INTERNATIONAL SERIES IN PHYSICS

LEE A. DuBRIDGE, Consulting Editor

THE PRINCIPLES OF OPTICS

INTERNATIONAL SERIES IN PURE AND APPLIED PHYSICS

G. P. Harnwell, *Consulting Editor*

Dr. Lee A. DuBridge was consulting editor of the series from 1939 to 1946.

THE PRINCIPLES
OF OPTICS

BY

ARTHUR C. HARDY, Sc.D.

Professor of Optics and Photography,
Massachusetts Institute of Technology

AND

FRED H. PERRIN, Ph.D.

Research Laboratories, Eastman Kodak Company

First Edition
Twelfth Impression

McGRAW-HILL BOOK COMPANY, Inc.
NEW YORK AND LONDON
1932

THE MAPLE PRESS COMPANY, YORK, PA.

PREFACE

This book is the result of experience in teaching the principles of optics at the Massachusetts Institute of Technology. It is intended to serve as a basis for a substantial first course for students in the third year of their undergraduate training, and presupposes merely the general knowledge of optical phenomena that is acquired in the average first and second year course in college physics. The scope of the book is such that it should provide a solid foundation for those who intend to select optics as a career and at the same time it should furnish an adequate knowledge of the subject in a comprehensible form for those who intend to specialize in other branches of physics or engineering.

The existing works on optics fall into two fairly well defined classes. Those dealing with what may be called pure optics treat the subject from a mathematical standpoint and commonly disregard the portions that are not amenable to mathematical treatment. Those dealing with what is sometimes called applied optics are devoted almost exclusively to the design of optical instruments. In this volume, we have attempted to steer a middle course and to treat the entire subject of optics as thoroughly as can be done in a work of this size. Such a procedure appeared to be desirable because, in a broader sense, there can be no distinction between pure and applied optics. An acquaintance with the entire subject is as necessary for those whose chief aim is to discover new optical phenomena as for those who intend to find new applications for the known phenomena.

There is as yet no profession that can truly be called optical engineering. In this respect, optics differs from the other branches of physics, such as mechanics, heat, electricity, and acoustics. Nevertheless, the ever-increasing importance of optics in industry makes it seem not unlikely that the profession of optical engineering will eventually assume its rightful place alongside the established engineering professions. The recent developments in such fields as illumination, motion pictures, and television, that depend primarily upon optics, have been brought about largely by engineers whose college training was received at a time when optics was not regarded as an essential part of an engineering education. In the selection of material for this volume we have had in mind the needs of engineers who may wish to work up the subject by themselves quite as much as the needs of college students who may some day call themselves optical engineers.

It is unfortunate that the study of optics must inevitably begin with the geometrical theory of image formation, which, although of little interest in itself, is a prerequisite to an adequate comprehension of all other branches of optics. This subject is disposed of in the five chapters that follow the introductory chapter. Chapter VII then deals with the phenomenon of diffraction and the limitation that it imposes on the performance of optical systems—a limitation that is not indicated by the purely geometrical theory. The next seven chapters discuss the properties of radiation and light sources, the various detectors of radiation, such as the eye, the photographic plate, the photoelectric cell, and the measurement of light and color. The next group of four chapters describes the properties of optical materials and the construction and testing of optical parts. This information does not appear in any of the standard works on optics, despite its importance to any one who intends to make optics his profession. The remainder of the book deals primarily with optical instruments. Chapter XIX develops the general principles underlying their design. It is followed by a discussion of the more important image-forming instruments, such as spectacles, photographic objectives, telescopes, microscopes, and projection systems. The last three chapters are concerned with spectroscopic apparatus, interferometers, and polarizing apparatus.

Those who are accustomed to regard optics as an exercise in applied mathematics will be disappointed in the present treatment because we have not considered it necessary to give a rigorous proof of every principle, since many of the proofs are extremely involved and may be found elsewhere. We trust that this lack of rigor is more than compensated by the greater emphasis that is thereby placed upon the principles themselves and upon the manner in which they can be applied. The references to original papers are more numerous in this volume than is customary in a work of this sort. These are intended to serve as a key to the literature and thus to encourage the student to obtain his information at first hand. In view of the impossibility of giving a complete bibliography of the entire field of optics we have attempted to select papers that are readily available, especially those which themselves contain extensive bibliographies.

Grateful acknowledgment is extended to all who have assisted in the preparation of this volume, especially to Professor J. C. Slater for his aid in connection with Chap. VIII, to Mr. Alden Handy and Mr. Ivan A. Getting for reading a large part of the manuscript, and to the various firms who have so generously contributed material for the tables and illustrations.

ARTHUR C. HARDY.

FRED H. PERRIN.

CAMBRIDGE, MASS.,
July, 1932.

CONTENTS

ix

THE PRINCIPLES OF OPTICS

CHAPTER I

GENERAL CONCEPTS

The term "light" is used to describe radiant energy that is capable of affecting our sense of sight. It may denote also the sensation produced by this form of energy in the brain of a human observer. Physicists generally use the term in its first or objective sense; psychologists and physiologists use it in its second or subjective sense. Occasionally its objective meaning is extended to include the energy propagated by waves that are either too long or too short to be perceived by our eyes but which can be studied by the methods that are used in the visible region.

Unlike other branches of physics, optics exhibits no simple phenomena, and there is, therefore, no logical point at which to begin the study of it. In mechanics, for example, one may begin with simple concepts like the equilibrium of forces, deferring more difficult ones until later, but in optics there are certain fundamental principles pertaining to all branches of the subject that must be grasped before a single branch can be studied intensively. Most of these principles are to be found in more elementary texts, but they are so important that they will be summarized in this first chapter. Inasmuch as a knowledge of the history of optics conduces to a better understanding of the subject, a brief historical sketch will be presented first.

1. The History of Optics.—The ancients were undoubtedly more familiar with optics than with any other branch of physics. The discovery in the ruins of Nineveh of a convex lens of quartz and tablets bearing inscriptions too minute to be decipherable by the naked eye indicates that the Chaldeans made use of magnifying glasses almost three thousand years ago. The use of a convex lens as a burning glass and as a magnifier is mentioned by Aristophanes and Pliny. Nevertheless, the knowledge of the ancient Greeks and Romans concerning the lens was probably

1

limited to its effects; for, although we know that they understood
the laws of reflection at plane and curved surfaces, there is
no evidence that they understood anything about the laws of
refraction. It was not until A.D. 50 that Cleomedes showed by
analogy with the appearance of a stick partially immersed in
water that the sun must be visible after it has set.

After the Dark Ages, the first outstanding figure in optical
history was the Arabian philosopher Alhazen, who died in Cairo
in 1038. Although he was distinguished in many branches of
science, he is best known because of his optical works, which were
later translated into Latin for the use of Europeans. He was
the first to explain the functions of the different parts of the eye
and to show that an image is formed by its optical system on the
retina. He anticipated Huygens and others by explaining why
we see objects singly with our two eyes. His astronomical
investigations led him to explain the phenomenon of twilight;
and with extraordinary sagacity he deduced that the atmosphere
of the earth extends less than sixty miles above the surface, thus
anticipating the epoch-making experiments that Torricelli and
Pascal were to make many centuries later.

The next figure of importance was Roger (Friar) Bacon, who
lived in England during the thirteenth century. Only a little
is known of this eccentric genius, who was centuries in advance
of his day. He may have invented spectacles, which appeared in
Europe about this time, and he is credited with having made
combinations of lenses that acted like telescopes and microscopes.
At least, his writings hint at a knowledge of these instruments,
but if he invented them he did not claim so. Brave would have
been the philosopher to admit being so manifestly a sophisticate
in the black art! As it was, his scientific curiosity resulted in his
spending some twenty-four of the last thirty-seven years of his
life in prison.

The Renaissance introduced a new era in science, which was
characterized by an openly expressed dissatisfaction with the
dogmatism of the Church and with the theories of the established
argumentative schools of philosophy. This era marked the
beginning of the experimental method in science, and the resulting
advances in optics were as outstanding as those in the other
branches of physics. Italy led the van with such pioneers as
Leonardo da Vinci (1452–1519), Maurolycus (1494–1575), della
Porta (1538–1615), and, foremost of all, Galileo (1564–1642).

There was but little specialization in those days, since all the known facts of natural philosophy could be comprehended by a single individual. As a consequence, the investigators who participated in the development of the branch of physics that is now called optics made contributions in other fields as well. The works of these sixteenth century pioneers are therefore too well known to require a detailed account here.

The optical history of the seventeenth century is predominantly the history of the telescope. It is true that spectacles had been in use for some years, but, as few could afford such a luxury, the field of ophthalmic optics remained quite undeveloped. Also, the compound microscope had been invented by the Janssens about 1590, but it was so imperfect that the sciences dependent upon it could not progress beyond the most embryonic stages. Astronomy, on the other hand, was in a well-organized state; and the age-old heavens invited observation as never before, now that the novel Copernican theory was battling for its life against the accepted theory of Ptolemy. The actual invention of the telescope was probably the result of a chance observation of a Dutch spectacle maker. News of the discovery reached Galileo in 1609, and, although he had not seen one of the instruments, he instantly grasped the principle and made one which he exhibited in Venice for several months. A second and somewhat improved instrument followed very shortly, and in January, 1610, he constructed one with a magnifying power of thirty-three times. These telescopes were similar to the modern opera glass, consisting of a double-convex objective and a double-concave ocular. Their definition was faulty, largely because of spherical and chromatic aberrations in the objective. It was soon found that these aberrations could be reduced without changing the magnifying power by increasing the focal length of the lenses. Such monstrosities as the 123-ft. telescope that Huygens presented to the Royal Society were the natural result. A more elegant solution was proposed by Gregory, who in 1663 suggested eliminating the chromatic aberration entirely by using a mirror instead of a lens. Newton adopted this suggestion and constructed a large number of reflecting telescopes, after hastily concluding that a combination of lenses could not be achromatized. But his conclusion was based upon inadequate evidence, and in 1733 an achromatic objective was constructed by Chester Moor Hall, an English gentleman.

In one sense, there are only two types of optical instruments: those that form images, like the telescope; and those that analyze radiation, like the spectroscope. It is quite fitting, therefore, that the seventeenth century should have witnessed the birth of the second type of instrument as well as the first. In fact, Newton's classical experiment on the composite nature of white light, which led to the development of the spectroscope, was nearly contemporaneous with the construction of the first good telescope.

The outstanding characters of the seventeenth century were Christiaan Huygens (1629–1695) and Sir Isaac Newton (1642–1727).[1] The contributions of both men to optical science are so numerous that they cannot be even mentioned here. Both made valuable experimental discoveries, but they are now remembered chiefly as the most famous supporters of rival theories of light propagation, notwithstanding that neither was satisfied with the adequacy of the theory he supported. Although these two investigators somewhat overshadowed all others of the period, mention must be made of Scheiner (1575–1650), who studied the optics of the eye, Snell (1591–1626), who discovered the true law of refraction, and Römer (1644–1710), who, by observations on the moons of Jupiter, was the first to prove that light travels with a finite velocity.

During the eighteenth and nineteenth centuries, developments in optics were more in the nature of improvements than fundamental inventions. Progress was slow because these developments had to await inventions in allied fields. Only at the end of the nineteenth century did the photographic film, the electric arc, and the incandescent lamp appear; and the present century had well started before the photoelectric cell could be put to practical use. Even optical glass was limited in variety until 1886, when the researches of Abbe and Schott made the modern highly corrected lenses possible. Optical research during this period was confined very largely to a study of the classical phenomena, such as interference and diffraction, which are explained so beautifully on the basis of the wave theory. The remarkable confirmation of optical theory afforded by these experiments led to the growing conviction that the work of the physicist of the future would be merely to determine the known

[1] Huygens's "Treatise on Light" was translated by Silvanus P. Thompson in 1912. Newton's "Opticks" was reprinted in 1931.

constants of nature with greater accuracy. But this attitude was suddenly changed just before the beginning of the present century by the discovery of new phenomena which opened unexplored fields of investigation. At the same time, the industrial applications of optics were enormously increased by the appearance of the inventions mentioned above and by the development of optical instruments by Abbe. In fact, the beginning of the twentieth century marks the entrance of optics, which had never been exploited in an engineering sense, into practical affairs.

The extraordinary progress in all branches of optics during the present century may be said to have resulted indirectly from the invention of the electric lamp by Edison in 1879. At that time there were no satisfactory sources of electrical energy, and this invention created a demand that led to the development of the electrical industry, which has lowered the cost of light to the point where it has revolutionized the habits of mankind. At the present time, developments in optical science are progressing along three well-defined courses. There is considerable activity in the improvement of sources of light and in methods of utilizing them. There are also many new applications of optics in science and industry, and the manufacturers of optical equipment are therefore constantly developing new instruments and modifying older ones to suit new purposes. In the field of pure science, it has come to be recognized that the branch of optics known as *spectroscopy* holds the key to the secrets of the constitution of matter and possibly to the nature of the universe. The activity in this field is so great that spectroscopy is rapidly assuming the status of an independent science.

2. The Nature of Light.—The nature of light is a puzzle that has absorbed the attention of philosophers and scientists since the earliest times. The ancient Greeks imagined that light consisted of a stream of corpuscles, but whether these emanated from the light source or from the eye was a subject of debate. Both theories accounted for the apparently rectilinear propagation of light and also for the facts of regular reflection, thus supplying the Greek geometers with an application for their newly developed mathematical methods.

No better theory concerning the nature of light was proposed until the seventeenth century, when experimental evidence of new kinds began to accumulate, especially the phenomena of interference, diffraction, double refraction, and polarization. Huygens showed about 1690 that the phenomena of reflection and refraction could be explained by assuming that light is propagated as longitudinal waves like sound. However, no method was found of explaining rectilinear propagation; and Newton, after considering this new theory carefully, was inclined to favor the older corpuscular theory. The weight of his opinion squelched the wave theory so effectively that it was in disrepute until about 1800, when Young and Fresnel attacked the problem anew. These investigators succeeded in explaining on the basis of the wave theory not only rectilinear propagation but the phenomena of interference and diffraction as well. Young later accounted for the phenomenon of polarization by assuming that the waves are transverse—that is, perpendicular to the direction of propagation—rather than longitudinal, or parallel to the direction of propagation. Finally, in 1850, Foucault gave the *coup de grâce* to the corpuscular theory by proving experimentally that the velocity of light in a material medium is less than in free space, a result that the proponents of both theories had always admitted would be conclusive.

But the wave theory had its difficulties. The propagation of waves necessitated some medium, and inexorable mathematics showed that the so-called *ether*, invented for the purpose, must be endowed with the most extraordinary physical properties. For example, to account for the enormous velocity of light, it must have a rigidity that is difficult to reconcile with the apparently unhampered motion of the planets. Then Faraday and Henry discovered electrical and magnetic phenomena that led Maxwell, in 1873, to announce his famous electromagnetic theory concerning the mode of propagation of electrical and magnetic disturbances. That this theory would also account for certain optical phenomena was proved about 1888, when Hertz showed that electrical waves possess many of the properties of light waves. In fact, the electromagnetic theory was so successful in interpreting the known phenomena in the field of optics that everyone believed that the final chapter on the subject had been written.

New experimental evidence began to make its appearance toward the end of the last century. Several investigators found that the space surrounding certain metals becomes electrically conductive when the metals are exposed to light. After J. J.

Thomson discovered the electron in 1897, it was naturally concluded that this *photoelectric effect*, as it is called, is due to the emission of electrons by the metal as a result of some action of the light. The expulsion of an electron from a metal requires a certain definite amount of energy, and this energy presumably comes from the beam of light. However, calculations showed that the rate at which an electron receives energy from a beam of light of ordinary intensity is so small that several years would be required for it to accumulate enough to bring about its expulsion. Actually, of course, the expulsion of electrons begins as soon as the metal is exposed. As a consequence it was necessary to assume that the energy in a beam of light is not distributed uniformly over the wave front but is concentrated at certain points, as if the light consisted of corpuscles instead. Other evidence in favor of this view soon began to accumulate. In arriving at a satisfactory explanation of the radiation from a black body, Planck found it necessary to assume that the radiating oscillators in the body radiate energy discontinuously in units called *quanta*. Then in 1905 Einstein suggested that the absorption of light in the photoelectric process might be in quantum units also, and experiment proved that these quanta are of the same size as those required by Planck.

During the last decade, the physicist has been forced to employ two seemingly contradictory theories: the wave theory for classical phenomena such as reflection, refraction, interference, diffraction, and polarization; and the quantum theory for the more recent discoveries in the field of X-rays, photoelectricity, and radiation. The inability of the physicist to fuse these two theories placed him in an anomalous position. We may smile at Newton's idea that corpuscles have alternate fits of easy reflection and refraction, but what shall we say when a modern physicist determines the energy of a corpuscle that causes the expulsion of a photoelectron on the basis of the wave length required by the wave theory to explain phenomena that the corpuscular theory is incapable of explaining? The reason for the existence of the two theories is that the human mind can conceive of but two ways by which energy can be transferred— either by the actual transfer of matter or by a wave motion. Both theories in their simple forms have been signally successful in explaining certain optical phenomena while failing to explain the others.

A deeper understanding of some recent experiments suggests that both theories are essentially correct as far as they go. The Compton effect has indicated that light corpuscles may behave much like particles of matter, while the work of Davisson and Germer has indicated that, under certain conditions, electrons behave like a group of waves. *Wave mechanics* is the name given to a new method of interpreting physical phenomena that may provide the fundamental principle necessary for reconciling the conflicting theories. While a detailed account is beyond the scope of this book, it may be stated here that the theory of wave mechanics accepts the equivalence of matter and energy at the outset, postulating that waves are always associated with particles of matter. This subject has been developed principally by de Broglie and Schrödinger and is intended to supplant the ordinary gross mechanics when treating particles of atomic and sub-atomic dimensions. In fact, it goes beyond this and makes the ordinary gross mechanics of Newton merely a special case of a more general theory.

In the present volume, the theory that "explains" a certain set of phenomena most conveniently will always be used, notwithstanding that it may not "explain" some other set. Thus, in arriving at the principles of image formation, it will be assumed merely that light travels in straight lines; in discussing interference, diffraction, and similar phenomena, that it is propagated as transverse waves; and in discussing radiation and the photoelectric effect, that it behaves more like corpuscles and is emitted or absorbed in multiples of the elementary quantum of energy. Despite the seeming inconsistency of such a procedure, it should be remembered that if a certain theory fits the observed facts once it will do so always. That the theory represents only a special case of a more general principle should not be an objection to utilizing it for what it is worth, especially in a book whose emphasis is laid more on the applications of the theories than on the proofs of their validity.

3. The Velocity of Light.—The ancients were undoubtedly familiar with the finite velocity of sound and must have speculated about the velocity of light. All the early terrestrial experiments failed of their purpose, however, because of the crudeness of the apparatus. It remained for Römer in 1675 to note with the aid of the newly discovered telescope that a peculiar variation in the apparent periods of the eclipses of the satellites of

Jupiter depends upon the distance between the planet and the earth. The remarkably precise value of 3.0×10^{10} cm/sec. for the velocity of light in free space was determined on the basis of his observations. The first terrestrial method of determining the velocity of light was successfully carried out by Fizeau in 1849. He allowed light to pass through a rotating toothed wheel, thus causing rapid interruptions in the beam. A mirror located some distance away redirected the light to the toothed wheel again, and the velocity could be computed by observing the speed of rotation at which the wheel moved through a distance equal to one tooth in the time required for the light to travel twice over the distance between the wheel and the mirror. Fizeau's method was improved by Foucault a year later by the substitution of a rotating mirror as the timing device in place of the toothed wheel. This resulted in the same precision with a much shorter optical path, so that Foucault was able to demonstrate also that the velocity of light in water is less than in air. The most accurate determinations of the velocity of light have been made by Michelson,[1] who concluded in 1926 that its velocity in free space is $(2.99796 \pm 0.00004) \times 10^{10}$ cm/sec. Michelson used the essential features of Foucault's method but employed a greatly improved technique, so that now the velocity of light is known with greater accuracy than almost any other physical constant.

4. Wave Motion.—The simplest wave motion that can be represented mathematically is the one shown in Fig. 1. The figure may be considered a snapshot of a longitudinal section of a transverse wave. Every particle in the wave is vibrating up and down, its maximum distance from the axis being a. If the origin is chosen at some particle that is on the axis for the moment, the distance of any other particle from the axis is

$$y = a \sin x, \tag{1}$$

where x is the distance of the particle from the origin, measured along the line of propagation.

The concepts relating to wave motion are so ingrained in our consciousness to-day that even the layman uses the terms appropriate to it without thinking. Nevertheless, it may be well to define a few of the more common ones, which is here done with reference to Fig. 1 in lieu of a more formal set of definitions.

[1] *Astrophys. Jour.*, **65**, 1 (1927).

Consider two particles m_1 and m_2 occupying corresponding positions in two successive waves of a train. The distance $x_2 - x_1$ between these particles is one *wave length*, the symbol for which is λ. Now m_1, m_2, and all the intermediate particles are vibrating up and down and therefore will return to their present positions again at the end of a time T called the *period*. During this time, the wave will have progressed from x_1 to x_2 with a velocity

$$c = \frac{\lambda}{T}. \tag{2}$$

The velocity may be expressed also in terms of the *frequency*, which is the reciprocal of the period. Then

$$c = \lambda f. \tag{3}$$

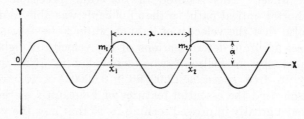

Fig. 1.

The position of a given particle in terms of these constants is

$$y = a \sin 2\pi f t, \tag{4}$$

where t is the time measured from some instant when y was zero. The graphical representation of this equation is similar to Fig. 1 with values of time as abscissae instead of distance.

When a given particle is acted upon simultaneously by two disturbances of the type represented by Eq. (4), the resultant displacement is the vector sum of the displacements that each disturbance would produce alone. A case of considerable importance in optics arises when the two disturbances lie in the same plane and pursue substantially the same course. If the disturbances have the same frequency, the equations may be written

$$y_1 = a_1 \sin 2\pi f t$$

and

$$y_2 = a_2 \sin (2\pi f t + \varphi),$$

where φ represents the phase of one disturbance with respect to the other. It is easily shown that the sum of these disturbances is a sinusoidal disturbance of the same frequency as the components and that it has an amplitude

$$a = \sqrt{a_1^2 + a_2^2 + 2\,a_1 a_2 \cos\varphi}.$$

If φ is zero or any multiple of 2π, the two waves are in phase and the resultant amplitude is the arithmetical sum of the amplitudes of the two components. Now in any wave motion, the rate at which energy is propagated is proportional to the square of the amplitude. Hence, the combination of two sine waves of the same amplitude and frequency results, if they are in phase, in quadrupling the rate of flow of energy instead of merely doubling it. This never causes a violation of the conservation of energy principle, however, because the surplus energy at one point is always accompanied by a deficiency somewhere else. This deficiency occurs at points for which

$$\varphi = \pi,\ 3\pi,\ 5\pi,\ \text{etc.}$$

The two disturbances are then 180° out of phase, and the resultant amplitude is zero. This phenomenon is known as *interference*. It is of great use in the precise measurement of distances, partly because of the convenient shortness of light waves but more because their length is so constant.

The velocity of light in any medium except free space depends on both the nature of the medium and the frequency of the light, the ratio of the velocity in free space to that in the medium being termed the *refractive index* of the medium. This quantity is commonly represented by n. Now from Eq. (3), either the wave length or the frequency or both must change by an amount sufficient to account for the change in the velocity. It so happens that the wave length changes, the frequency remaining constant. In other words, the frequency of a light wave is a property impressed on it by the source and is unaltered by the medium through which it is transmitted.

Light waves are so short that it is convenient to adopt special units for expressing their length. The shortest radiation that can ordinarily be seen has a wave length of about 0.0004 mm, which is generally expressed as 0.4 micron, 400 millimicrons, or 4000 Ångström units. The symbols for these units are μ, $m\mu$, and Å, representing 10^{-4}, 10^{-7}, and 10^{-8} cm respectively. Following the custom of most workers in the field of optics, wave length will be expressed in millimicrons in the present volume.

When a source of light and an observer are in motion relative to each other, the frequency is apparently altered.   If the source emits light of frequency ν and is moving relative to the observer with a velocity v, the frequency of the light appears to the observer to be

$$\nu' = \nu\left(\frac{c}{c \pm v}\right),$$ (5)

the negative sign applying when the source and the observer are approaching each other.   This *Doppler effect* is used by astronomers to determine the component of the velocity of stars in the line of sight from the change in frequency of the lines in their spectra.   It is also used in the same way to determine the velocity of gas within sun spots.

5. The Wave Front.—On the old elastic-solid theory, it was possible to visualize light as being propagated by waves in much

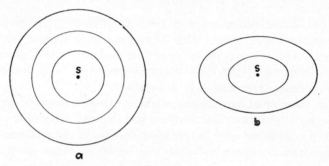

Fig. 2.

the same manner that waves are propagated along a string that is under tension.   Of course, the similarity is but slight because energy is transmitted by the vibrating string in one dimension only, whereas light energy is transmitted in three.   With the advent of the electromagnetic theory of light, these mechanical vibrations of the ether particles were replaced by oscillating electric and magnetic fields.   A simple conception of the mode of propagation, other than the purely mathematical one expressed by Maxwell's equations, is therefore impossible.   Huygens, however, had demonstrated many years before that the progress of a wave in a three-dimensional medium may be visualized in terms of the motion of a surface in which the phase of the disturbance is everywhere the same. Such a surface is termed a *wave front*. Regardless of our present ideas concerning the nature of light, Huygens's method still offers a simple interpretation of the facts of image formation and is generally used on this account.

Let the point source of light S in Fig. 2a be situated in a homogeneous isotropic medium—that is, one in which the velocity of propagation is the same at all points and in every direction.

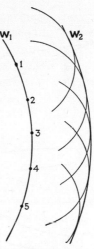

Under these circumstances the locus of any given phase of the disturbance is a sphere. Hence, the emission of light by the point S may be visualized in terms of a series of concentric spheres, each representing the locus of the same phase of the disturbance at successive intervals of time. Huygens showed that the wave front at any future time can be determined by assuming that every point on a given wave front acts as the center of a new disturbance emanating from that point. This is illustrated in Fig. 3, where W_1 is the wave front at some particular instant. Treating every point, 1, 2, 3, etc., on this wave front as an independent source, the envelope of the arcs representing the wavelets emitted by these points can be shown to be the new wave front

Fig. 3.

W_2. The radii of the wavelets are proportional, of course, to the time that has elapsed since the wave front was at W_1. If the original source is at infinity, the radius of the sphere becomes infinite and the wave front becomes a plane.

If the medium is not isotropic, like many crystals, the velocity of propagation is different in different directions. In such a case the wave fronts are ellipsoidal as shown in Fig. 2b.

6. Rays, Pencils, Beams.—It is impossible to describe the shape of a wave front in simple mathematical terms unless it is either plane or spherical. In the passage of a wave front through an optical system, small departures from the true plane or spherical form are always introduced. These are of great significance in estimating the perfection of the image, and the designers of optical instruments have therefore been forced to resort to a method that permits a portion of the wave front to be treated independently.   The procedure is to locate certain lines, such as r_1, r_2, r_3, r_4, etc., in Fig. 4a, which represent the directions in which the corresponding portions of the wave fronts W_1 and W_2 are moving.   These lines are known as *rays* of light, and they are perpendicular to the wave front when the medium is isotropic.   In the case of anisotropic media—crystals for example —the rays in general are not perpendicular to the wave front, as shown in Fig. 4b.

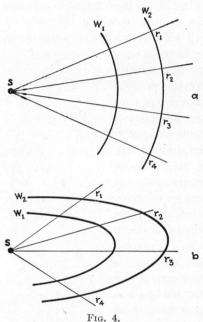

A bundle of rays originating at a single point is known as a *pencil*. The light used for all practical purposes comes from sources of finite area, every point of which emits a pencil.   Such a group of pencils is known as a *beam*. The distinction between these concepts is often illustrated by the statement that a ray of light will pass through two infinitely small holes, a pencil through one small hole and one large hole, while a beam requires two large holes.

Fig. 4.

7. Monochromatic Light.— The type of radiation represented in Fig. 1 has a definite frequency which can be expressed exactly in a mathematical sense.   This type of radiation is commonly called *monochromatic* or *homogeneous;* but neither term is entirely appropriate, the former because it implies a correspondence between the radiation and the color sense of a human observer, and the latter because in its usual sense it would imply merely that the radiation has the same character throughout space.   Of the alternatives, the term "monochromatic" is perhaps less objectionable and is certainly more widely used.   No actual source emits radiation that is truly monochromatic.   In fact, before Michelson could undertake his classical determination of the length of the standard meter in terms of the wave length of light, he was forced to make an extensive search for a source whose wave length could be expressed with sufficient precision to give significance to his results. He was fortunate in finding that an arc in cadmium vapor furnishes a comparatively monochromatic red radiation. It should be emphasized, however, that truly monochromatic light in the mathematical sense can never be produced. Even if all the atoms in a given mass of gas emitted continuously light of exactly the same frequency, the Doppler effect, due to the motion of the gas molecules, would prevent the radiation from appearing to be strictly monochromatic.

8. Heterochromatic Light.—If the term "monochromatic" is applied to radiation of a single frequency, the radiation from any actual source may be described as *heterochromatic* (or *non-homogeneous*). When analyzed by a spectroscope, such radiation produces either a line, a band, or a continuous spectrum. A *line spectrum* is characteristic of atoms and is usually produced by an element in a gaseous state. If the gas itself is excited, the lines are bright; if the gas is in the path of light from a source that would produce a continuous spectrum, the lines are dark. The solar spectrum contains dark lines, called *Fraunhofer lines*, because the light from the photosphere passes through the cooler outside layer of gases and this layer absorbs the radiations peculiar to the elements constituting it.

A *band spectrum* is characteristic of molecules and hence is produced by a compound in the gaseous state. It is really a line spectrum in which the lines are in groups, the lines of each group becoming more crowded toward one end, called the head. Of course, if the compound becomes dissociated into its constituent elements, the line spectrum of each element may appear.

A *continuous spectrum* is characteristic of incandescent solids. It has no detectable structure but is usually considered to consist of radiation of all possible frequencies. However, Gouy and others have shown that the light from incandescent solids could very well consist of pulses that are analyzed by the spectroscope into what appears to be a continuous spectrum. In other words, the colors that appear in the spectrum of the sun and other incandescent solids may be introduced by the prism or grating in much the same way that the reflection of a sharp sound at a tier of seats in an auditorium may give rise to a musical note.

The appearance of a continuous spectrum is characterized by a gradual change in hue from red at one end through orange, yellow, green, and blue to violet at the other. There is, of

course, no one-to-one correspondence between the wave length of
the radiation and the sensation of hue that it produces.   Nevertheless, it has been found convenient to divide the spectrum
somewhat arbitrarily into six or seven hues which, according to
Abney, have the following wave-length limits:

Violet	—— to 446 mμ
Indigo	446 to 464 mμ
Blue	464 to 500 mμ
Green	500 to 578 mμ
Yellow	578 to 592 mμ
Orange	592 to 620 mμ
Red	620 to —— mμ

9. Polarized Light.—In the simple type of wave motion
represented in Fig. 1, the vibrations take place in the plane of
the paper, and the kind of light this is supposed to represent is
said to be *plane polarized.*   An observer viewing an oncoming
beam of this light would notice, if he were able to see the vibrations, that they take place in one plane only.   The effect on
the retina is the same regardless of the azimuth of the plane of
vibration, but, if a substance like tourmaline is introduced into
the beam, the amplitude of the transmitted wave depends upon
the relation of the azimuth of the tourmaline crystal to that
of the plane of vibration.   In fact, the beam may be practically
extinguished for some positions of the crystal.

The *plane of polarization* can be defined in two ways.   The
early investigators of necessity defined it arbitrarily, and later
experiments proved that the vibrations of the ether particles,
assumed on the basis of the elastic-solid theory, take place in a
plane perpendicular to the plane that had been selected as the
plane of polarization.   The situation is analogous to that in
electricity, where the electrons carrying the current were found
to migrate in a direction opposite to that in which the early
experimenters had assumed the current to flow.   Ordinarily, the
term "plane of polarization" means the plane normal to the
plane of vibration, but, as the term is occasionally used to mean
the plane of vibration, it is necessary to ascertain the meaning
of the author in each case.   In the electromagnetic theory of
light, the electric and magnetic vectors lie in mutually perpendicular planes, and the plane of polarization is understood to be
the plane containing the magnetic vector.

If two beams of monochromatic light of the same frequency are plane polarized in mutually perpendicular azimuths, the result of their combination is *elliptically polarized* light. In this case, an ether particle would appear to an observer viewing the oncoming beam along the line of propagation to be vibrating in an elliptical orbit. The ratio of the major to the minor axis of the ellipse depends upon the relative intensity of the two beams. In the special case when the intensities are equal, the ellipse becomes a circle. The light is then said to be *circularly polarized*.

Ordinary or natural light is assumed to be composed of beams of plane-polarized light representing all possible azimuths. As it is impossible to imagine an ether particle vibrating in all directions at once, it is assumed that natural light is composed of a number of plane-polarized wave trains following one another in such rapid succession that, over any time interval which the eye can perceive or the photographic plate can record, all azimuths are represented equally. The same crystal of tourmaline that was suggested above as a detector of plane-polarized light can be used to produce plane-polarized light from natural light. In practice, Nicol prisms, cut from a crystal of Iceland spar, give better results.

Polarized light is used by chemists in the quantitative estimation of the concentration of solutions, especially of sugars, which have the property of rotating the plane of polarization. It is found that the amount of rotation is proportional to the concentration, and thus, when the constant for a given substance has been once determined, the concentration of an unknown solution may be found readily. The instrument employed for this purpose is called a polarimeter or, if designed especially for sugar solutions, a saccharimeter.

Polarized light has numerous other applications. It is of use to geologists because crystals can often be identified by means of it. Polarizing prisms are used in several types of photometers for controlling the intensity of light. Also, one method of recording sound on photographic film makes use of the change in the behavior of certain liquids toward polarized light when the liquid is placed in a strong electric field.

10. The Visibility of Radiant Energy.—The visibility curve of a normal human eye is shown in Fig. 5. The ordinates of this curve represent the *relative visibility*, which is the reciprocal of the relative amount of power required to produce a given brightness sensation. This curve is plotted from the data in Table I.

TABLE I.—RELATIVE VISIBILITY OF RADIANT ENERGY*

λ	Visibility	λ	Visibility	λ	Visibility
400	0.0004	520	0.710	640	0.175
410	0.0012	530	0.862	650	0.107
420	0.0040	540	0.954	660	0.061
430	0.0116	550	0.995	670	0.032
440	0.023	560	0.995	680	0.017
450	0.038	570	0.952	690	0.0082
460	0.060	580	0.870	700	0.0041
470	0.091	590	0.757	710	0.0021
480	0.139	600	0.631	720	0.00105
490	0.208	610	0.503	730	0.00052
500	0.323	620	0.381	740	0.00025
510	0.503	630	0.265	750	0.00012

* From *Bur. Standards Sci. Paper* 475, p. 174.

As the curve indicates, the normal eye is most sensitive to radiation at 555 mμ. No exact wave-length limits can be

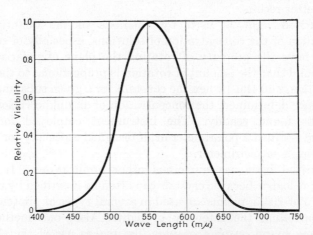

FIG. 5.—Visibility curve of the human eye.

assigned to the visible spectrum, but the region from 400 mμ to 700 mμ contains most of the visible radiation.

11. Photometric Units.—*Photometry* is the name applied to the science of measuring light. Just as current can be regarded as a flow of electricity, so light can be regarded as a flow or *flux* of radiant energy. If the human eye were uniformly sensitive to radiation of all wave lengths, the *radiant power* expressed in watts would provide an adequate method of evaluating the flux. However, the eye is so strikingly selective in its response that an arbitrary unit by which the flux is evaluated in terms of its visual effect is chosen instead. The name of this unit is the *lumen.* It obviously has the same dimensions as power, and it has been found by experiment that for a normal observer one lumen is equivalent to 0.00161 watt of monochromatic green light of a wave length corresponding to the maximum of the visibility curve ($\lambda = 555$ mμ); or, taking the reciprocal, one watt of monochromatic green light of this wave length is equivalent to 621 lumens.

The number of lumens associated with one watt of radiant power from a given source is called the *luminous efficiency* of the source. For a source of monochromatic light, the luminous efficiency is obtained by multiplying 621 by the value of the relative visibility for the wave length in question. In general, if the source has an energy distribution represented by E_λ, its *luminosity* in lumens is given by the expression

$$L = 621 \int_0^\infty V_\lambda E_\lambda d\lambda \, ,$$

where V_λ is the relative visibility function given in Fig. 5. The total power in watts is, of course,

$$W = \int_0^\infty E_\lambda d\lambda \, ,$$

and therefore the luminous efficiency is

$$l = \frac{621 \int_0^\infty V_\lambda E_\lambda d\lambda}{\int_0^\infty E_\lambda d\lambda} \, . \tag{6}$$

Because of the form of this function, the integration is usually performed either graphically or by a point-by-point method.

When a source of light does not radiate uniformly in all directions, a mere statement of the total flux may be inadequate. If the source is so small that it can be regarded as a point without introducing an appreciable error, a more complete description can be given in terms of the amount of flux radiated per unit solid angle in each direction. In this case, the *intensity* of the source in any given direction is defined as the number of lumens per unit solid angle radiated in that direction. That is, if a small source radiates dF lumens of flux within a small solid angle $d\omega$, the intensity

$$I = \frac{dF}{d\omega}. \tag{7}$$

The unit of luminous intensity is the *candle*. A point source emitting light uniformly in all directions radiates 4π lumens per candle.

It happens to be easier for standardizing laboratories to maintain a standard of intensity than a standard of flux. Because of this practice, it is often assumed that the candle is the fundamental unit. However, for the sake of a clear understanding of the work that is to follow, particularly in Chaps. XIII and XIX, it must be realized at the outset that the lumen is the fundamental quantity and that the candle represents merely the amount of flux that a point source radiates per unit solid angle in some specified direction.

The concept of intensity is applicable only when the source is so small that it can be treated as a point. If the source is too large to be treated as a point, the corresponding quantity is called *brightness*. By definition, the brightness in a given direction at any point of an extended surface is the quotient of the intensity of an element of the surface at that point by the area of the element projected in a plane perpendicular to the given direction. In mathematical symbols,

$$B = \frac{dI}{d\sigma \cos \theta}, \tag{8}$$

where dI is the intensity of an element of the surface in the specified direction, $d\sigma$ is the area of this element, and θ is the angle between the normal to the surface and the given direction. The unit of brightness is the candle per unit area.

The brightness of a surface depends in general upon the direction of observation, but there is a large class of materials for which the intensity varies as $\cos \theta$, and these therefore appear equally bright from every direction. Such materials are said to be diffuse radiators if self-luminous and diffuse reflectors if illuminated by some other source. Freshly fallen snow is a good example of a diffuse reflector, but it loses this property when a crust forms upon it.

The apparent brightness of an extended surface is independent of the distance at which it is observed; for, as the distance from the eye is increased, the area covered by the image on the retina decreases at a rate that almost exactly compensates for the smaller amount of flux entering the pupil. This is in contrast to the case of a point source, where all the flux entering the pupil falls on a single element of the retina regardless of the distance of the source. Hence in this case the source appears fainter as the distance is increased.

When light is incident upon a surface, the resulting *illumination* is expressed in terms of the amount of flux incident upon a unit area. In the English system, the unit of illumination is the lumen per square foot; in the metric system, it is the lumen per square meter. The illumination produced by a point source is given by the well-known inverse-square law, which is

$$E = \frac{I}{d^2} \cos i, \tag{9}$$

where I is the intensity of the source, d is its distance from the surface, and i is the angle of incidence measured from the normal to the surface. The method of computing the illumination produced by a source of finite area will be considered in Chap. XIX. In brief, it consists in dividing the source into areas that are small enough to be treated as points and then finding the total illumination due to all the elementary areas by the method of the integral calculus. Because of the relatively low precision of present methods of measuring illumination, the inverse-square law can usually be applied without appreciable error to any source whose greatest dimension is less than one-twentieth of the distance to the surface on which the illumination is computed.

Because the inverse-square relation is used so frequently, illuminating engineers have fallen into the habit of evaluating illumination in terms of a unit known as the *foot-candle*. By definition, a foot-candle is the illumination produced when the light from one candle falls normally on a surface at a distance of one foot. From a consideration of the illumination produced on the interior of a sphere by a point source at its center, it will be seen that one foot-candle is numerically equivalent to one lumen per square foot. The foot-candle is, of course, dimensionally incorrect and implies that the illumination is the product of the candlepower of the source and its distance from the surface. It is in common use in illuminating engineering practice, but it will be avoided whenever possible in the present work because of the confusion it causes; especially in Chap. XIX where the photometry of optical instruments is considered.

12. Reflection.—The result of allowing a plane wave to fall upon a smooth reflecting surface can be studied by Huygens's construction. Figure 6 shows such a surface with a plane wave front *I-I'* incident on it at *A*. If the surface were not present, the wave front would pass successively through positions *I-I'*, *II-II'*, *III-III'*, *IV-IV'*, etc., each new position being determined from Huygens' principle by describing arcs representing

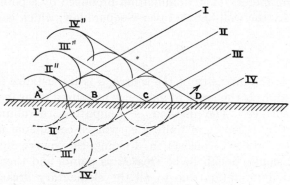

Fig. 6.

the secondary disturbances emanating from each point of the old wave front. With the reflecting surface present, only the portion of the secondary disturbances above the surface at the point of incidence of the wave front can go to form the new wave front. After reflection has occurred, the new wave fronts *II''-B*, *III''-C*, *IV''-D*, etc., are formed in exactly the same way as they would have been if the surface were absent. It will be seen from the geometry of the figure that the incident and the reflected wave fronts make equal angles with the surface.

The kind of reflection discussed above is said to be regular or *specular*. In the majority of cases of practical interest, the reflecting surface is rough in comparison with the wave length of light. If a sketch similar to Fig. 6 be drawn for such a surface, it will be seen that the character of the reflection is very different.

A plane incident wave is no longer plane after reflection because the roughness of the surface causes the wavelets to combine in such a way that light is scattered in all directions. If the surface is sufficiently rough, its brightness is the same in every direction; or, in other words, the reflection is *diffuse*. Specular reflection and diffuse reflection thus represent limiting cases, between which lie the cases of practical interest. A surface that partakes of more of the properties of specular reflection than diffuse is commonly called *glossy*, while a surface exhibiting the properties of diffuse reflection to a pronounced degree is called *matte*. Surfaces intermediate between these two kinds are known as *semi-gloss* or *semi-matte*. Figure 7 illustrates the manner in

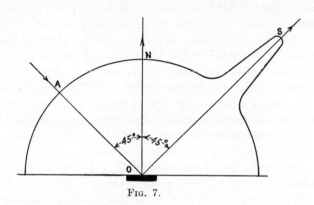

Fig. 7.

which light is reflected from a semi-matte surface. The incident light follows the path *AO*, and the proportion reflected in each direction is indicated in polar coordinates by the curve. The specular component is reflected in the direction *OS*, such that the angle *SON* equals the angle *AON*.

No surface ever reflects all the light incident upon it. Even a block of magnesium carbonate, which is about as white as any known substance, reflects only about 98 per cent of the incident light. If the reflecting power of a material is independent of the wave length, it is said to be *non-selective* and the material appears white, gray, or black depending upon the value of the reflecting power. In general, however, the reflection is *selective* and the material appears colored.

13. Absorption.—Of the light that enters a material, some is absorbed and some is transmitted. The *transparency* of a material is defined as the ratio of the intensity of the transmitted light to that of the incident light:

$$T = \frac{I}{I_o}.$$ (10)

The *opacity* is the reciprocal of the transparency. The *optical density* is defined as the common logarithm of the opacity:

$$D = \log_{10} O = \log_{10} \frac{1}{T}.$$ (11)

A non-homogeneous medium, such as a photographic emulsion, behaves toward transmitted light as a semi-matte surface does toward reflected light; that is, the light does not all pass directly through. Some does, but a considerable amount is scattered and emerges at various angles with the incident beam. If I in Eq. (10) refers to the light passing through the medium without change in direction, the density is said to be *specular;* if it refers to the total emergent light, the density is said to be *diffuse.* Inasmuch as some light is always scattered, the specular density of a material is always greater than the diffuse density.

In materials that are homogeneous, such as glass or clear liquids, the absorption depends upon the thickness in accordance with *Bouguer's law.*[1] Suppose that a layer of unit thickness transmits a fraction t of the light incident upon it. This layer will absorb a fraction $(1 - t)$. Consequently a thickness x of the material will transmit the fraction t^x, and the intensity of the light transmitted is

$$I = I_0 t^x,$$ (12)

where I_0 is the intensity of the incident light. This expression may be written

$$I = I_0 \epsilon^{-ax},$$ (13a)

where a, the *absorption coefficient*, equals $-\log_\epsilon t$. The absorption of a solution is in general proportional to the concentration of the solute. The absorption coefficient can therefore be written as

$$a = bc,$$

---

[1] Bouguer set forth this law in 1729. It was rediscovered by Lambert and consequently is frequently called *Lambert's law of absorption.*

where c is the concentration and b is the absorption coefficient for unit concentration. With this substitution, Eq. (13a) becomes

$$I = I_0 \epsilon^{-bcx}, \tag{13b}$$

which is known as *Beer's law*.

Absorption, like reflection, varies with the wave length of the light and is therefore said to be *selective*. In rare instances, when radiations of all wave lengths are absorbed equally, the absorption is *non-selective* and the material is said to be neutral in color.

14. Refraction.—Inasmuch as the velocity of light in a material medium is less than in free space, a wave front incident

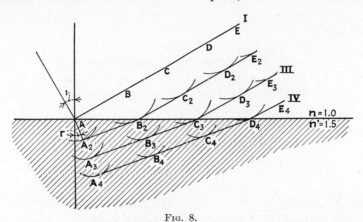

Fig. 8.

on the boundary of such a medium will be deviated or *refracted*. This can be shown with the aid of Fig. 8, in which Huygens's construction is used again. The first medium is supposed to be air, whereas the second is one in which light travels two-thirds as fast. The successive positions of the refracted wave front are the successive envelopes of wavelets emanating from the wave front in previous positions. These wavelets penetrate the second medium and travel two-thirds as fast as they did in the first. If the normals to the wave front before and after refraction make the angles i and r respectively with the normal to the surface, as shown in the figure,

$$n \sin i = n' \sin r. \tag{14}$$

This is known as *Snell's law*. The refractive indices n and n' here represent the ratios of the velocity of light in free space to the velocities in the media.   The ratio n'/n is sometimes called the *relative index*, but this term leads only to confusion and the invariant form of Eq. (14) is preferable.

15. Total Reflection.—If n is greater than n', it is obvious that sin r will become unity when i is still less than 90°.   It is of course impossible for sin r to have a value greater than unity, and experiment shows that this imaginary case represents a change from refraction to total reflection.   Thus in Fig. 9, the rays a, b, and c proceeding from a source S beneath the surface of the water emerge from the surface into the air above.   In each case, the angle of refraction is greater than the angle of incidence. The ray d strikes the surface at the so-called *critical angle* and

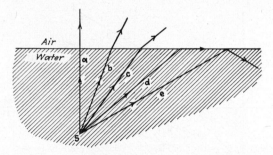

Fig. 9.

emerges parallel to the surface.   The ray e, on the other hand, is totally reflected on striking the boundary surface.

It must not be assumed that the transition from refraction to total reflection is abrupt.   As a matter of fact, there is some reflection at the surface in the case of even ray a, although most of the light is refracted into the air.   As the angle of incidence increases, more light is reflected and less refracted, the reflection finally becoming complete when the angle of incidence exceeds the critical angle.

A quantitative expression for the amount of light reflected at the boundary surface between two transparent media was first derived by Fresnel.   In Fig. 10, let I_0 represent the intensity of a beam of plane-polarized light that is incident at an angle i on the boundary surface between two media whose indices of refraction are n and n' respectively.   Let it be assumed first that the light is polarized in the plane of incidence—that is, in the plane of the figure.   In this case the vibrations are perpendicular to the plane of the figure. Fresnel showed that the intensity I of the reflected beam is given by

$$\frac{I}{I_0} = \frac{\sin^2 (i - r)}{\sin^2 (i + r)}.$$

The ratio I/I_0 is the reflecting power of the surface for light that is polarized in the manner assumed. The variation in the reflecting power with the angle of incidence is shown graphically by curve A in Fig. 11 for the case where the first medium is air and the second is ordinary spectacle glass of index 1.523. For

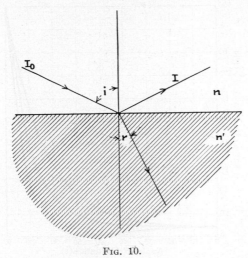

Fig. 10.

light polarized perpendicular to the plane of incidence, Fresnel showed that the reflecting power is

$$\frac{I}{I_0} = \frac{\tan^2 (i - r)}{\tan^2 (i + r)}.$$

The variation in the reflecting power with the angle of incidence is represented in this case by curve B in Fig. 11.

Natural or unpolarized light may be assumed to consist of equal amounts of two components that are plane polarized in mutually perpendicular azimuths. Hence the proportion of natural light that is reflected at the boundary surface between two transparent media is given by

$$\frac{I}{I_0} = \frac{\sin^2 (i - r)}{2\sin^2 (i + r)} + \frac{\tan^2 (i - r)}{2\tan^2 (i + r)}. \tag{15}$$

The variation in this quantity with the angle of incidence is shown by curve C in Fig. 11. For normal incidence, Eq. (15) can be transformed into the more convenient expression

$$\frac{I}{I_0} = \left(\frac{n-1}{n+1}\right)^2 \tag{16}$$

if one medium is air. Thus, a single glass surface reflects about 4 per cent of the light falling normally upon it and transmits 96 per cent. A sheet of glass, which of course has two air-glass

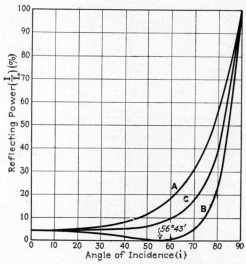

Fig. 11.—The variation of reflecting power with the angle of incidence for spectacle crown glass ($n = 1.523$). Curve A, reflecting power for light polarized in the plane of incidence; curve B, for light polarized perpendicular to the plane of incidence; curve C, for natural or unpolarized light.

surfaces, transmits approximately $(0.96)^2$ or a little more than 92 per cent, assuming no loss by absorption.

It will be noticed that if natural light falls upon the boundary surface at such an angle that $i + r = 90°$, the second term of Eq. (15) becomes zero and the reflected light is therefore completely plane polarized in the plane of incidence. The angle of incidence for which this occurs is called the *polarizing angle*. It is the angle whose tangent is the ratio of the index of the second medium to that of the first. It will be noticed also that, although the light reflected at the polarizing angle is completely polarized, the refracted light is only partially polarized.

16. Image Formation.—Since a large part of optics is concerned with instruments that form optical images, a clear understanding of the process of image formation is essential. As explained before, the most satisfactory interpretation is based on Huygens's wave-front concept. In Fig. 12*a*, the point *P* is a source of light emitting waves which are represented by wave fronts that are spherical when the material is homogeneous and isotropic. The velocity of the wave through the lens *L* depends upon the refractive index of the material of the lens, and in this case the lens is assumed to have a higher index than the surrounding media. Hence the wave will travel more slowly through the lens and, as

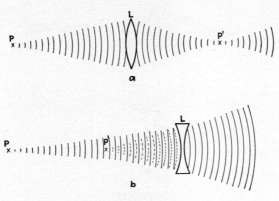

Fig. 12.

the center of the lens is thicker than the edges, the central part of the wave front will be retarded most. The curvature of the wave front will therefore be altered and may become of opposite sign, as in the case shown. Actually the wave front will be somewhat distorted by the lens unless the surfaces are especially figured, but, if the lens is properly corrected, the wave front will remain approximately spherical after refraction. That is, it will shrink until all the energy passes through the point *P'* and will expand again as though *P'* were a source. Then *P'* is said to be the *image* of the point *P* formed by the lens *L*. An observer situated at the right of the figure would see only *P'* and would be unaware of the presence of either the lens *L* or the point *P*, which in the theory of optics is called the *object*. The image at *P'* is said to be *real*. A lens that causes the wave front to converge in this manner is called a *converging* lens.

In Fig. 12*b*, the lens is *diverging* in its effect on the wave front so that the center of the latter after refraction lies at the left of the lens. As before, an observer stationed at the right of the figure would be unaware of the presence of either *P* or *L* and would see only *P'*. An image of this type is said to be *virtual*, because the wave front only *appears* to spread out from *P'* and does not actually do so.

It is difficult, as stated before, to describe in mathematical terms a wave front that is not exactly spherical. Consequently, those who work in geometrical optics visualize the process of image formation in terms of rays, since these can be traced

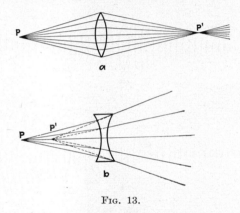

Fig. 13.

through the system by simple trigonometrical methods. To be sure, the path of a single ray gives information concerning only a single point on the wave front, but in practice the performance of an optical system can usually be judged from the behavior of a few properly selected rays.

The process of image formation on the basis of the ray method is shown in Fig. 13. In Fig. 13*a*, the pencil of rays emitted by the point source *P* is refracted by the two surfaces of the lens and recombined to form an image at *P'*. In Fig. 13*b*, the lens causes the rays to diverge after refraction as though they originated at *P'*, so this point is the image of *P*.

Now in any of these cases, there is no reason why the image *P'* should not serve as the object for a second lens. If *P'* lies at the left of the second lens, as in Figs. 14*a* and 14*b*, the rays from *P'* behave toward the second lens exactly as though *P'* were an actual source. Such an image can then be regarded as a *real* *object* for the second lens whether the rays actually diverge from it or only appear to do so; that is, whether the image is real (Fig. 14*a*) or virtual (Fig. 14*b*), it is, in effect, a real object for a second lens if it is situated at the left of the latter. If P' lies at the right of the second lens, as in Fig. 14*c*, the rays are converging toward P' when they enter the second lens, and are therefore intercepted before they can form the image P'. Nevertheless, P' may still be regarded as the object for the second lens, but in this case it is said to be a *virtual object*. It is clear that whether an object is real or virtual depends merely on whether the light is diverging or converging when it enters the lens. From a mathe-

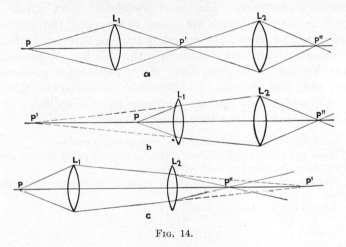

Fig. 14.

matical standpoint it is unnecessary to make any distinction between these two kinds of objects, except in choosing the algebraic signs of the involved quantities in the equations to be developed in later chapters.

For every position that an object may occupy with respect to a lens, there is a corresponding position for the image. The object and image are therefore said to be *conjugate* to each other with respect to the lens, and the corresponding distances of the object and its image from the lens are called *conjugate distances*. The mathematical equations expressing this conjugate relationship will be developed in later chapters, and it will be sufficient to note here that, in the most general sense, an optical system transforms a three-dimensional *object space* into a three-dimensional *image space*. Since the object may be either real or virtual, the object space extends from infinity in one direction to infinity in the other. A similar argument holds for the image, and consequently both object space and image space extend throughout the entirety of physical space. In other words, neither the object space nor the image space can be considered as a separate region, the expressions being used merely to differentiate between quantities relating to the object and those relating to the image.

17. Geometrical Optics.—The branch of optics that treats of the formation of images is called *geometrical optics* because the subject can be developed from a few fundamental postulates by geometrical methods. The four postulates upon which the subject is usually based are given below, and the next five chapters will be devoted to extending their significance by formal mathematical processes. Although the validity of these postulates should be obvious from the experimental phenomena described in this chapter, the best proof lies in the fact that the results to which they lead are confirmed by the excellence of the optical instruments that they have produced.

1. Light travels in straight lines in a homogeneous medium.

2. When two rays of light intersect, the subsequent paths of each are the same as though each ray existed separately.

3. When a ray is reflected, the angle of incidence equals the angle of reflection.

4. When a ray is refracted, $n \sin i = n' \sin r$.

CHAPTER II

REFRACTION AT A SPHERICAL SURFACE

Inasmuch as the most important problems in geometrical optics relate to lenses with spherical surfaces, a study of the subject must begin with a study of the formation of images by a spherical refracting surface. In Fig. 15, the point object P lies in a medium of refractive index n. A second medium at the right of P with an index n' is separated from the first by a spherical boundary surface whose center is at C. The line PC will be

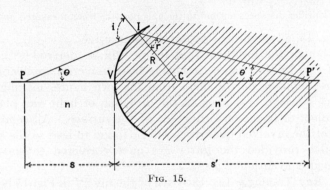

Fɪɢ. 15.

called the *axis* of this system and the point V, where it intersects the refracting surface, the *vertex*. Now a ray PV coincident with the axis before striking the surface will be coincident thereafter, because it strikes the surface normally and consequently is not deviated. Another ray from P, such as PI, will be refracted to intersect the axial ray at some point P'. This point where the two rays intersect is the image of the point P. The problem that arises most frequently is to determine the image distance $s' = VP'$, knowing the object distance $s = PV$ and the angle θ, which for convenience will be termed the *slope angle* of the ray PI.

18. Convention of Signs.—Since every distance involved in the problem must be measured from some origin, a convention of signs must be adopted to insure consistency in the derivation

33

and use of the formulae. No convention is universal, but the following coincides largely with the conventions of coordinate geometry and results in the greatest number of positive signs when applying the derived formulae:

1. Draw all figures with the light incident on the reflecting or refracting surface from the *left*.

2. Consider the *object distance s = PV* positive when *P* is at the *left* of the vertex.

3. Consider the *image distance s′ = VP′* positive when *P′* is at the *right* of the vertex.

4. Consider the *radius of curvature R = CV* positive when the center of curvature lies at the *right* of the vertex.

5. Consider *slope angles* positive when the *axis* must be rotated counterclockwise through less than $\pi/2$ to bring it into coincidence with the ray.

6. Consider *angles of incidence and refraction* positive when the *radius of curvature* must be rotated counterclockwise through less than $\pi/2$ to bring it into coincidence with the ray.

7. Consider distances normal to the axis positive when measured upward.

In Fig. 15, all quantities except θ' are positive.

Although the formulae that follow will be derived with the aid of Fig. 15, they can be proved to be of universal applicability. The reader may derive them from his own figure, making the surface concave or convex to the direction of light and placing the object or image on either side of the surface. All combinations of the involved quantities will be found to lead to the same formulae provided the latter are once corrected to suit the assumed convention of signs.

19. Ray Tracing.—Let the path of the ray *PI* in Fig. 15 before refraction be described in terms of s, the object distance, and θ, the slope angle. To find the corresponding quantities s' and θ' after refraction, the angle of incidence i must first be determined. In triangle *PIC*, by the sine law,

$$\frac{\sin \theta}{\sin (\pi - i)} = \frac{R}{R + s}.$$

Solving for i,

$$\sin i = \frac{R + s}{R} \sin \theta . \qquad (17)$$

Now the angle of refraction can be found from Snell's law, Eq. (14), which, for convenience, will be rewritten in the form

$$\sin r = \frac{n}{n'} \sin i . \qquad (18)$$

Then in triangle PIP' the sum of the angles is π. In other words,

$$\theta + (\pi - i) + r + \theta' = \pi$$

Making this equation explicit for θ' and remembering that the latter is negative,

$$\theta' = r + \theta - i. \tag{19}$$

This gives the slope angle of the refracted ray. To find the distance $s' = VP'$, consider the triangle $P'IC$ and, from the law of sines, set

$$\frac{s' - R}{R} = \frac{\sin r}{-\sin \theta'}.$$

Solving this for s', it becomes

$$s' = R - R \frac{\sin r}{\sin \theta'}. \tag{20}$$

The four equations, (17), (18), (19), and (20), are sufficient to locate the point P' for any ray in the object space whose intercept and slope angle are known.

If the refracting surface is plane, $R = \infty$ and the above formulae become indeterminate. For this special case, it can easily be shown that the following relations are sufficient:

$$\sin \theta' = \frac{n}{n'} \sin \theta \tag{21}$$

and

$$s' = -s \tan \theta \cot \theta'. \tag{22}$$

Another important special case[1] is illustrated in Fig. 16. Here the point P is at infinity so that PI is parallel to PV. Designating the height of the ray PI above the axis by h, it appears at once that

$$\sin i = \frac{h}{R}. \tag{23}$$

---

[1] Occasionally there arise certain other special cases that can be treated more conveniently by other methods of ray tracing, but they are beyond the scope of the present volume. They can be found in such works as von Rohr's "The Geometrical Investigation of the Formation of Images in Optical Instruments" and Steinheil and Voit's "Applied Optics." The latter contains many examples of trigonometrical computations.

The law of refraction, Eq. (18), applies as before. Then, in triangle $P'IC$, the exterior angle at C equals i, so

$$\theta' = r - i. \tag{24}$$

Finally the law of sines gives Eq. (20) just as in the general case. The four equations, (23), (18), (24), and (20), are sufficient in this case for tracing the course of a ray after refraction.

Most optical systems consist of many refracting surfaces; even a simple lens is bounded by two surfaces. When the system consists of more than one refracting surface, the procedure in ray tracing is to trace the given ray through each surface in turn, the object for each surface (after the first) being the image formed

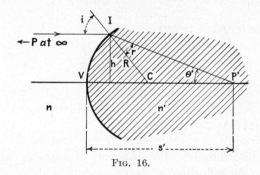

Fig. 16.

by the preceding surface. Almost invariably optical systems consist of successive media separated by spherical surfaces whose centers lie on a line known as the *axis* of the system. A ray intersecting this axis (or that would intersect it if extended) lies in a meridian plane and is known as a *meridional ray*. The preceding formulae apply to such rays. Although most of the rays emanating from an object do not lie in a meridian plane, except for the very special case of a point object on the axis, the performance of an optical system can usually be judged from the behavior of properly selected meridional rays. The rays that do not intersect the axis—the so-called *skew rays*—are so much more difficult to trace that they are usually ignored in practical lens design.

20. Numerical Calculations.—In practice, the designer of an optical system begins by selecting a set of glasses and radii of curvature that experience (or a rough preliminary calculation) has shown may produce a system capable of forming an image of the quality required. He then traces selected rays through each surface in turn to determine the performance of the system, and modifies the constants by successive trials until the desired performance is attained. Different establishments have different forms for the computation but they are all similar in essential details to the one about to be presented. This particular form is selected because of the ease with which it can be comprehended, and the reader who attempts lens computation will undoubtedly modify it to suit his own convenience.

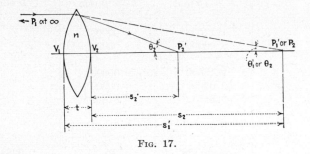

Fig. 17.

As an example of the process of ray tracing, let us determine the behavior of the simple lens sketched in Fig. 17. The constants of this lens are:

Radius of first surface R_1 .... $+100.00$ mm
Radius of second surface R_2 .. -100.00 mm
Refractive index n 1.51767
Axial thickness t .... 20.00 mm

Since the precision required in such a problem necessitates the use of logarithms, a formal argument facilitates the computation. This argument is merely a skeleton form, made out prior to beginning the calculation, into which the logarithms are inserted in the proper order for easy addition or subtraction in accordance with the operations indicated by the fundamental equations developed in the preceding section. The argument in Table II is for the first refracting surface and shows the calculations for three incident rays parallel to the axis—the axial ray ($h = 0$) and two others at an incident height of 10 mm and 15 mm respectively above the axis. The method of computing will be obvious by comparing the work with Eqs. (23), (18), (24), and (20).

Although five-place logarithms are used ordinarily, the value of θ' sometimes becomes so small that six-place tables must be used to attain the requisite precision. The difference between keeping in mind five and six figures is great, and therefore six-place tables should not be used unless it is necessary. Indeed, seven-place tables are but little more difficult for an inexperienced computer, and, as they are readily available, they are to be recommended when five-place tables are not sufficiently precise.

TABLE II.—ARGUMENT FOR FIRST SURFACE

(Incident rays parallel to the axis.)

	$h = 15$ mm	$h = 10$ mm	$h = 0$
$\log h$	1.17609^+	1.00000^+	
$\mathrm{colog}\ R$	8.00000^+	8.00000^+	
$\log \sin i$	9.17609^+	9.00000^+	
$\log n$	0.00000^+	0.00000^+	
$\mathrm{colog}\ n'$	9.81882^+	9.81882^+	
$\log \sin r$	8.99491^+	8.81882^+	
r	$5°\ 40'\ 20''^+$	$3°\ 46'\ 41''^+$	0.098835^+
i	$8°\ 37'\ 37''^+$	$5°\ 44'\ 21''^+$	0.150000^+
$\theta'(= r - i)$	$2°\ 57'\ 17''^-$	$1°\ 57'\ 40''^-$	0.051165^-
$\mathrm{colog} \sin \theta'$	1.28780^-	1.46571^-	1.29103^-
$\log \sin r$	8.99491^+	8.81882^+	8.99491^+
$\log R$	2.00000^+	2.00000^+	2.00000^+
$\log (R - s')$	2.28271^-	2.28453^-	2.28594^-
$R - s'$	191.74^-	192.54^-	193.17^-
s'	291.74^+	292.54^+	293.17^+

The axial ray, for which sin $i = 0$, is computed by means of an artifice.[1] The procedure is to trace any other ray parallel to the axis, and then, beginning with the operations represented by Eq. (18), to use the sines of the angles in place of the angles themselves. In the present case, the value of log sin r for $h = 15$ is 8.99491, and the corresponding value of r is 5° 40′ 20″. Now the number whose logarithm is 8.99491 is found in the table of logarithms of natural numbers to be 0.098835, and the latter

[1] For the proof of the validity of this method, see Lummer's "Photographic Optics," translated by Silvanus P. Thompson, p. 126.

value is entered in the table opposite r for the axial ray. A similar procedure is followed with respect to i, and the value of θ' is found by subtraction. Then against colog sin θ' is written simply the cologarithm of 0.051165, after which the procedure is the same as for any other ray. It is immaterial what ray is selected as the auxiliary provided it is used throughout.

The argument shown in Table II gives the distances s' from the vertex V_1 of the first surface to the point P_1' where each ray would intersect the axis if everything behind the first surface were

TABLE III.—ARGUMENT FOR SECOND SURFACE

	$\theta = 2° 57' 17''$	$\theta = 1° 57' 40''$	$\theta = 0$
log $(R + s)$	2.57024⁻	2.57117⁻	2.57191⁻
colog R	8.00000⁻	8.00000⁻	8.00000⁻
log sin θ	8.71220⁻	8.53429⁻	8.70897⁻
log sin i	9.28244⁻	9.10546⁻	9.28088⁻
log n	0.18118⁺	0.18118⁺	0.18118⁺
colog n'	0.00000⁺	0.00000⁺	0.00000⁺
log sin r	9.46362⁻	9.28664⁻	9.46206⁻
r	16° 54' 24''⁻	11° 9' 23''⁻	0.28977⁻
θ	2° 57' 17''⁻	1° 57' 40''⁻	0.05117⁻
i	11° 2' 50''⁻	7° 19' 28''⁻	0.19093⁻
$\theta'(= r + \theta - i)$	8° 48' 51''⁻	5° 47' 35''⁻	0.15001⁻
colog sin θ'	0.81406⁻	0.99596⁻	0.82388⁻
log sin r	9.46362⁻	9.28664⁻	9.46206⁻
log R	2.00000⁻	2.00000⁻	2.00000⁻
log $(R - s')$	2.27828⁻	2.28260⁻	2.28594⁻
$R - s'$	189.79⁻	191.69⁻	193.17⁻
s'	89.79⁺	91.69⁺	93.17⁺

glass. But the ray never reaches P_1' because it suffers a further refraction when it encounters the second surface, the vertex of which is V_2. The direction and intercept of the ray in the final image space can be found, of course, by tracing it through the second surface. This procedure is straightforward since the slope angle θ_2 for the second surface is identical with θ_1' for the first surface, and the image point P_1' which has just been located is the object point P_2 for the second surface. That the object is virtual is of no consequence provided proper recognition of the fact is made in the choice of algebraic signs. Thus in the present case for the ray at $h = 15$, s' for the first surface was 291.74. This distance is measured from V_1. The object distance s_2 for the second surface is the distance V_2P_1', which is obtained by subtracting the thickness of the lens from s_1'. Thus $s_2 = -271.74$, the negative sign being required because P_2 is at the right of V_2. The rays are traced through the second surface by following the argument illustrated in Table III, which is based on Eqs. (17), (18), (19), and (20). As a result, it is found that if rays from infinity are incident on the lens of Fig. 17 at the heights zero, 10 mm, and 15 mm, the intercepts are at distances 93.17 mm, 91.69 mm, and 89.79 mm respectively behind the second vertex. The inequality of these values is an indication of a defect known as spherical aberration, which will be treated more fully in Chap. VI.

The distance from the vertex of the last refracting surface to the image of an infinitely distant point object on the axis is called the *back focal length* of the lens. This term is a misnomer since this quantity has no direct relation to what is properly known as the focal length, as will be shown in Sec. 31. There is a need for a better term but none has been suggested.

21. Behavior of Rays in the Paraxial Region.—The sine of the slope angle θ can be expanded by Maclaurin's theorem into

$$\sin \theta = \theta - \frac{\theta^3}{3!} + \frac{\theta^5}{5!} - \frac{\theta^7}{7!} + \cdots \tag{25}$$

For a ray in the vicinity of the axis, a *paraxial ray*, θ becomes so small that $\sin \theta = \theta$ to a close approximation. The theory based upon this approximation is known as the *first-order theory* because the terms of higher order are neglected. It is also called the *Gauss theory* from the mathematician who first developed it.

If θ is small, i and r must be small to the same order of approximation. Then the fundamental equations become

$$i = \frac{R + s}{R} \theta, \tag{26}$$

$$r = \frac{n}{n'} i, \tag{27}$$

and

$$s' = R - R\frac{r}{\theta'}; \tag{28}$$

with Eq. (19),

$$\theta' = r + \theta - i$$

remaining the same as before. By direct algebraic methods, θ and θ' can be eliminated from these equations with the result that

$$\frac{n}{s} + \frac{n'}{s'} = \frac{n' - n}{R}. \tag{29}$$

This equation is in many respects the most important in geometrical optics. From a theoretical standpoint, the fact that θ and θ' do not appear in it shows that all rays near the axis emanating from a point object unite to form a point image. To be sure, the rays traced through the lens in the preceding section did not unite at a point after refraction, but if more rays had been traced, it would have been found that those within a small region about the axis do so to a very close approximation. From a practical standpoint, this equation is adequate for locating the image formed by any system of centered spherical surfaces regardless of its complexity. Of course, the equation applies only to rays in the paraxial region, but in a

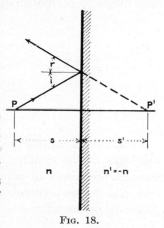

Fig. 18.

properly corrected system, the extra-axial rays come to focus at substantially the same point as the paraxial rays.[1] This equation does not become indeterminate when R becomes infinite and it may therefore be used for refraction at a plane surface. It may also be used for reflection by setting $n' = -n$. That this is possible can be shown by Fig. 18. Here, by convention, i and r are always of opposite sign, and so $\sin i = -\sin r$. Hence, from Eq. (18), $n' = -n$. By treating reflection as a special case of

[1] It is clear that Eq. (29) can be used for the treatment of the axial ray instead of the artifice used in the preceding section. In practical lens design, where several rays must be traced through a number of surfaces, the artifice is more convenient.

refraction, it is unnecessary to develop parallel sets of equations for the two phenomena.

22. Lateral Magnification.—If a point is not on the axis, it is usually desirable to know the distance of the image from the axis in addition to its position along the axis. Consider the point Q in Fig. 19. This point lies in a plane through P perpendicular to the axis, the distance PQ being represented by y. It is easily shown that, provided PQ is not too great, the image of Q lies at Q' in a plane perpendicular to the axis through P', the image of P. If the distance of Q' from the axis is represented by y', the *lateral magnification* in these planes is defined by

$$m = \frac{y'}{y}. \tag{30}$$

This quantity is frequently called simply the *magnification*.

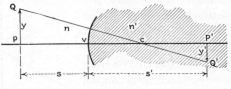

FIG. 19.

To derive an expression for the magnification in terms of other constants of the system, consider rays PCP' and QCQ' passing through the center of curvature C in Fig. 19. Obviously these rays will be undeviated at the refracting surface. From the geometry of the figure,

$$-\frac{y'}{y} = \frac{s' - R}{s + R}. \tag{31}$$

Now Eq. (29) may be written

$$\frac{n}{s} + \frac{n}{R} = \frac{n'}{R} - \frac{n'}{s'}$$

or

$$\frac{s' - R}{s + R} = \frac{ns'}{n's}. \tag{32}$$

Combining Eqs. (30), (31), and (32),

$$m = \frac{y'}{y} = -\frac{ns'}{n's}. \tag{33}$$

This equation determines the height y' of the image formed by a single refracting surface of an object of height y. For a system comprising a number of centered spherical surfaces, the size of the final image is found by multiplying the size of the object by the product of the magnifications produced by all the surfaces. It must be noted that the term "magnification" is used in its most general sense and so includes values of m less than unity.

23. Lagrange's Law.—In Fig. 20, a spherical refracting surface forms an image having a height y' of an object having a height y. Let the corresponding slope angles in the object and image

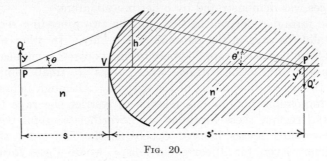

Fig. 20.

spaces be θ and θ' respectively, θ being so small that θ and θ' can be measured by their arcs. Then,

$$\theta = \frac{h}{s}$$

and

$$\theta' = -\frac{h}{s'}.$$

Therefore

$$\frac{s'}{s} = -\frac{\theta}{\theta'}. \tag{34}$$

Combining this with Eq. (33),

$$\frac{y'}{y} = \frac{n\theta}{n'\theta'} \tag{35}$$

or

$$ny\,\theta = n'y'\theta'. \tag{36}$$

This equation, which represents what is frequently called *Lagrange's law* after its discoverer, can be extended to include the case of refraction at any number of surfaces. Then the left-hand member refers to the quantities in the object space and the right-hand member to the corresponding quantities in the final image space. The validity of this extension of Lagrange's law can be demonstrated by writing it for each surface in succession. Then, since the image formed by one surface is the object for the succeeding surface and since the index of the intermediate media and the slope angles of the intermediate rays, taken successively, are the same, all the quantities referring to the intermediate refractions cancel in pairs. There remain only those quantities represented by Eq. (36). This equation will still be referred to as Lagrange's law, although its application to a series of surfaces was demonstrated by other investigators.

The formulae derived in this and the two preceding sections are valid for rays in the paraxial region only. In other words, these formulae can be applied only to small objects lying near the axis and to refracting surfaces whose areas are small compared with the other dimensions of the system. Although in practice it is impossible for obvious reasons to restrict the rays to the paraxial region, these formulae are nevertheless useful because well-corrected lenses behave closely as the first-order theory predicts. Even for ill-corrected lenses, where these formulae apply only approximately, the results are still of some value.

CHAPTER III

THE THIN LENS IN AIR

In the preceding chapter, formulae were developed for determining the size and location of an image formed by refraction at a spherical surface. It was also shown that a system composed of any number of coaxial spherical surfaces can be treated by considering the surfaces one at a time, the object for each surface being the image formed by the preceding one. No more formulae are necessary, but inasmuch as certain special cases arise in the overwhelming majority of problems involving the first-order theory, it is convenient to have formulae for treating them directly. The case considered in this chapter is that of the thin lens in air.

24. Formulae for Conjugate Distances.—In Fig. 21, let the refractive index of the lens be n, its axial thickness be t, and the

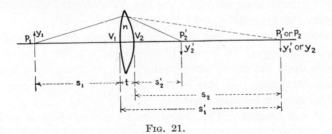

FIG. 21.

radii of its surfaces be R_1 and R_2. The paraxial rays emanating from P_1 unite after the first refraction at P_1' as given by Eq. (29), which here becomes

$$\frac{1}{s_1} + \frac{n}{s_1'} = \frac{n-1}{R_1} \tag{37}$$

because the first medium is air. In other words, if the medium at the right of the first surface consisted entirely of glass, an image of the point P_1 would be formed at P_1'. Now if P_1' is considered as the object P_2 for the second surface, and it is noted

45

that $s_2 = -(s_1' - t)$, Eq. (29) applied to the second surface becomes

$$\frac{n}{-(s_1' - t)} + \frac{1}{s_2'} = \frac{1 - n}{R_2}. \tag{38}$$

These two equations suffice to determine s_2' for any simple lens in air. If the lens is thin, s_2 can be set equal to $-s_1'$ and the latter eliminated. The result is that

$$\frac{1}{s_1} + \frac{1}{s_2'} = (n - 1)\left(\frac{1}{R_1} - \frac{1}{R_2}\right).$$

Inasmuch as t is assumed to be equal to zero, the distances s_1 and s_2' may be measured from any part of the lens and the subscripts lose their significance. Thus the thin-lens equation may be written

$$\frac{1}{s} + \frac{1}{s'} = (n - 1)\left(\frac{1}{R_1} - \frac{1}{R_2}\right). \tag{39}$$

It will be recalled that, by the convention of signs, s is positive when the object lies at the left of the lens and s' is positive when the image lies at the right. The radii R_1 and R_2 are positive when the center of curvature is at the right of the vertex of the corresponding surface. As Fig. 21 is drawn, all quantities appearing in Eq. (39) except R_2 are positive.

Inasmuch as no lens can have zero thickness Eq. (39) is always an approximation. Whether it is satisfactory for a given case depends upon the importance of the error resulting from neglecting the thickness. If this error would be too great, Eqs. (37) and (38) should be used instead.

25. Focal Length.—The quantities in the right-hand member of Eq. (39) are characteristic of the lens itself and do not involve the object or image distance. This member is often called the *power* D of the lens[1]; and its reciprocal, the *focal length f.* Thus

$$D = \frac{1}{f} = (n - 1)\left(\frac{1}{R_1} - \frac{1}{R_2}\right). \tag{40}$$

It will be seen that the value of f is the image distance s' when s is infinite. The sign of f evidently must follow from the

[1] The unit of power is the *diopter* (sometimes written dioptre, dioptrie, or dioptry). By definition, it is the power of a lens whose focal length is one meter.

convention already adopted. Thus, the focal length of the lens shown in Fig. 21 is positive. If this lens were in a medium of higher index than its own, its focal length would become negative. Since lenses are commonly used in air, they are called *positive* or *converging* when f is positive for the lens in air, and *negative* or *diverging* when f is negative.

26. Magnification Produced by a Thin Lens.—Consider an object of height y_1 in a plane through P_1 perpendicular to the axis (Fig. 21). From Eq. (33) the height y_1' of the image formed at P_1' by refraction at the first surface is

$$y_1' = m_1 y_1 = -\frac{s_1'}{n s_1} y_1. \tag{41}$$

If this image is considered as the object for the second surface, the height of the final image is

$$y_2' = m_2 y_1' = -\frac{n s_2'}{s_2} y_1'. \tag{42}$$

If Eqs. (41) and (42) are combined, the magnification produced by refraction at both surfaces is found to be

$$m = \frac{y_2'}{y_1} = \frac{s_1' s_2'}{s_1 s_2}. \tag{43}$$

It will be noted that when the initial and final media have the same index, as in the present case, the index of the lens disappears in the expression for the magnification. When the lens is so thin that s_2 can be set equal to $-s_1'$, Eq. (43) can be rewritten without the subscripts as

$$m = \frac{y'}{y} = -\frac{s'}{s}. \tag{44}$$

In this equation, s and s' are measured from any part of the lens and y and y' represent the size of the object and the final image respectively. By the convention of signs, y and y' are positive when measured above the axis. Therefore a positive value of m indicates an erect image and a negative value, an inverted image. Since s is always positive for a real object and s' for a real image, it follows that real images of real objects when formed by a *single* thin lens must always be inverted.

As before, the term "magnification" is used in the broad sense and is not restricted to cases where the value of m is greater than unity. As a matter of fact, reduction is more common in practical optics than enlargement.   A camera lens, for example, is used ordinarily to form images many times smaller than the objects photographed.   A more extreme example is the telescope objective, which forms an image of the moon, say, so small that the magnification is practically zero.   The image formed by the entire instrument appears larger than the object because the image formed by the objective is in a position where it can be magnified by the ocular, and this magnification is an enlargement that more than overbalances the first reduction.

27. Systems of Thin Lenses.—The position and size of the final image formed by any number of coaxial thin lenses in air

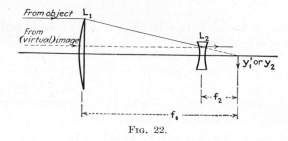

Fig. 22.

can be found by the use of Eqs. (39) and (44).   The method is the same as that used for a series of surfaces in the preceding chapter.   The image formed by each lens is found in turn, the object for each lens (after the first) being the image formed by the preceding lens.   An example will make the method clear.

Consider a converging and a diverging lens separated by a distance equal to the numerical difference of their focal lengths f_1 and f_2, as shown in Fig. 22.   This is the optical system of the opera glass or Galilean telescope.   The image of an infinitely distant object formed by lens L_1, called the objective, is at a distance f_1 behind it.   This image is the object for lens L_2, called the ocular.   It is a virtual object because it lies at the right of L_2. Inasmuch as it is at a distance f_2 from L_2 by the conditions of the problem, the image formed by this lens is at infinity also.

The magnification of the combination is the product of the magnifications produced by the individual lenses.   For the objective,

$$m_1 = \frac{y_1'}{y_1} = -\frac{s_1'}{s_1} = -\frac{f_1}{s_1}, \tag{45}$$

where y_1 is the assumed height of the original object. For the ocular,

$$m_2 = \frac{y_2'}{y_2} = \frac{y_2'}{y_1'} = -\frac{s_2'}{s_2} = -\frac{s_2'}{f_2}, \tag{46}$$

and so for the combination

$$m = m_1 m_2 = \frac{f_1}{s_1} \cdot \frac{s_2'}{f_2}. \tag{47}$$

Now the ratio s_2'/s_1 approaches unity as s_2' and s_1 become increasingly large. They are opposite in sign, however, because of the convention that was adopted. Hence,

$$m = -\frac{f_1}{f_2}. \tag{48}$$

Equation (48) shows that if f_1 is made very great and f_2 relatively small, the magnification may be made practically infinite. It will be shown in Chap. VII, however, that the limit of useful magnification is set by the wave length of light. This fact is not indicated by the formulae derived on the basis of the postulates of geometrical optics; and the postulates are, to this extent, an incomplete representation of the principles underlying the formation of optical images.

CHAPTER IV

THE THICK LENS

It was shown in Chap. II that Eqs. (29) and (33) suffice to determine the location and size of the image formed by the paraxial rays that traverse any system of coaxial spherical refracting surfaces. The application of these equations necessitates treating the surfaces one at a time, the object for each surface (after the first) being the image formed by the preceding one. In Chap. III, special formulae were developed as a matter of convenience for the case of a simple lens of negligible thickness. In the present chapter, formulae will be developed for any system of centered spherical refracting surfaces, which we shall term simply a *thick lens*. Such a lens may consist of a single piece of glass or it may consist of several elements, which may be either thick or thin. As in the preceding chapter, these formulae hold only for the paraxial region, but in practice they represent the behavior of corrected systems reasonably well.

These formulae involve conjugate distances, which must be measured from some point of reference, and they are much simplified by selecting two points of reference, one for the object space and the other for the image space. These points may be chosen quite arbitrarily, but a further simplification results from selecting certain pairs of points that are so important that they are called *cardinal points*. Of the cardinal points, those known as the principal points and the focal points are the most useful, and we shall therefore discuss them first.

28. Principal Points and Focal Points.—In Fig. 23, let the two conjugate planes AB and $A'B'$ be the two transverse planes for which the lateral magnification produced by an optical system (not shown) is unity and positive. Such planes are said to be the *principal planes* of the system. The points H and H', where the planes intersect the axis, are known as the *principal points* or *Gauss points*. Now all rays parallel to the axis in the object space, such as QA, may be considered to have arrived from an infinitely distant point object on the axis, and so, from

50

the first-order theory, they will converge, after refraction by the system, to form a point image at F'. This point is called the *second focal point*, and the distance $f' = H'F'$, the *second focal length* of the system. By turning the system end for end, it will be seen that the point F has similar properties for an infinitely distant object at the other side of the system. This point is called the *first focal point*, and the distance $f = FH$ is called the *first focal length* of the system. Following the convention of signs already adopted, the first focal length is positive when F lies at the left of H, and the second focal length is positive when F' lies at the right of H'. It will be shown in Sec. 32 that, if the initial and final media are the same, the two focal lengths are equal. Indeed, this is most commonly the case.

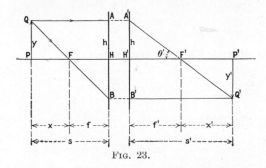

Fig. 23.

29. Conjugate Distances and Lateral Magnification Referred to the Focal Points.—Let PQ and $P'Q'$ in Fig. 23 lie in conjugate planes, PQ being considered the object and $P'Q'$, its image. Formulae for the position and size of $P'Q'$ will now be developed in terms of the position and size of PQ and certain constants of the system. Since P is on the axis, the object distance measured from the first focal point is $x = PF$. Similarly the image distance is $x' = F'P'$. It is evident from the figure that triangles PQF and HBF are similar, as are triangles $P'Q'F'$ and $A'H'F'$. Therefore

$$\frac{-HB}{AH} = \frac{f}{x} \tag{49}$$

and

$$\frac{-H'B'}{A'H'} = \frac{x'}{f'}. \tag{50}$$

In these equations, x and x' are assumed positive as drawn— that is, the object distance x from the first focal point is positive when the object lies at the *left* of F, while the image distance x' is positive when the image lies at the *right* of F'.

Now the lateral magnification between the object plane and the image plane was defined by Eq. (30) as $m = y'/y$. But $y = AH$ and $y' = H'B'$. Since by definition the lateral magnification is unity in the principal planes, any ray in the object space that would pass through the point A if it were not refracted emerges in the image space as though coming from the point A', where $AH = A'H'$. Similarly any ray through F that would intersect the first principal plane at B if it were not refracted emerges parallel to the axis after refraction as though coming from B', where $HB = H'B'$. In the light of these considerations, Eq. (30) combined with Eq. (49) results in

$$m = -\frac{f}{x}, \tag{51}$$

and combined with Eq. (50) results in

$$m = -\frac{x'}{f'}. \tag{52}$$

Combining Eqs. (51) and (52),

$$xx' = ff'. \tag{53}$$

This form of the expression for the conjugate distances is frequently referred to as the *Newtonian*[1] *form*. It is admirably suited to the use of the slide rule or logarithms, which can scarcely be said of other forms of the equation. It should be noted that, since f and f' always have like signs, x and x' must have like signs also. In other words, an object and its image always lie on opposite sides of the corresponding focal points.

30. Conjugate Distances and Lateral Magnification Referred to the Principal Points.—In the preceding section, the distance of the object was measured from the first focal point F while the distance of the image was measured from the second focal point F'. Occasionally it is more convenient to measure these distances from the principal points H and H'. Let $PH = s$ and $H'P' = s'$. Conformably to the convention already adopted, assume s

---

[1] "Opticks" (1704), Book I, Pt. I, Axiom VI, Case 4. Equation (53) was stated (in words) in the form $x'/f' = f/x$. Newton gave no proof because this axiom, like the others, had "hitherto been treated of in Opticks."

positive when P lies at the *left* of H, and s' positive when P' lies at the *right* of H'. From Fig. 23,

$$x = s - f \tag{54}$$

and

$$x' = s' - f'. \tag{55}$$

Substituting in Eq. (53),

$$(s - f)(s' - f') = ff',$$

which may be written more simply as

$$\frac{f}{s} + \frac{f'}{s'} = 1. \tag{56}$$

By substituting Eq. (54) in Eq. (51), and Eq. (55) in Eq. (52), the lateral magnification in terms of the conjugate distances from the principal points is found to be

$$m = -\frac{f}{s - f} = -\frac{s' - f'}{f'}. \tag{57}$$

The convention of the signs of all quantities has been consistent, so a positive magnification still indicates an erect image.

A more useful expression for the lateral magnification can be obtained by applying Lagrange's law to the principal planes. In Fig. 24, θ and θ' are the corresponding slope angles for a ray through H and H'. Since the lateral magnification is unity in these planes, Lagrange's law shows that

$$\frac{n}{n'} = \frac{\theta'}{\theta}, \tag{58}$$

where the quantities n and n' designate the refractive indices of the object and image spaces respectively. Since θ and θ' are small, they can be measured by their arcs, so

$$\theta = -\frac{y}{s}$$

and

$$\theta' = \frac{y'}{s'}.$$

The lateral magnification between the conjugate planes at P and P' is y'/y, so it follows at once that

$$m = -\frac{ns'}{n's}. \tag{59}$$

The method of treatment used in the present chapter is so general that Eqs. (56) and (59) apply even when the system consists of but a single refracting surface. The fact that Eq. (59) is identical in form with Eq. (33) in Chap. II, wherein the distances s and s' were measured from the vertex, indicates that the principal points of a single surface coincide at its vertex. The focal points can be located by assuming an infinitely distant object, first on one side and then on the other, and finding the position of its image in each case by means of Eq. (29). Although it is of theoretical interest to notice that the concept of cardinal points is applicable to a single surface, it is generally more convenient in practice to apply the formulae of Chap. II directly.

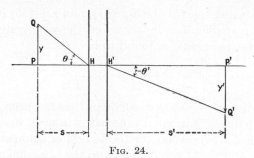

Fig. 24.

31. Focal Length.—The focal lengths f and f' can be determined by calculation when the radii, indices, and separations of the system are known. The procedure is to consider a point object at infinity in the object space, which we shall assume to have a refractive index n. If the index of the medium following the first refracting surface is n_1, Eq. (33) gives

$$m_1 = -\frac{n s_1'}{n_1 s_1}$$

for the magnification resulting from refraction at the first surface, s_1 and s_1' being measured from the first vertex, of course. Now in similar fashion,

$$m_2 = -\frac{n_1 s_2'}{n_2 s_2}$$

for the second refracting surface. Hence the magnification m produced by any number of centered spherical surfaces is

$$m = m_1 \times m_2 \times m_3 \times m_4 \ldots$$
$$= \left(-\frac{n s_1'}{n_1 s_1}\right)\left(-\frac{n_1 s_2'}{n_2 s_2}\right)\left(-\frac{n_2 s_3'}{n_3 s_3}\right)\left(-\frac{n_3 s_4'}{n_4 s_4}\right) \ldots \quad (60)$$

The same value for the magnification should result if it is computed by means of Eq. (59) instead of Eq. (60). Equating the two expressions for the magnification,

$$-\frac{ns'}{n's} = \left(-\frac{ns_1'}{n_1s_1}\right)\left(-\frac{n_1s_2'}{n_2s_2}\right)\left(-\frac{n_2s_3'}{n_3s_3}\right)\left(-\frac{n_3s_4'}{n_4s_4}\right)\cdots \quad (61)$$

Since the object was chosen at infinity, s and s_1 are equal and infinite and may therefore be eliminated; that is, the difference between s and s_1 is merely the distance between the first vertex and the first principal point, and this distance is small compared with infinity except in systems of infinite focal length. It will be noticed also that the refractive indices of the intermediate media, n_1, n_2, etc., cancel in pairs from the right-hand member, leaving only the index of the first medium n and the index of the final medium, which may be written n'. Hence the refractive indices cancel entirely from Eq. (61). But the object distance was assumed to be infinite, so $s' = f'$ and therefore

$$f' = s_1'\left(-\frac{s_2'}{s_2}\right)\left(-\frac{s_3'}{s_3}\right)\left(-\frac{s_4'}{s_4}\right)\cdots \quad (62)$$

The quantities involved in this equation can be determined by applying Eq. (29) in Chap. II to each surface in turn or by tracing a ray from infinity through the system trigonometrically. But if the latter procedure is adopted, there is a much simpler method for finding f'. In Fig. 23, the ray QA in the object space is at a height h above the axis and parallel to it. No matter how many refractions the ray may suffer, it will finally emerge into the image space as though it had passed through the point A', which is also at a height h above the axis. Now angle $A'F'H'$ is known from the trigonometrical computations since it is the value of θ' after refraction at the last surface. By definition, the focal length for the ray QA is the distance $A'F'$. Hence

$$\frac{h}{f'} = \sin\theta'$$

or

$$f' = \frac{h}{\sin\theta'}. \quad (63)$$

As a practical example of the foregoing, let us return to the problem in Sec. 20, Chap. II. The value of θ' after refraction at the last surface (in this case the second) for the ray at $h = 10$ is $\theta' = 5° 47' 35''$. Substituting in Eq. (63), $f' = 99.1$ mm. It should be noted that the argument (Table III) contains both log h and colog sin θ', so the calculation of f' is extremely simple when made by this method. Now if the ray at $h = 0$ is selected instead, colog sin $\theta' = 0.82388$. Remembering that this was computed by an artifice with the ray at $h = 15$ as the auxiliary, we find that $f' = 100.0$ mm for the axial ray.

The difference of 0.9 mm between the focal length of the axial ray and that of the ray at $h = 10$ gives rise to a defect called coma, which will be discussed in Chap. VI. Even though spherical aberration is entirely absent from a given system, as indicated by the equality of the back focal lengths for all rays, the true focal lengths may be different and hence the magnification will be different for different zones of the lens.

32. Case of the Same Initial and Final Medium.—Equations (57) and (59) can be combined in a manner to yield the expression

$$\frac{f}{f'} = \frac{n}{n'}. \tag{64}$$

Thus, if f' is found for a given system, f can be readily determined from the indices of the initial and final media. In the vast majority of cases, the initial and final media are air; and Eq. (64) shows that in this case $f = f'$. By making this substitution, Eqs. (51), (52), (53), (56), and (59) can be rewritten more simply as follows:

$$m = -\frac{f}{x}, \tag{65}$$

$$= -\frac{x'}{f}, \tag{66}$$

$$xx' = f^2, \tag{67}$$

$$\frac{1}{s} + \frac{1}{s'} = \frac{1}{f}, \tag{68}$$

$$m = -\frac{s'}{s}. \tag{69}$$

It will be noted that the last two equations have the same form as Eqs. (40) and (44) for the case of a thin lens. This does not mean that a thick lens can be replaced by a thin lens; for, although there can always be found a thin lens that will produce an image of a given object of the same size and in the same place as the image produced by the thick lens, this thin lens would be equivalent for only a single position of the object. For an object at infinity, the thin lens must lie in the second principal plane of the thick lens, and its focal length is of course the same as that of the thick lens. Such a thin lens is often called the *equivalent thin lens;* and its focal length is therefore called the *equivalent focal length.*

33. Location of the Cardinal Points by Calculation.—The calculations pertaining to a thick lens become so involved when it is treated surface by surface that it is usually advisable to determine the positions of the cardinal points immediately. This can be done in a number of ways, and the method to be selected depends somewhat upon the form in which the data are furnished. In the general case, the system is described in terms of the radii and separations of the surfaces and the refractive indices of the media. One method of locating the focal points is to apply Eq. (29) to each surface in turn, the object for the first surface being assumed to be at infinity. The value of s' for the last surface gives the position of the second focal point with respect to the vertex of the last surface. By turning the system end for end and repeating the process, the first focal point can be located with respect to the vertex of what is the first surface in the normal position. The two focal lengths of the system can then be computed by means of Eq. (62), since all the quantities appearing therein have been determined for both the normal and the reversed positions of the system. By definition, each of the principal points is separated from the corresponding focal point by the corresponding focal length, so the two principal points can be located at once.

The trigonometrical method of locating the cardinal points is essentially the same as the algebraic one that has just been described. As before, an axial ray from an object at infinity is traced through the system to locate the second focal point, and then the lens is reversed to find the first focal point. The only real difference between the two methods is in connection with the determination of the focal length, which, in this case, can be done by applying Eq. (63). As an example of the foregoing procedure, consider the lens discussed in Sec. 20. The second focal point was there found to be 93.2 mm to the right of the vertex of the last refracting surface. Now in Sec. 31, the axial focal length was found to be 100.0 mm. Consequently the second principal point must be 6.8 mm to the left of the vertex of the last (in this case, the second) refracting surface. The positions of the first focal point F and the first principal point H can be found by reversing the lens end for end and making similar calculations. As this lens is in air, the two focal lengths are equal, and this fact can be used as a check on the correctness of the calculations.

34. Formulae for a Simple Lens.—It is possible to derive algebraic formulae for the positions of the cardinal points of any optical system, but the formulae are generally so involved that it would be more laborious to substitute in them than to proceed in the straightforward manner outlined in the preceding section. They are sometimes convenient, however, in the case of a *simple lens*—that is, one containing only two refracting surfaces with air as the initial and final medium. The necessary steps in the

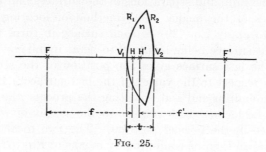

FIG. 25.

derivation of these formulae are so obvious that only the final expressions will be given.

In Fig. 25, let the focal points be F and F' and the corresponding principal points, H and H'. Let the thickness $t = V_1V_2$ be considered positive always. Since the initial and final media are the same, the first and second focal lengths are the same. The numerical value of the focal length is

$$ f = \frac{-R_1R_2}{(n-1)\left(R_1 - R_2 - \frac{n-1}{n}t\right)}, \tag{70} $$

which may be written also as

$$ \frac{1}{f} = (n-1)\left(\frac{1}{R_1} - \frac{1}{R_2} + \frac{(n-1)t}{nR_1R_2}\right). \tag{71} $$

The distance of the first principal point from the first vertex is

$$ V_1H = \frac{-(n-1)tf}{nR_2} = \frac{tR_1}{n(R_1 - R_2) - (n-1)t}. \tag{72} $$

By the sign convention, this distance is positive when H is at the *right* of V_1. Similarly,

$$H'V_2 = \frac{(n-1)\,tf}{nR_1} = \frac{-t\,R_2}{n(R_1 - R_2) - (n-1)t}, \qquad (73)$$

which is positive when H' is at the *left* of V_2. The principal points are separated by the distance

$$HH' = t - \frac{(R_1 - R_2)t}{n(R_1 - R_2) - (n-1)t}, \qquad (74)$$

which is positive when H is at the *left* of H'. This is considered the normal order. When this quantity is negative, the order is reversed and the principal points are said to be *crossed*.

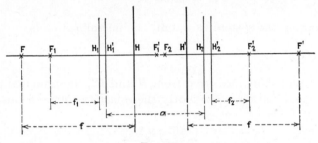

Fig. 26.

It will be seen from the above equations that no general statements can be made concerning the focal lengths or positions of the principal points of a thick lens. For example, even the familiar double-convex lens has a focal length that increases with the thickness until it becomes infinite when

$$t = \frac{n}{n-1}(R_1 - R_2).$$

A greater thickness results in a negative focal length.

35. Formulae for a System of Simple Lenses.—When the system consists, as it frequently does, of two simple lenses whose individual cardinal points have already been located, the focal length and cardinal points of the combination are easily found. In Fig. 26, let the quantities pertaining to the first lens or *element* be specified by the subscript 1 and those pertaining to the second element by the subscript 2. Let the distance $H_1'H_2$ from the second principal point of the first element to the first principal point of the second element be represented by a. Assume all quantities in the figure to be positive as drawn.

The formula for the focal length of the system can be derived by a procedure similar to that used in Sec. 31. The magnification produced by the first element is

$$m_1 = -\frac{s_1'}{s_1},$$

and that produced by the second element,

$$m_2 = -\frac{s_2'}{s_2},$$

so the total magnification is

$$m = m_1 m_2 = \frac{s_1' s_2'}{s_1 s_2}.$$

Considering the system as a unit, the magnification is

$$m = -\frac{s'}{s},$$

where s and s' are measured from H and H', the principal points of the combination. Evidently these last two expressions must be equal, whence

$$-\frac{s'}{s} = \frac{s_1' s_2'}{s_1 s_2}.$$

But the object is assumed to be at infinity, so $s = s_1$, $s_1' = f_1$, and $s' = f$. Therefore

$$f = f_1\left(-\frac{s_2'}{s_2}\right). \tag{75}$$

Now from the figure, $s_2 = a - f_1$; and from Eq. (68),

$$s_2' = \frac{f_2 s_2}{s_2 - f_2}.$$

By combining these equations, the focal length of the system is found to be

$$f = \frac{f_1 f_2}{f_1 + f_2 - a}, \tag{76}$$

which may be written

$$\frac{1}{f} = \frac{1}{f_1} + \frac{1}{f_2} - \frac{a}{f_1 f_2}. \tag{77}$$

The cardinal points can now be located, as before, by assuming an object at infinity at the left of the system. The first element then forms an image at its second focal point F_1'. This image is the object for the second element. Writing

$$x_2 x_2' = f_2^2$$

for this element, it is evident from the figure that

$$x_2 = F_1'F_2 = a - (f_1 + f_2)$$

and

$$x_2' = F_2'F' = f - f_2 - H'H_2',$$

since the image of F_1' formed by the second element must be at F'. By making the obvious substitutions, it is found that the distance of the second principal point of the system from the second principal point of the second element is

$$H'H_2' = \frac{af_2}{f_1 + f_2 - a}. \tag{78}$$

In a similar manner, the distance of the first principal point of the system from the first principal point of the first element can be shown to be

$$H_1H = \frac{af_1}{f_1 + f_2 - a}. \tag{79}$$

These formulae can be used when the elements are thin lenses by remembering that the principal points of the elements then coincide at the elements themselves. Thus Eq. (76) gives the focal length of two thin lenses separated by a distance a, and the subsequent formulae permit the focal points and principal points of a combination of two such lenses to be located.

The formulae developed in this section can be used for a system containing any number of lenses by combining the first lens with the second, this combination with the third, and so forth. Usually, however, it is easier to trace a ray from infinity as outlined in Sec. 31. When the lenses are thin, the equation

$$f = f_1\left(-\frac{s_2'}{s_2}\right)\left(-\frac{s_3'}{s_3}\right)\left(-\frac{s_4'}{s_4}\right)\dots, \tag{80}$$

wherein the quantities refer to the entire lenses instead of the individual surfaces, can be used instead of Eq. (62). This is merely an extension of Eq. (75). The distance from the last lens to the second principal point is the difference between the true focal length and the back focal length. The entire procedure is exactly analogous to that described in Sec. 31, except that lenses are treated instead of surfaces.

36. Angular Magnification.—Consider a ray passing through a lens from some axial point P in the object space to its conjugate P' in the image space, the slope angles in the object and image spaces being θ and θ' respectively. The ratio

$$\gamma = \frac{\theta'}{\theta} \tag{81}$$

is known as the *angular magnification* in the planes at P and P'. Lagrange's law may then be written as

$$\frac{n'}{n}m\gamma = 1. \tag{82}$$

Since n, n', and m (the lateral magnification between the conjugate planes at P and P') are constants, γ is seen to be a constant also for all rays through P in the paraxial region.

37. Nodal Points and Optical Center.—In Fig. 27, let the ray QN in the object space be refracted to cross the axis at O and

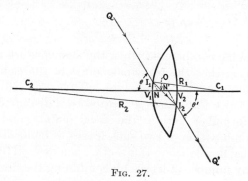

Fig. 27.

emerge as the ray $N'Q'$ in the image space. When QN and $N'Q'$ are parallel, the angular magnification referred to the conjugate points N and N' is unity and positive. These points are then said to be the *first* and *second nodal points* of the lens respectively. In other words, any ray in the object space directed toward N emerges in the image space from N' parallel to its original direction. The point O, where these rays cross the axis, is known as the *optical center* of the lens.

It will be seen from Eq. (82) that, when $n = n'$, the lateral magnification in the planes at N and N' is unity also. As this was the property by which the principal points were defined, it follows that the nodal points coincide with the principal points when the initial and final media have the same refractive index. This case is so common that the properties of the two pairs of points are frequently confused.

The nodal points can be located by means of Eqs. (51) and (52), since the lateral magnification in the planes at N and N' is known from Eq. (82) to be

$$m = \frac{n}{n'}.$$ \hfill (83)

Now from Eq. (51),

$$x = -\frac{f}{m} = -\frac{n'}{n}f,$$

where x is now the distance of the first nodal point from the first focal point. Similarly Eq. (52) gives

$$x' = -mf' = -\frac{n}{n'}f',$$

where x' is the distance of the second nodal point from the second focal point. By substituting in the above equations the values of f and f' respectively from Eq. (64), the distances of the nodal points from the corresponding focal points are found to be

$$x = -f'$$ \hfill (84)

and

$$x' = -f.$$ \hfill (85)

Thus the nodal points are related to the system in a manner that is just the inverse of the way the principal points are related; that is, whereas the distance of the first principal point from the first focal point is equal to the *first* focal length, the distance of the first nodal point from the first focal point is equal to the *second* focal length. The second nodal point is related to the second focal point in a corresponding manner. As a result, the formulae for conjugate distances and lateral magnification referred to nodal points as points of reference follow at once from Eqs. (56) and (57) by interchanging f and f'. Thus if *s* represents the distance of an object from the first nodal point and *s'* represents the distance of its image from the second nodal point,

$$\frac{f'}{s} + \frac{f}{s'} = 1$$ \hfill (86)

and

$$m = -\frac{f'}{s - f'} = -\frac{s' - f}{f}. \tag{87}$$

A simple expression for the lateral magnification in terms of s and s' can be found. Since the angular magnification is unity for the nodal points,

$$\frac{y'}{s'} = -\frac{y}{s}.$$

Therefore

$$m = \frac{y'}{y} = -\frac{s'}{s}. \tag{88}$$

It will be remembered that the corresponding expression given by Eq. (59) for the lateral magnification in terms of distances referred to the principal points was

$$m = -\frac{ns'}{n's}.$$

As before, the formulae become identical when the initial and final media are the same. If this were not generally the case, the nodal points would probably be used more often than the principal points because of the greater simplicity of Eq. (88).

The properties of the nodal points can be used as an aid in studying the properties of the optical center, since this is the point where a ray directed toward the first nodal point intersects the axis. Manifestly, if the optical system contains several refracting surfaces, this ray may cross the axis at more than one point so that the system possesses more than one optical center. It is customary, therefore, to consider the optical center only in connection with a simple lens, where it is unique and also possesses some useful properties. In this case, it will be evident from Fig. 27 that, since QN and $N'Q'$ are parallel, the tangent planes at the points of incidence and emergence must be parallel also, and so triangles OI_1C_1 and OI_2C_2 are similar. Hence, for the paraxial region,

$$\frac{V_1O}{R_1} = \frac{OV_2}{-R_2}.$$

Calling the thickness of the lens t, this equation can be transformed into

$$V_1O = \frac{R_1 t}{R_1 - R_2} \tag{89}$$

and

$$OV_2 = \frac{-R_2 t}{R_1 - R_2}. \tag{90}$$

It will be noted that the optical center of a simple lens possesses a property not shared by the other cardinal points. The positions of the latter depend upon the refractive index of the material of the lens, and hence they shift in position with a change in the color of the light. The position of the optical center, on the other hand, depends only on the radii of curvature, and consequently this point possesses the property that every ray through it, regardless of its color, is parallel to itself in the object and image spaces.

If the position of either of the nodal points of the lens is known, the optical center can be located by another method. It will be seen from Fig. 27 that O is the image of N formed by refraction at the first surface, and N' is the image of O by refraction at the second surface. Hence the optical center can be located immediately by applying Eq. (29).

38. Other Cardinal Points.—The principal points, focal points, and nodal points are the only cardinal points that are ordinarily of value in the solution of thick-lens problems. In rare instances, however, the treatment of the subject is simplified by using certain others, and for this reason they are encountered occasionally in the literature. Because of their comparative unimportance their properties will not be studied, although this could be done by the methods used hitherto in this chapter.

The *anti-principal points*, or negative principal points, are conjugate points for which the lateral magnification is unity and negative. They lie as far from the focal points as the corresponding principal points but on opposite sides.

The *anti-nodal points*, or negative nodal points, are conjugate points for which the angular magnification is unity and negative. They lie as far from the focal points as the corresponding nodal points but on opposite sides.

The *Bravais points* are hardly to be considered cardinal points but they may be mentioned here. They are the self-conjugate points of a system. Some systems have no such points, others have one, and still others have two. When two Bravais points exist, each is conjugate to itself, of course, and not to the other.

39. Transverse Axis.—Consider the thick lens shown in Fig. 28, the nodal points of which are N and N'. This lens may be of any form and need not be situated in air, although this is generally the case. Suppose that the lens is rotated through a small angle τ about an axis T perpendicular to the plane of the paper. After rotation, the point object P will lie at a distance from the axis $y = \tau(PT)$, provided τ is small. The distance of P' from the axis is now obtained by multiplying y by the magnification between the conjugate planes at P and P'. Hence

$$y' = my = m\tau(PT) = -\frac{s'}{s} \cdot \tau \cdot (PT), \qquad (91)$$

where s and s' are measured from N and N' respectively.

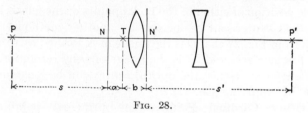

Fɪɢ. 28.

The *transverse axis* is, by definition, the axis of rotation for which there is no displacement of P' when the lens is rotated. This condition is satisfied for the point T when

$$\tau(TP') = -y'. \qquad (92)$$

By combining Eqs. (91) and (92),

$$\frac{TP'}{PT} = \frac{s'}{s}.$$

But from Fig. 28, $PT = s + a$, and $TP' = s' + b$. Hence

$$\frac{a}{b} = \frac{s}{s'}. \qquad (93)$$

It will be seen that, when s is very large, b becomes zero and the transverse axis coincides with the second nodal point. This is the basis of the so-called *nodal slide*, by means of which the position of the second nodal point can be found experimentally. The method consists in mounting the lens so that it can be rotated about an axis that is adjustable longitudinally. A position of the axis is found for which a small rotation of the lens produces no lateral movement of the image of an object at infinity. By turning the lens end for end, the first nodal point can be located in the same manner.

40. Longitudinal Magnification.—It is sometimes useful to know the amount of displacement of an image along the axis for a small longitudinal displacement of the object. Let the *longitudinal magnification* Γ be defined by

$$\Gamma = \frac{dx'}{dx}, \tag{94}$$

where dx' is the longitudinal displacement of the image corresponding to a small longitudinal displacement dx of the object. By differentiating Eq. (53), it can be shown that

$$\Gamma = \frac{dx'}{dx} = -\frac{ff'}{x^2} = -\frac{x'}{x}. \tag{95}$$

Since x and x' always have the same algebraic sign, it follows that Γ is always negative. But, since x and x' are measured in opposite directions under the convention of signs, this result indicates that the displacement of the image is always in the same direction as that of the object. It is interesting to note that the longitudinal magnification is the negative ratio of the distances of image and object from the corresponding focal points, whereas the lateral magnification is the negative ratio of the distances from the nodal points. By combining Eqs. (59) and (82), it can be shown that the angular magnification is the negative inverse ratio of the distances from the principal points.

By combining Eq. (95) with Eqs. (51), (52), and (64), it is found that

$$\Gamma = -\frac{n'}{n} \cdot m^2. \tag{96}$$

Then by combining this equation with Eq. (82), the following expression, relating the angular, the longitudinal, and the lateral magnification, results:

$$\frac{\gamma\Gamma}{m} = -1. \tag{97}$$

It must again be emphasized that this method of treating thick lenses, which was first used by Gauss, applies only to rays in the paraxial region. The method is extremely convenient when a large number of problems that relate to a given system are to be solved. For the solution of a single problem, the straightforward method of Chap. II is generally simpler.

CHAPTER V

THE LIMITATION OF RAYS BY APERTURES

In the most general sense, an optical system forms a three-dimensional image of a three-dimensional object. In other words, for every object plane there exists a corresponding or conjugate image plane. In practice, however, only a single plane of the object space can be in focus at any one time because the image is always received on a screen of some sort. This is the case even in visual instruments, wherein the retina of the eye acts as the screen upon which the final image is formed. The pencils that would form images of points in other planes are intercepted either before or after they have come to a focus, and thus they produce spots of finite area. Whether these spots are large enough to have a deleterious effect on the image depends upon the angular dimensions of the pencils producing them. These dimensions, in turn, depend upon the aperture of the system, which is determined by the diameters of the lenses and the stops that it contains. The theory of stops was first developed by Abbe, and it constitutes one of the most useful concepts in the theory of optical instruments.

41. Aperture Stop.—Although the theory of stops is applicable to any optical system regardless of its complexity, it can be illustrated best by a concrete example. Figure 29 represents an optical system, such as a photographic objective, in which the elements I and III are lenses, assumed here to be thin, while element II is the stop or diaphragm that such a system normally contains. The point P is imaged by the objective at P'. In the object space, the image-forming pencil has a half-angle θ; in the image space, it has a half-angle θ'.

It is clear from the figure that the value of θ is determined by the diameter of the diaphragm II, which is therefore called the *aperture stop* in the terminology developed by Abbe. The method of determining the value of θ consists in finding first the image of the aperture stop in the object space. In Fig. 29, the image of the aperture stop II formed by lens I is at E. It

is obvious from the theory of optical imagery, of course, that
any ray from P that would pass through E if it were not refracted
will pass through II after being refracted.   In other words, the
size of the pencil at P in the object space is limited effectively by
E, just as it is limited actually by II.   In fact, an observer
at P could not see the aperture stop II itself but only its magnified
image at E.   In a similar manner, the size of the emergent pencil
at P' is limited by E', the image of II formed by lens III.

Figure 29 illustrates a case in which the diaphragm is the
aperture stop.   It is obvious that the rim of either lens I or

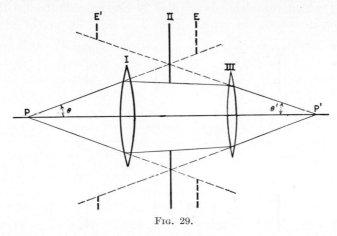

FIG. 29.

lens III (or both) might become the aperture stop if the diameters
of these lenses were decreased sufficiently.   In the general case,
it is not known which element of the system is the aperture stop,
and the effectiveness of each element must then be investigated
in turn to determine which one leads to the smallest value for
θ.   As the precision required is not great, the first-order formulae
are sufficiently exact for such computations.   For lens I in
the present example, the maximum value of θ is simply the angle
subtended at P by the radius of the lens itself; for stop II, the
value of θ is the angle subtended at P by the radius of the stop
image E, as has already been seen; for lens III, the maximum
value of θ is the angle subtended at P by the image of lens III
formed by lens I (not shown in the figure).   Stop II in this case
leads to a smaller value of θ than the others, which means that
it is the aperture stop of the system with respect to the point P.
In rare cases, two stops may be equally effective, and either may

then be considered as the aperture stop. It is clear that the procedure just described might be conducted as well with respect to the image space because, of course, the aperture stop is the one that leads to the smallest value of θ' also.

The fact that stop II is the aperture stop with respect to the point P does not imply that it is necessarily the aperture stop for any other point on the axis. For example, it is clear from Fig. 29 that, if the point P had been chosen at a great distance from the objective, lens I rather than stop II would have been the aperture stop of the system. This is better illustrated by Fig. 30, in which the elements of Fig. 29 are represented by their images in the object space. Lens I is actually in the object

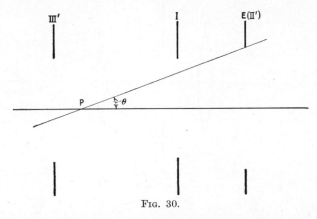

Fig. 30.

space, of course. The image of II in the object space is already known to be at E. The image of lens III in the object space is formed by lens I at III'. For an axial point in the vicinity of P, E is obviously the image of the aperture stop. At a certain point at the left of P, lens I and stop II are equally effective in limiting the aperture; and for a point still farther to the left, lens I is the aperture stop. It should be mentioned that this behavior of the aperture stop is not typical of actual photographic objectives. On the contrary, in any well-designed optical system, the diaphragm that is introduced to limit the aperture performs its function over the entire range of object distances for which the instrument is intended to be used.

42. Entrance and Exit Pupils.—In the nomenclature developed by Abbe, the image of the aperture stop in the object space is called the *entrance pupil* of the system. Thus in Fig. 29, diaphragm II is the aperture stop with respect to the point P, and E is the corresponding entrance pupil. Similarly, the image of the aperture stop in the image space is called the *exit pupil*. In Fig. 29, E' is the image of the aperture stop by lens III and hence is the exit pupil. Any ray through P that would pass through E if it were not refracted traverses the entire system and takes part in the formation of the image at P', and it will appear in the image space to have passed through E'.

The aperture stop and entrance and exit pupils have here been discussed with reference to a relatively simple optical system. It should be obvious, however, that the method described is applicable to any system regardless of its complexity. The computation may be more tedious, of course, because many lenses may be involved, but the procedure of finding the aperture stop is exactly the same. No matter how complicated a system may be, it usually contains but a single aperture stop. The entrance pupil is then the image of this stop formed by all the lenses preceding it; and the exit pupil is the image formed by all the lenses following it. Since the entrance pupil is conjugate to the aperture stop with respect to the part of the system at the left of the latter and since the exit pupil is conjugate to the aperture stop with respect to the part of the system at the right, it follows that the entrance and exit pupils are conjugate to each other with respect to the entire system.

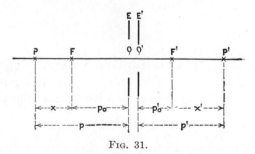

Fig. 31.

43. Conjugate Distances Referred to the Entrance and Exit Pupils.—The position and size of the image formed by an optical system can be determined when the only data available are the positions and sizes of the entrance and exit pupils and the focal length of the system. In Fig. 31, F and F' represent the focal points of an optical system, and E and E' the entrance and exit pupils for some point P on the axis. Let the radius of the entrance pupil be ρ and that of the exit pupil, ρ'.   Let the distance from the first focal point to the entrance pupil be p_0 and the distance of the second focal point from the exit pupil be p_0'. Let the object distance referred to the entrance pupil be p and the image distance referred to the exit pupil be p'. It can then be seen from the figure that

$$p = x + p_0$$

and

$$p' = x' + p_0'.$$

When these quantities are substituted in Eqs. (65), (66), and (67) of Chap. IV, the latter become

$$(p - p_0)(p' - p_0') = f^2, \tag{98}$$

$$m = -\frac{f}{p - p_0}, \tag{99}$$

and

$$m = -\frac{p' - p_0'}{f}. \tag{100}$$

The magnification between the conjugate planes E and E' is

$$m_{EE'} = \frac{\rho'}{\rho} \tag{101}$$

$$= \frac{f}{p_0}. \tag{102}$$

$$= \frac{p_0'}{f}. \tag{103}$$

Solving Eqs. (101), (102), and (103) for p_0 and p_0' and substituting the results in Eqs. (98), (99), and (100), the following formulae for the conjugate distances and the lateral magnification result:

$$\frac{\rho^2}{p} + \frac{\rho'^2}{p'} = \frac{\rho\rho'}{f}, \tag{104}$$

$$m = -\frac{1}{m_{EE'}} \cdot \frac{p'}{p}, \tag{105}$$

and

$$m = -\frac{\rho p'}{\rho' p}. \tag{106}$$

The convention of signs adopted in the derivation of these formulae is consistent with that already used—namely, p is positive when P lies at the left of E, and p' is positive when P' lies at the right of E'.

It should be noted that Eqs. (104), (105), and (106) do not depend in any way upon the properties of the entrance and exit pupils but are applicable to any pair of conjugate planes in which the lateral magnification is ρ'/ρ. The equations are still valid, therefore, for object points for which E and E' may not be the entrance and exit pupils.

In general the two pupils lie in different planes and are of different sizes. In special cases, however, they may lie in the same plane or may be of the same size. The second case is very common and is exemplified by the so-called symmetrical photographic objective. This objective consists of two similar lenses with a stop midway between, the second lens being reversed in position with respect to the first. Inasmuch as the entrance pupil is identical in size with the exit pupil because of the symmetry of the system, the two pupils lie in the principal planes. A little reflection will show that in this case the entrance pupil lies in the first principal plane.

44. Relative Aperture.—It can be seen from Fig. 29 that the angle subtended at P by the entrance pupil determines the amount of light traversing the system and hence the illumination of the image, other conditions being constant. This angle is represented by a quantity known as the *relative aperture*, which is expressed in various ways that have been found to be most suitable for the different types of instruments. Thus, the *numerical aperture* of a microscope objective is defined by

$$\text{N.A.} = n \sin \theta, \tag{107}$$

where n is the index of the object space and θ is the half-angle of the extreme ray from the object (Fig. 29). For telescope and photographic objectives, the object is usually at infinity and it is more convenient to define the relative aperture as the ratio of the focal length of the objective to the diameter of the entrance pupil. In photographic practice, this ratio is called the *f/-number*. Thus the "speed" of a lens is said to be $f/4.5$ when the focal length is 4.5 times the diameter of the entrance pupil.

45. Chief Ray.—The ray in the object space that passes through the center of the entrance pupil is known as the *principal ray* or *chief ray* of the pencil. This ray also passes through both the center of the aperture stop and the center of the exit pupil because of the conjugate relationship between them, but only in rare cases does it pass through the center of any of the lenses. Evidently the chief ray defines the direction of a pencil in its passage through the optical system; and the place where it intersects the various surfaces is of great importance in correcting the aberrations of a lens, as will be shown in the following chapter.

46. Telecentric Systems.—When the aperture stop is at the second focal point of the system, the entrance pupil is at infinity

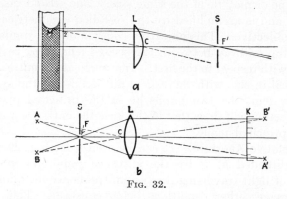

Fig. 32.

and all chief rays in the object space are parallel to the axis. Such a system is said to be *telecentric on the side of the object*. It is often used to advantage in making measurements where parallax must be avoided. Thus in Fig. 32*a*, the lens *L* is used as a simple magnifier to facilitate the reading of the height of the meniscus against the scale engraved on the outside of the burette. With the telecentric stop *S* at the second focal point of the lens, the chief rays in the object space are parallel to the axis and the error due to parallax is eliminated, the meniscus *M* and the point 1 on the scale appearing to be in line even though they are not on the axis of the lens. On the other hand, if the stop were at some other position, such as *C*, the chief ray from *M* (shown by the broken line) would intersect the scale at the point 2, and a false reading would result.

The system of Fig. 32*b* is *telecentric on the side of the image*, since the aperture stop *S* is at the first focal point, and the exit pupil is therefore at infinity. This type of system lends itself to the determination of the size of an object by measuring the size of

its image. In microscopy, for example, it is customary to determine the size of an object on the stage from the size of its image
formed by the objective. In the figure, the object points A
and B are imaged by the lens L at A' and B'. Suppose that the
scale K is not exactly in the plane of the image $A'B'$. With the
telecentric stop S in position, the chief rays in the image space
are all parallel to the axis and a true reading of the distance
$A'B'$ is obtained notwithstanding. On the other hand, if the
stop were placed at any other position, such as C, the chief rays
(shown by the broken lines) would intersect the scale as shown,
thus producing a false reading.

In telecentric systems, one of the pupils is at infinity and is
therefore infinitely large. Nevertheless, the angle it subtends

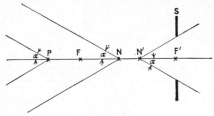

Fig. 33.

from points in the vicinity of the optical system is finite. Thus,
in Fig. 33, the telecentric stop S is at F', and its image is therefore
at infinity in the object space. Now, by the properties of the
nodal points N and N', the entrance pupil subtends the same
angle α at N that the stop S does at N'. Since the entrance pupil
is at infinity, it subtends the same angle from any other point,
such as P, unless this point is also at infinity.

47. Entrance and Exit Windows.—The method used in Sec.
41 for determining the effective rays in an optical system can be
extended to include the case of extra-axial points. In Fig. 34
the system of stop images is identical with that of Fig. 30, but
we shall now consider an extra-axial point, such as Q, in the plane
of P. The size of the pencil through Q will be limited by the
entrance pupil E as before, but it may be further restricted by
one or more of the other stop images. As the figure has been
drawn, the chief ray through Q grazes the edge of the stop image
III'. It will be recalled that III' is the image of the rim of lens
III by lens I. Lens III is then said to be the *field stop*, and its

image III' in the object space is known as the *entrance window*. In more general terms, the entrance window is the stop image in the object space that subtends the smallest angle at the center of the entrance pupil. The field stop is the real diaphragm of which the entrance window is an image. A diagram similar to that of Fig. 34 can of course be constructed for the image space. The *exit window* is then the stop image subtending the smallest angle at the exit pupil. Since it is the image of the field stop in the image space, the entrance and exit windows are seen to be conjugate to each other with respect to the entire system.

It is evident from Fig. 34 that, when the chief ray from a point such as Q grazes the edge of the entrance window, approximately

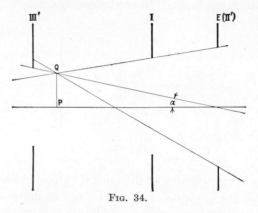

FIG. 34.

one-half of the pencil that would otherwise enter the entrance pupil is obscured by the entrance window. If Q were at a greater distance from the axis, even more of the pencil would be obscured until finally no ray through Q could pass through both the entrance pupil and the entrance window. It is seen, therefore, that there is a definite limit to the size of the field that can be imaged by any optical system. As this limit is set effectively by the size of the entrance window but really by the size of the field stop, the reason for the choice of the latter term is obvious.

In practice, it is usually undesirable to have the illumination at the edge of the field fall sensibly below that at the center. The useful field is, therefore, arbitrarily said to be limited by the ray that passes through the edge of the entrance window and the center of the entrance pupil. This ray passes through the point Q in Fig. 34, and hence PQ is the radius of the useful field.

It should be pointed out, however, that the useful field of a photographic objective, taken here as an example, is usually smaller than the illuminated area because the aberrations in the outer portions of the field become excessive. Hence the plate itself is made the field stop of the system. The plate is the exit window as well, and its image in the object space—the entrance window—is at the object. In visual instruments, the field is usually given a definite boundary by introducing a diaphragm where it will appear sharply focused to the observer. Here again, the entrance window coincides with the object, and the exit window with the image.

The *field of view* in the object space is said to be limited in angular measure by the angle α that the radius of the entrance window subtends at the center of the entrance pupil. The angular field of view in the image space is likewise limited by α', the angle subtended by the radius of the exit window at the center of the exit pupil. The values of α and α' are usually different, except in the special case of a single lens in air. The total angular field covered by an optical instrument is, of course, 2α in the object space and $2\alpha'$ in the image space.

48. Depth of Field.—In Fig. 35, let ρ and ρ' represent the radii of the entrance and exit pupils respectively of an optical system for which the point P' is conjugate to the point P. To make the example concrete, suppose that the optical system is a photographic objective forming an image of the point P on a photographic plate at P'. Evidently the point P_1 will be imaged in front of the plate at P_1', thus forming a *circle of confusion* of radius z' on the plate. Whether the circle of confusion is injurious to the quality of the image depends upon its size compared with the structure of the emulsion on the plate. Now let us find an expression for d_1, the distance of P_1 from P, that will produce a circle of confusion of radius z' in the plane of P'. From the geometry of the figure,

$$\frac{p_1 - p}{z} = \frac{p_1}{\rho}.$$

Then, by definition,

$$d_1 = p_1 - p$$

and hence

$$\frac{d_1}{z} = \frac{d_1 + p}{\rho}$$

or

$$d_1 = \frac{zp}{\rho - z}. \tag{108}$$

A similar argument with respect to an axial point P_2 between P and E would show that

$$d_2 = \frac{zp}{\rho + z}, \tag{109}$$

where d_2 is the distance of P_2 from P. Equations (108) and (109) together give for the total depth of field

$$d_1 + d_2 = \frac{zp}{\rho - z} + \frac{zp}{\rho + z}. \tag{110}$$

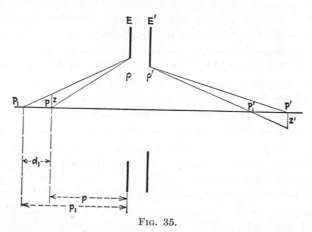

FIG. 35.

Usually the values of d_1 and d_2 can be determined more easily from the magnification in the conjugate planes at P and P', since this quantity is usually known or may be considered constant when comparing two optical systems designed to perform the same function. Now

$$m = \frac{z'}{z}$$

for the conjugate planes at P and P', and it follows therefore that

$$d_1 + d_2 = \frac{z'p}{m\rho - z'} + \frac{z'p}{m\rho + z'}. \tag{111}$$

Since both z' and m always have like signs, it can be readily seen that d_1 is always either equal to or greater than d_2.

The maximum value of z' that can be tolerated in any practical case depends upon factors other than those involved in the geometrical theory of image formation. In photography, for example, a rather common value for z' for precise work with good objectives is 0.05 mm. If the lens is poor, even the points that are in focus are blurred, and a larger value for z' must be assumed. Thus a poor lens has apparently a greater depth of field than a good one of the same relative aperture.

49. Depth of Focus.—In the preceding section, consideration has been given to the depth of field in the object space for a given amount of blurring of the image. It is occasionally of

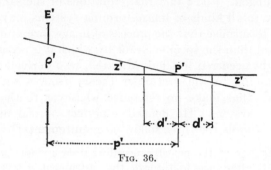

Fig. 36.

interest to know the amount by which the plane on which the image is received can be moved without causing a similar effect. In Fig. 36, ρ' represents the radius of the exit pupil, and P' an axial point image of an object point P. If a photographic plate or a suitable screen were inserted in the plane at P', the image of P would be a point. This plate or screen could be moved a distance d' along the axis in either direction until the circle of confusion became large enough to be observable. Let z' represent the radius of this circle as before. It follows at once that

$$\frac{z'}{d'} = \frac{\rho'}{p'}$$

or

$$d' = \frac{z'p'}{\rho'}. \tag{112}$$

The latter expression is useful in determining, for example, how much the film in a camera may buckle without causing an appreciable blurring of the image.

CHAPTER VI

LENS ABERRATIONS

The laws developed in the preceding chapters to interpret the behavior of paraxial rays in systems of centered spherical surfaces were first deduced by Gauss in his famous "Dioptrische Untersuchungen." The fact that equations of the same general form apply to all kinds of image-forming systems may have led the reader to surmise that the process of image formation is more fundamental than the specific means by which it is accomplished. This thought occurred to Clerk Maxwell, who derived the equations pertaining to the first-order theory from a set of three assumptions that make no reference whatever to the physical form of the system. He defined a perfect optical instrument as one that fulfills the three following requirements:

I. Every ray of the pencil, proceeding from a single point of the object, must, after passing through the instrument, converge to, or diverge from, a single point of the image. . . .

II. If the object is a plane surface, perpendicular to the axis of the instrument, the image of any point of it must also lie in a plane perpendicular to the axis. . . .

III. The image of an object on this plane must be similar to the object, whether its linear dimensions be altered or not. . . .

While these assumptions do not mention specifically the form that the optical instrument must take, the second implies an axis and the third that it must be an axis of symmetry.

A more general theory of the formation of optical images was developed by Abbe in 1872 from postulates which assume only that a transformation of a certain kind does take place between the object space and the image space. In the assumed transformation, points, lines, and planes of the object space have corresponding to them points, lines, and planes in the image space. In geometry, this type of transformation is called homographic or collinear. An analytical statement of this transformation is expressed by three equations relating the three Cartesian coordinates of any point in the image space to those of the conjugate point in the object space. Abbe showed that all the fundamental laws pertaining to the first-order theory follow at once when these equations are reduced to their simplest form.[1] It is also of interest to note that Silberstein[2] has demonstrated that this principle of optical collineation is independent of metrics In other words, optical collineation may be considered a purely projective transformation from the object space to the image space. It is therefore "independent of the usual measuring processes and of the particular metrical nature of the contemplated space—Euclidean, Riemannian (elliptic), or Lobatchevskyan (hyperbolic)."

Unfortunately, perfect images in the ordinary sense cannot be formed by this type of transformation, unless the lateral magnification is unity. Consider the problem of forming an image of a small cube. If the image is to be cubical in form, the lateral and longitudinal magnifications must be equal. Now Eq. (96) shows that, when the initial and final media are the same, the longitudinal magnification is equal to the square of the lateral magnification, and hence the two magnifications can be equal only when both are equal to unity. In general, it is impossible to satisfy this condition for more than a single plane of the object space, so that, unless the dimensions of the cube are vanishingly small, the longitudinal and lateral dimensions of the image will be disproportionate. Moreover, optical instruments are usually designed to produce magnified images, which can never be faithful representations of three-dimensional objects. The plane mirror is a notable exception because the lateral magnification is always unity regardless of the object distance. It is the only optical instrument of any importance that yields perfect images in the ordinary sense.

50. Third-order Theory.—The theory of optical imagery that has been developed up to this point applies only to those rays in meridian planes which lie so close to the axis that terms above the first order in the expansion of the sine of the slope angles can be neglected. In practical optical systems, the apertures are always so large that these paraxial rays constitute but a small fraction of the image-forming rays. As we have already seen

[1] See, for example, von Rohr's "Geometrical Investigation of the Formation of Images in Optical Instruments," Chap. III. An English translation is available from His Majesty's Stationery Office, London.

[2] *Jour. Optical Soc. Amer. and Rev. Sci. Instruments,* **8,** 675 (1924).

that the representation is collinear for rays in the paraxial region, the problem now is to discover the conditions that must be fulfilled if this is to be true of the extra-axial rays also. In 1855, Ludwig von Seidel extended the Gauss theory by including the third-order term in the sine expansion and by considering the skew rays also. He developed the third-order theory as a series of five correction terms to be applied to the Gauss theory when considering the behavior of the more oblique rays. When these rays perform in the same manner as those in the paraxial region, the value of the five terms is zero. On the other hand, when one or more of these terms differ from zero, it is an indication that the rays outside the paraxial region do not behave according to the first-order theory, and the lens is then said to possess aberrations. The same five aberrations have been obtained by Rayleigh from Hamilton's characteristic function, thereby avoiding the laborious trigonometrical analysis used by von Seidel.[1]

In theory, the problem of producing an aberrationless optical system consists merely in choosing the radii of curvature for the various refracting surfaces in such a manner that each of the five Seidel equations shall equal zero. In practice, these equations are of little assistance because no optical system ever contains a sufficient number of refracting surfaces to permit all five equations to equal zero simultaneously. Also, the form of these equations is such that each is meaningless unless those preceding it have been satisfied. In other words, the equation for the fifth Seidel aberration has no significance unless each of the four others is zero. Moreover, these equations cannot be solved explicitly for the quantities of greatest interest to the lens designer—namely, the required radii of curvature. Although a notable attempt to reduce the equations to a more usable form was made by H. Dennis Taylor,[2] the algebraic method is still unduly involved.[3] Lens designers find it easier to trace a few selected rays through the system trigonometrically and to estimate the aberrations from the performance of these rays. Notwithstanding the slight practical value of the algebraic

[1] Probably the simplest direct deduction of the aberration equations is found in Whittaker's "Theory of Optical Instruments." See also Lummer's "Contributions to Photographic Optics."

[2] See "A System of Applied Optics."

[3] The application of the algebraic method is excellently treated in *Bur. Standards Sci. Paper* 550. This is also a useful introduction to practical lens design.

method, von Seidel's equations do supply a logical basis for classifying the five third-order aberrations.

It should be kept in mind that these five aberrations refer to light of a single wave length. Inasmuch as von Seidel's equations contain terms involving the indices of the refracting media, it follows that the aberrations depend to some extent upon the wave length of the light. This is taken into account in designing systems for critical work by minimizing the aberrations for two or more wave lengths well separated in the spectrum. These variations of the Seidel aberrations with wave length are unimportant, however, compared with the relatively large variation in focal length with wave length. This is the cause of two additional aberrations that are not included in von Seidel's treatment. For the present these will be ignored and the discussion will be confined to those aberrations with which a system is afflicted when light of a single wave length is used.

51. Spherical Aberration.—When von Seidel's first condition is not satisfied, the system is said to be afflicted with *spherical aberration*. Physically, it means that the rays from a point object on the axis do not recombine to form a point image in the manner required by the first-order theory. This was illustrated in Sec. 20 by the trigonometrical computation for the lens shown in Fig. 17. The amount of spherical aberration that is present in a given lens is usually expressed by the distance measured along the axis between the intercept of a ray through the zone in question and the intercept of the paraxial rays. In the lens of Sec. 20, the spherical aberration for the ray at a height of 10 mm was 1.5 mm, which is 1.5 per cent of the focal length. Spherical aberration varies approximately as the square of the incident height of the ray and depends also upon the distance of the object. For purposes of comparison, it is always computed for a lens with a focal length of 100 mm and an object at infinity. It is generally considered positive when, as in this example, the extra-axial ray intersects the axis at the left of the intercept of the paraxial rays.

As might be expected, spherical aberration can be eliminated by giving the reflecting or refracting surfaces the proper form. For example, in the case of a mirror, an ellipsoidal surface is free from spherical aberration for its foci. When one of the foci is at infinity, the ellipsoid becomes a paraboloid, and such a surface is free from spherical aberration for a point at the focus

and its conjugate at infinity. Refracting systems are less easy
to correct because the required surfaces are rarely of a simple
geometrical form, and the only practical method yet devised
for grinding lenses in quantity requires that their surfaces be
either plane or spherical.[1] Aspherical surfaces are used to a
limited extent for telescope objectives where the improvement
in definition justifies the large amount of hand work that must
be done to bring each zone to the proper curvature. Parabolic
surfaces are ground commercially from a template, but, when
produced in this way, their figure is not sufficiently exact to form
sharply defined images. Nevertheless, this method is sometimes
used for high-aperture condensers, since these are required only
to concentrate light within a small area, and the poor quality
of the image is of little importance compared with the elimination
of spherical aberration in the outer zones of the lens. As most
optical systems require surfaces of better quality than are produced
by this method, and, furthermore, do not justify the additional
expense that hand figuring would entail, it is common practice
to adhere to plane and spherical surfaces and to reduce spherical
aberration by a judicious choice of the radii of curvature.

The effect of the choice of radii on the spherical aberration
of a simple lens is illustrated in Fig. 37a. Each of the curves
in this figure represents the aberration in a lens of the form
shown directly below it in Fig. 37c. The ordinates of these curves
represent the incident height of the ray; the abscissae, the spherical aberration measured along the axis. These curves were
plotted through points computed by tracing rays through the
lenses trigonometrically. Lens 6 is the one used as an example
in Sec. 20. The numerical values for the aberration of the lenses
will be found in Table IV.

The differences in the shapes of the lenses shown in Fig. 37c
are produced by what the lens designer calls *bending* the lens. It
will be seen that lens 8 has the form that results in the least
spherical aberration for an object at infinity on the left. As
might be expected, the condition for minimum spherical aberration obtains when the deviation of a given ray is divided equally

---

[1] For a more extensive theoretical discussion of the application of aspherical surfaces to lens design, the reader should consult a paper by Silberstein,
Jour. Optical Soc. Amer. and Rev. Sci. Instruments, **11**, 479 (1925). The
aberrations of certain aspheric lenses used in practice are discussed by
Rayton, *idem*, **7**, 197 (1923).

TABLE IV.—EFFECT OF THE SHAPE OF A SIMPLE LENS ON THE SPHERICAL ABERRATION AND COMA

Each lens has an index of 1.51767, a thickness of 20.00 mm, and a focal length of 100.00 mm. Although all values are expressed in millimeters, any other consistent set of units may be substituted.

Number	Type of lens	R_1	R_2	u	V_1H	$H'V_2$	V_2F''	Spherical aberration			Sine condition			Coma
								10.0	12.5	15.0	10.0	12.5	15.0	15.0
1	Concavo-convex	−150.0	−40.23	−1.73	17.0	−4.4	104.4	7.7	12.4	18.1	5.5	8.8	12.7	−5.4
2	Plano-convex	∞	−51.77	−1.00	13.2	0.0	100.0	4.4	6.9	10.1	2.9	4.6	6.6	−3.5
3		599.4	−56.02	−0.83	12.2	1.1	98.9	3.7	5.8	8.5	2.4	3.8	5.5	−3.0
4		425.2	−58.00	−0.74	11.8	1.6	98.4	3.5	5.4	7.9	2.2	3.5	5.1	−2.8
5		187.1	−68.97	−0.46	9.8	3.6	96.4	2.5	3.8	5.8	1.5	2.3	3.5	−2.3
6	Equiconvex	100.0	−100.0	0	6.8	6.8	93.2	1.5	2.4	3.4	0.9	1.5	2.1	−1.3
7		68.97	−187.1	0.46	3.6	9.8	90.2	1.0	1.6	2.3	0.8	1.3	1.8	−0.5
8		58.00	−425.2	0.74	1.6	11.8	88.2	1.0	1.5	2.2	1.0	1.5	2.2	0
9		56.02	−599.4	0.83	1.1	12.2	87.8	1.0	1.6	2.3	1.1	1.6	2.4	+0.1
10	Convexo-plane	51.77	∞	1.00	0.0	13.2	86.8	1.1	1.7	2.3	1.2	1.9	2.8	+0.5
11	Convexo-concave	40.23	150.0	1.73	−4.4	17.0	83.0	1.7	2.8	4.0	2.5	3.9	5.6	+1.6

between the two refracting surfaces. Hence, for an object at one of the anti-principal points, a lens of the equiconvex form (6) has a minimum of spherical aberration.

When the thickness of the lens is negligible, a simple algebraic formula[1] can be derived for computing the spherical aberration.

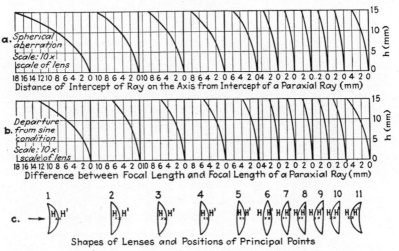

FIG. 37.—Effect of bending a lens upon the spherical aberration and the sine condition. All the lenses have an axial thickness of 20, an axial focal length of 100, and an index of 1.51767, differing only in their radii of curvature. The curves at a represent the spherical aberration; the curves at b, the departure from the sine condition. These curves are plotted from the data in Table IV.

This has the simplest form when the aberration is expressed in terms of the error in $1/s'$ rather than s' itself.
The formula is

$$\Delta\left(\frac{1}{s'}\right) = \frac{h^2}{f^3}(Au^2 + Buv + Cv^2 + D) \tag{113}$$

$$= \frac{h^2}{f^3}S, \tag{114}$$

where the shape factor

$$u = \frac{R_2 + R_1}{R_2 - R_1}, \tag{115}$$

the position factor

$$v = \frac{s' - s}{s' + s} = \frac{2f}{s} - 1 = 1 - \frac{2f}{s'}, \tag{116}$$

[1] A detailed description of the method, with charts and tables to facilitate the computations, will be found in *Bur. Standards Sci. Paper* 461.

and the constants

$$A = \frac{n+2}{8n(n-1)^2},\tag{117}$$

$$B = \frac{n+1}{2n(n-1)},\tag{118}$$

$$C = \frac{(3n+2)}{8n},\tag{119}$$

and

$$D = \frac{n^2}{8(n-1)^2}.\tag{120}$$

The value of the longitudinal spherical aberration $\Delta s'$ is evidently

$$\Delta s' = -s'^2 \Delta\left(\frac{1}{s'}\right).\tag{121}$$

The accuracy with which the formula represents the spherical aberration of a lens of moderate thickness may be inferred from Fig. 38, wherein the aberration of the lenses shown in Fig. 37c is plotted against the shape factor u for an incident height of 15 mm. The full curve represents values determined by tracing rays through the lenses trigonometrically; the circles represent points determined by substitution in the formula (113). It will be seen that the formula is a satisfactory approximation in the region where the spherical aberration is small, notwithstanding that the thickness of these lenses is one-fifth of their focal length.

Another use of the formula is to find the shape of a lens that will have a minimum of spherical aberration under any assumed set of conditions. Setting Eq. (113) equal to zero and solving for u leads to imaginary roots for values of n greater than 0.25. This means that spherical aberration cannot be eliminated from a single lens for any combination of radii. It can be minimized, however, as may be seen by differentiating the formula with respect to u and setting the derivative equal to zero, the result being that

$$u = -\frac{Bv}{2A}.\tag{122}$$

If this condition is satisfied, the lens will have a minimum of spherical aberration. Lens 8 satisfies this condition for an object at infinity and, as shown in Fig. 38, it has the least spherical aberration of all the lenses in the series.

Although spherical aberration cannot be eliminated from a single thin lens, it can be eliminated from a system of two or more lenses by shaping them so that the amount of spherical aberration introduced by the negative elements is equal and opposite to that introduced by the positive ones. This is possible because spherical aberration varies as the cube of the focal length, as shown by Eq. (113), and hence changes sign with the latter. The method of elimination will be apparent from considering the problem of correcting a doublet consisting of a positive and a

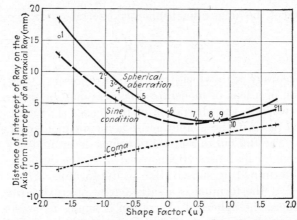

Fig. 38.—Variation of spherical aberration, coma, and departure from the sine condition with shape factor for a lens having an axial thickness of 20, an axial focal length of 100, and an index of 1.51767. The values represented are for a ray at an incident height of 15. The data are taken from Table IV. The numbered circles represent the values for spherical aberration computed by means of Eq. (113).

negative element. Suppose that the focal length of the combination is to be positive. Then the positive element will normally be the stronger of the two, and, other conditions being equal, it will have more spherical aberration. But by choosing its shape to minimize its aberration and choosing the shape of the negative element to increase its aberration, the total aberration of the combination can be made zero.

This process is particularly simple when the system consists of two thin lenses in contact like a telescope objective. The focal length of the combination is shown by Eq. (77) to be

$$\frac{1}{f} = \frac{1}{f_1} + \frac{1}{f_2}, \tag{123}$$

in which f is the focal length of the combination, and f_1 and f_2 are the focal lengths of the elements. Now the spherical aberration of the combination vanishes when

$$\Delta\left(\frac{1}{s_1'}\right) + \Delta\left(\frac{1}{s_2'}\right) = 0. \tag{124}$$

From Eq. (114) this may be written as

$$\frac{h_1^2}{f_1^3} S_1 + \frac{h_2^2}{f_2^3} S_2 = 0; \tag{125}$$

and, since $h_1 = h_2$ for thin lenses in contact, this becomes simply

$$\frac{S_1}{f_1^3} + \frac{S_2}{f_2^3} = 0. \tag{126}$$

This is not the only condition to be satisfied because the position factors of the two elements are always related to each other by an independent equation. The position of the object and the focal length of the first element determine the position factor v_1 for this element. The image distance s_1' for this element is the object distance s_2 for the second element since the elements are in contact, and consequently the position factor v_2 for the second element is determined in terms of f_2. By writing Eq. (116) for each element in turn and combining the two expressions, it is found that

$$v_1 - 1 = \frac{f_1}{f_2}(v_2 + 1). \tag{127}$$

Now the behavior of a thin doublet to monochromatic light is completely determined by the indices of the two elements and the radii of the four surfaces, six quantities in all. If the combination is to have a predetermined focal length, Eq. (123) must be satisfied; and if it is to be free from spherical aberration in addition, Eqs. (126) and (127) must be satisfied also. Frequently such a combination is cemented, a condition requiring that the radius of the first surface of the second element shall equal the radius of the second surface of the first, or

$$(R_1)_{\mathrm{II}} = (R_2)_{\mathrm{I}}. \tag{128}$$

This leaves two independent variables, which are available for eliminating other aberrations.

For the ideally thin lenses that have just been discussed, it has been possible to assume that the incident height of a ray

is the same at each surface.   An actual lens, of course, must have
a finite thickness; and consequently, except in special cases, the
condition for freedom from spherical aberration is a function of
the height of the ray.   This means that spherical aberration
cannot be reduced to zero for more than a single zone.   In
practice, a system is said to be "corrected" if the aberration is
zero for one zone and negligible for the others.   The diameter
of the zone for which the aberration is made zero is usually about
two-thirds of the aperture of the lens.   Clearly, such a lens falls
far short of the ideal expressed by von Seidel's condition; but it

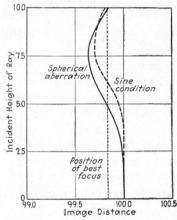

should be recalled that in his
equation all terms of the sine
expansion above the third order
are neglected and consequently
his condition does not apply
strictly to lenses of high aperture,
where the fifth-order term is important.   An extension of the
algebraic method to include the
fifth-order terms would be well-
nigh impossible; and, as the third-
order theory is only approximate
in systems of high aperture, lens
designers prefer to use the trigonometrical method, which is exact
for the rays that are selected for
the computations.

Fig. 39.—The variation of spherical
aberration and the departure from
the sine condition for a typical
photographic objective.

An idea of the degree to which spherical aberration is corrected
in practice may be gained from Fig. 39.   The full curve in this
figure represents the spherical aberration of a common type of
photographic objective.   It will be seen that, as the incident
height increases, the negative aberration increases faster than
the positive, so the total aberration reaches a maximum and then
diminishes.   The useful aperture of a lens is determined by
the rate at which the negative aberration in the outer zones
increases.   Frequently the plane of best focus is not the focal
plane for the paraxial rays.   Thus in Fig. 39, the vertical dotted
line represents the position of best focus, which in this case lies
slightly ahead of the focal point for the paraxial rays.

The total spherical aberration of this lens amounts to 0.35 per
cent of the focal length, which is satisfactory for a photographic

objective because other aberrations are present due to the high aperture of the lens and the wide field that it is expected to cover. In telescope objectives, on the other hand, the relative aperture and the field are both small, and a much higher degree of correction is not only possible but necessary.

52. Coma.—The second of von Seidel's equations refers to a third-order aberration known as *coma*. Of the five monochromatic aberrations, this is probably the most difficult to visualize, partly because it can be represented in such a variety of ways. The cause of it was disclosed in Sec. 31, where it was shown that, although the absence of spherical aberration implies a common intercept for all rays from a single point on the axis,

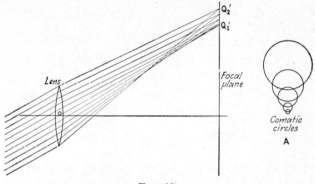

Fig. 40.

the focal length along the various rays may be different. Since the lateral magnification depends upon the focal length, it follows that the magnification will be different for the different zones of the lens. This is of no consequence for an object point on the axis, but it becomes important when the point lies even a short distance off the axis. In the latter case, the image is formed principally by the skew rays, which behave in a most unexpected manner and form a pattern such as is shown at *A* in Fig. 40.

To illustrate the behavior of skew rays in a two-dimensional diagram is difficult, so it will facilitate the discussion to consider first the behavior of the meridional rays. Figure 40 shows the path of the meridional rays traversing a lens from an infinitely distant point slightly off the axis. This lens is assumed to be free from all aberrations except coma. The rays through the central zone unite to form a point image Q_1', as would be expected from the first-order theory. The rays through the outer zones unite at points that lie farther from the axis, such as Q_2', a result that would be expected if the magnification is greater for the outer zones of the lens than for the central zone.   If the magnification for the outer zones were less than for the central zone, Q_2' would lie closer to the axis than Q_1'.   In the first case, which is represented in the figure, the coma is said to be positive; in the second case it is said to be negative.

If the image were formed entirely by the meridional rays, it would consist of a line of light $Q_1'Q_2'$ in the focal plane.   For a point off the axis, however, the skew rays are of far greater importance than the meridional rays.   Their behavior can be

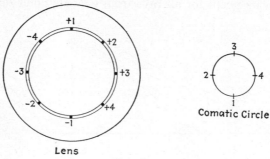

Fig. 41.

represented by means of Fig. 41, which shows on the left a section of a lens through its own plane.   By tracing rays through a circular zone, it is found that the image is a circle, called by H. Dennis Taylor a *comatic circle*.   The ray through the point $+1$ unites with the ray through the point -1 at the point 1 on the comatic circle.   Similarly the other points on the comatic circle are formed by the union of rays passing through opposite points of the zone.   The diameter of the comatic circle and its distance from the focus for the central rays both increase as the square of the diameter of the zone.   Consequently the image formed by the entire lens is made up of a series of these overlapping comatic circles, as illustrated at A in Fig. 40.   It is evident that most of the light is concentrated in the region where the circles are the smallest, and hence the figure is brightest at its small end and shades off at its large end.   The resemblance of the comatic pattern to a comet is most striking and is responsible for the name of the aberration.   Only in rare instances does a lens exhibit pure coma because other aberrations are almost invariably great enough to mask the typical comatic pattern.

The condition for the absence of coma can be stated in various ways but the simplest is due to Abbe. In Fig. 42, let a small element y be imaged at y', and let the refractive indices of the object space and image space be n and n'. It can be shown that the slope angle θ' of any ray in the image space is given by

$$n\,y\,\sin\,\theta = n'y'\,\sin\,\theta',* \qquad (129)$$

where θ is the slope angle in the object space. The condition for freedom from coma requires that the lateral magnification

$$m = \frac{y'}{y}$$

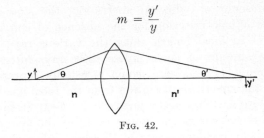

Fig. 42.

be constant for all zones of the lens. In other words, a system is free from coma when the ratio

$$\frac{\sin\,\theta}{\sin\,\theta'} = \text{a constant} \qquad (130)$$

for all values of θ. This is known as Abbe's *sine condition*.

It may be worth while to note in passing that Eq. (129) has been derived from the first law of thermodynamics by Clausius and others, and hence it ranks as one of the most important principles in optical theory. Being so fundamental in nature, it frequently conflicts with approximations based on the first-order theory; and in such cases one should remember that it takes precedence over whatever principles it contravenes.

In the absence of other aberrations, the sine condition is a true measure of coma. It is usually represented quantitatively by plotting the ratio $\sin\,\theta/\sin\,\theta'$ against the incident height of the rays. Usually the object is assumed to be at infinity and consequently $\sin\,\theta$ is proportional to h, the height of the incident ray. In this case, the condition for the absence of coma is that

$$\frac{h}{\sin\,\theta'} = \text{a constant}. \qquad (131)$$

* This is a more general form of Lagrange's law and becomes equivalent to it for small values of θ.

By comparison with Eq. (63) in Chap. IV, it will be seen that this ratio gives the focal length for the ray at a height h.   The sine condition can therefore be plotted on the same diagram with the spherical aberration, and it is so represented by the broken curve in Fig. 39.   The ordinates of this curve represent the height of the incident ray; and the abscissae, the focal length measured along the ray.   Figure 37b shows the departure from the sine condition for the lenses of Fig. 37c, the curves being plotted from the data in Table IV.

In the presence of spherical aberration, the sine condition ceases to be a true criterion for the absence of coma because the variation in focal length along the various rays does not indicate the amount of coma unless these rays intersect at a common point.   In this case, coma is usually represented by subtracting the spherical aberration from the focal lengths along the various rays.   This procedure will be clear from Fig. 38. The broken curve shows the departure from the sine condition for the ray at an incident height of 15 mm.   When this curve is corrected by subtracting the ordinates of the spherical-aberration curve, the pure coma curve, shown by the dotted line, results. Evidently this curve approximates a straight line.   Since it crosses the axis for real values of the shape factor, it follows that, unlike spherical aberration, coma can be eliminated from a simple lens.   In the present case, the thickness is such that the lens with the least spherical aberration is also practically coma-free.

Lest it be inferred that both coma and spherical aberration are manifestations of the same fault, it is well to note that, whereas spherical aberration is concerned with the position of the focal point, coma is concerned with the position of the princi- pal point.   This will be clear from Fig. 43, which shows the path of a ray from infinity incident on the lens at a height h.   If the lens is corrected for spherical aberration, this ray will inter- sect the axis at F', the focal point for the paraxial rays.   If it is also free from coma, the distance $C'F'$ must be equal to the axial focal length $H'F'$.   The second principal plane of the first-order theory must therefore be in reality a spherical surface, called the *principal surface*, which has its center at F'.   The point C', where the ray intersects this surface, is sometimes called the *chief point*.   The second principal point for this ray is located at $H_h{}'$, the foot of the perpendicular from C'.   Evidently a curve of

$h/\sin \theta'$ against incident height (such as the broken curve in Fig. 39) represents the departure of the principal surface from a spherical form when spherical aberration is absent.

A fairly simple analytical expression can be derived for the amount of coma in a thin lens. For this purpose, coma may be represented best in terms of the angle subtended at the center of the lens by the length of the comatic figure. In Fig. 40, this is the angle subtended by $Q_1'\ Q_2'$ at O. This angle can be shown to be

$$\zeta = \frac{h^2 \tan \alpha}{f^2}(Pv + Qu), \tag{132}$$

where

$$P = \frac{3(2n + 1)}{4n} \tag{133}$$

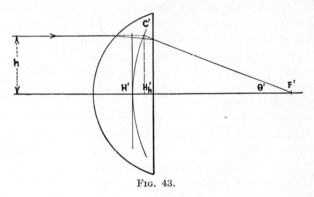

FIG. 43.

and

$$Q = \frac{3(n + 1)}{4n(n - 1)}. \tag{134}$$

The quantities u and v are the shape and position factors respectively described by Eqs. (115) and (116) in the preceding section. The angle α is the angle between the chief ray of the pencil and the axis. It will be seen that, for a given lens, coma increases directly as the tangent of the angle of obliquity and as the square of the relative aperture.

Unlike Eq. (113) for spherical aberration, Eq. (132) is linear in u and passes through zero for a value that can be satisfied physically. This value is evidently

$$u = -\frac{P}{Q}v, \tag{135}$$

a result that can also be deduced from the sine condition. The coma of a simple lens can therefore be eliminated by satisfying this equation. Lens 9 in Figs. 37 and 38 was designed to satisfy this equation, and, although the thickness of the lens is such that lens 8 instead of 9 has zero coma, it is evident from the dotted curve of Fig. 38 that Eq. (135) is a close approximation for even such a thick lens.

The elimination of coma from a doublet is effected in a manner very similar to that used in the correction of spherical aberration. For two thin lenses in contact, the condition is obviously that

$$\frac{1}{f_1^2}(P_1v_1 + Q_1u_1) + \frac{1}{f_2^2}(P_2v_2 + Q_2u_2) = 0, \qquad (136)$$

since the incident height is the same for both. Just as in the case of spherical aberration, the combination is then free from coma for all zones. In practice, lenses have a finite thickness, and the consequent separation of the surfaces makes it impossible to assume that the height of a ray is constant as it traverses the system. A lens is said to be "corrected" for coma when it is made coma-free for a single zone and the coma in the other zones is reduced to a negligible amount.

An optical system that is free from both spherical aberration and coma for one object point was called by Abbe *aplanatic*. Frequently, a system is said to be aplanatic with respect to a certain pair of conjugate points when it is merely corrected for those points as described above; but a better course is to restrict the term to the type of system conceived by Abbe—namely, one that is free from the aberrations for every zone. There are several such systems but most of them are of merely academic interest. Two, however, are of importance in microscopy. The first is a cardioid refracting surface combined with a spherical reflecting surface, the combination being aplanatic for an object at infinity.[1] The second is a spherical refracting surface, which is aplanatic for a single pair of conjugate points lying on a line passing through the center of the sphere. As an illustration of the behavior of aplanatic systems,[2] the proof of the aplanatism of this system will be given.

In Fig. 44, a point P is imaged at P' by the second refracting surface of a sphere whose center is C and whose index is n.

[1] A sketch of this combination is shown at B in Fig. 246 (Chap. XXIV).

[2] For a description of other aplanatic systems, Gleichen's "The Theory of Modern Optical Instruments," Chap. XVI, may be consulted.

It will now be proved that the sphere is aplanatic for P and P' when

$$PC = \frac{R}{n}.$$

The most direct method is to trace a ray through the surface in the manner outlined in Chap. II. Consider a ray from P incident on the surface at any point I; after being refracted it will emerge as though coming from P'. Remembering that R

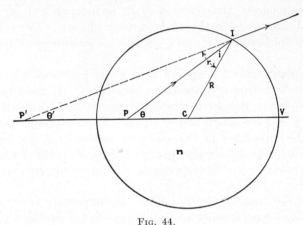

Fig. 44.

is negative, it follows that the object distance measured from the vertex V is

$$s = PV = -R\frac{(n+1)}{n}.$$

Substituting this in Eq. (17),

$$\sin i = -\frac{1}{n}\sin \theta. \tag{137}$$

Substituting this in turn in Eq. (18),

$$\sin r = -\sin \theta. \tag{138}$$

Considering this in connection with Eq. (19),

$$\sin \theta' = -\sin i.$$

Combining this with Eq. (137), it appears that

$$\frac{\sin \theta}{\sin \theta'} = n. \tag{139}$$

This shows that the sine condition is fulfilled for all zones of the sphere. Finally, substituting Eqs. (138) and (139) in Eq. (20), it appears that

$$s' = VP' = R - R\frac{-\sin\theta}{\dfrac{\sin\theta}{n}} = R + nR. \tag{140}$$

The negative sign of R indicates that the image P' is at a distance nR at the left of the center of the sphere. Since all terms in θ have disappeared, the position of P' is independent of θ, and spherical aberration is therefore entirely absent. The sphere is therefore aplanatic for P and P', which are known as its *aplanatic points*.

The aplanatism of a sphere is of great practical importance in the construction of microscope objectives. If the front lens of an objective is spherical and the specimen is located at P, the image at P' is magnified n^2 times. The specimen cannot be physically embedded in the glass, of course, but, by grinding away part of the sphere and placing a drop of liquid of the same index between it and the specimen, the latter can be embedded optically.

There remains to be discussed an important relationship between spherical aberration and coma that is not immediately evident. If an optical instrument is to be used for the examination of objects at various distances, it might be thought that the performance of the instrument could be improved by correcting the spherical aberration for object points at various distances. Sir John Herschel put this idea into practice by designing a telescope objective in which spherical aberration was corrected for two object points. The theoretical treatment of this procedure is difficult unless the points are close together. It has been shown that, to eliminate spherical aberration for two such points, the condition that

$$\frac{n\sin\theta/2}{n'\sin\theta'/2} = \text{a constant} \tag{141}$$

must be satisfied for all values of θ. This is commonly called the *Herschel condition* although it had not been formulated mathematically when Herschel constructed his objective. Evidently this condition and the sine condition cannot be satisfied simultaneously. In other words, a system cannot be corrected for coma if it is to be corrected for spherical aberration for more than a single object distance. Thus a system can be corrected so that it will form a faithful image of either a small element perpendicular to the axis or a small element along the axis but not both.

53. Astigmatism.—We have seen that, if von Seidel's first condition is satisfied, all rays from a single object point on the axis unite at a common image point; and that, if his second condition is satisfied also, all rays from an object point at a short distance from the axis likewise unite at a common image point. If his third condition is satisfied in addition, rays from an object point at a considerable distance from the axis unite at a single image point. Such an image is said to be *stigmatic*, from the Greek word "stigma," meaning a point. A pencil that fails to unite at a single image point after refraction is said to be *astigmatic*, and the system is said to be afflicted with *astigmatism*. Although spherical aberration and coma are forms of astigmatism, the term is usually restricted to the aberration peculiar to the rays from point objects lying at a considerable distance from the axis.

In Fig. 45, a pencil of rays from an extra-axial object point Q is incident on the lens $ABCD$. The rays in the *meridional* or *primary* plane, defined by Q, A, and C, intersect one another at the point Q_1' in the absence of coma. The rays in the *sagittal* or *secondary* plane, defined by Q, B, and D, intersect one another at the point Q_2'. Since these secondary rays are still converging as they pass Q_1', the image at this point, the *primary image*, is a line perpendicular to the chief ray. Similarly, the *secondary image* is a line at Q_2' perpendicular to both the primary image and the chief ray. If rays in the oblique planes were traced, it would be found that these also pass through the two line images at Q_1' and Q_2'.

The appearance of an astigmatic image can be understood best by considering the problem of photographing the point Q. If the plate is inserted at Q_1', the image is a line perpendicular to the meridional plane; at Q_2', the image is a line in the meridional plane; at an intermediate position, the image is an ellipse. At a point approximately midway between Q_1' and Q_2', the major and minor axes of the ellipse are equal and the image is circular. This is known as the circle of least confusion and represents the optimum position for the plate.

It is interesting to consider the appearance of the image of such an object as a spoked wheel coaxial with the lens. At the point of intersection of one of the spokes with the rim, it is clear that the rim is perpendicular to the spoke. Since the spoke lies in a meridional plane, it will be imaged sharply at the secondary focus, whereas the rim will be imaged sharply at the primary focus. As this holds for any point on the rim, it follows that the

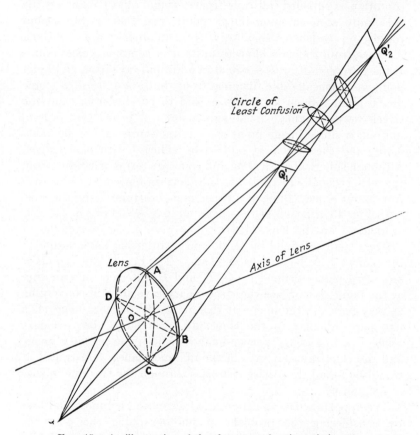

Fig. 45.—An illustration of the character of astigmatic images.

entire rim is in focus in the primary image plane while all the spokes are in focus in the secondary image plane. For this reason, the primary image plane is sometimes called the *tangential image plane;* and the meridional rays, the *tangential rays.* Similarly, the term "radial" might be applied to the secondary image plane and the secondary rays, but the term "sagittal" is far more common.

The method of representing the amount of astigmatism in a lens is illustrated in Fig. 46, which is a cross section through the axis of the lens. When astigmatism is present, the primary and secondary images of the plane object normal to the axis are ellipsoidal surfaces. The amount of astigmatism for any point on the object plane is generally represented by the *astigmatic difference*, which is the distance between these surfaces measured along the chief ray. This astigmatic difference is zero on the axis, where the image surfaces coincide, and, in an uncorrected

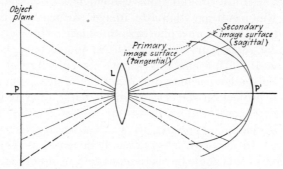

FIG. 46.—Astigmatic images of a plane object.

system, it increases approximately as the square of the tangent of the angle of obliquity. It also depends somewhat upon the object distance. It is said to be positive when, as in the figure, the primary surface lies between the secondary surface and the lens.[1]

The method of eliminating astigmatism consists in so choosing the elements of a lens that the primary and secondary image surfaces are brought into coincidence. When this is done, von Seidel's third condition is satisfied, but even then a serious

[1] It is important to note here that the astigmatism of a system of spherical surfaces is quite different from the defect of the eye known by the same name. The latter is caused by a lack of sphericity of one or more of the refracting surfaces of the eye, usually the cornea. That is, one of the surfaces has a shape resembling a combination of a sphere and a cylinder. Since a cylindrical surface forms a line image of a point, it is obvious that a person afflicted with astigmatism will see points drawn out into lines *even if the points are on the axis of the eye*. If the object consists of two sets of parallel lines in mutually perpendicular directions, like the wires of a window screen, only one set can be in focus at a given time. This is the analogue of the spoked wheel mentioned above in connection with the astigmatism of a system of spherical surfaces.

defect remains because the resulting image surface is usually curved. This curvature of the image surface is so intimately related to astigmatism that the elimination of both aberrations will be considered together in the next section.

54. Curvature of Field.—A system satisfying von Seidel's first three conditions meets Maxwell's first requirement only: it forms point images of point objects lying in a plane normal to the axis, but these images do not lie in a plane unless the system satisfies von Seidel's fourth condition also. Now, if the astigmatic surfaces are brought into coincidence to eliminate astigmatism, the resulting stigmatic image surface will in general be curved, and therefore a photographic plate or projection screen would have to be curved if the entire image is to be sharply defined on it. This effect is known as *curvature of field*. It must be corrected because, for practical reasons, photographic plates and projection screens are made flat. Like astigmatism, curvature increases rapidly with the angle of obliquity, being important chiefly, therefore, in systems designed to cover a wide field. In uncorrected systems, it increases as the square of the tangent of this angle but is independent of the object distance.

The precise determination of the amount of astigmatism and curvature in a system requires the tracing of skew rays. As this is a time-consuming process, lens designers prefer to use a method which, although less exact, is good enough for practical purposes. This method consists in tracing a number of chief rays through the system and locating the position of the primary and secondary images upon them. This is done by means of approximate formulae, derived for an elementary pencil surrounding the chief ray in much the same manner that Eq. (29) in Chap. II was derived for the paraxial rays.

It can be shown[1] that for a single refracting surface the distances of the object and the primary image from the refracting surface are related by the expression

$$\frac{n \cos^2 i}{s} + \frac{n' \cos^2 r}{s'} = \frac{n' \cos r - n \cos i}{R}, \qquad (142)$$

where s and s' are measured from the point of incidence along the chief ray, and i and r are the angles of incidence and refraction.

---

[1] CzAPSKI, "Theorie der Optischen Instrumente nach Abbe," Chap. III B.

The corresponding expression for the position of the secondary image is

$$\frac{n}{s} + \frac{n'}{s'} = \frac{n' \cos r - n \cos i}{R}. \tag{143}$$

The difference between the values of s' computed from these two equations is, of course, the astigmatic difference. If the astigmatic difference is small enough to give significance to the position of best focus, the curvature of the field can be found by comparing the position of best focus for several angles of obliquity with the position of the focus of the paraxial rays. Curvature is considered positive when the field is concave toward the lens.

Coddington[1] has shown that, for a simple thin lens with the stop at the lens, the distances of the primary and secondary images from the lens are determined from the following relations respectively:

$$\frac{1}{s} + \frac{1}{s'} = \frac{1}{\cos \alpha} \left(n \frac{\cos \alpha'}{\cos \alpha} - 1 \right) \left(\frac{1}{R_1} - \frac{1}{R_2} \right) \tag{144}$$

and

$$\frac{1}{s} + \frac{1}{s'} = \cos \alpha \left(n \frac{\cos \alpha'}{\cos \alpha} - 1 \right) \left(\frac{1}{R_1} - \frac{1}{R_2} \right). \tag{145}$$

In both equations, s and s' are measured along the chief ray. The angle α is the angle of obliquity of the chief ray before refraction, and α' is the slope angle of this ray while within the lens. Thus $\sin \alpha = n \sin \alpha'$. These equations correspond to Eq. (39) just as Eqs. (142) and (143) correspond to Eq. (29).

It can be shown from Eqs. (144) and (145) that the astigmatism and curvature of field of a thin lens are nearly proportional to the focal length and are almost independent of the shape of the lens. Bending the lens, therefore, is of no avail in eliminating these aberrations, nor is constructing the lens of a positive and a negative element in contact, since both elements would have the same focal length and thus would neutralize each other. The indices of the elements might be chosen so as to reduce the aberrations, but the effect is slight because of the small range of index available.

---

[1] "Reflexion and Refraction," p. 120; also TAYLOR, "A System of Applied Optics," p. 127.

On the other hand, astigmatism and curvature can be eliminated if the elements are separated. The extreme example is a combination consisting of two elements made of the same glass and having the same focal length, one lens being positive and the other negative. Their combined field can be shown to be flat and stigmatic whatever their separation, whereas their combined focal length is finite and positive if they are separated by a distance less than their individual focal lengths. Conversely, a combination of two separated positive elements has more pronounced astigmatism and curvature than a single lens. Such is the case for certain oculars. But this reasoning must not be carried too far because other aberrations modify the conclusions. For instance, if astigmatism and curvature are to be eliminated, both elements must be corrected for spherical aberration and coma for the position of the stop, and this cannot be done if they are to be corrected for the position of the object also.

From the many references to the position of the stop in this section, it might be surmised that this is a factor of prime importance in affecting the astigmatism and curvature of field of a system. That such must be the case will be apparent at once on recollecting that the chief ray is, by definition, the ray through the center of the entrance pupil, and that the position of the latter depends upon the position of the stop. Equations (144) and (145) hold only when the stop is coincident with the lens. By locating the stop properly, either the astigmatism can be reduced or the field can be flattened, but the two results cannot be achieved simultaneously unless the *Petzval condition* is satisfied in addition. This condition is that

$$n_1 f_1 + n_2 f_2 = 0, \tag{146}$$

which holds for two thin lenses whether they are in contact or separated. It is of importance chiefly in connection with photographic objectives because of the wide field they must cover. Although the elements of such lenses are not thin, the Petzval condition is a useful approximation.

The importance of the position of the stop is illustrated by the success of the cheap lenses found in simple box cameras. These lenses are usually of the meniscus type and are provided with a front stop as shown in Fig. 47. If the stop is properly placed, the rays can be made to pass through the lens in such a manner that the two image surfaces are curved in opposite directions. As the circles of least confusion lie approximately midway between the two image surfaces, this results in *artificially*

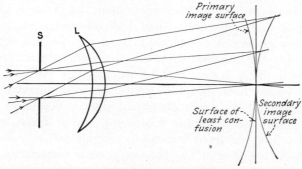

Fɪɢ. 47.—Artificial flattening of the field by a front stop.

flattening the field. Under these conditions, the astigmatic difference is increased and consequently the definition suffers, especially at the margins of the picture, but this is less objection-

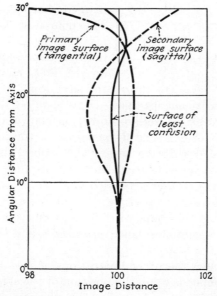

Fɪɢ. 48.—Astigmatism of a typical photographic objective.

able than would be the elimination of the astigmatic difference at the expense of a curved field.

Artificial flattening is not used for lenses of which critical definition is required, partly because the astigmatic difference is increased, as was just mentioned, and partly because the method depends for its effectiveness upon the presence of coma. It was in common use until about 1886, however, because, with the glasses produced before that time, the Petzval condition could rarely be satisfied when the chromatic aberrations were eliminated. This matter will be discussed in Sec. 56, but it may be stated here that this limitation was removed by the development of new types of optical glass. Nowadays all the better quality photographic objectives, except those designed for portraiture, are freed from both astigmatism and curvature without the sacrifice of the necessary color corrections. Such lenses in which the field is astigmatically flattened are called *anastigmats.* The type of correction possible in a modern high-quality anastigmat is shown in Fig. 48.

55. Distortion.—With the first four Seidel conditions satisfied, the image of a transverse plane in the object space is a transverse plane in the image space, every point on the first plane being imaged sharply on the second.

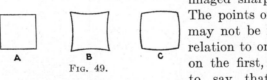

A   B   C

Fig. 49.

The points on the second plane may not be in the same spatial relation to one another as those on the first, however, which is to say that Maxwell's third requirement may not be met. This can be illustrated with the aid of Fig. 49. A square object, as shown at A, is imaged as shown at B or C. The deformation of the image, which is known by the descriptive term "distortion," is caused by a variation in the magnification with the distance from the axis. If the magnification increases with distance, as shown at B, the distortion is considered positive; if it decreases, as shown at C, negative. From the shape of the image of a square object, the two types are sometimes called *pincushion* and *barrel* distortion respectively.

Distortion, like the other aberrations of rays at large angles of obliquity, depends upon the position of the stop. A common practical illustration is furnished by the simple camera lens discussed above in connection with artificial flattening of the field. It is shown in Fig. 47, but to prevent confusion it has been redrawn in Fig. 50. As shown here, it is forming an image at P' of a plane normal to the axis at P. Von Seidel's first four conditions are assumed to be satisfied for the points P and P', and so the image at P' is also a plane normal to the axis. The entrance pupil E is coincident with the aperture stop S, which is in front of the lens. This stop has been shown outside the first focal point to simplify the figure by bringing the exit pupils E_1', E_2', etc., to the right of the lens, but in practice its distance from the lens is only approximately $\frac{1}{5}f$.

Under the conditions shown, the chief rays differ from one another in two respects: (1) their chief points C_1, C_2, etc., are not in the same plane; and (2) their corresponding exit pupils

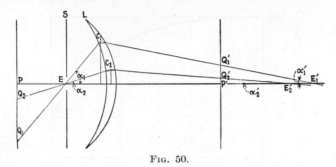

Fig. 50.

E_1', E_2', etc., are not coincident. Unless both conditions are fulfilled, the expression

$$\frac{P'Q'}{PQ} = m$$

will not be a constant for every extra-axial object point Q. Denoting the angles that the chief rays make with the axis by α and α' in the object and image spaces respectively, the conditions for distortionless imagery are:

1. The ratio $\tan \alpha'/\tan \alpha$ must be a constant for all values of α.
2. The system must be corrected for spherical aberration with respect to the entrance and exit pupils.

An examination of the figure will show that the lens under discussion is afflicted with negative distortion, and this would still be true if the stop were within the focal point. On the contrary, if the stop were behind the lens, the distortion would be positive. The behavior of a negative lens is exactly the opposite. Now, if the type of distortion depends upon whether the stop is in front of the lens or behind it, one might expect that a lens consisting of two similar elements placed in opposition to each other with a stop midway between would be free from distortion. This type of lens, which is the photographer's familiar symmetrical objective, is indeed quite distortionless at unit magnification. Under any other conditions, it must be corrected for spherical aberration with respect to the entrance and exit pupils. That is, it must satisfy the second condition set forth above, but only this one. The impossibility of doing this in general is evident on recollecting that the lens must be corrected for spherical aberration for the object and image planes in addition.

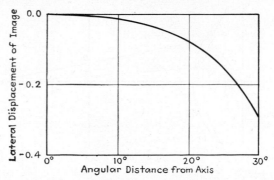

Fɪɢ. 51.—Distortion of a typical photographic objective.

The formulae for distortion are so complicated and of such little value in practice that they will not be given. They involve the position of the aperture stop, but if von Seidel's five conditions were fulfilled, the system would be free from distortion regardless of the position of the stop. Such a consummation appears to be unattainable, but lenses that are almost distortionless for a single position of the stop are on the market. These lenses are designed for such critical work as photo-engraving and aerial mapping. Ordinary photographic objectives, even high-quality anastigmats, suffer to some extent from distortion; Fig. 51 shows the curve for such a lens having a focal length of 100 units. The ordinates of this curve represent the displacement of the actual image from the position indicated by the first-order theory. The distortion of this particular lens is entirely negative, but that of some lenses is entirely positive, while an occasional lens will exhibit one kind of distortion at small angles of obliquity and the other at large angles. Symmetrical objectives exhibit so little distortion, even for magnifications other than unity, that they are called *orthoscopic* or *rectilinear*, if they are not anastigmatic.

56. Chromatism.—Up to this point, no account has been taken of any change in the wave length of the light; the light has been assumed to be monochromatic, and the indices of the media, therefore, have been considered to be constant.   Now the index

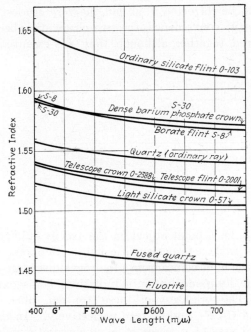

Fig. 52.—Variation of refractive index with wave length for typical optical glasses and other common optical materials listed in Table V.   The positions of the sodium and hydrogen lines are indicated at the bottom of the chart.

of all optical materials increases with the frequency of the light (increases with decreasing wave length, as shown in Fig. 52). Therefore, even if the Seidel conditions could be satisfied, it would be for light of but a single wave length, and perfect images for all colors would be formed only if these conditions could be satisfied simultaneously for all wave lengths.   But such a result would be of little practical value, even if it could be realized, because the images would probably be formed at different positions along the axis and, moreover, would probably be of different sizes.   The displacement of an image along the axis due to a change in wave length is called *axial chromatism* or *longitudinal chromatism;* the variation in the size of the image is called *lateral chromatism, oblique chromatism,* or sometimes *chromatic difference of magnification.* These two chromatic aberrations transcend in importance the relatively inconsequential variations of the Seidel aberrations. Only in systems requiring corrections of the highest order are the variations in the Seidel aberrations considered, whereas the chromatic aberrations must be corrected in all but the very crudest of systems. As a matter of convenience, the two chromatic aberrations will be considered together although they are essentially separate aberrations.

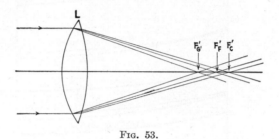

Fig. 53.

In Fig. 53, let a point object on the axis at infinity be imaged by the lens with heterochromatic light. Suppose, for convenience, that the light comes from a hydrogen discharge tube, which emits practically monochromatic radiations well separated in the spectrum. The brightest of these are red, blue, and violet, the so-called C-, F-, and G'-rays respectively. In this case, the "image" consists of a series of monochromatic images on the axis, and, of course, only one at a time can be in focus on a receiving surface, such as a photographic plate. This effect is due to *axial* chromatism. It is clear that the seriousness of the effect depends upon the relative aperture of the lens, which accounts for the long telescopes in vogue before the discovery of achromatism. If, in a manner to be described later, the lens in the figure is achromatized by making the three focal points coincide, the three focal lengths will not be equal unless the principal points coincide also. Since the magnification depends upon the focal length, the images of an extended object, although lying in the same plane, will in general differ in size. This effect is due to *lateral* chromatism.

In studying these aberrations, it will be convenient to consider first the method of achromatizing the focal length. This will be illustrated by a doublet consisting of thin elements separated by an interval a. The focal length of the combination, f, is related to the focal lengths of the two elements, f_1 and f_2 respectively, according to Eq. (77), which is

$$\frac{1}{f} = \frac{1}{f_1} + \frac{1}{f_2} - \frac{a}{f_1 f_2}.$$

The focal length of a thin lens is related to its index and radii according to Eq. (40), which is

$$\frac{1}{f} = (n - 1)\left(\frac{1}{R_1} - \frac{1}{R_2}\right).$$

Representing the quantity $\left(\dfrac{1}{R_1} - \dfrac{1}{R_2}\right)$ by K and substituting for f_1 and f_2 in Eq. (77), the latter becomes

$$\frac{1}{f} = (n_1 - 1)K_1 + (n_2 - 1)K_2 - a(n_1 - 1)(n_2 - 1)K_1 K_2. \quad (147)$$

In the language of the calculus, the condition for constancy of the focal length is that

$$\frac{d}{d\lambda}\left(\frac{1}{f}\right) = 0,$$

which, applied to Eq. (147), becomes

$$[K_1 - a(n_2 - 1)K_1 K_2]\frac{dn_1}{d\lambda} + [K_2 - a(n_1 - 1)K_1 K_2]\frac{dn_2}{d\lambda}$$

$$= 0. \quad (148)$$

The quantity $dn/d\lambda$ depends upon the type of glass and is also a function of the wave length; it will be called the *dispersion* of the glass. Now if the elements of the doublet under consideration are made of the same kind of glass, their refractive indices and dispersions are the same at every wave length. Utilizing this fact and substituting for $(n_1 - 1)K_1$ and $(n_2 - 1)K_2$ the values $1/f_1$ and $1/f_2$ in Eq. (148), it becomes simply

$$a = \frac{f_1 + f_2}{2}. \quad (149)$$

Hence, by separating the elements in accordance with this equation, the rate of change of f is zero at the wave length for

which f_1 and f_2 are computed. For visual instruments, this
wave length is preferably chosen near the middle of the visible
spectrum. Many oculars for telescopes and microscopes are
achromatized in this manner, and curve B in Fig. 54 shows the
variation in focal length with wave length for a typical ocular.
The elements of this ocular are made of light silicate crown
(O–57), for which data are given in Table V. Like the other

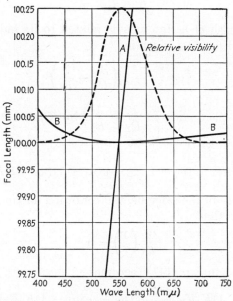

Fig. 54.—Curve A shows the variation in focal length with wave length of a
single lens of light silicate crown glass (O–57) having a focal length of 100 mm
at 550 mμ. Curve B shows the variation in focal length of a doublet made of
the same glass achromatized at 550 mμ by separating the elements according to
Eq. (149). The focal lengths of the elements at this wave length are respectively
200.00 mm and 66.67 mm, and the separation is 133.3 mm.

glasses in the table, this is one manufactured by Schott of Jena.
The focal lengths of the elements were chosen so that the combination would have a focal length of 100 mm at 550 mμ and
would be achromatic at this wave length also. It is clear that
glass having a low dispersion is best suited for this method of
achromatizing. The remarkable effectiveness of the method
can be appreciated by comparing curve B with curve A, which
is for a single lens of the same focal length and the same kind of
glass.

TABLE V.—REFRACTIVE INDICES AND OTHER CONSTANTS OF A FEW TYPICAL OPTICAL GLASSES AND OTHER OPTICAL MATERIALS

The quantities n_0, c, and λ_0 are the constants in Hartmann's formula computed from the published values of index at the A'-, D-, and G'-lines. The materials are arranged in the order of increasing values of λ_0.

Type	Fused quartz		Quartz (ordinary ray)		Light silicate crown		Dense barium phosphate crown		Borate flint		Telescope crown		Fluorite		Telescope flint		Ordinary silicate flint	
Catalogue number	....		....		O-57		S-30		S-8		O-2388		....		O-2001		O-103	
n_D	1.4585		1.5443		1.5086		1.5760		1.5736		1.5254		1.4338		1.5211		1.6202	
ν	67.9		70.0		61.8		65.2		50.8		61.7		95.4		51.8		36.2	
n_0	1.4421		1.5261		1.4909		1.5570		1.5494		1.5071		1.4243		1.5001		1.5882	
c	7.49		8.06		7.42		7.96		10.09		7.60		8.96		8.55		12.00	
λ_0	131.0		144.7		170.3		170.9		172.9		173.1		176.7		181.4		214.4	
λ	n	$-\sigma \times 10^7$	n	$-\sigma \times 10^7$	n	$-\sigma \times 10^7$	n	$-\sigma \times 10^7$	n	$-\sigma \times 10^7$	n	$-\sigma \times 10^7$	n	$-\sigma \times 10^7$	n	$-\sigma \times 10^7$	n	$-\sigma \times 10^7$
400	1.4700	1035	1.5577	1236	1.5232	1407	1.5917	1517	1.5938	1956	1.5406	1476	1.4420	793	1.5393	1789	1.6528	3484
450	1.4656	736	1.5519	865	1.5174	949	1.5855	1022	1.5858	1314	1.5346	991	1.4387	530	1.5320	1185	1.6391	2162
500	1.4624	550	1.5488	638	1.5134	683	1.5812	735	1.5802	943	1.5304	711	1.4365	379	1.5270	842	1.6302	1471
550	1.4600	427	1.5460	491	1.5104	515	1.5780	554	1.5761	709	1.5273	535	1.4349	284	1.5233	629	1.6240	1066
600	1.4581	341	1.5438	389	1.5082	402	1.5755	432	1.5730	553	1.5249	417	1.4336	221	1.5206	488	1.6193	807
650	1.4566	278	1.5421	316	1.5064	323	1.5736	347	1.5705	443	1.5231	334	1.4326	179	1.5184	389	1.6157	632
700	1.4553	231	1.5407	261	1.5049	265	1.5720	284	1.5685	363	1.5216	274	1.4318	145	1.5166	318	1.6129	509
750	1.4542	196	1.5395	220	1.5037	221	1.5707	237	1.5669	303	1.5203	228	1.4312	120	1.5152	264	1.6106	418

For two thin lenses in contact, the condition for achromatism expressed by Eq. (148) becomes simply

$$K_1 \sigma_1 + K_2 \sigma_2 = 0 , \tag{150}$$

where σ_1 and σ_2 represent the dispersions $dn_1/d\lambda$ and $dn_2/d\lambda$ respectively. If this equation is satisfied for some particular wave length, the rate of change of the focal length of the combination with wave length is zero at that point in the spectrum. This is illustrated by curve A in Fig. 55, which shows the variation in focal length with wave length for a typical combination of a

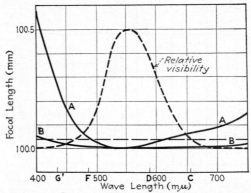

Fig. 55.—Curve A shows the variation in focal length with wave length for a doublet consisting of a positive element of light silicate crown (O–57) in contact with a negative element of ordinary silicate flint (O–103). The focal lengths of the elements at 550 mμ, for which the doublet is achromatized, are respectively +40.97 mm and −69.40 mm. The horizontal broken line indicates the effective focal length for visual use with white light. Curve B is a similar curve for a pair of glasses especially recommended for eliminating the secondary spectrum. These are dense barium phosphate crown (S–30) and borate flint (S–8). The focal lengths at 550 mμ are respectively 22.14 mm and −28.44 mm.

positive crown element in contact with a negative flint element. The particular glasses are the light silicate crown (O–57) and the ordinary flint (O–103) for which data are given in Table V. This lens was achromatized at 550 mμ by means of Eq. (150). Because of the shape of the visibility curve, the effective focal length will be somewhat greater than the minimum value when white light is used as a source and will be more nearly as represented by the horizontal broken line. It will be seen that the focal lengths for the red and violet regions are longer than the effective focal length, while the focal length for the yellow is shorter. This residual chromatism gives rise to a fringe of color surrounding the image of an extended object, which is known as the *secondary spectrum*.

The condition that must be satisfied if a pair of thin lenses in contact is to be completely achromatic—that is, if the focal length is to be the same at all wave lengths—will now be investigated. To do this, we must first consider the type of optical materials that are available for the purpose. A few curves giving the variation of n with λ were shown in Fig. 52. These curves can be represented very accurately by an empirical formula due to Hartmann, which is

$$n = n_0 + \frac{c}{\lambda - \lambda_0}, \tag{151}$$

where n_0, c, and λ_0 are constants for a given material. Throughout the relatively short wave-length interval comprised by the visible spectrum, this equation represents the variation in index of all optical materials within a few units in the fifth decimal place.[1] The dispersion can be found by differentiating this expression, whence

$$\sigma = \frac{dn}{d\lambda} = -\frac{c}{(\lambda - \lambda_0)^2}. \tag{152}$$

If Eq. (150) is to be satisfied for all wave lengths, the ratio

$$\frac{\sigma_1}{\sigma_2} = -\frac{K_2}{K_1}$$

must be a constant. In other words,

$$\frac{d}{d\lambda}\left(\frac{\sigma_1}{\sigma_2}\right) = 0.$$

Substituting the values of σ_1 and σ_2 from Eq. (152) and differentiating with respect to λ, this condition becomes

$$(\lambda_0)_1 = (\lambda_0)_2. \tag{153}$$

The fact that this equation contains no quantities dependent on λ means that, if both it and Eq. (150) are satisfied simultaneously, the doublet will be achromatic for all wave lengths.

[1] The form of this formula expressed by Eq. (214) in Chap. XV contains four constants and is therefore more exact. The three-constant form is, however, much easier to handle and is sufficiently exact for the present purpose.

The superiority of the achromatism that results when the two elements have approximately the same value of λ_0 will be apparent from curve B in Fig. 55. The elements of this doublet were made of glasses especially designed to eliminate the secondary spectrum. They are respectively the dense barium phosphate crown (S-30) and the borate flint (S-8) in Table V. The values of λ_0 for this pair differ by only about 1 per cent whereas the values for the pair represented by curve A differ by approximately 25 per cent. These special glasses almost completely abolish the secondary spectrum, but they were found to be unstable and were replaced by others which, although less effective in abolishing the secondary spectrum, have fewer disadvantages as a whole.

The achromatism produced by such special glasses is sometimes slightly different from that shown by curve B in Fig. 55. For such a small aberration, the departures from Hartmann's formula may be sufficient to produce two points at which the focal length is stationary instead of the single minimum allowable if the formula held exactly; that is, whereas ordinarily a given focal length is common to two wave lengths, for such materials a given focal length is common to three. Lenses made of these materials and corrected for spherical aberration for two wave lengths were invented by Abbe and called by him *apochromatic*. The custom now is to avoid the special glasses because of their instability and to obtain the apochromatic correction by using three or more glasses of orthodox characteristics. This procedure also allows the other aberrations to be more fully corrected. The finest microscope objectives are apochromatic. Objectives that are nearly as good but are much simpler and cheaper are made by combining fluorite with a glass that has a similar λ_0-value. Such objectives are called *semi-apochromatic*. They are made only for microscopy, because fluorite of optical quality is not readily obtainable in large pieces.

The problem of achromatizing a thin doublet was undertaken by Newton, who concluded that it was impossible of solution because, for all the materials he examined, σ was approximately proportional to $(n-1)$. For such materials, Eqs. (77) and (150) can be satisfied simultaneously only for a focal length of infinity. In other words, if the ratio of σ to $(n-1)$ is the same for both glasses, an achromatic combination is impossible when the lenses are in contact. Any pair of glasses having different ratios can be used, but, unless the ratios differ widely, the focal lengths of the elements must be short, and hence the curves must be undesirably steep. Thus the suitability of a glass for achromatism in this sense is measured by the ratio of σ to $(n - 1)$. For practical purposes, it is sufficiently accurate to use as a criterion the quantity

$$\frac{1}{\nu} = \frac{n_F - n_C}{n_D - 1}, \tag{154}$$

which is known as the *dispersive power* of the glass. In these terms, the condition for achromatizing the focal length of a thin doublet in contact (corresponding to Eq. [150]) is that

$$\nu_1 f_1 + \nu_2 f_2 = 0. \tag{155}$$

Satisfying this equation has the effect of making the focal length stationary near the D-line and of making the focal length for the C- and F-lines approximately equal. For this reason, it is sometimes stated that this procedure achromatizes for the C- and F-lines. It obviously achromatizes for an infinite number of pairs of wave lengths also, but, because of the shape of the visibility curve, the effective focal length lies in the vicinity of the C- and F-lines.

A feature of Eq. (155) that is not immediately evident is its relation to the Petzval condition, Eq. (146):

$$n_1 f_1 + n_2 f_2 = 0.$$

By combining the two equations, it will be found that, if a combination of two ideally thin elements in contact is to be achromatized for focal length and is to have a flat, stigmatic field at the same time, the glasses must satisfy the relation

$$\left(\frac{n}{\nu}\right)_1 = \left(\frac{n}{\nu}\right)_2. \tag{156}$$

Even when the combination has a finite thickness, this relation holds closely enough to be a good working rule. Now the glasses known before 1886 did not even approximately satisfy this relation because the more refractive glasses were the more dispersive and hence ν diminished as n increased. For example, the silicate crown and flint of Table V, O–57 and O–103, have n/ν ratios of 0.0244 and 0.0447 respectively. The various new glasses developed by Abbe and Schott will be described in Chap.

XV, but by way of anticipation it may be stated that certain pairs have ratios as similar as 0.0262 and 0.0264. These glasses are anomalous in the sense that the one having the lower index has the greater dispersion; and combinations made of them are known as *new* or *anomalous achromats* in contradistinction to the *old* or *normal achromats*.

The constant ν is used in practice for convenience because the hydrogen tube and the sodium flame are generally employed in the determination of refractive indices. The quantity $(n_F - n_C)$ appearing in Eq. (154) is known as the *mean dispersion*. It can be computed directly from the refractometric determinations, as can also the *partial dispersions*, $(n_D - n_{A'})$, $(n_F - n_D)$, and $(n_{G'} - n_F)$; and therefore the amount of secondary spectrum is usually estimated by lens designers from the similarity of the corresponding *partial dispersion ratios*, $\dfrac{n_D - n_{A'}}{n_F - n_C}$, $\dfrac{n_D - n_C}{n_F - n_C}$, etc., of the glasses of the pair.

It must be remembered that this entire treatment holds only when the lenses are ideally thin; and it is found that, unlike the conditions for correcting spherical aberration and coma, the conditions for achromatism are greatly influenced by the thicknesses and separations of the elements. Partly for this reason but more because the choice of glass affects the monochromatic aberrations, no simple algebraic method is adequate for the design of even so simple a lens as a doublet.

Up to this point, the achromatism of focal length alone has been considered. If the lens is achromatic in this sense, the image of an extended object at a great distance will be of the same size regardless of the wave length. In other words, the lateral chromatism will be eliminated. For near objects, some lateral chromatism may be present, but usually it is so small as to be negligible. Let us now investigate the condition for the elimination of axial chromatism also. *Stable achromatism* is the term sometimes used to indicate the simultaneous elimination of both chromatic aberrations.

In an ideally thin lens, stable achromatism is achieved if the lateral chromatism is eliminated, because the principal points are always at the lens and do not vary in position with wave length. In a thick element or a separated system, the principal points for the different wave lengths are differently situated, even when lateral chromatism is eliminated, and hence the variously colored images lie at different positions along the axis. It will now be shown that stable achromatism is impossible in a separated system unless each element is individually achromatized. This will be demonstrated for a separated doublet, but the result is more general.

The lateral magnification produced by a doublet is given by the expression

$$m = \frac{s_1' s_2'}{s_1 s_2},$$

where the object and image distances are measured from the lenses to which the subscripts pertain. The object distance for the first lens, s_1, is obviously the same for all colors; and, if the system is to be free from axial chromatism, s_2' must also be the same for all colors. Hence the ratio

$$\frac{s_1'}{s_2} = \text{a constant}.$$

But the separation

$$a = s_1' + s_2 = \text{a constant}.$$

These two simultaneous equations uniquely determine s_1' and s_2, and therefore these quantities must be constant for all wave lengths. This proves that each element must be achromatized individually.[1]

57. The Balancing of Aberrations.—We have seen that a lens is afflicted with seven major aberrations—five monochromatic aberrations of the third order and two chromatic aberrations. In addition, there are monochromatic aberrations of higher order, and hybrid aberrations arising from the variations of the monochromatic aberrations with wave length. Rarely is it possible to eliminate a single aberration completely, and no optical system contains a sufficient number of elements to enable all the aberrations to be eliminated even for a single position of the object. In view of this, one might wonder that a lens could be designed to function satisfactorily at all! Indeed, the balancing of aberrations to produce a useful lens out of a reasonable number of elements is an intricate process—one that calls for the highest degree of skill and experience in addition to almost unlimited patience.

[1] An outline of the methods by which achromatism is achieved in practice and the other corrections made simultaneously will be found in Hovestadt's "Jena Glass," translated by J. D. and A. Everett.

With our present methods of attack, no direct method of balancing aberrations can be formulated that will apply in any but the simplest cases. The lens designer must select the aberrations most detrimental to the purpose for which the lens is destined and reduce them to negligible amounts—despite von Seidel's requirement that each of his sums must be reduced to zero before the next can become mathematically significant. But the proof of the pudding is in the eating. In fairness to the designer, it must be stated that, despite the clumsiness of the methods he is forced to employ and the human fallibility of those who execute his designs, he usually produces a better lens than the skill of its user warrants. Indeed, if the demands upon the lens as to size of aperture and field are not excessive, the aberrations can be reduced to such an extent that the limit of perfection of the image is set by the finite length of a wave of light. This ultimate limitation is the next matter to be investigated.

CHAPTER VII

THE RESOLVING POWER OF OPTICAL INSTRUMENTS

The subject of image formation has been approached in the preceding chapters from the standpoint of geometrical optics, and the results apply if light behaves in accordance with the four postulates assumed in Sec. 17. Unfortunately these postulates represent the behavior of light only in an ideal case that is never realized in practice. The present chapter returns to the physical method of regarding image formation and discusses a limitation to the perfection of optical images that is brought about by the finite length of a wave of light.

58. Diffraction.—The first of the four postulates of geometrical optics is that "light travels in straight lines in a homogeneous medium." Although this postulate is a satisfactory foundation for such sciences as navigation and surveying, it is inadequate to explain in detail the formation of optical images. In fact, the reader may have detected a certain artificiality in the treatment of image formation by Huygens's method in Chap. I. It was stated there that the new wave front could be found by treating each point of the old wave front as a new source from which a secondary wavelet emanates. This implies that every point of the old wave front is the center of a new disturbance radiating light in all directions, whereas the principle of rectilinear propagation would seem to necessitate that each point radiate in but a single direction, namely, the direction perpendicular to the wave front. Before considering the behavior of light in optical systems, therefore, Huygens's principle must be correlated with the principle of rectilinear propagation.

In Fig. 56, the surface $ABCD$ is part of an infinite plane wave front moving in the direction of the normal to the surface OP'. Since this wave front is the result of a disturbance originating at a single point source P at infinity, all portions of it may be considered to be vibrating with the same frequency, amplitude, and phase. Consider now some elementary area such as

$$ds = r\, dr\, d\phi,$$

121

which, according to Huygens's principle, may be considered as a new source radiating light in all directions. This elementary area will produce at P' a disturbance whose amplitude is directly proportional to ds and inversely proportional[1] to the distance of the elementary area from P'. The effect at P' due to the entire wave front is obtained by adding together the disturbances due to all the elementary areas. This was not a part of Huygens's original concept, but Fresnel showed that it is a necessary modification. The integral calculus is especially suited to this operation, but the actual process of integration is complicated by the circumstance that the disturbances do not arrive at P' in the same phase because the elementary areas are at different

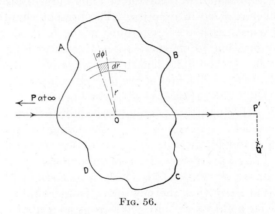

Fig. 56.

distances. The formal mathematical operations[2] will be avoided because they contribute very little to the present argument. It will be sufficient to assume that the resultant amplitude of the disturbance at P' due to the entire wave front has been found. Let us now consider some other point Q' lying in a plane through P' perpendicular to OP'. If the wave front $ABCD$ is unlimited in extent, the frequency, amplitude, and phase of the disturbance at Q' are the same as at P'. This is true also for

---

[1] This follows from the inverse-square law, since in any wave motion the rate of propagation of energy is proportional to the square of the amplitude. Hence, if the energy decreases as the square of the distance, the amplitude must decrease as the first power.

[2] To be found in all standard textbooks on physical optics. The subject of diffraction is well discussed in Rayleigh's article Wave Theory of Light, Encyclopædia Britannica, 9th ed. It is reprinted in "Scientific Papers of Lord Rayleigh," Vol. III, p. 47.

every point in the transverse plane through P'.   It is therefore evident that a plane wave front of infinite extent through O gives rise to a new plane wave front through P'.   A similar treatment of a spherical wave front would show that the new wave front in this case is spherical.   In other words, the principle of rectilinear propagation can be derived from Huygens's principle provided the wave front is unrestricted in extent.[1]

The same sort of reasoning can be applied when the wave front is restricted by a diaphragm placed between O and P' as shown in Fig. 57.   If it is assumed, as before, that a plane wave of infinite extent is incident on the diaphragm, which is also infinite in extent but contains an aperture of finite area, it is clear that the amplitude of the disturbance at any point such as P' can be

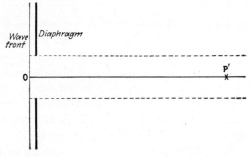

Fig. 57.

obtained by finding the resultant disturbance due to all the elementary areas of the wave front within the area of the aperture.   The actual integration is difficult, but a satisfactory idea of the behavior of the light in this case can be obtained by considering the extreme cases of very large and very small apertures.

If the aperture is very large compared with the wave length of light, the behavior of the wave front approximates that of a wave front of infinite extent.   A plane wave will therefore be confined within the region indicated by the dotted lines.   On the other hand, if the diameter of the aperture is less than half a wave length of light, it may be treated as an elementary area because all portions of it will produce at any distant point a disturbance of substantially the same amplitude and phase. An aperture of these dimensions will therefore cause a dis-

[1] A complete treatment of this subject explains satisfactorily the absence of a back wave in the reverse direction.

turbance to emanate in all directions. For an aperture of intermediate dimensions, the distribution of light in a transverse plane through P' depends upon the size and shape of the aperture. If the aperture is many wave lengths in diameter, this plane will contain an illuminated patch of approximately the dimensions of the aperture. There will be, however, some spreading of the light into the geometrical shadow which lies outside the dotted lines. This apparent bending of light around an obstacle is known as *diffraction*. The diffracted light is not distributed uniformly but appears as fringes or bands which are separated by intervals of darkness. The energy diffracted outside the geometrical shadow is provided at the expense of the energy within the geometrical shadow, where similar dark fringes appear. These fringe systems are known collectively as a *diffraction pattern*.

During the nineteenth century, when evidence for the wave theory of light was so earnestly sought, the diffraction patterns produced by apertures of various shapes became highly important. The experimental verification of the mathematical computations did indeed form one of the strongest arguments in favor of the wave theory. At the very least, it indicated that Huygens's principle, as modified by Fresnel, provides a satisfactory interpretation of diffraction phenomena.

Diffraction is usually a difficult phenomenon to understand, not because it is inherently abstruse but because of the manner in which it is ordinarily approached. The common procedure is to accept the rectilinear propagation of light as axiomatic and to treat diffraction as a sort of aberration that appears when the wave front is restricted by a small aperture. In other words, diffraction is regarded as a bending of light around obstacles in defiance of the geometrical theory. That this is a misleading concept is evident from what has preceded: diffraction is a fundamental property of light, and rectilinear propagation is merely a special case occurring when the wave front is unrestricted. The effect of a diaphragm is not to produce a bending of the light in the usual sense but rather to eliminate those wavelets which, if present, would produce a resultant effect in accordance with the geometrical theory.

59. Diffraction at a Circular Aperture.—Of all the apertures whose diffraction patterns have been investigated, the circular aperture is the most important. This is used, for example, in the pinhole camera, which, under proper conditions, is capable of producing pictures equal if not superior to those produced with a lens. This subject was investigated by Petzval in 1859, and the substance of his argument will be followed here.

In Fig. 58, suppose that a circular pinhole of radius ρ' is situated at a distance p' in front of a photographic plate.[1] According to the geometrical theory, the "image" on the plate of a distant point would be a circular spot with a radius

$$z' = \rho' .$$

On the other hand, if the pinhole is small, the size of the image will be determined by the diffraction pattern it produces. An approximate idea of the distribution of light on the plate with a

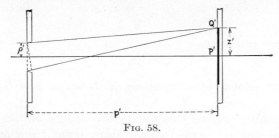

FIG. 58.

small pinhole can be obtained by considering the effect at some point Q' whose distance from the top of the pinhole is just one wave length less than from the bottom. The resultant disturbance at Q' produced by the portion of the wave front incident on the upper half of the pinhole is then almost exactly neutralized by that produced by the portion of the wave front incident on the lower half. Consequently, the intensity at Q' is zero, and the bulk of the energy entering the pinhole falls within the circle whose radius $P'Q' = z'$. If the pinhole is small, the above condition will obtain when

$$z' = \frac{p'}{\rho'} \frac{\lambda}{2} .$$

Adding together the two values of z', as Petzval did, the radius of the image of an infinitely distant point object is found to be

$$z' = \rho' + \frac{p'}{\rho'} \frac{\lambda}{2} . \tag{157}$$

---

[1] The symbols ρ' and p' are used in conformity with the terminology adopted in Chap. V, although the concept of entrance and exit pupils is scarcely applicable here.

Although Lord Rayleigh has shown that it is not permissible to add the values of z' representing the extreme cases of very large and very small apertures, the results based on this equation are sufficiently accurate for most practical purposes. For further details, the reader should consult Lord Rayleigh's original paper on pinhole photography.[1]

Let us now find the value of ρ' that will give the best definition under a given set of conditions. That is, with light of a definite wave length and the plate at a fixed distance from the pinhole, let us see what value of ρ' produces the smallest value of z'. Differentiating Eq. (157) with respect to ρ' and equating the result to zero, we find that the optimum value is

$$\rho' = \sqrt{\frac{p'\lambda}{2}}. \tag{158}$$

Under these conditions

$$z' = 2\rho', \tag{159}$$

as is easily shown by eliminating p' between Eqs. (157) and (158).

The quantity z' here represents the radius of the smallest image that can be formed of a distant point by a camera of length p'. This quantity alone is not a true measure of the ability of the pinhole to reproduce fine detail, since the size of the picture is proportional to p'. The real criterion is therefore the ratio z'/p'. By combining Eqs. (157) and (158), this ratio is found to be

$$\frac{z'}{p'} = \sqrt{\frac{2\lambda}{p'}} = \frac{\lambda}{\rho'}. \tag{160}$$

To record fine detail in the picture, z'/p' should be small, which means that ρ' and p' must be large. But this involves a new difficulty in the form of an increase in the time of exposure. It will be shown subsequently that, for extended objects at a great distance from the camera, the time of exposure is directly proportional to the square of the $f/$-number. From the definition of this quantity given in Sec. 44, it will be seen that, in the present instance,

$$f/\text{-number} = \frac{p'}{2\rho'} = \frac{1}{z'/p'}. \tag{161}$$

[1] *Phil. Mag.*, **31**, 87 (1891).

A quantitative notion of the length of the camera and the time of exposure can be gathered from Table VI, which is computed for $\lambda = 0.00045$ mm, the wave length for which ordinary photographic plates are most sensitive. The values of p' are the optimum for the given values of ρ' or, conversely, the values of ρ' are the optimum for the given values of p'.

TABLE VI

ρ'	p'	z'	z'/p'	$f/$-number
0.01 mm	0.44 mm	0.02 mm	$\frac{1}{2}22$	$f/22$
0.10 mm	4.44 cm	0.20 mm	$\frac{1}{2}222$	$f/222$
1.00 mm	4.44 m	2.00 mm	$\frac{1}{2}2222$	$f/2222$

60. Diffraction at a Lens.—The function of a lens has hitherto been regarded from the standpoint of its action on rays of light, a procedure that furnishes no information about the diffraction pattern that it must produce according to the physical method of interpreting its behavior. Let us return to Fig. 57, therefore, and consider the effect of filling the aperture with a converging lens. From the physical standpoint, the effect of the lens is merely to retard the elementary wavelets differentially because the lens is thicker at the center than at the edges. By choosing a lens of the proper shape, the disturbances from all parts of the incident wave front can be made to arrive at P' simultaneously; that is, all the elementary wavelets can be made to arrive at P' in the same phase, which is but another way of stating that P' is the image of the original infinitely distant source.

Now let us consider the effect at any other point in a plane through P' normal to OP'. Every such point experiences the effect of disturbances originating at each point of the incident wave front, but in general these disturbances arrive in different phases. As before, the resultant amplitude must be computed by integration, but a sufficient understanding can be gained by considering extreme cases. If the lens is infinitely large, the disturbances at every point except P' neutralize one another and the illumination is zero except at P' itself; on the other hand, if the lens has a diameter smaller than $\lambda/2$, the entire receiving plane is illuminated. For some intermediate value of the lens diameter, the result is a diffraction pattern appearing somewhat as shown in Fig. 59.

The nature of this diffraction pattern was investigated mathematically by Airy in 1834. He demonstrated that the illumination E at any point Q' in the pattern depends upon the wave length λ of the light, the radius ρ' of the exit pupil of the system, and the angular distance α' of the point from the axis. Airy's result expressed in mathematical terms is that

$$E = K\rho'^4\left[1 - \frac{1}{2}m^2 + \frac{1}{3}\left(\frac{m^2}{2!}\right)^2 - \frac{1}{4}\left(\frac{m^3}{3!}\right)^2 + \frac{1}{5}\left(\frac{m^4}{4!}\right)^2 - \cdots\right]^2,$$

(162)

where K is a constant and

$$m = \frac{\pi\rho'}{\lambda}\sin\alpha'. \tag{163}$$

By substituting various values for the quantity α', it is found that the illumination is a maximum in the center of the diffraction

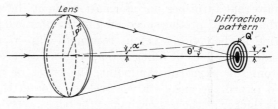

Fig. 59.

pattern. As α' increases, the illumination diminishes gradually to zero and then passes through a series of secondary maxima separated by points of zero illumination. The following table gives the values of m corresponding to the first few maxima and minima, together with the relative illumination E at those points:

m	E	
0	1	First maximum
$0.61\,\pi$	0	First minimum
$0.81\,\pi$	0.174	Second maximum
$1.116\,\pi$	0	Second minimum
$1.333\,\pi$	0.0041	Third maximum
$1.619\,\pi$	0	Third minimum

This diffraction pattern appears to consist of a central disk of light surrounded by a series of rings of decreasing intensity. The central disk receives approximately 84 per cent of the energy transmitted by the lens, and the rings receive only 7, 3, 1.5, 1, etc., per cent, respectively. For practical purposes, the diffraction pattern may be assumed to consist merely of the central disk. The size of this disk can be determined in terms of the angle θ' by substituting in Eq. (163) the value of m corresponding to the first minimum and noting that

$$\sin \alpha' = \tan \alpha' = \frac{z'}{p'}$$

(α' being small), and that

$$\tan \theta' = \frac{\rho'}{p'}.$$

The result is

$$z' = \frac{0.61 \lambda}{n' \tan \theta'}, \tag{164}$$

where n' is the refractive index of the image space. This quantity is introduced to make the equation of general application since λ/n' is the actual wave length of the light in the image space when the index is other than unity. It should be noticed that, for light of a given wave length, the size of the diffraction pattern depends only on the angle subtended at the image by the exit pupil of the system. That this equation is qualitatively correct will be seen by noting that it holds for the extreme cases of vanishingly small and infinitely large apertures. In the former case, $\theta' = 0$ and hence $z' = \infty$, which means that the entire receiving plane is illuminated; in the latter case, $\theta' = \pi/2$ and hence $z' = 0$, which means that the image is a true point, as it should be on the basis of the geometrical theory.

This description of the image has been based on the tacit assumption that the light is monochromatic. If the light is heterochromatic—white, for example—the image consists of the superposed diffraction patterns produced by light of every wave length. Since z' depends on λ, these patterns are of different sizes and the resultant image is characterized by variously colored rings. To determine the order of the colors theoretically would require a complicated analysis, because the intensity of the light in a single monochromatic pattern passes through its various maxima and minima gradually. Certain salient features can be readily deduced, however. Within the area covered by the violet disk, which is the smallest, light of all wave lengths combines to produce an approximate white. Just outside the violet disk, the violet alone is absent and the resultant is yellow.   From this point outwards a colored ring pattern of complex design appears.   At the outer portion of this pattern, the rings due to light of so many different wave lengths overlap that the field becomes practically white although, of course, very faint.

61. Resolving Power.—It is clear from the foregoing that the image of a point object is always a diffraction disk whose size depends principally on the angle subtended at its center by the exit pupil of the instrument.   If the object consists of two points, the image consists of two diffraction disks; and, if the points are close together, the disks may overlap to such an extent

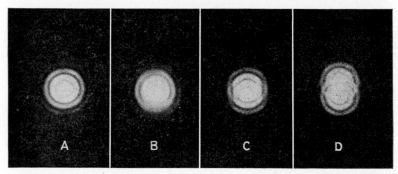

Fig. 60.—Enlargements from photographs of typical diffraction patterns produced by a lens: *A*, for a single distant point object; *B*, for two distant point objects whose diffraction patterns are separated by a distance equal to half the radius of the central disks; *C*, the same when the separation is equal to the radius of the disks; *D*, the same when the separation is equal to twice the radius of the disks.   (*Photographs by A. G. Hall.*)

that they cannot be distinguished separately.   In Fig. 60, *A* is an enlargement of an actual photograph of the image formed by a high-quality objective of a distant point object; *B* is a similar photograph of the image of two points whose separation is such that the distance between the centers of their diffraction patterns is equal to half the radius of the central disks; in *C*, the distance between the centers is equal to the radius of the disks; and in *D*, to twice the radius.   It is evident that, unless the separation of the diffraction patterns is at least equal to the radius of the central disk, the two points might appear as one. In other words, they could not be *resolved*.   Increasing the magnification by any means whatever would not improve the power of the lens to resolve the two points because the size of the diffraction disks would increase at the same rate as their

separation.   On the other hand, increasing the diameter of the
lens would decrease the size of the diffraction disks without
altering their separation.   In other words, the resolving power
of an optical system is a function of its aperture alone.   Even
before the theory of diffraction was understood, astronomers
had discovered that the ability of a telescope to resolve double
stars depends only on the diameter of the objective, and that
increasing the magnification beyond a certain point does not
improve the resolution.

It is fairly easy to derive an expression for the separation of
a pair of points in the object space that can just be resolved

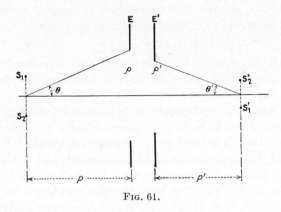

Fig. 61.

according to the criterion that the distance between the centers
of the diffraction patterns must be equal to the radius of the
first dark ring.   In Fig. 61, let S_1 and S_2 be two point objects
at a distance p from the entrance pupil of an optical system.
The images of S_1 and S_2 will then be formed at a distance p'
from the exit pupil.   Let the radii of the entrance and exit pupils
of the system be ρ and ρ' respectively.   Then the separation
of S_1' and S_2' which, according to the criterion, will just permit
resolution is, from Eq. (164),

$$\overline{S_1'S_2'} = z' = \frac{0.61\ \lambda}{n'\ \tan\ \theta'} = \frac{0.61\ \lambda\ \cos\ \theta'}{n'\ \sin\ \theta'}.$$

From the sine law,

$$\overline{S_1S_2}\ n\ \sin\ \theta = \overline{S_1'S_2'}\ n'\ \sin\ \theta'$$
$$= 0.61\ \lambda\ \cos\ \theta',$$

or

$$\overline{S_1 S_2} = \frac{0.61 \lambda}{n \sin \theta} \cos \theta'.$$

In most optical systems, the image distance is so great compared with the diameter of the exit pupil that $\cos \theta'$ can be set equal to unity without introducing an appreciable error, especially in view of the arbitrariness of the criterion of resolution. Usually, therefore,

$$\overline{S_1 S_2} = \frac{0.61 \lambda}{n \sin \theta}. \tag{165}$$

This equation gives the smallest separation of two points in the object space that can be resolved in light of wave length λ with an optical system whose numerical aperture

$$\text{N.A.} = n \sin \theta,$$

as defined in Chap. V. Obviously the numerical aperture cannot exceed unity when the object is situated in air, but by filling the space between the object and the first lens of the objective with a suitable liquid, as is done in microscope practice, the numerical aperture can be increased considerably. Microscope objectives to be used dry are made with numerical apertures up to 0.95, while those designed to be used with an oil having the same index as the first lens may have a numerical aperture as high as 1.40. For such an objective, the distance between two points that can just be resolved is approximately one-half a wave length of light. The advantage of using light of short wave length is plainly evident.

The resolving power of a system designed for viewing objects at a considerable distance is expressed more conveniently in terms of the angular separation of two points that can just be resolved, rather than the linear separation. By calling this minimum angle α and assuming it to be small, it can be expressed as

$$\alpha = \frac{\overline{S_1 S_2}}{p} = \frac{0.61 \lambda}{p \, n \sin \theta}. \tag{166}$$

Since p is large compared with ρ,

$$\sin \theta = \theta = \tan \theta = \frac{\rho}{p}.$$

Hence Eq. (166) becomes simply

$$\alpha = \frac{0.61 \lambda}{n \rho}. \tag{167}$$

Setting $n = 1$, as is almost invariably the case for distant objects, and introducing the diameter of the entrance pupil $D = 2\rho$ as a matter of convenience, the resolving power can be written as

$$\alpha = \frac{1.22\,\lambda}{D}. \tag{168}$$

The smaller the value of α, the higher the resolving power is said to be. Thus the resolving power of a telescope is directly proportional to the diameter of its objective when the latter is the entrance pupil of the system.

The resolving power of a telescope when computed by means of the above equation agrees fairly well with values that are obtained by experience. The astronomer Dawes, who made an extensive investigation of observations on double stars, arrived at the conclusion that the resolving power of a telescope of moderate dimensions is approximately 4.6 seconds of arc divided by the diameter of the objective in inches. Equation (168) indicates that for green light ($\lambda = 555$ mμ) the value should be 5.5″, a remarkable agreement in view of the arbitrariness of the criterion of resolution on which the equation depends. It is clear that this criterion holds only for two point objects of equal brightness. It does not hold if the points are of unequal brightness nor does it hold for detail in an extended object, the resolution of which depends in large measure upon the contrast in the object. Hence, except in the special case of double stars, these formulae supply merely a useful working rule for determining the capability of an optical instrument in a rough sort of way.

In practice, the term "resolving power" is used in a rather broad sense to describe the limit upon the ability of a system to record fine detail in the object, whether this limit is imposed by diffraction, by aberrations in the system, or by poor workmanship in preparing and centering the elements of which it is composed. Optical systems vary enormously in the closeness with which their resolving power in this sense approaches the ultimate limit set by diffraction. The resolving power of photographic objectives, for example, falls far short of it. Telescope and microscope objectives, on the other hand, which are required to cover only a small field, are commonly corrected so well that their resolving power very closely approaches the limit set by diffraction. Lord Rayleigh has investigated the degree to which small departures from perfection in the construction of an optical system injure its performance.[1]   He concluded that the imagery is practically perfect if the length of the optical path along every ray is the same to within one-quarter of a wave length.   This does not mean that an inferior system will not produce images that are entirely satisfactory for the purpose for which the system was designed, but it indicates a limit for the most exacting work that is worth striving for but is hardly worth exceeding.

[1] *Phil. Mag.*, **8**, 403 (1879).   Reprinted in "Scientific Papers of Lord Rayleigh," Vol. I, p. 428.

CHAPTER VIII

RADIATION

The six preceding chapters have been devoted principally to the subject of image formation. Now there are, of course, three essential elements in any optical system: the source of light, the image-forming system itself, and the light-sensitive receiving surface. The subject of image formation can be studied independently because the behavior of an optical system does not depend upon the amount of light present; that is, the quality of the image, whether limited by diffraction or by aberrations, is the same in a weak light as in a strong one. In the succeeding seven chapters, the characteristics of light sources and of receivers of radiant energy are presented. The present chapter will be devoted to the general subject of radiation.

62. The Electromagnetic Spectrum.—The entire electromagnetic spectrum is customarily divided, in the order of increasing frequency, into Hertzian waves, heat rays, light, ultraviolet rays, X-rays, gamma rays, and cosmic rays. The divisions between these regions are shown in Fig. 62. Until recent years, these regions were separated by gaps, but now that these gaps have been closed, it appears that the essential properties of all electromagnetic radiations are the same. Any classification of radiation with respect to frequency is therefore significant only when considering the interactions between radiation and matter that occur during the process of emission or absorption. In Fig. 62, the wave length and frequency are both plotted on a logarithmic scale so that an octave may be represented by an equal interval everywhere in the spectrum. It will be observed that the visible region corresponds to slightly less than a single octave while the figure represents more than seventy octaves. There are, of course, no limits to the electromagnetic spectrum; frequencies as close to zero as desired can readily be generated, and it is also conceivable that frequencies higher than those of the cosmic rays will some day be discovered. An investigation of the phenomena associated with the electromagnetic

135

spectrum would naturally involve nearly every branch of physics, and we shall therefore confine this discussion to the phenomena most closely associated with the visible region.

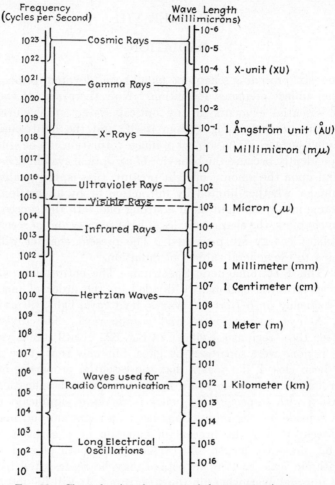

FIG. 62.—Chart showing the gamut of electromagnetic waves.

Because of the enormous frequency range of the electromagnetic spectrum, it is to be expected that the mechanisms by which the various radiations are produced must be widely different. Electromagnetic waves which are identical with light waves, except that their frequency is very much lower, are radiated into free space from the ordinary transmission line carrying a 60-cycle alternating current. The wave length in free space corresponding to this frequency is 5×10^6 meters. To increase the frequency, the generator might be rotated more rapidly, but mechanical difficulties impose a limit upon this procedure. Radiation of higher frequency can be produced by the oscillations of an electrical circuit, thus avoiding the movements of mechanical parts. In this case, the frequency of the oscillation is

$$f = \frac{1}{2\pi\sqrt{LC}},$$

where L is the inductance and C the capacitance of the oscillating circuit. The radiations employed in radio communication are generated in this manner. The required energy can be supplied either by means of a spark gap, which periodically shocks the circuit into oscillation, or by means of a vacuum-tube oscillator, which supplies the energy continuously. The shortest waves that have been produced by means of a vacuum-tube oscillator have a wave length of 56 mm, the limit being set by the inherent inductance and capacitance of the tube. Radiations of still shorter wave length have been produced by spark-excited oscillations, the electrodes being made very small to reduce the inductance and capacitance of the circuit to a minimum. By using electrodes only 0.2 mm long and 0.2 mm wide, Nichols and Tear produced waves as short as 1.8 mm. More recently, Glagolewa-Arkadiewa, with a somewhat modified form of apparatus, has produced electromagnetic waves as short as 0.1 mm. This represents the present limit (1929) of waves produced by electrical oscillations of the kind discovered by Hertz.

Radiations of higher frequency than can be generated by oscillating electrical circuits are produced by the oscillations of the molecules themselves. Waves as long as 0.4 mm have been detected in the radiation from such a common source of light as the mercury-vapor lamp. This radiation is identical in every respect with that of the same frequency produced by electrical oscillations. Radiations of higher frequency than can be produced by the oscillations of molecules result from the vibrations within the molecules—that is, the vibrations of the atoms of which they are composed. These radiations extend into the visible region, the boundary between the visible region and the infrared being determined solely by the spectral sensitivity of the human eye. These radiations, when analyzed, appear as band spectra. They are usually observed as absorption spectra, but emission and absorption are produced by the same mechanism.

All the radiations of higher frequency than can be produced by the vibrations of either atoms or molecules as a whole are attributed to changes that take place within the atom. To understand the process, it is necessary to assume some sort of atomic model, and the one that most nearly fulfills the requirements of the spectroscopist is that devised by Rutherford. According to this model, atoms consist of charges of positive and negative electricity, the positive charges being known as *protons* and the negative charges as *electrons*. Hydrogen is the first element in the periodic table, and, as might be expected, its atom has the simplest form. It is assumed to consist, as shown in Fig. 63, of a single proton about which a single electron revolves. Actually both elements revolve about their common center of mass, but, as the mass of the proton is known to be 1846 times that of the electron, the proton is at rest in comparison. The electron can be removed from the atom in various ways; for example, by bombardment with another electron. The denuded atom is then said to be *ionized*.

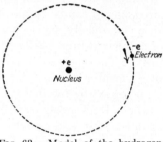

FIG. 63.—Model of the hydrogen atom.

The position of an element in the periodic table determines the complexity of its atom. Thus helium, the second element in the table, has a nucleus containing four protons and two electrons about which two more electrons revolve, much as the planets revolve about the sun. One or both of these planetary electrons can be removed from the atom, thus making the latter either singly or doubly ionized. The third element in the periodic table, lithium, has several isotopes, and the number of protons and electrons in the nucleus is different for each isotope. However, each isotope has three more protons than electrons in the nucleus, so the latter is surrounded by three planetary electrons when the atom is in its normal or electrically neutral state. The ordinal number representing the place of an element in the periodic table represents the excess of protons over electrons in the nucleus of the atom. It is known as Moseley's *atomic number* and represents also the number of planetary electrons revolving about the nucleus when the atom is in its normal state.

With the Rutherford atomic model as a basis, a very complete and satisfactory interpretation of spectroscopic data has been evolved during the last decade. A hint as to the type of change that takes place within an atom when it radiates energy will be given in the following section; so it is sufficient to state here that when the change involves the outermost group of electrons, the resulting radiation occurs principally in the visible and ultraviolet regions. If these changes produce vibrations of the atoms composing the molecule, band spectra in the same regions result. The present short-wave limit of the ultraviolet spectrum is at 13.7 mμ, which is the wave length of a line observed by Millikan in the optical spectrum of oxygen. Radiations of shorter wave length are called X-rays and are produced by bombarding a metal with a stream of high-velocity electrons. This causes one or more of the inner planetary electrons to undergo changes similar to those undergone by the outer electrons when the latter radiate line spectra in the visible and ultraviolet regions. X-rays with wave lengths as great as 27 mμ have been observed, thus bridging the gap that once existed between the ultraviolet and X-ray regions. At the other end of the X-ray spectrum, the limit depends upon the potential difference that tubes can be made to withstand. The gigantic tubes that have been developed in recent years are capable of withstanding a potential difference of a million volts, and the rays emitted have a wave length in the neighborhood of 0.001 mμ.

One characteristic feature of X-rays is the facility with which they penetrate matter. Although very long X-rays, like ultraviolet rays, are absorbed by the atmosphere, the penetrating power increases as the wave length decreases so that the very short X-rays, which are produced by the use of high voltages, are capable of penetrating several inches of steel.

The radiations that remain to be discussed—the gamma rays and the cosmic rays—are associated with changes within the nucleus of the atom. Since the constitution of the nucleus is determined by the atomic number of the element, it follows that the changes in the nucleus are associated with the actual trans-

mutation of elements.   The gamma rays accompany the break-
down of the so-called radioactive materials, such as radium and
uranium.   Radiations produced in this way have wave lengths
as long as 0.14 mμ, which overlaps the X-ray region.   As might
be expected, the gamma rays are also very penetrating.   The
cosmic rays, which are the shortest radiations known at present,
are still more penetrating and are capable of discharging an
electroscope even when the latter is thoroughly shielded from all
other radiations.   Because of their great penetrating power, their
wave length can not be measured directly but can be predicted
from certain theoretical considerations.   Thus the formation
of helium from hydrogen should produce a radiation with a wave
length of 0.000046 mμ; and the absorption coefficient at this wave
length for a layer of water 1 meter thick should be 0.30.   Similarly, the transmutation of hydrogen into oxygen or into silicon
in a single act should produce radiations having absorption
coefficients of 0.08 and 0.041 per meter of water respectively.
These absorption coefficients correspond closely with those
observed for the cosmic rays; and since helium, oxygen, and
silicon appear in great abundance in the heavenly bodies, it is
surmised that these rays are due to a process of formation of
atoms that may be taking place in other parts of the universe.

   63. The Origin of Spectra.—The striking feature about
atomic and molecular spectra is that they consist of sharp lines,
representing vibrations of definite frequencies.   This would not
be expected from the simple model of the atom presented above;
the electron in a hydrogen atom, for example, would be
expected to revolve in any orbit whatever, determined solely
by the amount of energy it happens to possess at the moment.
If this were the case, it would pursue a spiral path toward the
nucleus as it radiates energy, the period of revolution becoming
constantly shorter.   If it is assumed that the frequency of the
emitted light is the same as the frequency of revolution of the
electron, it is clear that the total radiation from a large number
of radiating atoms should produce a continuous spectrum.
This failure of classical mechanics to account for line spectra led
to the development of the quantum theory of spectra by Bohr,
Sommerfeld, and others.   When treating the behavior of such
small things as atoms and molecules, this theory must be substituted for classical mechanics, although it reduces to the familiar
classical mechanics for bodies of ordinary size.

The fundamental postulates of the quantum theory are that systems cannot take on any energy value whatever but only a certain discrete set of energies; and that the frequency of the radiation emitted by such a system is to be computed, not by setting it equal to mechanical frequencies, but by the equation

$$h\nu = E - E', \tag{169}$$

where E and E' are two permissible values of the energy (*energy levels*, as they are called), ν is the frequency of the radiation, and h is a fundamental constant equal to 6.55×10^{-27} erg-second. As applied to an atomic model, this means that the electrons revolve in orbits representing definite energy levels. When an atom absorbs energy, an electron is caused to jump to an outer orbit; when an electron jumps to an inner orbit, it emits energy in the form of radiation. Since the energy levels are definite, the frequencies are also definite, in agreement with experiment, and the spectrum consists of sharp lines.

The frequencies of the spectral lines permit the values of the energy levels of the atoms to be deduced; and, in this way, far-reaching information about the structure of atoms can be obtained. The various possible electronic orbits are classified according to certain indices, called *quantum numbers*. Thus, one of these is called the principal quantum number n, which can take the value 1 for the smallest orbit, 2 for the next larger, etc. In hydrogen, the electron can be in any one of these orbits, but that for $n = 1$ has the lowest energy. This is the normal state of the atom to which it always falls, unless it is bombarded by electrons or is otherwise excited. More complicated atoms, containing many electrons, tend at ordinary temperatures to fall to as low a level as possible. They would all go to the level $n = 1$ except for a most important principle, called the *exclusion principle*, which states that there can be no more than two electrons in an atom with $n = 1$, eight with $n = 2$, etc. It is this principle that results in the formation of the groups of elements of the periodic table. Thus helium, neon, etc., with 2, $2 + 8$, etc., electrons, have closed shells and are inert gases; lithium, sodium, etc., with $2 + 1$, $2 + 8 + 1$, etc., electrons, have one electron that is easily removed and thus they readily become ionized. These complicated atoms can be excited, as can hydrogen, some of their electrons going to higher levels and placing the atoms in a condition to permit the emission of radiation. To excite the outer electrons, only a comparatively small amount of energy is needed (that supplied by a bombarding electron falling through a difference of potential of a few volts) and the resulting radiation is in the visible region. On the other hand, if the inner electrons are to be removed to outer orbits, a very large amount of energy is needed (corresponding to electrons of thousands of volts of energy) and the radiation is in the X-ray region. These are examples of the general rule expressed by Eq. (169), that the greater the energy of excitation, whether as a result of bombardment by more energetic particles or as a result of a higher temperature, the greater the frequency and the shorter the wave length of the resulting radiation.

To understand how the quantum theory goes over into ordinary mechanics for large systems or low frequencies, it must be noted that as ν gets smaller, which of course it does for a heavy system, the energy levels get closer together. Thus for the rotation of a molecule, the energy levels are so close together that only a good spectroscope will resolve the lines, and the spectrum ordinarily appears to consist of continuous bands. It can be proved that in this case the emitted light approaches more and more closely the result predicted by ordinary mechanics. Thus, although the quantum theory is indispensable in the X-ray, ultraviolet, and visible regions, it is more accurate but not essential in the infrared region, and is quite unnecessary in the region of Hertzian waves.

64. Thermal Radiation.—It is a fact of common experience that all liquids and solids emit light when their temperature is raised above approximately 500°C. This light is at first a dull red, and becomes successively orange, yellow, and then white as the temperature is increased, the total amount of energy radiated increasing simultaneously at a rapid rate. When this *thermal radiation*, as it is called, is analyzed with a spectroscope, the spectrum is found to be continuous. To borrow an analogy from the field of acoustics, thermal radiation may be likened to the sound of a sand blast, whereas the type of radiation discussed in the preceding section corresponds to musical notes or chords. Thermal radiation is characteristic of the temperature of the radiating body rather than the material of which it is composed. It is due to the thermal agitation of the molecules which, in the closely packed condition existing within liquids and solids, are unable to radiate in their characteristic manner. Many of the laws pertaining to thermal radiation are derived, therefore, on the basis of thermodynamical considerations involving the energy of the entire system, rather than on the basis of the behavior of its component parts.

It must not be assumed that thermal radiation is associated solely with high temperatures. As a matter of fact, it is emitted at every temperature above the absolute zero. According to Prévost's famous theory of exchanges, every body is constantly exchanging energy with its surroundings; and any body whose temperature is constant must radiate energy at a rate exactly equal to the rate at which it absorbs energy from its surroundings, assuming it to be insulated and in a vacuum.

Before the laws of radiation can be discussed, it will be necessary to define certain properties of radiating surfaces. The emissive power of a surface at a given temperature will be defined as the amount of energy radiated per unit time per unit area. This quantity will be designated by E. Conversely, the amount of incident radiant energy falling per unit time on a unit area of a surface will be designated by I. Now, in general, the radiation falling on a body is partly reflected, partly transmitted, and partly absorbed. Let it be supposed that a fraction R of the incident radiation is reflected and a fraction A is absorbed. The quantities R and A are known as the *reflectivity* and the *absorptivity* of the surface respectively. If the fraction transmitted can be neglected,

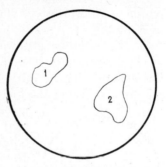

Fig. 64.

$$R + A = 1 .$$

There is a fundamental relationship between the absorptivity of a body and its emissive power which we shall now investigate. In Fig. 64, assume that the two bodies, 1 and 2, are placed within an evacuated enclosure, the walls of this enclosure being maintained at a constant temperature. In the course of time, both bodies will acquire the same temperature as the walls of the enclosure, whereupon they will radiate in a given time an amount of energy exactly equal to the amount they absorb. If S_1 represents the superficial area of body 1, the total energy radiated per unit time by this body is $E_1 S_1$. The amount of energy it absorbs from its surroundings is IA_1S_1.   When thermal equilibrium has been reached,

$$E_1S_1 = IA_1S_1.$$

The corresponding expression for body 2 is

$$E_2S_2 = IA_2S_2.$$

From these equations, it follows that

$$\frac{E_1}{A_1} = \frac{E_2}{A_2}. \tag{170}$$

This argument is valid for any number of bodies, and hence we may state that, at any given temperature, the ratio of emissive power to absorptivity is the same for all bodies.   This is known as *Kirchhoff's law*.

Since the emissive power of a body is directly proportional to its absorptivity, a body for which the reflectivity is zero and the absorptivity is unity is the best possible radiator.   Such a body absorbs all the incident radiation and is therefore called

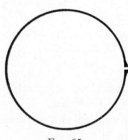

FIG. 65.

a *black body*.   No substance is known that is truly black in this sense, even lampblack reflecting about one per cent. Hence the desired condition is approximated, both in theory and in experiment, by a hollow enclosure containing a small hole through which the radiation may enter or leave, as shown in Fig. 65.   If the size of the hole is small compared with the size of the enclosure and the reflectivity of the walls has a value less than unity, any radiation entering the enclosure will be reflected and re-reflected until, after an infinite number of reflections, it becomes completely absorbed.   Conversely, the radiation from such an enclosure is identical with that from an ideal black body.

It can be proved theoretically that any body within an enclosure radiates like a black body after thermal equilibrium with the walls of the enclosure has been reached.   This fact was observed experimentally by Draper as long ago as 1847.   Draper placed an assortment of metals, crockery, and other materials in a gun barrel which he heated in a furnace until it reached a dull red color. He then found it impossible, on looking into the gun barrel, to distinguish these substances from the wall of the barrel. Since the black body is the only perfect radiator and since, furthermore, all bodies within an enclosure radiate like a black body, it represents an ideal case for study.

65. The Stefan-Boltzmann Law.—In 1879 Stefan suggested, on the basis of an experiment by Tyndall, that the total emissive power of a body is proportional to the fourth power of its absolute temperature. In other words,

$$E = \sigma T^4, \tag{171}$$

where σ is a constant and T is the temperature on the absolute or Kelvin scale.[1] This fourth-power law was subsequently derived for a black body by Boltzmann from theoretical considerations of a thermodynamic nature.[2] The clue to the method was supplied by Maxwell's proof that radiation exerts a pressure when it falls on a surface.[3] Hence, if radiation is introduced within a cylinder, it will exert a pressure tending to force the piston outward. If the inside of the cylinder is made of a material whose reflectivity is unity, the radiation within the cylinder will persist forever and will exert a continuous pressure on the piston. In this respect, therefore, radiation behaves very much like a gas confined within a cylinder. Now Carnot had previously found the relationship between the mechanical energy and the thermal energy when a gas undergoes a cyclical process consisting of alternate isothermal and adiabatic expansions and compressions. By following the same sort of reasoning with radiation substituted for the gas, Boltzmann proved that the total emissive power of a black body is proportional to the fourth power of its absolute temperature. The quantity σ in Eq. (171) is called the *Stefan-Boltzmann constant*. Its accepted value is 5.709×10^{-5} when E is in ergs per second per square centimeter and the temperature is measured on the Kelvin scale.

[1] The Kelvin temperature is obtained by adding 273.1 to the temperature measured in centigrade degrees.

[2] See any textbook on heat, such as Preston's "Theory of Heat."

[3] This pressure is exceedingly feeble, amounting to only 4.5×10^{-5} dyne/cm² for solar radiation at the earth's surface. A layer of water less than half a millimicron thick would produce this pressure! Nevertheless, the existence of this pressure was verified by Nichols and Hull in a classical experiment performed in 1901, and an apparatus for measuring it was described by Tear, *Jour. Optical Soc. Amer. and Rev. Sci. Instruments*, **11**, 135 (1925).

The experiment that led Stefan to propose the fourth-power law consisted in measuring the amount of energy radiated by a platinum wire at two different temperatures. The results were in good agreement with Eq. (171), notwithstanding that the reflectivity of platinum is not zero and hence it is not a black body. However, it very closely approximates what is known as a *gray body*—namely, one that radiates at every wave length an amount of energy bearing a constant ratio to the amount radiated by a black body at the same temperature. In other words, the spectral distribution of the energy from a gray body is exactly the same as that from a black body, but the total energy radiated is smaller in amount. A gray body is sometimes said to be a *non-selective radiator*. Such materials as platinum, iron, tungsten, and carbon are very nearly non-selective; and the success of Stefan's explanation was due to the fact that the fourth-power law holds for these non-selective radiators also, the only difference being in the value of the constant. The constant in this case is the product of the Stefan-Boltzmann constant and a quantity e, which is known as the *emissivity* of the gray body. The emissivity is, of course, the ratio of the emissive power of the gray body to that of a black body at the same temperature.

A *selective radiator* is one whose spectral distribution of energy differs from that of a black body at the same temperature. The Welsbach mantle is a good example of such a radiator, the whiteness of its light being due to the disproportionately large amount of energy in the blue end of the spectrum. Obviously, the laws that have been developed for pure thermal radiation do not apply to such radiators.

66. The Spectral Distribution of Black-body Radiation.— Although thermal radiation always gives a continuous spectrum when analyzed, the distribution of the power within the spectrum is found to vary with the temperature of the radiating body in a characteristic manner. Figure 66 shows the distribution of power in the spectrum of a black body at various temperatures computed by means of a formula that will be discussed presently. The abscissae represent wave length and the ordinates, power. The plots have been made on a logarithmic scale because of the great range of values that must be represented. It will be seen that, as the temperature increases, the maximum of the distribution curve shifts toward the short-wave end of the spectrum.

This accounts qualitatively for the fact that a heated body becomes first a dull red and then successively orange, yellow, and white.

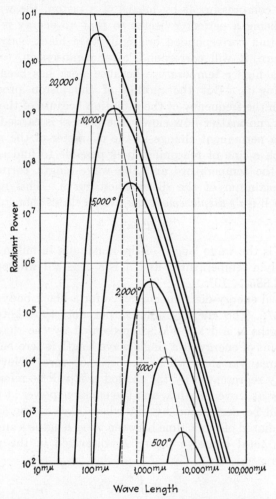

FIG. 66.—Black-body radiation curves for various absolute temperatures plotted on a logarithmic scale. The power is expressed in ergs per second per square centimeter per millimicron. The dotted lines define the visible region; the broken line is the locus of the maximum of the radiation curves. These curves are similar in their dimensions and orientation and differ only in their positions along the locus of the maximum. The curve for 5000°K. is plotted on a natural scale in Fig. 67.

The position of the maximum of the distribution curve for a black body can be found theoretically by continuing the sort of reasoning that led Boltzmann to the fourth-power law. The details of the proof would be out of place here, but the method in brief consists in introducing some radiation into a cylinder and then compressing it by means of a piston, the wall of the cylinder being a perfect reflector so that no energy is lost. If the radiation corresponded originally to a black body at some temperature, it will correspond, after compression, to a black body at a higher temperature because work has been done in compressing it. But the motion of the piston produces an increase in the frequency of the radiation because of the Doppler effect; for, no matter how slowly the process is carried out, the result is a permanent change in the character of the radiation. From such a line of reasoning, it is possible to find a relation between the temperature and the wave length corresponding to the maximum of the distribution curve. This relation is known as *Wien's displacement law*, which states that

$$\lambda_m T = A, \qquad (172)$$

where λ_m is the wave length of the maximum in millimicrons, T is the Kelvin temperature,[1] and A is a constant whose accepted value is 2.885×10^6.

A typical energy-distribution curve for a black body is shown in Fig. 67. The energy radiated per unit time between the wave lengths λ and $\lambda + d\lambda$ is represented by the shaded area. The amount of energy at a single wave length is zero because the shaded area vanishes when $d\lambda$ becomes zero. Nevertheless, the energy represented by the shaded area will be referred to as the energy at wave length λ, and the emissive power at this wave length will be designated by E_λ, where $E_\lambda d\lambda$ is the amount of energy radiated per unit time between wave lengths λ and $\lambda + d\lambda$. Then the total emissive power E, discussed in the preceding section, is

$$E = \int_0^\infty E_\lambda d\lambda.$$

Let E_m represent the emissive power corresponding to λ_m in

---

[1] It is interesting to observe that a black body at 5200°K. radiates most copiously at 555 mμ, the point in the spectrum where the human eye is most sensitive. Solar radiation after passing through the earth's atmosphere corresponds approximately to this temperature, indicating the degree to which the eye has adapted itself to the source of radiation to which it is most frequently subjected.

Wien's displacement law. By following an argument similar to the one previously outlined, Wien was able to show that

$$\frac{E_m}{T^5} = B, \qquad (173)$$

where B is a constant whose value is 1.300×10^{-11} when T is the Kelvin temperature and E_m is in ergs per second per square centimeter per millimicron.

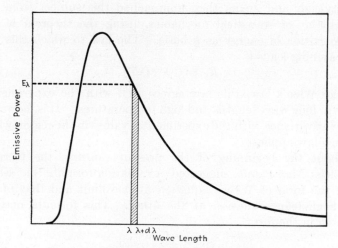

Fig. 67.—A typical black-body radiation curve.

From the generalized form of Wien's two laws, it follows that the distribution of energy in the radiation from a black body is representable by

$$E_\lambda = C\lambda^{-5} \cdot f(\lambda \cdot T), \qquad (174)$$

where C is a constant and $f(\lambda \cdot T)$ is some function of λ and T which thermodynamical reasoning alone is incapable of evaluating. Wien then made the following assumptions:

1. Each molecule sends out rays whose wave length depends only on the velocity of the molecule, and of which the intensity is a function of this velocity. Since the wave length is a function of the velocity, the velocity may be regarded as a function of the wave length.

2. The energy of radiation between the wave-length limits λ and $\lambda + d\lambda$ is proportional to the number of molecules sending out waves of this period and to a function of the molecular velocity v.

The number of molecules whose velocities lie between the limits v and $v + dv$ is known from the kinetic theory. Wien was therefore able to derive a law for the distribution of energy radiated by a black body, which is

$$E_\lambda = C_1\lambda^{-5}\epsilon^{-\frac{C_2}{\lambda T}}. \tag{175}$$

At short wave lengths and low temperatures, this law is in close agreement with the experimentally determined values, but at long wave lengths and high temperatures the deviations become excessively great.

Rayleigh and Jeans then approached this subject from the standpoint of statistical mechanics, using the theorem of the equipartition of energy as a basis. The law to which this line of reasoning leads is

$$E_\lambda = C_1\lambda^{-5}(\lambda T). \tag{176}$$

Unlike Wien's law, this law agrees well with the experimental facts at long wave lengths and high temperatures. It is, however, quite at variance with the experimental values in the region where Wien's law applies.

About the beginning of the present century, the German physicist Max Planck suggested[1] a radiation formula that would take the form of Wien's equation at one limit and that of the Rayleigh-Jeans equation at the other. This formula may be written in the form

$$E_\lambda = \frac{C_1\lambda^{-5}}{\epsilon^{C_2/\lambda T} - 1}, \tag{177}$$

where C_1 and C_2 are constants whose numerical values are 3.703×10^{23} and 1.433×10^7, respectively, when E_λ is measured in ergs per second per square centimeter per millimicron, λ is in millimicrons, and T is in absolute degrees.[2] This law has been found to fit the observed data within the experimental error throughout the entire spectrum. For comparison, curves representing the Wien, the Rayleigh-Jeans, and the Planck radiation formulae are plotted together in Fig. 68 for a black body at 5000°K.

Of course, no physicist is ever satisfied with a situation like this, where both the Wien and the Rayleigh-Jeans expressions seem to contain a certain measure of correctness, although neither

[1] *Verhandl. deutsch. physik. Gesells.*, **2**, 202 (1900).

[2] Calculations involving Planck's law are greatly facilitated by the use of the data in the "International Critical Tables," Vol. V, pp. 237 *et seq.* The charts and tables published by the Bureau of Standards as their *Miscellaneous Publication* 56 are also valuable, especially in the visible region.

is adequate for a complete interpretation of the phenomenon. Planck attempted, therefore, to find some concept to reconcile

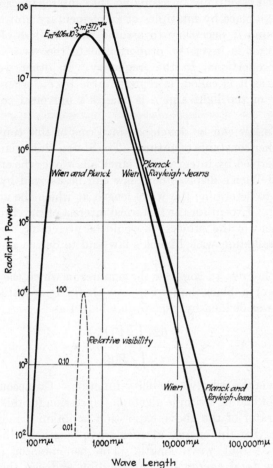

Fig. 68.—A comparison of the various radiation formulae for a black body at 5000°K.

the differences between the two results. The concept he introduced[1] is too well known, both on its own account and because

[1] *Ann. Physik*, **4**, 553 (1901). His line of reasoning is set forth in his Nobel Prize address, "The Origin and Development of the Quantum Theory" (1922). His derivation of the radiation law has been simplified by Einstein, *Verhandl. deutsch. physik. Gesells.*, **18**, 318 (1916) and *Physik. Zeits.*, **18**, 121 (1917). See Ruark and Urey's "Atoms, Molecules, and Quanta," Chap. III.

of the profound influence it has had on the development of modern physics, to require more than a brief mention here. It consisted essentially in assuming that interchanges of energy always take place by multiples of an elementary unit of energy. Planck found it necessary to assume that the size of this elementary unit is inversely proportional to the wave length, or directly proportional to the frequency. In other words, this quantum, as it is called, is representable by $h\nu$, where ν is the frequency of the light and h is Planck's universal constant of action.

Planck's law can be developed in terms of this constant and certain other constants of nature. The Stefan-Boltzmann law can then be derived by integrating Planck's law over the entire spectrum, and Wien's displacement law can be derived by differentiating it to determine the wave length at which the energy is a maximum. Except for the historical interest of the chronological development of the subject, it would be preferable to begin the study of radiation with Planck's law and to derive all the other laws from it.

It is of interest to consider the manner in which the luminous efficiency of a black body varies with its temperature. This quantity was defined by Eq. (6) in Chap. I as

$$l = \frac{621 \int_0^\infty V_\lambda E_\lambda d\lambda}{\int_0^\infty E_\lambda d\lambda},$$

where V_λ is the relative visibility function. On account of the difficulty of finding a simple algebraic expression for this function, the numerator of the above expression is obtained most readily by multiplying the energy at each wave length by the relative visibility at that wave length. The denominator represents merely the total energy of the radiation and can therefore be found directly from the Stefan-Boltzmann law, Eq. (171). Figure 69 indicates the variation of the luminous efficiency of a black body with its absolute temperature. It will be observed that the luminous efficiency rises to a maximum at approximately 6500°K. and then decreases slowly. The temperature of the maximum is in the neighborhood of the color temperature of daylight—that is, of sunlight plus sky light. The inefficiency of artificial sources of light is due very largely to the fact that their temperatures are rarely much above 3000°K.

In the case of radiators that are not true black bodies, a distinction must be made between true temperature, black-body temperature, and color temperature. The *true temperature* is defined as the temperature of the body as measured on the Kelvin thermodynamic scale. A gas thermometer using hydrogen indicates temperatures on this scale very closely. The *black-body* or *brightness temperature* of a body is the temperature of a black body whose brightness is the same as that of the body in question for some fairly narrow spectral region. Usually this region is taken in the neighborhood of 650 mμ, chiefly because of the ease with which this region can be isolated with filters. Since the radiation from a body which emits non-selectively can never exceed that from an ideal black body at any part of the spectrum,

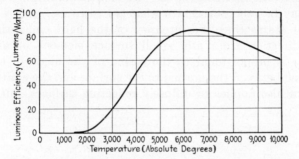

Fig. 69.—Curve showing the relationship between the luminous efficiency of a black body and its absolute temperature.

the black-body temperature of such a body is always lower than its true temperature. The *color temperature* of a body is the temperature of a black body that emits light of the same color as the body in question. The color temperature of a gray body is of course the same as its true temperature. A selective radiator, on the other hand, may appear either too blue or too red, and so its color temperature may be either higher or lower than its true temperature. Frequently the concept of color temperature is applied in cases where temperature is not the cause of the radiation. Thus the color temperature of the sky, which appears blue merely because of molecular scattering, is said to be about 25,000°K., although any concept of temperature in this connection is quite meaningless.

67. Lambert's Law.—It is an experimental fact that a heated metal sphere appears to be of nearly uniform brightness over its entire surface. It follows, therefore, that the brightness of the surface must be independent of the angle at which it is observed. In Fig. 70, consider the small element of a radiating surface, which we shall assume appears equally bright from every angle of observation. Such a surface will be called a *diffuse radiator*. Now the brightness of any surface, according to the definition given in Sec. 11, Chap. I, is given by the quotient of its luminous

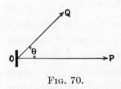

FIG. 70.

intensity (candlepower) by its projected area. Since the projected area varies as the cosine of θ, it follows that the intensity must vary in the same manner if the brightness is to remain constant. In other words, the intensity in the direction OQ is equal to the intensity in the direction OP multiplied by cos θ. This may be generalized into what is known as *Lambert's cosine law*. It states that the intensity of the light emanating in a given direction from any small surface element of a diffuse radiator is proportional to the cosine of the angle of emission measured between the normal to the surface and the emitted ray. This law also applies to diffusely reflecting surfaces, but it does

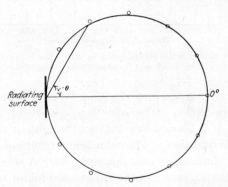

FIG. 71.—Comparison between the distribution of radiation from a polished tungsten surface and from a perfectly diffuse radiator. The large circle represents in polar coordinates the distribution from a diffuse radiator (obeying Lambert's cosine law); the points represent the observed values for tungsten.

not follow that a surface which radiates diffusely is also a diffuse reflector. A polished metal surface may be a good diffuse radiator although it is far from being a diffuse reflector.

The usual method of representing the distribution of flux from a source of light is by means of a diagram showing the distribution of intensity in polar coordinates. A typical curve, plotted from Worthing's[1] values for the radiation from a tungsten surface, is shown in Fig. 71. If this surface obeyed Lambert's law, the distribution of intensity would be represented by the circle. The points indicate that, for angles close to the normal, a tungsten surface behaves very like a diffuse radiator. Most common sources of light tend to obey Lambert's law, although this is not always evident from the distribution curves. In the case of an arc, for example, the negative carbon and the supporting mechanism may obscure the light in certain directions.

68. Radiometry.—The science of measuring radiant energy is called *radiometry*. Radiometric methods may be divided into two classes, depending upon whether the detector of radiation employed is selective or non-selective with respect to wave length. Non-selective detectors usually depend upon the heating effect of the radiation, so they respond equally to a given amount of energy regardless of its wave length if precautions are taken to make the surface on which the radiation is absorbed non-selective. This type of radiation detector is represented by the radiometer, the radiomicrometer, the thermopile, and the bolometer. As a class, these instruments are less sensitive than the selective detectors of radiation such as the human retina, the photographic plate, and the photoelectric cell. The sensitivity of the latter class varies enormously with wave length, and hence, unless they are carefully calibrated, they can be used only for comparing radiations of the same spectral quality. Sometimes, however, the selective property of a detector is invaluable when a small amount of energy in one spectral region must be measured in the presence of a much larger amount of energy in some other region. Thus, it is difficult to measure the amount of ultraviolet energy in solar radiation with a non-selective detector because of the presence of such a large proportion of energy in other spectral regions. On the other hand, a selective detector, such as a photoelectric cell of the proper type, may be insensitive to the powerful visible and infrared radiations and, hence, may be used for measurements in the ultraviolet region quite as readily as though the other radiations were not present. As subsequent chapters are to be devoted to the subject of selective detectors

---

[1] *Jour. Optical Soc. Amer. and Rev. Sci. Instruments*, **13**, 635 (1926).

of radiation, we shall discuss only non-selective detectors in this chapter.[1]

One of the simplest and earliest instruments for measuring radiant energy was the radiometer, invented more than fifty years ago by Sir William Crookes. This instrument was later improved by Nichols,[2] and its behavior was treated theoretically by Maxwell. It consists essentially of two similar thin vanes, usually of mica or platinum, blackened on one side and attached to a horizontal member that is suspended by means of a fine quartz fiber. The radiation to be measured is allowed to fall on one of the vanes, thereby warming the surface slightly.

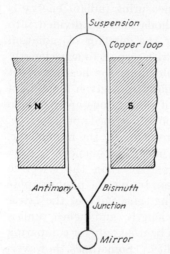

Fig. 72.—The Boys radiomicrometer.

The case containing the instrument is evacuated, but enough gas molecules are allowed to remain to rebound more vigorously from the heated side of the vane than from the cool side. This causes the vanes to rotate until the force-moment is balanced by the torsion in the quartz fiber. The amount of rotation, which is observed by means of a mirror carried by the horizontal member, is very nearly proportional to the total radiation received by the vane.

The principle of the radiomicrometer, invented almost simultaneously by d'Arsonval and by Boys, is illustrated in Fig. 72. As designed by Boys,[3] it consists of a thermal junction of bismuth and antimony soldered into a loop of copper wire that is suspended in a strong magnetic field. When radiation falls on the bismuth-antimony junction, the temperature of the latter is raised and the resulting thermo-electromotive force causes a current to flow in the loop. This, in turn, causes the loop to rotate by an amount that depends upon the stiffness of the sus-

---

[1] A critical survey of these instruments will be found in *Bur. Standards Sci. Papers* 85 and 188.

[2] The technique of the Nichols radiometer is described by Tear, *Jour. Optical Soc. Amer. and Rev. Sci. Instruments*, **11**, 81 (1925).

[3] *Proc. Roy. Soc.*, **42**, 189 (1887).

pending fiber. Both this instrument and the radiometer are relatively insensitive to stray magnetic disturbances but are seriously affected by mechanical vibrations.

A plurality of thermal junctions connected in series is called a thermopile.[1] In the radiomicrometer just described, there is no advantage in increasing the number of junctions because the resistance of the circuit is nearly all in the junction itself and not in the loop. Therefore, although increasing the number of junctions would increase the voltage applied to the circuit, the resistance of the circuit would be increased proportionately and the current through the loop would be practically unaltered. The thermopile does not suffer from this defect when used with a separate galvanometer. It is easily shown that the condition for maximum sensitivity is satisfied when the resistance of the galvanometer is the same as that of the thermopile. The chief advantage of the thermopile over the two instruments previously mentioned is its convenience. The thermopile itself, not being affected by mechanical vibrations, can be incorporated as part of the optical system. The galvanometer can then be mounted at a convenient location in some suitable manner, preferably on a Julius suspension. The thermopile should be evacuated to avoid spurious effects due to air currents. If it must be used in the open, it should be designed so that air currents affect both sets of junctions equally. The sensitivity of a thermopile varies as the square root of the area of the receiving surface— a condition that imposes a low practical limit upon the number of junctions.

The bolometer is a minute Wheatstone bridge, one arm of which receives the radiation to be measured. This arm is usually made of platinum for mechanical reasons, although from a theoretical standpoint it would be preferable to use a material having the highest possible temperature coefficient of resistance. It is generally made in the form of a ribbon and is blackened to absorb as much of the radiation as possible. The bolometer shares with the thermopile the advantage of being relatively immune to mechanical vibrations, but it is rather sensitive to magnetic disturbances because the arms of the bridge cannot be concentrated in a small space. The chamber containing the bolometer should be evacuated because the current carried by the wires raises their temperature slightly above that of their

[1] *Bur. Standards Sci. Papers* 229, 261, and 413. Also Chapter VIII of Strong's "Procedures in Experimental Physics" (Prentice-Hall, 1938).

surroundings, and the convection currents that would otherwise be produced would cause the zero point to drift. A drift of the zero point may also be caused by variations in the voltage applied to the bridge, but this can be largely eliminated by using a storage battery of generous capacity.

The sensitivity of the various instruments appears to depend more upon the skill of the builder and observer than upon any inherent characteristics of the instruments themselves. The practical limit of sensitivity of the thermopile may be placed at 10^{-12} or 10^{-13} watt/mm^2, and that of the other instruments is of this order of magnitude.[1] It must be realized that, however simple in principle the measurement of radiation may appear to be, the amount of energy available is ordinarily so minute that the technique can be acquired only by long experience. In fact, there is probably no other type of measurement that contains so many pitfalls for the novice; and even the simplest measurement should not be undertaken without a thorough acquaintance with the literature.[2]

69. Spectroradiometry.—*Spectroradiometry* is the term used to designate the measurement of the spectral distribution of radiant energy, which is usually accomplished by determining successively the energy within narrow regions of the spectrum. Spectroradiometry is commonly associated with the infrared region, primarily because the radiation from incandescent solids has been studied more extensively than that from other sources and, at the temperatures that are realizable in the laboratory, most of the energy from such sources is in the infrared. For this reason, the infrared region is sometimes called the region of heat radiation, thereby encouraging a common misconception that there is more heat in an erg of energy in this region than elsewhere in the spectrum.[3]

The separation of radiation into narrow spectral regions for measurement is usually accomplished by means of either a

[1] Cartwright has discussed the sensitivity of radiometric instruments in *Physics*, **1**, 211 (1931).

[2] See the series of papers by Coblentz previously mentioned and Forsythe's "Measurement of Radiant Energy."

[3] It may be remarked in this connection that some stars have such a high temperature that only a small fraction of their energy is in the infrared. If these stars are surrounded by planetary systems, the inhabitants might conceivably regard the ultraviolet region as the region of heat radiation!

prism or a calibrated filter. A prism is used in some form of spectroscopic apparatus; and the results obtained in this way must be corrected both for the selective absorption of radiation within the instrument and for the variation in the width of the spectral band resulting from the irrationality in the dispersion of the prism. Filters[1] are simpler to use and are eminently satisfactory when their absorption curves are such that they isolate definite spectral regions.

Spectroradiometric measurements[2] are especially difficult because the amount of energy to be measured decreases as the purity of the spectral band under examination is increased. Some idea of the difficulties can be obtained from the recent papers by Abbot,[3] who has measured the energy distribution of stars as faint as magnitude 3.8. The vanes of his radiometer were constructed from flys' wings coated with lampblack. This procedure resulted in a system of extraordinary lightness since eight of these wings, having an area of approximately 70 mm^2, weighed but slightly more than three milligrams. The quartz-fiber suspension was so fine that, in spite of the small mass it had to support, 44 complete revolutions of the torsion head were required before the suspended system began to rotate in response. This was before the chamber was evacuated and filled with hydrogen at a low pressure, the air at atmospheric pressure acting on the vanes "as if viscous, like tar." When this radiometer was used with the 100-in. reflector at Mount Wilson, the maximum deflections were of the order of one millimeter although the scale was 6 meters away. Nevertheless, the energy distribution curves were well delineated, indicating the extent to which spurious effects had been avoided.

[1] The characteristics of a number of filters that are useful for this purpose will be found in Chap. XVIII.

[2] A survey of the subject will be found in *Jour. Optical Soc. Amer. and Rev. Sci. Instruments*, **7**, 439 (1923).

[3] *Astrophys. Jour.*, **69**, 293 (1929).

CHAPTER IX

LIGHT SOURCES

The production and distribution of large amounts of light is to-day recognized as a branch of engineering. Practically all modern sources of light operate on electrical energy and, hence, illuminating engineering has developed as a specialized field for the electrical engineer. This is quite logical because the optical problems involved in the distribution of light in bulk are relatively simple compared with the electrical and economic problems. In the field of pure optics, however, there are many problems for which the solution is not the economic one generally sought by the illuminating engineer. In fact, the properties of image-forming systems are such that the efficiency of the source is less important than such characteristics as its shape, size, and intrinsic brightness. These characteristics will therefore be given more consideration in this chapter than the adaptability of the sources for general illumination; and, as the human eye has apparently adapted itself to utilize daylight most effectively, a discussion of solar radiation will be given first.

70. The Sun.—To the unaided eye, the sun appears as a circular disk of practically uniform brightness subtending a mean angle of 32′ 04″. This angle varies, of course, with the time of year from about 31′ 32″ at aphelion, early in July, to 32′ 36″ at perihelion, early in January. If the earth had no atmosphere, the illumination falling on its surface would be due entirely to direct radiation from the sun. The intensity of the illumination would then vary as the cosine of the angle of incidence of the sun's rays.

The curves in Fig. 73 show the variation in illumination on a horizontal surface with the time of day on a typical clear day in midsummer at a latitude of 42° north. The maximum illumination due to both sunlight and sky light is approximately 10,000 foot-candles. A day is considered dreary if the level of illumination outdoors is as low as 1000 foot-candles, and it is a dark day indeed when the level drops to 100 foot-candles. This

160

is in marked contrast to the levels of illumination that are ordinarily produced indoors, where the illumination is commonly in the neighborhood of 20 foot-candles by natural light and less than 10 foot-candles by artificial light.

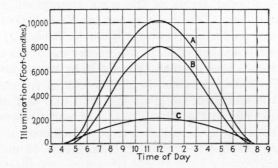

FIG. 73.—Illumination on a horizontal surface on a typical clear day in mid-summer at Cleveland. Curve *A* represents the total illumination; curve *B*, the component due to direct sunlight; curve *C*, the component due to diffuse sky light. If these curves had been plotted for the illumination on a surface normal to the incident radiation, the variation in illumination with time of day would have been less marked. (*From Luckiesh's "Artificial Sunlight," by courtesy of D. Van Nostrand Company.*)

It is possible to compute the apparent brightness of the sun from the illumination that it produces on the surface of the earth and the angle that it subtends. Assuming the illumination on a

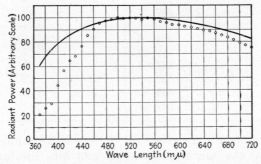

FIG. 74.—The spectral distribution of mean noon sunlight at Washington in the visible and near ultraviolet regions (circles) compared with the radiation curve of a black body at 5400°K.

horizontal plane in Cambridge at the summer solstice to be 8000 foot-candles and the angle subtended by the sun to be 31' 30'', the apparent brightness of the sun, computed by means of Eq. (223) in Chap. XIX, is 140,000 candles/cm.[2] If allowance is made for atmospheric absorption, the true brightness is in the neighborhood of 225,000 candles/cm².

The solar spectrum is continuous with the exception of the so-called *Fraunhofer lines,* which are produced by absorption either in the upper layers of the sun's atmosphere or in the earth's atmosphere. The most important Fraunhofer lines and the elements producing them are listed in Table VII. These lines have only a slight effect on the energy distribution of sunlight, which has been studied extensively by numerous investigators. The values obtained in 1917 by Abbot for mean noon sunlight at Washington are given in Table VIII and are represented graphically in Fig. 74. The smooth curve represents the energy distribution in the radiation from a black body at 5400°K., which is approximately the color temperature of mean noon sunlight.

TABLE VII.—THE CHIEF FRAUNHOFER LINES IN THE VISIBLE SOLAR
SPECTRUM

Certain Fraunhofer lines really consist of groups of lines, which may be due either to a single element or to several elements. The wave lengths of such lines, indicated by asterisks (*), are given to the number of figures that are the same for all the lines.

Line	Element	$\lambda(m\mu)$	Line	Element	$\lambda(m\mu)$
A^*	Atm. O	763.	F	H	486.13
B^*	Atm. O	687.	d	Fe	438.35
C	H	656.28	G'	H	434.05
D_1	Na	589.59	G^*	Ca, Fe	430.8
D_2	Na	589.00	g	Ca	422.67
D_3	He	587.56	h	H	410.17
E^*	Fe, Ca	527.	H	Ca	396.85
b_1	Mg	518.36	K	Ca	393.37
b_2	Mg	517.27			

If it were not for the presence of the earth's atmosphere, the spectrum of the sun would extend well into the infrared and ultraviolet regions. Actually, the long wave-length limit of the radiation reaching the earth is about 20,000 mμ, the exact limit varying enormously with the amount of water vapor in the earth's atmosphere and the altitude of the sun. The short wave-length limit is about 290 mμ, the exact limit varying also with atmospheric conditions and the altitude of the sun. The spectral region between 290 mμ and 310 mμ has assumed con-

TABLE VIII.—SPECTRAL DISTRIBUTION OF MEAN NOON SUNLIGHT AT
WASHINGTON ACCORDING TO ABBOT*

λ(mμ)	Relative power	λ(mμ)	Relative power	λ(mμ)	Relative power
370	20.2	490	98.8	610	93.5
380	24.6	500	100.0	620	91.6
390	29.6	510	99.4	630	90.6
400	44.5	520	99.4	640	89.4
410	56.3	530	99.3	650	88.1
420	64.6	540	98.1	660	86.9
430	68.0	550	99.9	670	84.8
440	76.4	560	98.2	680	83.2
450	85.3	570	96.6	690	81.2
460	90.6	580	95.5	700	79.0
470	95.2	590	93.9	710	76.7
480	97.3	600	93.5	720	74.8

* *Bur. Standards Misc. Pub.* 114, p. 16.

siderable importance within the last few years because of the discovery of its antirachitic action. This is the so-called *vital-ray* region. Energy measurements by Fabry and Buisson and by Abbot have been compiled by Forsythe and Christison to indicate the hourly and daily variations of solar radiation in this region. These data are represented by Figs. 75 and 76.

The total amount of energy radiated by the sun varies somewhat from day to day and seems to be related in some manner to the sunspot activity. The mean value of the *solar constant* is 1.94, which is the number of calories received per minute on a square centimeter of surface normal to the radiation outside the earth's atmosphere at the earth's mean solar distance.[1] The variation in this "constant" is from 1.92 cal. when no spots are present to a maximum of approximately 1.97. It is thought by some that the sunspot activity has a profound effect on the weather and that the variations of the solar constant can be used as a basis of long-range forecasts. This subject is one that must be studied statistically over extended periods, and it may be some time before enough data will have been accumulated to make the method practical.

[1] ABBOT *et al.*, *Smithsonian Misc. Pub.*, **77**, No. 3, p. 31 (1925). This is equivalent to 8.1×10^7 ergs per minute per square centimeter or 0.135 watt/cm².

The luminous efficiency of solar radiation can be determined from a comparison of the illumination that it produces with the solar constant. It can be computed that, if the earth had no atmosphere, the illumination on a surface normal to the radiation would be 13,600 foot-candles or 14.5 lumens/cm². Since the mean value of the solar constant is 0.135 watt/cm², the luminous efficiency of solar radiation is evidently slightly more than 100 lumens/watt. It will be recalled that the maximum luminous efficiency of a black body is about 84 lumens/watt, which occurs

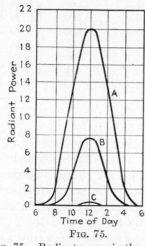

FIG. 75.

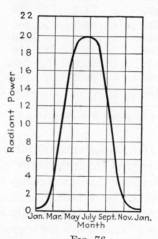

FIG. 76.

FIG. 75.—Radiant power in the ultraviolet below 310 mμ in solar radiation at 42° north latitude. The ordinates represent power in microwatts per square centimeter on a horizontal surface. Curve *A*, at summer solstice; curve *B*, at spring and fall equinoxes; curve *C*, at winter solstice. (*Gen. Elec. Rev.*, **32**, 666–667, *by permission.*)

FIG. 76.—Radiant power below 310 mμ in solar radiation at noon at 42° north latitude. The ordinates represent power in microwatts per square centimeter on a horizontal surface. The abscissa above each month denotes its beginning. (*Gen. Elec. Rev.*, **32**, 666–667, *by permission.*)

at a temperature of approximately 6500°K. (see Fig. 69). Although solar radiation outside the earth's atmosphere closely corresponds in color to the radiation from a black body at this temperature, its higher luminous efficiency is due to its relative deficiency in the violet and ultraviolet regions. This is shown by Fig. 77, where curve *A* represents the spectral distribution of solar radiation outside the atmosphere according to Abbot. It must be noted, however, that the deficiency in the violet and ultraviolet regions may be only apparent, since it is probably caused by the absorption of an extremely thin layer of ozone in the upper regions of the earth's atmosphere. The usual method of correcting for atmospheric absorption by making measurements when the sun is at various altitudes does not correct for the absorption of this layer.

71. Sky Light.—It is shown in Fig. 73 that approximately one-fifth of the total illumination on a clear day is due to light from the sky. This light results from the scattering of sunlight in its passage through the atmosphere. If the earth had no atmosphere, the sky would be perfectly black. At first thought, it would seem that the spectral composition of this scattered light should be the same as that of sunlight. This is very nearly

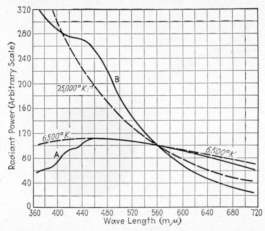

Fig. 77.—Curve *A* represents the spectral distribution of solar radiation outside the earth's atmosphere according to Abbot (1917). Curve *B* represents the theoretical spectral distribution of sky light, obtained by dividing each ordinate of curve *A* by the fourth power of the wave length. The spectral distribution of the radiation from a black body at 6500°K. and at 25,000°K. are presented for comparison. All the curves are adjusted to equal 100 at 560 mμ.

true on a completely overcast day, when the scattering particles are droplets of water of comparatively large size. However, when the particles are small, the short waves are scattered more than the long ones. This accounts for the blue color of the sky and the redness of sunsets, as will be clear from Fig. 78. To an observer at *A*, the sun appears to be just rising. Since the blue end of the solar spectrum is scattered more than the red, the light reaching the observer will predominate in red. On the other hand, the atmospheric layer above the observer at *B*, for whom the sun is on the meridian, is so thin that the amount of scattering is small and the color of the sun is but little affected. When this observer looks at any other part of the sky, he sees only scattered light, which predominates in blue. In very clear atmospheres, where smoke and dust particles are absent, this color is such an indescribably deep blue that one faintly grasps the medieval concept of the empyrean.

The phenomenon of scattering can be illustrated very easily by means of a dilute solution of sodium thiosulphate (hypo), the chemical that is used in a photographer's fixing bath. The addition of a few drops of dilute sulphuric acid causes sulphur to be precipitated in a finely divided state. The color of the light scattered by this solution is remarkably like the blue of the sky, while the light transmitted through the solution takes on

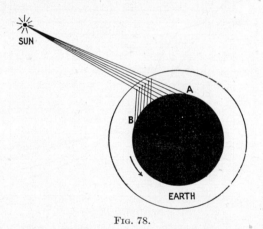

Fig. 78.

the orange or reddish cast frequently seen at sunrise or sunset. When the process has gone on for some time, the size of the sulphur particles becomes so great that the scattering is no longer selective and the solution appears white from every direction of observation.

The scattering of light by small particles was investigated experimentally by Tyndall[1] and, for this reason, it is frequently called the *Tyndall effect*. The subject has since been studied both theoretically and experimentally by many investigators. Lord Rayleigh[2] was the first to deduce on theoretical grounds

[1] *Proc. Roy. Soc.*, **17**, 223 (1868–1869) and *Phil. Mag.*, **37**, 384 (1869).

[2] *Phil. Mag.*, **41**, 107 and 274 (1871). Reprinted in "Scientific Papers," Vol. I, p. 87. The scattered light is also polarized, as described in Sec. 214, Chap. XXIX.

that the phenomenon is a true scattering and not a variety of reflection or refraction. He showed that the intensity of the scattered light should vary inversely as the fourth power of the wave length when the size of the particles is of the order of magnitude of the length of a light wave. On the basis of this law, the spectral distribution of sky light on a perfectly clear day is represented by curve *B* in Fig. 77. This curve was obtained by dividing Abbot's values for the spectral distribution of solar radiation outside the earth's atmosphere (curve *A*) by the fourth power of the wave length. The color temperature of the sky when clear is ordinarily found to be between 20,000°K. and 25,000°K. This temperature is somewhat lower than would be predicted from the fourth-power law, indicating that a considerable proportion of the scattering is non-selective even when the sky is perfectly clear.

The brightness of the sky on a clear day is about 0.8 candle/cm². On a day that is partly cloudy, white clouds on which the sun is shining directly may be considerably brighter than the blue sky. On a dark overcast day, the brightness of the sky may fall to as low a value as 0.004 candle/cm². By way of comparison, the brightness of a candle flame is in the neighborhood of 1 candle/cm², approximating that of a white cloud on a partly cloudy day; and the brightness of the moon is in the neighborhood of 0.25 candle/cm².

72. The Incandescent Lamp.—It was found at the beginning of the last century that electrical energy could be converted into light by sending a current through a wire of high resistance, thereby heating it to incandescence. The incandescent lamp did not attain a practical form, however, until nearly eighty years later. In the meantime, the electric arc had been discovered and was used to a limited extent after the development of a suitable dynamo for supplying the current. The arc lamp was not entirely satisfactory as a light source and was efficient only in the large sizes. Inventors did not cease their attempts, therefore, to devise a practical incandescent lamp, but the difficulties of obtaining a high vacuum and of making a suitable filament were not solved until 1879. In December of that year, Edison demonstrated a lamp that incorporated all the essential features of the modern incandescent lamp. The distinguishing features of this lamp, as disclosed by the patent, were a completely sealed glass bulb with platinum leads, and a filament of such a high resistance that the lamp could be operated in a parallel circuit. This filament was obtained by bending a thin strip of bamboo into the form of a hairpin and then carbonizing it.

In comparison with our modern tungsten filament lamp, this carbon filament lamp had to be operated at a relatively low temperature to make its life satisfactorily long. This was an extremely serious drawback because, as was shown in the previous chapter, the luminous efficiency of thermal radiators increases rapidly with the temperature throughout the temperature range with which we are concerned. Hence, the subsequent improvements in incandescent lamps have always been in the direction of a higher operating temperature. Various processes for coating the carbon filament with graphite were tried with some success. Then followed the metal filament lamps of wire-drawn tantalum, which were quickly superseded by lamps having filaments of pressed tungsten. It was subsequently discovered that tungsten, when suitably purified, can be drawn into wires as fine as 0.0005 in. in diameter. At first these filaments were operated in a vacuum, but it was later found that their tendency to evaporate is very much reduced by filling the bulb with some inert gas, such as nitrogen or argon, under moderate pressure. Some gas-filled tungsten lamps are operated to-day at temperatures as high as 3290°K., at which temperature the luminous efficiency is 27.3 lumens/watt. There seems to be little hope of making any marked increase in the efficiency of incandescent lamps because tungsten melts at 3655°K. and no other suitable material having a higher melting point has been discovered. It seems likely, therefore, that the light source of the future will be some sort of selective radiator that emits a larger proportion of its energy in the visible region.

Because of the unique importance of tungsten, its properties have been studied very extensively. One of the most exhaustive papers on the subject is that by Forsythe and Worthing,[1] and it is from this paper that Table IX, showing the chief optical properties of tungsten surfaces, was compiled. This table is for a perfectly smooth surface of tungsten situated in free space where the only energy loss is by radiation. In the practice of lamp design, consideration must be given to the various losses due to conduction by the leads, convection by the gas within the bulb, and absorption and reflection by the bulb. The

---

[1] *Astrophys. Jour.*, **61**, 146 (1925).

TABLE IX.—SPECIFIC CHARACTERISTICS OF TUNGSTEN

True temp. (T), °K.	Color temp. (T_c), °K.	Power radiated (W), watts/cm²	Flux radiated (F), lumens/cm²	Luminous efficiency (F/W), lumens/watt	Brightness (B), candles/cm²	Emissivity (e), black body = 1
500	....	0.019	....	....	....	0.053
1000	1006	0.654	0.0004	0.0006	0.00012	0.114
1100	1108	1.072	0.0033	0.0031	0.0010	0.128
1200	1210	1.691	0.020	0.012	0.006	0.143
1300	1312	2.576	0.095	0.037	0.029	0.158
1400	1414	3.82	0.34	0.09	0.11	0.175
1500	1517	5.55	1.11	0.20	0.33	0.192
1600	1619	7.77	3.10	0.40	0.92	0.207
1700	1722	10.59	7.52	0.71	2.26	0.222
1800	1825	14.22	16.48	1.16	5.05	0.236
1900	1920	18.55	34.8	1.88	10.40	0.249
2000	2033	23.72	65.9	2.78	20.0	0.260
2100	2137	29.82	117.9	3.95	35.6	0.270
2200	2242	37.18	204.	5.47	61.3	0.279
2300	2347	45.9	332.	7.25	100.5	0.288
2400	2452	55.8	523.	9.37	157.0	0.296
2500	2557	67.6	788.	11.67	237.5	0.303
2600	2663	80.8	1,150.	14.28	347.0	0.311
2700	2770	96.2	1,660.	17.26	498.0	0.318
2800	2878	112.9	2,300.	20.43	694.0	0.323
2900	2986	132.1	3,140.	23.80	949.	0.329
3000	3094	153.9	4,170.	27.10	1257.	0.334
3100	3202	177.5	5,500.	31.0	1647.	0.337
3200	3311	203.	7,030.	34.6	2110.	0.341
3300	3422	232.	8,940.	38.5	2685.	0.344
3400	3533	264.	11,270.	42.6	3370.	0.348
3500	3646	300.	13,800.	45.9	4220.	0.351
3655	3817	360.	19,150.	53.1	5740.	0.354

characteristics of some typical commercial lamps are shown in Table X. The luminous efficiency F/W is expressed in terms of flux emerging from the bulb per unit of power supplied to the filament. The color temperature of the filament varies along its length because of the cooling by the leads, and the values given represent the average. The last four columns give the fractions of the radiant energy emitted within the indicated spectral regions. These values were not corrected for absorption by the bulb. As will be seen later, ordinary glass absorbs strongly below approximately 360 mμ, so bulbs of quartz or special glass are required to transmit the radiations of shorter wave length.

It may be remarked in passing that this table provides a simple means for determining the amount of energy in the various spectral regions from measurements of the luminous flux. For

TABLE X.—CHARACTERISTICS OF TUNGSTEN FILAMENT LAMPS
The last four columns were computed by Holladay's method.[1]

Power input (W), watts	Type	Color temperature, °K.	Flux radiated (F), lumens	Luminous efficiency (F/W)	Fraction of radiant energy in			
					Vital ray 280-310 mμ	Near ultraviolet 300-400 mμ	Visible 400-760 mμ	Infrared 760-∞
10	Vacuum	2400	80	8.0	0.0000061	0.000276	0.058	0.942
40	Vacuum	2460	400	10.0	0.0000090	0.00036	0.062	0.938
50	Gas filled	2670	500	10.0	0.000029	0.00085	0.090	0.909
100	Gas filled	2740	1,290	12.9	0.000041	0.00110	0.099	0.900
200	Gas filled	2810	3,040	15.2	0.000057	0.00141	0.109	0.889
500	Gas filled	2920	9,050	18.1	0.000089	0.00198	0.120	0.878
1,000	Gas filled	2980	20,000	20.0	0.000116	0.00239	0.133	0.865
30,000	Gas filled	3300	930,000	31.6	0.000353	0.00548	0.182	0.812

[1] Jour. Optical Soc. Amer. and Rev. Sci. Instruments, 17, 329 (1928).

example, dividing the illumination on a surface by the luminous efficiency of the lamp gives the corresponding radiant power in watts per unit area, assuming that all the energy supplied to the lamp is radiated. The amount of radiant power within a given spectral region can be found by multiplying the total power by the appropriate value in one of the last four columns. Such a calculation is only approximate because of the losses within the lamp. In a gas-filled lamp, the losses by convection may amount to 20 per cent or more of the power input.

Two little-known lamps that are useful to the optical experimenter are sketched in Fig. 79. At A is shown a ribbon-filament lamp that requires 18 amp. at a potential of 6 volts. The filament is about 2 mm wide and 20 mm long, but it is bent as shown at B so that its useful length is only 7 mm. This lamp is admirably suited to photomicrography, and it is regularly supplied for this purpose by at least one leading manufacturer. The lamp shown at C has a straight wire filament about 20 mm long, kept taut by a spring in one of the leads. This lamp was designed principally for use in oscillographs, but its long straight filament makes

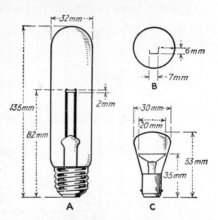

Fig. 79.—Two useful laboratory lamps. A, a 6-volt 108-watt ribbon-filament lamp, front view. B, top view of same showing the shape of the filament. C, a 4-volt straight wire-filament lamp. A spring in one support holds the filament taut.

it useful for many other purposes. It operates on a 4-volt supply and is made in 2- and 8-watt sizes, the difference being only in the diameter of the filament.

73. Artificial Daylight.—Long before the incandescent lamp was invented, daylight had become the traditional standard of illumination for matching colors. Sunlight itself is much too intense for this purpose and therefore color technologists have generally used the light from the north sky. On a clear day, the color of this light is approximately that of a black body at a temperature of 25,000°K., whereas on an overcast day its color is that of a black body at approximately 6500°K. As can be seen from Fig. 77, this variation is extremely great, and therefore a need has long been felt for a better standard of daylight. From a strictly scientific standpoint, it is preferable to define daylight as the radiation falling on the earth from the entire sky, including the sun if present. The absorption in the atmosphere is so nearly non-selective that daylight as thus defined has almost the same spectral quality as solar radiation outside the earth's atmosphere. This radiation is closely matched in color by a black body at 6500°K. regardless of the time of day or the state of the weather.

The obvious method of producing artificial daylight is to use a tungsten lamp in conjunction with a suitable filter for removing

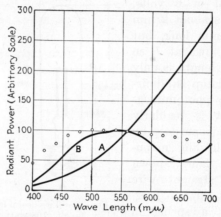

Fig. 80.—Comparison of screened tungsten light with sunlight. *A*, spectral distribution of the radiation from a black body at 2360°K. *B*, the same screened with a Wratten No. 79 filter. The circles represent Abbot's values for mean noon sunlight from Table VIII. All three curves are adjusted to equal 100 at 560 mμ.

the excess of energy at the red end of the spectrum. This is done in the Mazda C-2 lamp by using a blue bulb, which is entirely satisfactory for general illumination where only a rough approximation to daylight quality is required. For matching colors, special daylight units are available which, although necessarily inefficient, provide a very close approximation to daylight quality.

In photometry, it is often necessary to compare the intensity of two sources of different color temperature. Many photometric standards, notably the standard acetylene burner to be described presently and tungsten lamps of the vacuum type, operate at a color temperature of 2360°K. Other standards, such as the gas-filled tungsten lamp, operate at a color temperature of 2848°K. Several gelatin filters are available from the Eastman Kodak Company for making the radiation from these sources correspond to radiation at other color temperatures. As an example, curve *A* of Fig. 80 shows the distribution of energy in the radiation from a black body at 2360°K., and curve *B*, the relative distribution of this radiation after modification by the Wratten No. 79 filter. The circles represent Abbot's values for mean noon sunlight. Although such a filter can be made to produce a satisfactory color match in a photometric field, the spectral distributions of the two radiations are noticeably different.

The problem of obtaining a source having exactly the same energy distribution as mean noon sunlight has recently become important in connection with the standardization of a light source to be used in testing photographic materials. Since these materials vary in their spectral sensitivity within very wide limits, a mere visual color match is not sufficient. The problem of establishing a definite standard was undertaken by the International Congress of Photography, this country being represented by a committee composed of members of the Optical Society of America. Out of this investigation has come a liquid filter[1] that provides the most accurate means known at the present time for producing mean noon sunlight artificially.

Because of the difficulty of maintaining a tungsten filament at 2360°K., many laboratories use an acetylene lamp for routine purposes. One type of lamp using a Bray burner tip has been described by Jones.[2] In this lamp, there is a cylindrical flame about 3 mm wide and 50 mm high, but the portion that is used is only 3 mm high. The intensity of this lamp is remarkably constant, varying only slightly with the humidity of the atmosphere, the barometric pressure, or even the pressure of the acetylene. The controlling apparatus is very simple, consisting of an open-tube water manometer and a gas cock. The pressure required is 9 cm of water, and a regulation of 2 per cent is entirely

---

[1] This filter consists of two separate solutions containing copper sulphate and cobalt ammonium sulphate. The data for this filter and also for other filters of the same type designed to produce radiation similar in spectral quality to black-body radiation at various temperatures will be found in *Bur. Standards Misc. Pub.* 114, by Davis and Gibson. It will be sufficient here to state that these filters are easily prepared and have proved to be very stable and quite reproducible.

[2] *Trans. Illum. Eng. Soc.*, **9**, 716 (1914).

adequate.   The great advantage of this burner is its reliability in the hands of an unskilled operator; the greatest disadvantage is its low intensity, which is a trifle more than one candle.

The spectral distribution of the light of this acetylene burner[1] corresponds very closely to that of a Planckian radiator at 2360°K. throughout the spectral range from 480 mμ to the red end of the visible spectrum.   Below 480 mμ, the radiation is somewhat in excess of that of the Planckian radiator.

74. The Carbon Arc.—The electric arc was discovered by Sir Humphry Davy in 1801.   Davy was experimenting with the powerful batteries that had just been installed at the Royal Institution and found that a current could actually be maintained across the air gap between two charcoal electrodes.   The bow shape of the discharge led him to call the phenomenon an arc.   Many attempts were made to devise a practical system of lighting on the basis of this discovery, but they were unsuccessful until a practical dynamo was invented about 1875.   For a while thereafter the arc enjoyed a period of popularity, but to-day it is used only for special purposes because the incandescent lamp is so much more convenient.

The characteristics of the carbon arc are very unlike those of the incandescent lamp.   In the first place, the resistance of the arc diminishes as the current increases, so a ballast resistance or some other suitable current-limiting device must always be connected in series.   The voltage across the arc itself is usually from 40 to 70 volts and is nearly a linear function of the separation of the electrodes.   Increasing the current through the arc has the effect of increasing the size of the crater without affecting its brightness materially.   The arc usually operates most satisfactorily when the current is so adjusted that the crater approximately fills the positive electrode.

The spectrum of the carbon arc consists of a continuous background produced by the thermal radiation from the hot electrodes combined with line and band spectra from the vapors.   In the ordinary arc, most of the light is supplied by the positive crater, which has a brightness in the neighborhood of 13,000 candles/cm^2 and a color temperature of 3700°K.   The line and band spectra of the arc stream are faint in comparison, but the arc stream can be made to contribute more to the radiation by drilling the electrodes lengthwise and filling them with a core of inorganic

[1] *Bur. Standards Sci. Paper* 362.

salts. The white-flame arc, used for photographic purposes and for the comparison of colors, has a core consisting of the fluorides of the rare earths. The blue-flame arc, used for therapeutic purposes, has a core of iron salts, which emit copiously in the vital-ray region. The nickel arc, which has a nickel wire within its core, emits copiously in the near ultraviolet and is also used for therapeutic purposes. These are only a few of the many special types of arcs that have been devised, and the literature of the subject must be consulted for more specific information.[1]

It will be shown in Chap. XXVI that the most desirable characteristic in a source of light for projection purposes is a

Fig. 81.—High-intensity searchlight arc lamp. The positive carbon is 16 mm in diameter and the current consumption is 150 amp. (*By courtesy of Sperry Gyroscope Company.*)

high intrinsic brightness. The brightness of the crater of an ordinary arc cannot easily be increased because increasing the arc current merely causes the crater to become larger in area. In the high-intensity arc, which was invented about 1914, the crater is confined to a small area in which the current density is very high.[2] One type of high-intensity arc is illustrated in Fig. 81. The electrodes are extremely hard tubes of carbon, the positive being cored with cerium and thorium fluorides, and the

[1] A study of the radiation characteristics of some of the more important types of arcs has been made at the Bureau of Standards and is reported in *Sci. Paper* 539.

[2] A very interesting description of this type of arc has been given by Benford in *Trans. Soc. Motion Picture Eng.*, **24,** 71 (1926).

negative with soft carbon. The core of the positive electrode boils away slightly faster than the carbon tube itself and forms a deep crater in which the vapors are confined. This electrode is kept in rotation to prevent the hot vapors from breaking down the hard carbon shell unevenly. The current density in the crater is about four times that of an ordinary arc, and the brightness is more than five times as great, 85,000 candles/cm² being a representative value. The crater is so uniform in brightness and so constant in position that in motion-picture projectors it is

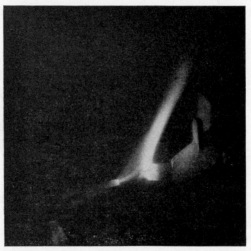

Fig. 82.—Discharge of the 150-amp. high-intensity arc shown in Fig. 81.
(*By courtesy of Sperry Gyroscope Company.*)

commonly focused directly on the film gate and therefore on the screen.

The discharge of a high-intensity arc is quite spectacular as can be seen from Fig. 82, which is a photograph showing the 150-amp. searchlight arc illustrated in Fig. 81 in operation. The positive electrode in this arc is 16 mm in diameter and has a core 8 mm in diameter; the negative electrode is 11 mm in diameter. The faint blue arc stream from the negative electrode forcibly strikes the crater gas emerging from the positive electrode and blows it upwards as a long flame. This prevents the fullest use of the arc in projection apparatus because the intense heat may injure the reflector and lenses if they are placed too close.

75. The Mercury Arc.—A type of arc radically different from those just described was invented by Peter Cooper-Hewitt in 1901. One electrode is a pool of mercury and the other is a metal wire, the arc being formed by vapor from the mercury. The entire unit is sealed within an evacuated tube, of course. Since mercury boils at a low temperature, the electrodes can be kept comparatively cool, so the light is due almost entirely to the glowing vapor. The radiation is therefore characteristic of the mercury spectrum and has but a faint continuous background. The chief lines in the spectrum of the mercury arc are given in Table XI and are shown graphically in Fig. 85.

TABLE XI.—CHIEF LINES IN THE ARC SPECTRUM OF MERCURY

The intensities of the lines in the spectrum of a mercury arc are greatly affected by the conditions under which the arc is operated, but the lines listed here are the ones most likely to be observed.

Ultraviolet.   253.6, 296.7, 302.1, 312.6, 313.2, 334.1, 365.0, 365.4, 366.3.
Visible.
  Violet: 404.7, 407.8, 433.9, 434.7, 435.8.
  Green: 546.1.
  Yellow-green: 577.0, 579.1.
  Red: 623.4, 690.8.

There are two ways of starting a mercury arc. The simpler is to tilt the tube until a stream from the mercury cathode touches the metallic anode. When the tube is returned to its normal position, the stream breaks and an arc usually forms across the gap thus created. If this procedure is impracticable, the arc can be started by applying a high potential across the electrodes to ionize the vapor that is present even when the tube is cold. In the industrial units, this potential is generated by breaking a current through a large inductance.

The brightness of the mercury arc and the distribution of energy in its spectrum depend upon its design and the conditions under which it is operated.[1] The industrial units are large in dimensions and have a low brightness, thus producing a soft, shadowless illumination. The unit most commonly used is 4 ft. long and 1 in. in diameter and has a brightness of approximately 2.3 candles/cm². On the other hand, the unit for therapeutic use is only a few inches long and has a brightness of approxi-

[1] This matter has been studied extensively by Harrison and Forbes, *Jour. Optical Soc. Amer. and Rev. Sci. Instruments*, **10**, 1 (1925); Stockbarger, *loc. cit.*, **14**, 356 (1927); and Buttolph, *Rev. Sci. Instruments*, **1**, 487 (1930) among others.

mately 350 candles/cm². It is made with a quartz tube, not only to transmit the ultraviolet rays but also because the discharge is so hot that a glass tube would soften.

The deficiency of energy in the red end of the spectrum gives the mercury arc a ghastly hue that militates against its wide adoption for general lighting and for those types of photography in which the true rendering of color values is important. It is unrivaled for blueprinting and photostating, because so much of its energy is in the blue and ultraviolet. A 3000-watt unit 6 ft. long and 3 in. in diameter is made for such purposes.

FIG. 83.—Cooper-Hewitt "Lab-arc." This is a self-contained quartz mercury arc operating on 115 volts. (*By courtesy of General Electric Vapor Lamp Company.*)

To the optical experimenter, the mercury arc is a tool of the highest value because the spectral lines are very bright and are so far apart that they can easily be isolated with filters. Many styles of arc lamps suitable for laboratory use have been devised, but perhaps the one most generally useful in the optical laboratory is the Cooper-Hewitt "Lab-arc," illustrated in Fig. 83. The tube is of quartz and is enclosed in a lamp house in which is a window fitted with adjustable shutters. The brightness of the arc stream is approximately 10 candles/cm². The necessary resistances and a switch for arranging the circuit for operation on either direct or alternating current are located in the base. The arc is started by tilting the lamp house backwards.

It may not be amiss to mention here a precaution that applies not only to this arc but to quartz arcs in general: All finger-prints on the tube must be removed before the arc is started. If this is not done, the salts contained in the grease on the fingers will unite with the quartz when the latter is heated and may cause the tube to crack.

A modified form of the mercury arc has been used by Edgerton[1] as a source of light for stroboscopic observations. If a rotating

[1] *Jour. Soc. Motion Picture Eng.,* **18,** 356 (1932).

machine is observed with a light source that flickers at the proper frequency, the machine can be made to appear stationary. The difficulty with most sources intended for stroboscopic work is that each flash persists for a sufficient length of time to cause some blurring of the motion. In the arrangement described by Edgerton, the duration of the flash is less than 10 microseconds. The average intensity of the arc is the same as when it is operated continuously.

76. Tungsten Arcs.—Before the ribbon-filament lamp shown in Fig. 79 was developed, the tungsten arc was widely used where a steady source of approximately uniform brightness was required. In this lamp, the filament is used only for starting the arc, which forms between one of the filament leads and a sphere of tungsten supported on a third lead. Nearly all the radiation from this lamp is emitted by the white-hot tungsten sphere, which has a color temperature of 3100°K. The radiation characteristics are essentially those of tungsten at this temperature. The usual type of lamp is made for operation on direct current, but a type designed for alternating current is also available.

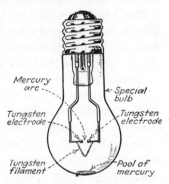

Fig. 84.—Type S-1 sunlight lamp. In use, the lamp is equipped with an aluminum oxide reflector. (*From Luckiesh's "Artificial Sunlight," by courtesy of D. Van Nostrand Company.*)

The lamp is known as the "Point-o-lite" or the "Tungsarc" and is made in several sizes. The chief disadvantage of this kind of lamp is the large control box necessary for energizing the filament at starting and for regulating the current during operation.

By introducing mercury vapor into the tungsten arc, the characteristics can be modified by the addition of the arc spectrum of mercury. A lamp based on these principles has recently been placed on the market by the General Electric Company. It is known as the type S-1 lamp and is intended primarily for therapeutic purposes. The lamp itself is illustrated in Fig. 84. It is generally used with an aluminum oxide reflector, which serves also to raise the temperature of the lamp and thus to increase the proportion of the radiation in the ultraviolet region.

This lamp is operated from a transformer that supplies 9.5 amp. at a potential of 33 volts across the filament at starting. As the filament becomes hot, the arc strikes and the current rises to 30 amp. By virtue of the drooping voltage characteristic of the transformer, the voltage across the terminals drops to 11 volts, which almost extinguishes the filament. When fitted with the reflector, the lamp emits about 6300 lumens, which corresponds to a luminous efficiency of 19 lumens/watt. Of the total luminous flux, about 75 per cent is supplied by the tungsten electrodes, 18 per cent by the arc stream, and only 7 per cent by the filament. The color temperature is about 4000°K.

The brightness of this lamp is extremely high, so that in a quartz bulb it would be an excellent source for spectroscopic work in the middle ultraviolet. The bulb as ordinarily supplied is of a special glass that has a short-wave cut-off just below 300 mμ. A considerable amount of information about this lamp has recently appeared in the literature.[1]

77. Flashlights.—When an extremely intense source of short duration is desired, recourse is had to the intense light that accompanies the rapid oxidation of metals like aluminum and magnesium. Magnesium is usually the base of the so-called flashlight powders used by photographers. It is supplied either as pure magnesium powder or as a mixture of magnesium with some oxidizing material like potassium chlorate. Magnesium alone is slow burning and is used in an alcohol lamp of special design, the powder being blown through the flame. The chlorate mixtures are explosive, of course, and must be handled with great care. They can be ignited by means of either a fuse or an electrically heated wire.

The duration of the flash depends upon the composition of the powder, the fineness of the particles, the total quantity of powder present, and the method of igniting it. In the case of pure magnesium powder blown through an alcohol lamp, the duration is usually a matter of several seconds. This type of powder is useful chiefly for inanimate objects at rest. For portraiture, the duration of the flash should be less than $\frac{1}{12}$ sec. to prevent blinking of the eyes. This speed is usually exceeded with the flash powders of the explosive type.

The luminous intensity of flash powder cannot be measured by ordinary photometric methods because of the short duration of

[1] *Jour. Optical Soc. Amer.*, **21**, 20 (1931).

the flash. It has been measured photographically by Huse,[1] however, and the results for three different types of photographic materials are given in Table XII. These results are expressed in candle-seconds—that is, in terms of the number of candles of white light which, acting for 1 sec., would produce the same photographic effect.

TABLE XII.—PHOTOGRAPHIC INTENSITY OF FLASHLIGHT MATERIALS
Expressed in equivalent candle-seconds of white light per gram of powder.

Flashlight material	Ordinary plate	Orthochromatic plate	Panchromatic plate
Eastman flash powder......	1900	1200	1400
Pure magnesium powder...	2300	4600	7700
Magnesium ribbon........	2850	4800	5600

A new type of flash lamp has been recently described by Forsythe and Easley.[2] It consists of approximately 50 mg of aluminum foil within a glass bulb filled with oxygen. The bulb is about the size of the ordinary 100-watt lamp and contains a special filament for igniting the flash that can be operated on any voltage between 1.5 and 150. As these lamps are made at present, the flash begins approximately 0.02 sec. after the filament is energized and lasts about 0.066 sec. A maximum intensity of about 4,500,000 candles is reached at approximately 0.014 sec. after the flash begins. The total flux radiated is of the order of 50,000 lumen-seconds, and the color temperature is approximately 5000°K.

78. Sources of Monochromatic Light.—No source of light emits radiation that is truly monochromatic. The purest radiations yet discovered are the three cadmium lines used first by Michelson in his measurement of the length of the standard meter in terms of the wave length of light. Benoit, Fabry, and Perot repeated the work some years later and determined the wave lengths of these lines in air at a temperature of 15° and a pressure of 760 mm to be

Red: 643.84696 mμ
Green: 508.5823
Blue: 479.9912

The locations of these lines in the spectrum are shown graphically in Fig. 85. The red radiation is the purest; and the value of its

[1] *Jour. Franklin Inst.*, **196**, 391 (1923).
[2] *Jour. Optical Soc. Amer.*, **21**, 685 (1931).

wave length has been adopted as the primary standard of wave length. Because of the purity of these radiations and their wide separation in the spectrum, the cadmium arc would be much used except for certain practical difficulties. The tube must be of quartz to withstand the high temperature at which the lamp must be operated, and pure cadmium adheres to the quartz as it solidifies and thus breaks the tube. This difficulty has been overcome by Bates, who found that a trace of gallium added to the cadmium prevents the latter from solidifying but does not affect the cadmium radiations.[1]

The need for secondary standards of wave length has been filled by certain iron lines.[2] These lines were chosen not only

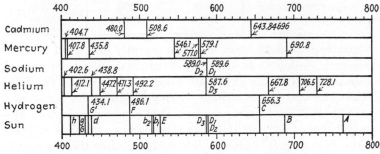

Fig. 85.—Spectra of certain monochromatic sources. The principal Fraunhofer lines in the solar spectrum are shown for comparison.

for their stability but also because they are so numerous that several are likely to be found on a spectrogram, even when the dispersion is high. Numerous tables are available that give the wave lengths of the lines in the spectra of the various elements.[3]

Many measurements in the optical laboratory must be made by means of light that is substantially monochromatic. For this purpose, the sodium flame is unexcelled because of its simplicity. The only two bright lines in the visible region (589.0 and 589.6 mμ) are so close together that this source is sufficiently monochromatic for ordinary purposes.[4]

[1] A lamp using this cadmium-gallium alloy is described in *Bur. Standards Sci. Paper* 371.

[2] The wave lengths of the stable iron lines determined by direct comparison with the primary standard are given in *Bur. Standards Sci. Paper* 478.

[3] The "International Critical Tables," Vol. V, contain extensive tables of this sort. See also Kayser and Runge, "Handbuch der Spectroscopie."

[4] A simple method of producing a sodium flame is to wrap the upper end of the tube of a Bunsen burner with a piece of asbestos soaked in a salt

When a source of greater brightness is required, a mercury arc like the one shown in Fig. 83 is a convenient source of monochromatic light. The lines in its spectrum are so far apart that a single line can be readily isolated by means of filters. Sets of filters for this purpose are supplied by several firms. The most useful line is the one at 546.1 mμ, which is very close to the maximum of the visibility curve. With the proper filter to transmit this line alone, the mercury arc is used extensively as a source for such purposes as polarimetry.

Gaseous discharge tubes are generally used for calibrating spectral apparatus and for determining the refractive indices of optical materials. The traditional source for measuring the optical constants of glass is the hydrogen tube. The chief lines in the hydrogen spectrum—at 656.28 (*C*), 486.13 (*F*), and 434.05 (*G'*)—are conveniently located for this purpose. But the index for the *D*-line of sodium is also required, and to avoid the use of two sources, the proposal has been made to specify the constants for the helium lines instead. The chief lines in the visible portion of the helium spectrum are the following:

Violet: 388.86, 402.62, 412.08, 438.79, 447.15.
Blue: 471.31.
Green: 492.19, 501.57.
Yellow: 587.56.
Red: 667.82, 706.52, 728.14.

The achromatism of lenses is so much a matter of convention that the substitution of the 706.52, 587.56, 471.31, and 438.79 lines of helium for the customary *C*-, *D*-, *F*-, and *G'*-lines should not affect the performance of an optical instrument, as can be seen from Fig. 85. For calibrating spectral apparatus, the helium tube is excellent because of the large number of lines in the helium spectrum and their wide distribution.

The brightness of a discharge tube can be greatly increased by constructing the tube in such a manner that the discharge can

---

solution. A neater method is to prepare cakes of asbestos fiber, plaster of Paris, and salt. One of these cakes held at the base of a Bunsen flame will impart a strong yellow color for a long time. As the color weakens, the cake can be scraped to expose a fresh surface. An alcohol lamp equipped with such a cake or fed with salt can be used if gas is not available. The familiar borax bead placed at the base of the flame is also satisfactory. For specifying the constants of optical glass, the *A'* line of the potassium flame spectrum is often useful. It consists of two lines whose mean wave length is 768.2 mμ.

be viewed end on.   The life of a tube can be prolonged by attaching a bulb of generous capacity to act as a reservoir for maintaining the pressure constant.   Where an ordinary tube will become useless in a few weeks, a tube fitted with a reservoir will continue to function satisfactorily for as many months.

For producing metallic spectra, a type of arc devised by Pfund[1] is very satisfactory.   The lower electrode, which is the negative, consists of a massive rod of iron with a depression in the top to hold a bead of the oxide of the metal under examination.   The positive electrode consists of a rod of iron or carbon, depending on whether iron or some other metal is being examined.   This type of arc is easy to construct and is remarkably steady.   The secondary standards of wave length mentioned above are certain iron lines in the Pfund arc when operated under carefully specified conditions.

The monochromatic radiations that we have briefly discussed[2] are sensibly pure but require special lamps for their production. There are many problems in the fields of physics, chemistry, and biology where the isolation of a fairly narrow spectral region is sufficient.   For this purpose, a source emitting a continuous spectrum is satisfactory if used with suitable filters. Filters for this purpose will be described in Chap. XVIII.   Very narrow spectral regions can be isolated with a special form of spectrometer known as a monochromator, which will be described in Sec. 201, Chap. XXVII.   Many light sources that lack of space forbids describing here are described in Chapter II of Forsythe's "Measurement of Radiant Energy" (McGraw-Hill, 1937).

[1] *Astrophys. Jour.*, **27,** 296 (1908).

[2] An extensive description of the production and use of monochromatic light has been published by Fabry in *Rev. d'Optique*, **1,** 413 and 445 (1922).

CHAPTER X

THE EYE

If the eye could be regarded solely as an optical instrument, its behavior could be explained satisfactorily by the methods of geometrical optics, notwithstanding that the eye is an organic structure which differs in some respects from the systems of spherical refracting surfaces that were previously considered. But image formation is only a small part of the phenomenon of vision, and a retinal image is of no use until it has been interpreted by the brain. Hence, any study of the eye involves physiology and psychology quite as much as physics; and to few investigators is given the ability to comprehend the phenomena included within these three branches of science. An outstanding exception was Hermann von Helmholtz, whose monumental "Physiological Optics"[1] remains to-day, more than sixty years after its first appearance, the most valuable source of information on the subject of vision.

79. The Anatomy of the Eye.—The human eye is an almost globular organ approximately an inch in diameter. As shown in Fig. 86, it is surrounded by a tough, white, outer skin S, called the sclera, to which are attached the six muscles that hold the eye in place. Two of these muscles are shown at Z_1 and Z_2. At the front of the eye, the sclera is replaced by a tough transparent membrane C, called the cornea. Light entering the eye passes successively through the cornea C, the aqueous humor AH, the crystalline lens L, the vitreous humor VH, and falls on the retina R. The aqueous humor is essentially a weak salt solution; the vitreous humor is a thin jelly consisting largely of water. The crystalline lens is a capsule containing a fibrous jelly that is

---

[1] Translated into English in 1924 by J. P. C. Southall under the auspices of the Optical Society of America. A summary of some of the more important characteristics of the eye may be found in the report of the Standards Committee on Visual Sensitometry, *Jour. Optical Soc. Amer.*, **4**, 55 (1920). An extensive bibliography of the literature concerning the visual functions that are of importance in illuminating engineering has been given by Troland in *Trans. Illum. Eng. Soc.*, **26**, 107 (1931).

hard at the center and progressively softer at the outer parts. This lens is held in place by the suspensory ligament G, which fastens it to the ciliary muscle Y.   When this muscle is relaxed, the second focal point of the normal eye is at the retina and distant objects are therefore in focus.   For viewing near objects, the ciliary muscle tenses and allows the lens to assume a more nearly spherical form.   This process is known as *accommodation*. The range of accommodation is great in young people but diminishes with age as the lens becomes less elastic.

The retina consists of a delicate film of nerve fibers that branch out from the optic nerve O to form the lining of a large part

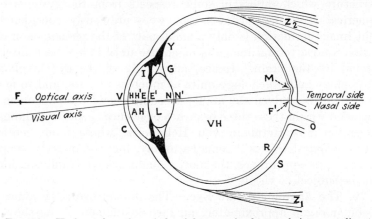

Fig. 86.—Horizontal section of the right eye of a human being according to Helmholtz; approximately to scale.   The significance of the symbols is stated in the text.

of the interior of the eyeball.   These nerve fibers terminate in minute structures called rods and cones.   Figure 87 shows their general appearance.   These rods and cones, together with a bluish liquid known as the visual purple which circulates in and about them, receive the optical image and transmit it along the optic nerve to the brain.   The slight depression in the retina at M is called the macula lutea or yellow spot.   It is about two millimeters in diameter and contains principally cones and but few rods.   At its center is the fovea centralis, which is about 0.25 mm in diameter and contains cones exclusively.   In this region, the cones vary in size from about 0.0015 mm to about 0.0054 mm in diameter.   They are considerably larger in the outer portions of the retina, where they are outnumbered by the rods in the ratio of ten to one. Foveal vision is so much more acute than extra-foveal vision that the muscles controlling the eye always involuntarily rotate the eyeball until the image of the object toward which the attention is directed falls on the fovea. Thus the outer portions of the retina serve to give a general view of the scene and to warn of an object approaching within the field, while the fovea enables the object of chief interest to be examined minutely.

80. The Optical System of the Eye.— Because of the inhomogeneity of the media in the eye, no system of spherical refracting surfaces can be devised that will replace it exactly. Nevertheless, many investigators have devised *schematic eyes*, as they are called, which closely simulate the optical system of the living eye. The one sketched in Fig. 86 from the data of Table XIII is due to Helmholtz. Two sets of constants appear in the table, the first for an unaccommodated eye and the second for an eye focused on an object 152.5 mm in front of the vertex V of the cornea. Since the refractive indices of all the eye media are so nearly alike, most of the refraction occurs at the anterior surface of the cornea, the function of the crystalline lens being chiefly to alter the accommodation. The defects of vision that can be corrected by spectacles are usually caused either by an irregularly shaped cornea or by an improper relation

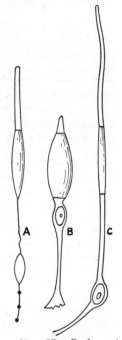

Fig. 87.—Rods and cones of the retina. *A*, a typical rod; *B*, a typical cone from the extra-foveal region; *C*, a typical cone from the center of the fovea.

between the radius of curvature of the cornea and the length of the eyeball. These defects will be discussed in Chap. XX. In the present chapter, the eye will be assumed to be normal.

The cardinal points of Helmholtz's schematic eye are located approximately to scale in Fig. 86. The principal points are at H and H', the nodal points at N and N', and the focal points at F and F'. It is noteworthy that the macula is more than a millimeter from the second focal point, making the eye unique among optical instruments in that the portion of the image where the resolution is the highest is not on the optical axis.

The amount of light entering the eye is controlled by the iris I, which is a ring-shaped involuntary muscle adjacent to the anterior surface of the lens. The iris varies in diameter from 2 mm to 8 mm, according to the field brightness, as shown in Fig. 88. The entrance pupil E and the exit pupil E' are its images in the

TABLE XIII.—PROPERTIES OF HELMHOLTZ'S SCHEMATIC EYE

The first column is for the unaccommodated eye; the second, for the eye accommodated for 152.5 mm. The first nine pairs of values are measured, the remaining ten computed. All dimensions are in millimeters.

	Far	Near
Refractive Indices:		
Aqueous humor..............................	1.337	1.337
Vitreous humor..............................	1.337	1.337
Crystalline lens..............................	1.437	1.437
Positions (distances from vertex of cornea):		
Crystalline lens, anterior surface...............	3.6	3.2
Crystalline lens, posterior surface..............	7.2	7.2
Fovea..	24.0	24.0
Radii:		
Cornea, anterior surface......................	7.83	7.83
Crystalline lens, anterior surface...............	10.0	6.0
Crystalline lens, posterior surface..............	− 6.0	− 5.5
Focal Lengths:		
First..	15.5	14.0
Second......................................	20.7	18.7
Positions of Cardinal Points (distances from vertex of cornea):		
Principal point, first.........................	1.75	1.86
Principal point, second.......................	2.10	2.26
Focal point, first............................	13.74	12.13
Focal point, second..........................	22.82	20.95
Nodal point, first............................	6.97	6.57
Nodal point, second..........................	7.32	6.97
Entrance pupil..............................	3.05	2.67
Exit pupil..................................	3.71	3.30

object space and image space respectively. The magnification ρ'/ρ between the pupils is 0.923 for the unaccommodated eye and 0.941 when the eye is accommodated for an object distance of 152.5 mm.

The size of the field of distinct vision can be computed from the dimensions of the fovea. Assuming a diameter of 0.25 mm for the fovea, the angle that it subtends at the center of the exit pupil is $\alpha' = 0.70°$. The corresponding angle[1] in the object space is $\alpha = 0.87°$. In a similar manner, the angle subtended in the object space by the macula can be found to be approximately seven degrees. It is not often appreciated that the field of distinct vision is so small, but that such is the case can be realized by attempting to focus on both dots of this colon (:) simultaneously. The angle that these subtend at the normal

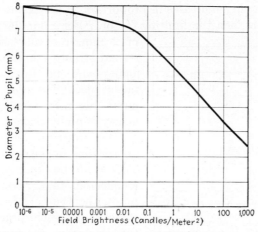

Fig. 88.—Variation of pupillary diameter with field brightness. (*Reeves, Jour. Optical Soc. Amer.*, **4**, 38 [1920].)

reading distance (250 mm) is 0.3°. The natural consequence is that the eye roams incessantly when examining an extended field.

It is easily computed that the fineness of the retinal structure is well adapted to the optical system of the eye. If the optical system were aberrationless, the resolving power of the image-forming system would be limited only by diffraction and it could therefore be computed by means of Eq. (168) in Chap. VII. Of course, the diameter of the pupil is variable, but assuming the value for the diameter of the entrance pupil as 2 mm and the wave length as 555 mμ, the resolving power is 70'' or slightly more than one minute of arc. Now the diameter of the central diffraction disk on the retina under these circumstances can be shown by computation to be 0.011 mm. This is but slightly

[1] This can readily be computed from Lagrange's law, since the magnification between the entrance and exit pupils and the refractive indices of the initial and final media are known.

greater than the diameter of the cones in the fovea and corresponds rather closely to the distance between adjacent cones. It may therefore be concluded that, with a pupillary diameter in the neighborhood of 2 mm, the resolving power of the eye is limited about equally by diffraction and by the coarseness of the retinal structure. This is borne out by some visual acuity experiments of P. W. Cobb,[1] the results of which are shown in Fig. 89. It will be noted that when the pupillary diameter is small, the visual acuity increases in proportion to the diameter because diffraction is then the limiting factor. For a pupillary diameter of 2 mm, the coarseness of the retinal structure limits the visual acuity and no further increase takes place. Indeed, when the pupil becomes very large, the acuity actually decreases because of the spherical and chromatic aberrations in the optical system. This would be expected when it is recollected that, with a 2-mm pupil, the eye constitutes an $f/8$ system in which practically all the refraction takes place at a single surface. For larger values of the relative aperture, the optical system would certainly be expected to perform less perfectly. Ordinarily, the resolving power of the eye is taken for practical purposes as one minute of arc or one part in 3438. This value is for two point objects of equal brightness, of course, and it may be quite different for any other type of object or for an observer with impaired vision.

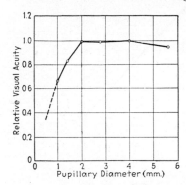

Fig. 89.—Effect of pupillary diameter on visual acuity. The experiments were performed with an artificial pupil and the brightness of the field was adjusted to maintain a constant retinal illumination.

81. The Spectral Sensitivity of the Eye.—One of the earliest determinations of the spectral sensitivity of the eye was made by König and Dieterici in 1893. Their method consisted in determining the least amount of energy that is just perceptible at each wave length. This is known as the threshold method. The same sort of curve has been obtained by other investigators using less direct methods. One such method is to determine the amount of monochromatic radiation required at each wave length to give a certain constant value of the visual acuity;

[1] *Amer. Jour. Physiol.*, **36**, 335 (1915).

another is to determine at each wave length the critical frequency at which flicker just disappears. The more recent determinations of the visibility curve have been made by means of a direct measurement of the relative brightness of equal amounts of energy throughout the spectrum. One way of making this measurement is to compare the brightness of two monochromatic radiations at wave lengths so close together in the spectrum that the color difference does not reduce the precision of the photometric setting. This is known as the step-by-step method. Another method involves the use of the flicker photometer, which will be described in Chap. XIII.[1]

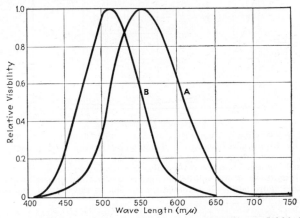

FIG. 90.—Visibility curves for a normal eye. *A*, at ordinary field brightnesses according to Gibson and Tyndall. *B*, at the threshold of vision according to König. Both curves are plotted for an arbitrary maximum of unity.

The sensitivity of the eye is found to shift toward the blue end of the spectrum at low levels of illumination. This effect is illustrated in Fig. 90, where curve *A* is identical with the curve in Fig. 5 and indicates the relative visibility for a normal observer at ordinary levels of illumination. Curve *B*, on the other hand, was determined by the threshold method and indicates the relative visibility at very low levels of illumination. This shift in the spectral sensitivity of the eye is probably due to a transition from cone to rod vision. The first evidence of such a shift was discovered by Purkyně more than a hundred years ago. He

[1] For a more extensive description of these methods and references to the literature of the subject, the reader should consult *Bur. Standards Sci. Papers* 303 and 475.

found that if a red field and a blue field are matched photo-
metrically at a high brightness level, a reduction in the illumination of both fields in the same proportion causes the red field to
appear darker than the blue. This *Purkyně phenomenon* is
responsible for much difficulty in the photometry of lights of
different color. It is often suggested as an explanation of the blue
appearance of objects seen by moonlight, an effect that artists
have long recognized.

82. The Contrast Sensitivity of the Eye.—The contrast
sensitivity of the eye relates broadly to the least perceptible

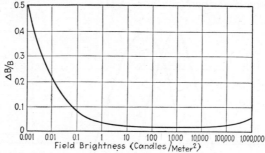

Fig. 91.—Variation of contrast sensitivity with field brightness from data
obtained by König and Brodhun. These investigators used an artificial pupil
one square millimeter in area and expressed the field brightness in *photons*, one
photon being by definition the retinal illumination produced by viewing a surface
having a brightness of one candle per square meter through such a pupil. The
curve in this figure has been adjusted for the size of the natural pupil according
to Fig. 88.

difference in the brightness of two contiguous areas. A more
precise definition can be made only in terms of the details of an
actual experiment by which the quantity is measured. In
general, experiments of this sort consist in viewing an extended
field of uniform brightness to which the eye of the observer is
allowed to become adapted. The brightness of a small area
near the center of the field is then varied until it is just noticeably different from that of the surrounding field. If the brightness of the surrounding field is represented by B and the least
perceptible difference by ΔB, the *contrast sensitivity* is, by
definition, the ratio $B/\Delta B$. The variation in the contrast
sensitivity with field brightness is more conveniently represented
by $\Delta B/B$, as is done in Fig. 91. The sensitivity is practically
the same for all colors at high levels of illumination, but for
levels below 0.1 candle/meter² it is higher for blue light and
lower for red than for white.

The most significant feature of this curve is the nearly uniform contrast sensitivity over the great range of brightness levels between about 1 and 100,000 candles/meter². This great range of adaptation of the eye must be associated with a change in the sensitivity of the retina, since the maximum variation in the pupillary diameter accounts for only a sixteen-fold variation in the retinal illumination. This change in the adaptation level of the retina requires an appreciable amount of time, and it is found that more time is required for adaptation to a lower level of brightness than to a higher. At least ten minutes are required for the eye to become dark adapted after exposure to daylight, and as much as an hour after exposure to a very intense source.

The significance of Fig. 91 will be enhanced by considering the levels of field brightness to which the eye is ordinarily required to adapt itself. These levels vary enormously, but representative values for various conditions are given in the following table:

Exteriors by daylight	10,000	candles/meter²
Interiors by daylight	100	candles/meter²
Interiors at night	1	candle/meter²
Exteriors at night	0.01	candle/meter²

The minimum brightness of an extended object that can just be perceived by a normal observer when dark adapted has been investigated by Prentice Reeves.[1] He found that when the field is large enough to cover a substantial portion of the retina, the least perceptible brightness is 5×10^{-11} candle/cm².* As the size of the field is reduced below a certain point, the least perceptible brightness increases rapidly, as shown in Fig. 92. When the field becomes so small that it is below the limit of resolution of the eye, all the energy entering the eye falls on a single rod or cone of the retina. Under these circumstances, Reeves found that a source having an intensity of 2×10^{-8} candle was just perceptible at a distance of 3 meters. We can, therefore, compute that, if it were not for atmospheric absorption, one candle should be just visible at a distance of 13 miles.

This value is in fairly good agreement with that determined from astronomical observations on faint stars. Ordinarily stars

[1] *Astrophys. Jour.*, **47**, 143 (1918).

* The brightness of the night sky outside the region of the Galaxy is in the neighborhood of 5×10^{-9} candle/cm².

fainter than the sixth magnitude are invisible to the naked eye, but H. N. Russell[1] has found that, under the optimum conditions, stars of magnitude 8.5 can just be perceived. The scale of magnitudes used by astronomers to express the "brightness" of stars is an arbitrary one in which the ratio of successive magnitudes is taken to be $\sqrt[5]{100}$ or approximately 2.5. Hence, if E_1 represents the illumination produced at the earth's surface

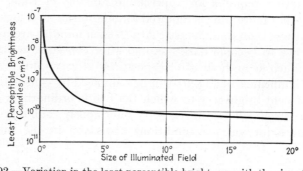

Fig. 92.—Variation in the least perceptible brightness with the size of the test object. It will be observed that the least perceptible brightness is sensibly constant when the test object subtends an angle of more than 5°. When the test object is below the limit of resolution (subtends an angle of less than 1′), the least perceptible brightness varies inversely as the area of the test object.

by the star that is arbitrarily selected as being of the first magnitude, the illumination produced by a star of magnitude m is

$$E_m = E_1\left(\frac{1}{2.5}\right)^{m-1}. \tag{178}$$

Fabry[2] has determined that the illumination at the earth's surface produced by a star of the first magnitude at the zenith on a clear night is 8.3×10^{-7} lumen/meter². It can, therefore, be computed that a star of magnitude 8.5 produces an illumination of 8.3×10^{-10} lumen/meter². This illumination would be produced by a candle at a distance of 21 miles if there were no atmospheric absorption.

The sensitivity of any physical instrument can be expressed as the change in its indication produced by a given change in the quantity that it measures. In a voltmeter, for example, the sensitivity can be expressed as the change in scale reading produced by a given change in voltage. It can also be

[1] *Astrophys. Jour.*, **45**, 60 (1917).
[2] *Trans. Illum. Eng. Soc.*, **20**, 12 (1925).

expressed in terms of the ratio $V/\Delta V$, where ΔV is the least perceptible change in voltage at the voltage V. If the eye is regarded as a physical instrument, its sensitivity can likewise be expressed in terms of the ratio $B/\Delta B$, where ΔB is the least perceptible change in brightness at the brightness level B. The visual sensation, which corresponds to the scale reading in the case of the voltmeter, is then given by the integral

$$S = \int_0^B \frac{B}{\Delta B} dB.$$

Now the ratio $B/\Delta B$ is simply the contrast sensitivity, and hence a sensation scale for the eye can easily be constructed. The

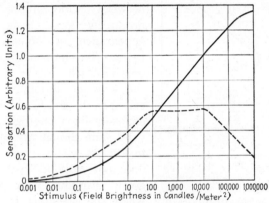

Fig. 93.—Visual sensation as a function of the stimulus. The value at 10,000 candles/meter² is arbitrarily taken as unity. The broken curve represents the contrast sensitivity $B/\Delta B$ in arbitrary units. Each ordinate of the sensation curve is proportional to the accumulated area under the broken curve.

broken curve in Fig. 93 represents the contrast sensitivity; the full curve represents the sensation, which is obtained by measuring the accumulated area under the broken curve. This sensation curve may be regarded as a sort of calibration curve for the visual apparatus. The significant feature of this curve is that, to a very close approximation, the sensation varies directly as the logarithm of the stimulus over the useful range of field brightness. This result is in accordance with the law stated by Fechner[1] in 1858 that, as the stimulus of the eye is increased in geometrical progression, the resulting sensation is increased in arithmetical progression. The ratio $\Delta B/B$ is sometimes termed *Fechner's fraction.*

[1] But which is only a corollary of Weber's more general law of sensation.

In most experiments devised to determine contrast sensitivity, the eye is allowed to view an extended field of uniform brightness and to become adapted to this brightness level before observations are begun.   Now in ordinary vision, the field is seldom of uniform brightness, but the eye nevertheless adjusts itself to a certain *adaptation level,* which is a sort of average field brightness.   The curve in Fig. 93 shows that the appearance of a given object does not change with the amount of illumination on it, provided that its brightness is always kept within the range where the sensation curve is a straight line.   In other words, the level of illumination in a room could be varied slowly between wide limits without producing any change in the appearance of objects in the room.   This indicates how utterly unreliable the eye is for judging the level of illumination as, for example, in gauging the time of exposure for a photograph.

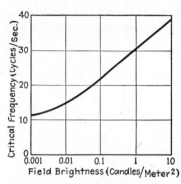

Fig. 94.—Critical frequency in flashes per second as a function of field brightness. The flashes and dark intervals are of equal duration.

83. The Sensitivity of the Eye to Flicker.—The visual apparatus does not respond instantly to a given stimulus, nor does the sensation cease immediately when the stimulus is removed. Hence, if the eye is exposed to a source whose intensity is varied rapidly, the *persistence of vision* may prevent the flicker from being detected.   The highest frequency at which flicker is just perceptible is known as the *critical frequency.*   This quantity is measured by interrupting a beam of light by means of a rotating sector wheel containing equal opaque and transparent sectors and noting the speed of rotation at which the sensation of flicker disappears.   The curve in Fig. 94 gives the critical frequency in cycles per second as a function of the field brightness for a source of white light.   This curve is for foveal vision, the critical frequency being somewhat higher for the extra-foveal region.

In the experiment from which this curve was determined, the flashes of light were separated by equal periods of total darkness. The critical frequency as a function of the degree of modulation of the light has been studied by J. S. Dow,[1] and a typical set

[1] *Electrician,* **59,** 255 (1907).

of his curves is reproduced in Fig. 95. It will be observed that, under the most favorable conditions of brightness and frequency, the least perceptible change in brightness is of the order of 1.5 per cent.

One of the common methods in photometry for reducing the intensity of a source of light is to use a wheel from which sectors of known angular aperture have been cut and to rotate this wheel in the path of the light at such a speed that the flicker is imperceptible. If the eye responded instantaneously to the stimulus and if the response were proportional to the stimulus instead of to its logarithm, no proof would be required for the validity of this method; a light seen through a wheel from which two 90°

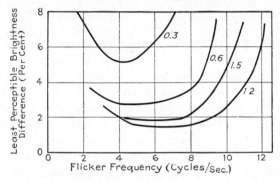

Fig. 95.—Least perceptible brightness difference as a function of the flicker speed for several brightness levels. The brightness level in candles per square meter is indicated on each curve.

sectors had been cut would appear to have exactly half its true brightness. But since the eye does not fulfill the required conditions, an experimental proof of the validity of the method must be sought. As long ago as 1834, Fox Talbot performed an experiment which indicated that the apparent brightness of an object viewed through a sector wheel is proportional to the angular apertures of the openings if the speed of the wheel is so high that the flicker is imperceptible. This principle of the integrating action of the eye is commonly called *Talbot's law.* It has been found[1] to hold at all flicker speeds above the critical frequency to within the limit of experimental error in photometric measurements, provided the eye is exposed to the light for at least 3 per cent of the cycle.

[1] *Bur. Standards Sci. Paper* **26.**

The persistence of vision of the human eye is utilized in the projection of motion pictures. The camera makes a series of photographs of the subject, usually at the rate of 24 per second if the pictures are synchronized with sound. These pictures are projected on the screen in succession, the film being held stationary during the projection of each picture. To prevent blurring of the screen image by the movement of the film, a shutter eclipses the beam while the film is in motion. At this speed of projection, the frequency of interruption of the light is below the critical frequency for the screen brightness that is ordinarily used. To minimize the flicker, the shutter is commonly constructed with three blades instead of one. Three flashes of light are projected through each picture, and the shift to the succeeding picture is made to occur during one of the dark intervals.

84. Other Visual Phenomena.—No discussion of the eye is adequate without some consideration of the subject of color vision. Although this subject might properly be discussed here, it is so important to an understanding of the methods of measuring color that it will be treated in connection with that subject in Chap. XIV. There are, however, many other visual phenomena that have perforce been omitted in this brief treatment of the eye. This should not be taken as an indication that such phenomena are unimportant. On the contrary, the physicist must be especially warned against the all too common tendency to embark upon investigations of the visual process without acquainting himself with all the visual phenomena known to the physiologist and the psychologist. This tendency among physicists is as common as the custom among physiologists and psychologists of employing physical apparatus in a wholly improper manner. The situation is probably a result of the attempt to classify all science into divisions separated by artificial boundaries. Fortunately for visual science, these boundaries are going out of fashion; and it is to be hoped that the result will be a renewed activity in this field, which has received little consideration by adequately prepared investigators since the days of Helmholtz and his immediate followers.

CHAPTER XI

PHOTOGRAPHY

Photography in the broadest sense relates to the applications of photochemical reactions between light and matter, the matter being usually one or more of the silver halides in a gelatin emulsion. Some photochemical effects, such as the tanning of the human skin on exposure to sunlight, must have been known to the ancients, but it was not until the middle of the eighteenth century that photochemical reactions were found that proceeded rapidly enough to suggest the idea implied in the word "photography"—namely, to write with light.

85. The History of Photography.—The earliest use of photography was for the production of silhouettes. The materials used were sheets of paper or leather sensitized with either silver nitrate or one of the halides of silver, usually the chloride. The sheets thus treated darkened on exposure to light because part of the silver salt was reduced to black metallic silver. The results were not permanent, of course, because further exposure darkened the unexposed portions also. There were two other outstanding difficulties: the exposures required were very long, and the result was a negative—that is, the greatest amount of darkening occurred where the light from the subject was most intense. In 1839, Sir John Herschel overcame the first of these difficulties by his discovery of sodium thiosulphate ($Na_2S_2O_3 + 5H_2O$), a material that has the ability to dissolve the relatively insoluble silver halides. This discovery permitted the removal of the unexposed halides, a process known as *fixing*. The term "hypo" that is almost universally applied to this salt resulted from its being mistaken at first for sodium hyposulphite.

The other objectionable features were eliminated by Fox Talbot about two years later. He found it possible to reduce the exposure in the camera until only an invisible or *latent* image was formed on the sensitized surface. This image was then "developed" in a solution of gallic acid. The portions of the silver halide that had been exposed to light were thus reduced to metallic silver, but the unexposed portions were only slightly affected. This procedure shortened the required exposure because most of the energy necessary for the reduction of the silver halide was supplied by the developer rather than by the exposing light. Fox Talbot used transparent paper as the support for the light-sensitive material and was therefore able to make positive prints from his negatives. It will be seen that this method differed only in minor details from that in common use to-day. In fact, some of his pictures were surprisingly good.

The early investigators tried almost every substance that might conceivably be affected by light in the hope of circumventing the difficulties of the silver halide process. Niepce experimented with plates of metal or stone upon which he coated a solution of bitumen of Judea dissolved in oil of lavender. These plates were exposed in the camera, the action of the light being to make the bitumen insoluble. They were then developed in oil of lavender, which removed the unexposed material. Then, by etching the plate in acid, a relief image was obtained from which prints could be made in an ordinary printing press. This process was the forerunner of the present photomechanical methods.

In 1829, Niepce formed a partnership with a scene painter named Daguerre, who also was experimenting with photography. A few years later Niepce died, whereupon Daguerre discarded the bitumen for silver and, aided by a lucky accident, developed what became known as the daguerreotype process. In its final form, this process consisted in exposing a polished silver surface to iodine vapor, thereby forming a thin coating of silver iodide. The plate was exposed in the camera for three or four minutes and was then developed by subjecting it to the action of mercury vapor. In this operation, metallic mercury gradually condenses on the portions that have been exposed to light—the reaction being but little understood even at the present time. The plates were fixed in a solution of hypo as usual. The daguerreotype is a direct positive of high quality, and it was deservedly popular for portraits until Scott-Archer discovered the wet-collodion process in 1851.

The developments in the photographic art since the middle of the nineteenth century have been largely in the nature of improvements in the sensitized material rather than modifications in the method. The wet-collodion process of Scott-Archer gave excellent results, but it involved sensitizing the plates in the field and exposing them while still wet. Nevertheless it was extensively used until the advent of the gelatino-bromide emulsion, which was first described in 1871 by Dr. Maddox, an English amateur photographer. Our present-day emulsions are merely improved varieties of this one.

Photography started on its road to popularity about 1880 with the introduction by George Eastman of the cellulose nitrate film support for the emulsion instead of glass. Without this invention, neither amateur nor motion-picture photography in their present forms would have been possible. One difficulty with the early film was that, after being developed, it curled into a tight roll or spiral because of the shrinking of the emulsion on drying. To overcome this, the reverse side of the film base was coated with plain gelatin. With the exception of motion-picture film, practically all film made to-day is of the non-curling type.

86. The Nature and Manipulation of Photographic Materials. In modern negative materials—that is, those intended for use in a camera—the emulsion consists of silver bromide and a small amount of silver iodide in gelatin. The emulsion is prepared by adding a moderately concentrated silver nitrate solution to a solution containing potassium bromide, potassium iodide, and gelatin. The silver bromide precipitates in the form of crystals or grains. The silver iodide enters directly into these crystals instead of precipitating separately. Curiously enough, it produces a marked increase in the sensitivity of the silver bromide grains although alone it is relatively insensitive. The chemistry of the preparation of high-speed emulsions is only beginning to be understood. For obvious reasons, many of the important details of the method are trade secrets and, although seemingly explicit directions have been published, the art of making high-speed emulsions is possessed by only a few experts. This, however, causes no hardship because so many types of materials are available that the user has but to select the one best adapted to his purpose.

The diffusion of light in an undeveloped emulsion is so great that examination with a microscope reveals very little. The grains of which it is composed can be studied by diluting the emulsion with water and recoating it on glass slides in a layer only one grain deep. A typical photomicrograph of a single layer of emulsion from a fast portrait (Eastman 40) plate is shown in Fig. 96. It will be seen that the large grains are generally either triangular or hexagonal in shape, whereas the smaller ones tend to be more nearly circular. These grains are, in reality, flat plates which, in the drying-down process that the emulsion undergoes after coating, tend to orient themselves parallel to the support. The grains vary enormously in size, even in a single emulsion. Many are too small to be resolved

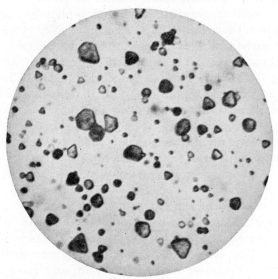

Fig. 96.—Photomicrograph of the grains in a fast portrait emulsion before development. Magnification, 2500 times. (*By courtesy of Dr. E. P. Wightman, Kodak Research Laboratories.*)

by a microscope (less than 0.0002 mm across), whereas a few grains in a high-speed emulsion may be as large as 0.003 mm across. The distribution of grain sizes has been studied extensively,[1] the curve for the material of Fig. 96 being shown in Fig. 97.

Although many investigators have studied the photographic process both theoretically and experimentally, no eminently satisfactory theory of the latent image has yet been devised. The difficulty in understanding the process probably results as much from our insufficient knowledge of the nature of light as

[1] See a series of papers by E. P. Wightman and others in *Jour. Phys. Chem.* between 1921 and 1924.

from a lack of comprehension of the physical and chemical changes that are produced in the light-sensitive substance itself. Whatever the effect of light is, there is one outstanding experimental fact upon which photography in the modern sense may be said to rest—namely, that there exist certain chemical substances, known as photographic developers, which are capable of distinguishing between the exposed and the unexposed grains. The act of exposing a photographic material renders a certain number of grains *developable*. In other words, these grains are placed in a condition to be reduced to metallic silver when acted upon by a suitable developer. Since the penetration of the developer into the emulsion is a relatively slow process, the number of developable grains that are actually developed depends

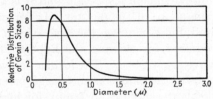

Fig. 97.—Frequency distribution of the grains shown in Fig. 96 as a function of their diameter. There were 4.9×10^7 grains per square centimeter in the single-layer emulsion and 1.5×10^9 in the original emulsion from which the single-layer emulsion was prepared. The grains are more hexagonal than circular, but the abscissae are plotted in terms of a circular grain of equal area. (*By courtesy of Dr. E. P. Wightman, Kodak Research Laboratories.*)

upon the length of time that the material is allowed to remain in the developing solution. By inference, the unexposed grains should not be developable, but this is only partially true since some unexposed grains may be developed also if the time of development is excessive. This produces what is known as chemical fog—that is, a silver deposit where there has been no exposure to light.

The essential steps in making a photograph are exposing, developing, fixing, and washing. The first two steps have such a profound influence on the quality of the reproduction that they will be discussed at some length in the ensuing sections. Fixing and washing are relatively unimportant except as regards the permanence of the result. Fixing is usually carried out in a bath containing some sort of acid hardener in addition to the hypo. Except in the tropics, where an especially powerful hardener is required, the following fixing solution is satisfactory:

Hypo....................................... 480 grams
Water, to make.............................   2 liters

Then add the following hardener solution slowly to the above hypo solution while stirring the latter rapidly:

Water (about 125°F.)........................ 160 cc
Sodium sulphite (dry)........................ 30 grams
Acetic acid (28 per cent)..................... 96 cc
Potassium alum (powdered) .... 30 grams

Dissolve in the order given.

The plate or film need remain in the fixing bath only long enough to dissolve the undeveloped silver halide. There is no difficulty in judging by inspection when the material has been fixed because the undeveloped halide dissolves most slowly in the regions where the density of the developed image is lowest. The proper time for washing is not evident on inspection, but it is of great importance to the permanence of the picture. It depends upon both the time required for removing the hypo from the emulsion and the time required for clearing the hypo from the vessel in which the negatives are washed. The former depends principally upon the thickness of the emulsion and varies from about 3 min. for materials like lantern plates to 7 min. for high-speed plates and films. Papers retain hypo more tenaciously and thus require much more washing. A representative value for the chloride ("gas-light") papers is 20 min. and for bromide papers, 1 hr. As a rough guide, the minimum safe time for washing may be taken as the time required to remove the hypo from the emulsion plus the time required to clear the hypo from the vessel.[1] For further details concerning the manipulation of photographic materials, the reader should consult the numerous handbooks published by the manufacturers.[2]

87. The Laws of Exposure and Development.—The discovery of the laws of exposure and development of photographic materials is due principally to two investigators, Ferdinand Hurter and Vero C. Driffield,[3] who began their investigations about

---

[1] The time required to clear the hypo from the vessel can be determined by adding a few drops of red ink and finding how long it takes the solution to clear. It may be mentioned in this connection that there are several simple chemical tests for hypo that may be used to insure sufficient washing.

[2] Such as "Elementary Photographic Chemistry," published by the Eastman Kodak Company.

[3] Their papers were collected in 1920 by Ferguson under the auspices of the Royal Photographic Society and published under the title, "The Photographic Researches of Hurter and Driffield."

1880. It was known at that time that photographic materials obeyed the so-called *reciprocity law* of Bunsen and Roscoe, which had been found to hold for many photochemical reactions. According to this law, if E represents the illumination on the sensitized surface and t represents the time that this illumination is allowed to act, the resulting photochemical effect is proportional to the product

$$\Sigma = E\,t, \tag{179}$$

where the quantity Σ is called the *exposure*.[1] A more careful investigation of this subject has since indicated that all photographic materials fail to obey the reciprocity law to such an extent[2] that account must be taken of the failure in any quantitative work such as photographic photometry. For most purposes, however, the reciprocity law may be regarded as a remarkably accurate statement of the observed facts over the ordinary range of illumination intensities.

The reciprocity law was almost the only quantitative information that was available at the time that Hurter and Driffield undertook their investigation. One of their first acts, therefore, was to decide upon a unit for measuring the amount of blackening of a developed photographic image. They selected the optical density for this purpose, which has already been defined by Eq. (11) in Chap. I as

$$D = \log_{10} \frac{1}{T},$$

where T, the transparency, is the ratio of the light transmitted by the developed image to the light incident on it. The density of a photographic deposit was found to be very nearly proportional to the mass of reduced silver per unit area, the constant of proportionality being sometimes called the *photometric constant*. Its value varies somewhat with the type of material but is usually in the neighborhood of 0.0001 gram of silver per square centimeter per unit density.

---

[1] The illumination is commonly measured in lumens per square meter (meter-candles), and the time of exposure in seconds. The unit of photographic exposure is therefore the lumen-second per square meter or, more frequently, its numerical equivalent, the meter-candle-second.

[2] See a series of papers by L. A. Jones and others in *Jour. Optical Soc. Amer. and Rev. Sci. Instruments* between 1923 and 1927.

The manner in which the density of an image increases with the time of development will now be investigated. A set of typical curves is shown in Fig. 98, each curve being for a different value of exposure. The shape of these curves indicates that the rate of development corresponds to what is known in chemistry as a first-order reaction—that is, one in which the rate of the reaction at any time is proportional to the amount of material

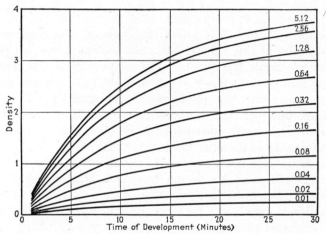

FIG. 98.—Curves showing, for a typical portrait film, the rate of growth of density with the time of development. The exposure in meter-candle-seconds is indicated on each curve. These curves have been slightly idealized to emphasize the more important features.

that remains to be acted upon. Expressed in mathematical symbols, the rate of increase in density is

$$\frac{dD}{dt} = k(D_\infty - D), \qquad (180)$$

where D is the density at the time t, and D_∞ is the density that would be produced if the development were indefinitely prolonged. The proportionality constant k is called the *development constant.* Its value depends on the concentration and temperature of the developing solution, on the type of emulsion and developer, and, of course, on the units in which the quantities are measured. The solution of this differential equation is

$$D = D_\infty (1 - \epsilon^{-kt}), \qquad (181)$$

which represents the experimental curves of Fig. 98 as satisfactorily as any equation containing only two arbitrary constants.

Actually, there is always a short induction period before the developer begins to act, so a better correspondence with the experimental facts is obtained by an equation of the form

$$D = D_\infty [1 - \epsilon^{-k(t-t_0)}]. \tag{182}$$

For most purposes, however, the two-constant equation is quite precise enough, and its greater simplicity justifies its use.

The exposure steps in Fig. 98 are in geometrical progression, which is found to result in spacing the curves equally except for

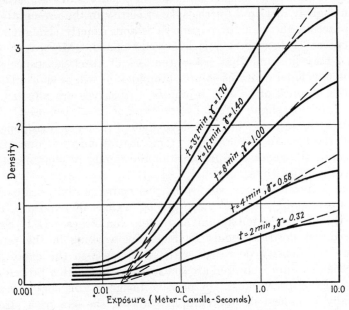

Fig. 99.—Characteristic curves of a typical portrait film. These curves are plotted from those of Fig. 98. The development time and the value of gamma for each curve are indicated.

very small and very large values of exposure. For small values, the curves approach a limit set by the development of the fog density. For large values, the limit is set by the "saturation" of the emulsion by light—that is, with sufficient exposure all the grains in the material are made developable.

In any actual photograph, the development time is constant and the exposure varies from point to point of the material. The curves in Fig. 98 can be replotted at once to show the variation of density with exposure for any time of development, as is done in Fig. 99. The exposure is plotted on a logarithmic scale, partly because of the simplicity in interpreting the results but more because of the great range of exposure values to be represented. These curves are called *characteristic curves* or, sometimes, *H and D curves* because Hurter and Driffield were the first to plot them in this manner.

The significant features of these curves are the long straight portion, the common point of intersection on the axis, and the steadily increasing slope which tends toward a definite limit for an infinite time of development. The curves in Fig. 99 have been slightly idealized for the sake of clarity in the presentation. In practice, the straight portion is seldom exactly straight and the point of intersection is less well defined. Moreover, this point may lie somewhat below the axis of abscissae, especially if the developer contains soluble bromides, as will be shown later. In the absence of soluble bromides, the curves are affected to a surprisingly slight extent by the type of developer used. To be sure, the rate at which the development proceeds does depend upon the type of developer, its temperature, and its concentration, but the general appearance of the family of characteristic curves remains the same.

The exposure range shown in the figure is that ordinarily encountered in practice. For greater values of exposure, the density attains a maximum and then diminishes. It is clear that direct positives could be made by working in the range where the density decreases with an increase in the exposure, but the exposures required are so excessive that such a procedure is usually impracticable. A positive image of this sort is occasionally produced in photographs showing the sun or a street light at night. These objects are so very bright that, when the exposure is correct for the rest of the picture area, they are overexposed to such an extent as to be reversed. The phenomenon was formerly called *solarization* but is now more frequently called *reversal*.[1]

---

[1] A so-called reversal process is used for making direct positives in amateur cinematography and in certain methods of color photography. It consists in developing the latent image in the ordinary manner, dissolving the silver in a "bleaching" solution, exposing the remaining silver bromide, and developing the material a second time. A dark-room lamp that is unsafe will sometimes produce weird reversal effects in much the same way by exposing the lower layers of the emulsion through the upper layers that have already been developed.

88. Sensitometry.—Hurter and Driffield undertook their investigation of the laws of blackening in the hope of finding a satisfactory method of specifying the sensitivity of photographic materials. For this reason, the technique of determining the characteristic curves is known as *sensitometry*,[1] although it furnishes much more information about the materials than

Fig. 100.—A typical sensitometric strip.

merely their sensitivity. In outline, the procedure in determining a set of characteristic curves is as follows: Several strips of the material to be tested are given a graded series of exposures, usually varying in a geometrical progression. These strips are developed for different lengths of time under known conditions of temperature and concentration. The general appearance

Fig. 101.—The non-intermittent sensitometer used at the Massachusetts Institute of Technology. The controls for keeping the light intensity constant are in the top of the lamp house at the left. A film holder, which accommodates three strips, is lying against the instrument. In use, it is inserted in the slot above the switch at the right. The openings in the sector wheels are visible under the raised cover.

of a developed strip is shown in Fig. 100. The density of each step is then measured optically and plotted as a function of the logarithm of the exposure.

[1] This subject is summarized exhaustively in a series of papers by L. A. Jones, *Jour. Soc. Motion Picture Eng.*, **17,** 491 and 695 (1931) and **18,** 54 and 324 (1932).

The instrument used for exposing the material is called a sensitometer. It consists of a box containing a light source and some means for producing the graded series of exposures. Hurter and Driffield used a rapidly rotating sector wheel just in front of the plate or film. This is open to the objection that the photographic material does not properly integrate intermittent exposures. In modern instruments, this difficulty is avoided by causing the sector wheel to make only a single revolution during the exposure. A photograph of such an instrument[1] in use in the photographic laboratory of the Massachusetts Institute of Technology is shown in Fig. 101. This instrument contains two concentric sector wheels, which provide for a much greater exposure range than a single wheel.

The density of each step is measured by means of an instrument called a densitometer. Such an instrument usually consists

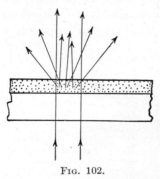

Fig. 102.

of a photometer for comparing two beams from the same source of light, one beam passing through the strip and the other passing around it. Although instruments for this purpose will be discussed in Sec. 107, Chap. XIII, it may be mentioned here that the optical density of a photographic deposit depends somewhat upon the method by which it is measured. This will be clear from Fig. 102, which shows a beam of light incident on a developed photographic image. Since the silver grains composing the image scatter some of the incident light, the density of the deposit depends upon whether the densitometer collects all the light passing through the material or only the portion that is unscattered. In the first case, the instrument is said to measure the diffuse density; and in the second case, the specular density.

It is impossible to find a simple mathematical equation that is adequate to express the relationship between density and exposure which is represented by a characteristic curve. We shall see presently, however, that the straight portion of the curve is the region of greatest interest, and this can be described very simply by an equation of the form

[1] *Jour. Optical Soc. Amer. and Rev. Sci. Instruments*, **10,** 149 (1925).

$$D = \gamma \left(\log \Sigma - \log i \right) = \gamma \log \frac{\Sigma}{i}, \qquad (183)$$

where γ and i are constants. The quantity γ is the tangent of the angle between the straight portion of the curve and the horizontal axis. The quantity i is the exposure corresponding to the intersection with the horizontal axis of the straight portion of the curve (extended). In Fig. 99, this exposure is 0.017 m.c.s. This exposure will here be called the *inertia*, although the quantity has sometimes been defined in a slightly different manner.

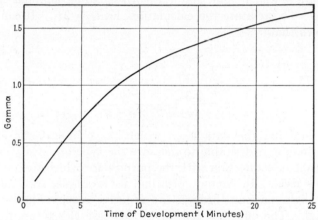

Fig. 103.—Curve showing the variation of gamma with development time for a typical portrait film. This curve is plotted from the curves in Fig. 99 and is represented analytically by Eq. (184).

Assuming that i is independent of γ—in other words, that the curves intersect the horizontal axis at a common point—Eq. (183) indicates that, for a given exposure, the density is proportional to γ. This result, combined with Eq. (181), means that γ is related to the development time according to the expression

$$\gamma = \gamma_\infty (1 - \epsilon^{-kt}), \qquad (184)$$

where γ_∞ is the value of γ that would result if the development were indefinitely prolonged. A plot of γ as a function of the time of development is shown in Fig. 103.

The value of γ indicates what the practical photographer calls the *degree of contrast* to which the material has been developed. If γ_∞ and k are known for a given material and a given set of development conditions, the time of development required to produce any desired degree of contrast can be found at once from Eq. (184), which becomes

$$t = \frac{2.3}{k} \log_{10} \frac{\gamma_\infty}{\gamma_\infty - \gamma} \tag{185}$$

when solved explicitly for t.   The values of γ_∞ and k can be found by developing two sensitometric strips for different lengths of time, plotting the characteristic curve for each strip, and determining the value of γ for each.   Suppose that the development times are t_1 and t_2 and that the corresponding gammas are γ_1 and γ_2.   To facilitate the calculation, let $t_2 = 2t_1$.   It can then be shown that

$$\gamma_\infty = \frac{\gamma_1{}^2}{2\gamma_1 - \gamma_2} \tag{186}$$

and

$$k = \frac{2.3}{t_1} \log_{10} \frac{\gamma_1}{\gamma_2 - \gamma_1}. \tag{187}$$

In obtaining the data from which the characteristic curves are plotted, it is desirable to measure the type of density that is significant in connection with the purpose for which the material is to be used.   In contact printing, for example, substantially all the light passing through the negative reaches the positive material.   The effective density in this case closely approaches the diffuse-density value.   In projection printing, on the other hand, almost none of the scattered light reaches the positive material.   The effective density approaches more closely, therefore, the specular-density value.[1]   The relationship between specular and diffuse density is usually associated with the work of Callier.   It is found that *Callier's coefficient*, which is the ratio of the specular density of a deposit to the diffuse density, is approximately constant over a considerable density range.   Its value is ordinarily about 1.3, which means that specular densities are 30 per cent higher than diffuse densities.[2]   Obviously the characteristic curve has the same general shape regardless of the type of density that is measured, but the value of gamma

[1] This assumes that the projection printer contains a condenser behind the negative instead of a diffusing glass.   See the discussion of transmission measurements, p. 283.

[2] For a recent investigation of this subject, see a paper by Tuttle, *Jour. Optical Soc. Amer. and Rev. Sci. Instruments*, **12,** 559 (1926).

determined from specular-density measurements is approximately 30 per cent higher than the corresponding value for diffuse-density measurements. This explains why a given negative appears to have more contrast when printed by projection than when printed by contact.

89. Speed.—The method of measuring the sensitivity of a photographic material that was in vogue before the time of Hurter and Driffield consisted in giving the material a graded series of exposures and then determining by inspection the exposure that produced a just perceptible deposit. This is a difficult determination to make because the conditions of observation have considerable influence upon the observer's judgment. Furthermore, the results at best are not very significant.

Although the characteristic curves of Hurter and Driffield give a complete specification of the relationship between density and exposure, it is obviously desirable to express the sensitivity by means of a single constant, if possible. This can be done if the characteristic curves have a common point of intersection on the axis of abscissae, as in Fig. 99. The inertia is then independent of the extent of development and might properly be chosen as a measure of the sensitivity of the material. Hurter and Driffield chose, however, to measure the *speed* in terms of the reciprocal of the inertia and adopted the arbitrary definition

$$S = \frac{34}{i},$$

where i is measured in meter-candle-seconds.

Whatever method of measuring speed is used, the results will obviously depend upon the spectral quality of the lamp used in the sensitometer, unless the spectral sensitivity of the photographic material is identical with that of the eye. As this is never true, the only fair method is to use a lamp of the same spectral quality as that to which the material will be exposed in the camera. Even this is generally impossible because the subject to be photographed usually contains areas with widely different spectral-reflection characteristics and the subject itself may be illuminated by light of almost any spectral quality. It is customary nowadays to use in the sensitometer a light source that very closely corresponds in spectral quality to mean noon sunlight.[1] Photographic materials are about six times faster,

[1] The method of producing radiation of this spectral quality was described in Sec. 73, Chap. IX.

on the average, when the speed is measured with this type of source instead of the pentane standard used by Hurter and Driffield. This is because the pentane lamp is relatively deficient in the blue end of the spectrum, where photographic materials are ordinarily most sensitive. As a matter of convenience, therefore, the speed has been redefined as

$$S = \frac{10}{i}. \tag{188}$$

This definition has been adopted by the International Congress of Photography[1] and is now used by all the leading photographic laboratories.

It may not be amiss to mention that much criticism has been directed toward Hurter and Driffield's method of specifying the speed of a photographic material. A part of this criticism arises from a failure to realize that a single constant is incapable of representing the speed of a material under a wide variety of conditions. It cannot be expected, for example, that the speed of a material determined with a source of sunlight quality will give more than a rough indication of its speed when exposed to an ordinary artificial source. Then, too, there are many applications of photography in which the useful criterion of speed is merely the exposure required to produce a given density. This is true, for example, in the so-called variable-width method of recording sound on motion-picture film. It is true also in many scientific applications of photography, such as spectroscopy, where a minimum density of about 0.6 above the fog density is required for the detection and measurement of weak absorption lines. The exposure required to produce this density obviously depends upon the extent of development, and in practice it is found that a development to approximately $0.8\gamma_\infty$ is the highest that is feasible. Since materials with a low H and D speed commonly have a high value of γ_∞, it frequently happens that a material that is slower according to Hurter and Driffield's definition may require less exposure when used for the special purposes just mentioned. For general purposes, however, the Hurter and Driffield definition of speed provides the best indication of sensitivity that can be provided by a single constant. Its principal disadvantage appears when the intersection of the

[1] See the series of reports on the photographic unit of intensity that have been published in *Jour. Optical Soc. Amer.* since 1925.

characteristic curves is not on the axis of abscissae, in which case the inertia depends upon the time of development.

90. Other Sensitometric Characteristics.—The *latitude* of a photographic material is defined as the ratio of the exposure at the upper end of the straight portion of the characteristic curve to the exposure at the lower end. Thus in Fig. 104, the exposure at the upper end is 1.7 m.c.s., and the exposure at the lower end is 0.04 m.c.s. The latitude of the material is therefore 42. Because of the difficulty of determining the exact point where the characteristic curve breaks away from a straight line, the precision of latitude determinations is very low. In this

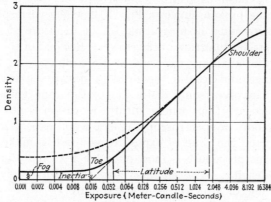

Fig. 104.—A typical characteristic curve with its various features indicated. The broken curve shows the effect of giving the film an auxiliary exposure equal to the exposure at the lower end of the straight portion (0.04 c.m.s.).

figure, for example, it is easy to see that a relatively small error in judgment would change the measured latitude enormously.

The latitude of an emulsion depends largely upon its thickness. For a material that is to be used in the camera, it is desirable to have a great latitude to allow for errors in exposure. On the other hand, for positive materials, such as cine positive film and lantern slides, a great latitude is unnecessary. In fact, it is even undesirable, because a thick emulsion requires more time and material to process.

Another property of an emulsion that can be read directly from the H and D curves is the *fog density*—that is, the density in the unexposed regions. The fog density for the curve in Fig. 104 is 0.14. The amount of fog increases with the time of development according to approximately the same laws as the

image [Eq. (181)]. Some investigators are in the habit of subtracting the fog density from the density of each step before
plotting the characteristic curve, but this procedure seems
scarcely justifiable when it is remembered that the fog density
is greatest where there is no image density and drops to zero where
all the silver bromide is exposed. The growth of fog density is
restrained by the addition of soluble bromides to the developer,
but these have other effects that will be discussed in another
section.

The effective speed of a photographic material can be somewhat
increased at the expense of an increased fog density by giving it
an auxiliary flash exposure. The result of this procedure is
shown by the broken curve in Fig. 104, which corresponds to a
flash exposure equal in magnitude to the exposure at the lower
end of the straight portion of the curve. Because of the logarithmic scale, the auxiliary exposure is more effective in the lower
density range and results therefore in destroying the straight
line. This involves some distortion of the tone values, as we
shall see presently; but where faithful rendition is not required,
as in astronomy or spectroscopy, it is a useful expedient because
it does shorten the time of exposure required to make a visible
record. This procedure is most effective with materials having
a low fog density. The auxiliary exposure can be given either
before, during, or after the regular exposure.

Until recently, photographic establishments have been reluctant to publish data concerning the materials they manufacture.
There was adequate reason for this policy. The lack of scientific
knowledge on the part of most photographers would have led
to the misinterpretation of such information, and the lack of
standardization in sensitometric procedure would have led to
unfair comparisons. A step in the right direction was recently
taken by Mees,[1] who has published invaluable data concerning
the characteristics of the materials that are most widely used for
scientific purposes. The ideal procedure from the standpoint of
the technically trained photographer would be to have this
information supplied with each package of material. Until this
procedure is adopted, the only practical course seems to be to
give the average characteristics for the materials supplied by

[1] *Jour. Optical Soc. Amer.*, **21**, 753 (1931). The authors understand
that this article is to be reprinted by the Eastman Kodak Company as a
pamphlet and revised at intervals to keep the information up to date.

one leading manufacturer, as is done in Table XIV. It must be emphasized, however, that the materials are being constantly improved and that their characteristics therefore change from time to time. The characteristics given in this table are for development at 68°F. in a developer composed of equal parts of the following solutions:

A

Sodium sulphite..............................	70 grams
Sodium bisulphite............................	17 grams
Pyrogallic acid...............................	20 grams
Water, to make...............................	1 liter

B

Sodium carbonate............................	75 grams
Potassium bromide...........................	1 gram
Water, to make..............................	1 liter

The first column in Table XIV gives the inertia in meter-candle-seconds for a light source approximating mean noon sunlight in its spectral quality. In the determination of these values, the level of illumination was held constant at 0.2 meter-candle and the time of exposure was varied. The second column gives the corresponding H and D speeds, computed according to Eq. (188). The next three columns give respectively the values of k, γ_∞, and the time in minutes required to produce a gamma of unity. These values were determined by developing a large number of strips for various lengths of time and plotting the time-gamma curve. The time for a gamma of unity was then read directly from the curve, and γ_∞ was estimated by extrapolation. The value of k was found by measuring $d\gamma/dt$ at the point where $\gamma = 1$ and substituting in the equation

$$\frac{d\gamma}{dt} = k(\gamma_\infty - \gamma).$$

This procedure gives results that are more consistent than those obtained by using only two strips and computing by means of Eqs. (186) and (187).

The values of fog density are not included because when the materials receive the development that is ordinarily used in practice, the fog density of even high-speed materials seldom exceeds 0.12. The fog density of very slow materials, such as lantern-slide plates, is often as low as 0.02. These values represent the density due to the photographic deposit alone. The

TABLE XIV.—SENSITOMETRIC CHARACTERISTICS OF PHOTOGRAPHIC MATERIALS MANUFACTURED BY THE EASTMAN KODAK COMPANY (1932)

Material	i	$10/i$	k	γ_∞	Time for $\gamma = 1$, minutes
Motion-picture film:					
Supersensitive panchromatic negative.......	0.011	900	0.25	1.60	4.0
Type 2 panchromatic negative..............	0.017	600	0.25	1.60	4.0
Ordinary negative........................	0.020	500	0.22	1.80	3.7
Duplicating positive......................	0.140	70	0.37	2.40	1.5
Ordinary positive........................	0.250	40	0.37	2.40	1.5
Cine Kodak (reversal) film:					
Supersensitive panchromatic..............	0.017	600	0.27	2.10	2.5
Panchromatic...........................	0.025	400	0.27	2.10	2.5
Aero film:					
Supersensitive panchromatic..............	0.011	900	0.25	1.60	4.0
Type 2 panchromatic.....................	0.017	600	0.25	1.60	4.0
Ortho..................................	0.020	500	0.22	1.80	3.7
Roll film and film pack:					
Verichrome.............................	0.017	600	0.22	1.70	4.0
Non-curling............................	0.025	400	0.22	1.60	4.5
Cut film:					
Supersensitive panchromatic..............	0.011	900	0.25	1.70	3.6
Portrait panchromatic....................	0.014	700	0.25	1.50	4.5
Commercial panchromatic.................	0.017	600	0.22	1.80	3.7
Portrait................................	0.022	450	0.25	1.40	5.0
Commercial Ortho......................	0.029	350	0.25	2.20	2.4
Commercial............................	0.050	200	0.28	2.40	2.0
Panchromatic process....................	0.130	75	0.37	3.00	1.2
Process................................	0.200	50	0.37	3.00	1.2
Plates:.					
Eastman Hyper Press....................	0.011	900	0.22	1.40	5.5
Wratten hypersensitive panchromatic.......	0.011	900	0.25	2.00	3.0
Eastman Speedway......................	0.014	700	0.22	1.50	5.0
Eastman 40............................	0.017	600	0.25	1.60	4.0
Wratten panchromatic...................	0.020	500	0.30	2.60	1.7
Eastman 36............................	0.022	450	0.25	1.70	3.6
Eastman D. C. Ortho....................	0.022	450	0.22	1.80	3.7
Eastman S. C. Ortho.....................	0.025	400	0.22	1.70	4.0
Eastman Universal......................	0.025	400	0.22	1.70	4.0
Eastman Polychrome....................	0.029	350	0.27	2.00	2.5
Eastman Commercial....................	0.033	300	0.27	2.00	2.5
Eastman 33............................	0.033	300	0.28	2.20	2.1
Wratten process panchromatic.............	0.050	200	0.35	3.00	1.2
Wratten "M"...........................	0.050	200	0.35	3.00	1.2
Eastman process.......................	0.200	50	0.37	3.00	1.2
Eastman lantern-slide, regular.............	0.500	20	0.40	3.20	1.0

density of the support, due to losses by reflection, is ordinarily in the neighborhood of 0.03. No values of latitude are given in the table, partly because of the difficulty of assigning a definite value and partly because the latitude depends to a considerable extent on the degree of development. In general, the latitude is greater for high-speed materials than for slow materials like process film and lantern-slide plates.

91. The Rendition of Tone Values.—In the ordinary use of photographic materials, the camera is directed toward a subject that can be described in terms of the brightness of each elementary area in the field of view. To be sure, these elementary areas are usually of different colors also, but we shall assume that the reproduction is to be in monochrome so that only the brightness can be reproduced. Let B represent the brightness of the subject, which varies, of course, from point to point of the subject area. For the sake of concreteness, let it be assumed that a lantern slide is then made from the negative and projected on a screen. Let b represent the brightness of the screen, which likewise varies from point to point. Now if b is equal to B at all points, the reproduction is perfect—that is, the brightnesses, or tones, of the subject are faithfully reproduced. But this condition is difficult to realize, owing to limitations in projection equipment. Fortunately it is unnecessary, provided the adaptation level of the eye is on the straight portion of the sensation curve of Fig. 93 when both the subject and its reproduction are viewed. In other words, if b is proportional to B, the reproduction will ordinarily look exactly like the original.

The exposure Σ_n of the negative is proportional to B in a properly designed camera; and the relationship between the density of the negative and the exposure is given by Eq. (183) for the straight portion of the characteristic curve. This equation can be rewritten in terms of the transparency as

$$\log \frac{1}{T_n} = \gamma_n \log \frac{\Sigma_n}{i_n} \tag{189}$$

or

$$T_n = \left(\frac{i_n}{\Sigma_n}\right)^{\gamma_n}. \tag{190}$$

If the time of development of the negative is so adjusted that $\gamma_n = 1$, the transparency of the negative will be inversely proportional to its exposure. In the printing process, of course, the exposure Σ_p of the positive is proportional to the transparency T_n of the negative, and the transparency of the positive is

$$T_p = \left(\frac{i_p}{\Sigma_p}\right)^{\gamma_p}. \tag{191}$$

Hence if the positive is also developed to a gamma of unity, its transparency is inversely proportional to the exposure it receives and is therefore directly proportional to the brightness of the subject. But the brightness of the projection screen is proportional to the transparency of the positive, and hence the conditions for the faithful reproduction of tone values are satisfied. If the algebra of this argument is carried out in a more formal manner, it will be seen that the γ-values of the negative and positive need not be unity individually, but that only their product need be unity. In other words, developing the negative to a gamma of 0.5 and the positive to a gamma of 2.0, which may be more satisfactory in some cases, would produce exactly the same result. It must be emphasized that this entire argument holds only when all the densities involved lie on the straight portions of the characteristic curves.

It is not always realized that the quantity γ is an exponent and therefore has a profound effect on the rendition of tone values. By way of example, consider an average subject, which usually has a brightness range of approximately 32—that is, the brightness of the high light is 32 times that of the deepest shadow.[1] Let the brightness of the high light be represented by B_1 and that of the deepest shadow by B_2. The *brightness range* or *contrast of the subject* is

$$\frac{B_1}{B_2} = 32.$$

It is easily seen from Eq. (190) that the corresponding transparency ratio in the negative is

$$\frac{T_2}{T_1} = \left(\frac{B_1}{B_2}\right)^{\gamma_n}. \tag{192}$$

Similarly, the transparency range of the positive is

$$\frac{T_1}{T_2} = \left(\frac{B_1}{B_2}\right)^{\gamma_n \cdot \gamma_p}. \tag{193}$$

[1] In the average landscape, the high light is usually a white cloud or a bit of blue sky, and the deepest shadow may be a tree trunk illuminated by full sky light but no sunlight. Subjects having a contrast greater than 100 rarely make satisfactory pictures. Similarly, subjects having a contrast less than 8 are ordinarily too flat to be interesting. The first case usually occurs in interiors or in deep woods, while the second occurs in distant views without foreground.

Thus it is clear that only a slight variation in the gamma-product will cause a relatively great change in the character of the result. If the gamma-product is greater than unity, the contrast of the subject is said to be enhanced; if less than unity, it is said to be reduced.

In some of the scientific applications of photography, the enhancement of contrast is of great practical importance. In microscopy, for example, the slide under examination may be

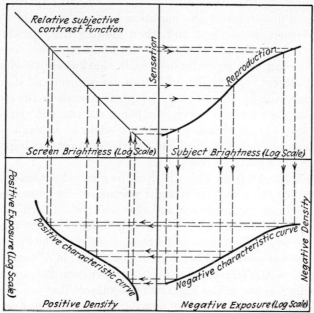

Fig. 105.—Graphical method of determining the faithfulness of the tone rendition.

so thin that certain details are invisible to the eye because the contrast is less than the contrast sensitivity of the eye (about 1.8 per cent, as shown by Fig. 91). It will be seen from Table XIV that values of gamma as great as 2.0 are attained quite easily and that values approaching 3.0 can be attained with difficulty. Taking the latter value for both the negative and the positive, the gamma-product is 9. Thus a brightness difference as small as 0.2 per cent will be increased to 1.8 per cent in the positive and will therefore become perceptible to the eye.

So far we have assumed that the densities lie entirely on the straight portion of both negative and positive curves. This assumption does not conform to practice, where it is frequently necessary to use the toe of the negative curve and both the toe and the shoulder of the positive curve.   Since any equation that represents a characteristic curve satisfactorily is necessarily complicated, the determination of the rendition of tone values in the general case is best accomplished graphically.   An ingenious method due to L. A. Jones[1] is represented in Fig. 105. In brief, it consists in using the fourth quadrant for the negative characteristic curve, the third quadrant for the positive curve, the second quadrant for the variation in the response of the eye when viewing the subject and when viewing the reproduction, and the first quadrant to compare the resulting visual sensation when viewing the reproduction with that when viewing the original subject.   As explained before, the subject and its reproduction are usually viewed under adaptation levels on the straight portion of the sensation curve, and hence the curve in the second quadrant is a straight line through the origin at an angle of 45°. In other words, only the third and fourth quadrants are important in the vast majority of cases.

It is easily seen from Fig. 105 that the greatest contrast occurs for densities lying on the straight portion of the characteristic curves of both the negative and the positive.   It will be seen also that the curvatures of the toe and shoulder of the negative are in the wrong directions to be compensated by the curvatures of the positive curve.   Therefore, if the rendition of tone values is correct for the straight portions of the curves, the contrast is necessarily too low in the regions of the subject that are recorded on the curved portions of either curve.   The reduction in contrast gives the appearance of loss of detail.   This will be clear from Fig. 106, which shows the portion of the negative characteristic that is used under a variety of exposure and development conditions.   Underexposing the negative results in loss of detail in the shadows, whereas overexposure results in loss of detail in the high lights.   It will be obvious also that overdevelopment is not a cure for underexposure, nor is underdevelopment a cure for overexposure.   If the subject has a short brightness range, overdevelopment of the negative in the case of underexposure may occasionally seem to improve the result.   However, if the tones of the subject lie on both the toe and the straight portion

[1] *Jour. Optical Soc. Amer.*, **5**, 232 (1921); *Jour. Franklin Inst.*, **190**, 39 (1920).

of the curve, the enhancement of contrast on the straight portion often makes the lack of contrast in the shadows even more evident than it would be with normal development. Overexposure is so infrequent that it might almost be passed without comment. If a good negative material is properly developed, satisfactory prints can often be made when the negative is so dense that no image whatever can be seen. However, if the photographer yields to the natural temptation to snatch the film from the developer before the proper gamma has been attained, the result will be unsatisfactory, not because the negative was overexposed but because it was underdeveloped.

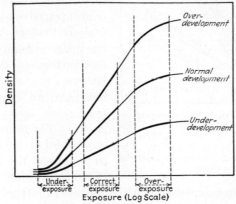

Fig. 106.—Characteristic curves showing the effects of improper exposure and development.

92. The Technique of Development.—The developer usually contains four components: a reducing agent, an accelerator, a preservative, and a restrainer. The reducing agent is the active ingredient and nowadays is frequently some coal-tar derivative. The accelerator is an alkali, usually sodium carbonate, or, occasionally, sodium hydroxide. The preservative, whose function is chiefly to protect the reducing agent from atmospheric oxidation, is usually sodium sulphite or sodium bisulphite. When the developer must be stored for some time, it is common practice to prepare it in two solutions, the reducing agent and the preservative in one and the accelerator in the other. Frequently both sodium sulphite and sodium bisulphite are used in proportions that will make the solution neutral in reaction, since many reducing agents keep best in neutral solution. The restrainer is usually potassium bromide. Its action will be discussed presently.

The choice of developer formula and concentration is very largely a matter of convenience. The important feature is that the time of development required to attain the desired gamma should be long enough to permit the developer to diffuse uniformly into the emulsion but short enough to keep the time of processing within reasonable limits. The same gamma can be obtained by a short development in a concentrated solution or by a long development in a dilute solution. With a concentrated developer and a short time of development, the image is confined more to the surface of the emulsion because the developer does not have an opportunity to penetrate into the lower layers. The dilute developer, on the other hand, has time to penetrate the lower layers of the emulsion but is too weak to develop completely. Although this difference in behavior can easily be seen in photomicrographs of transverse sections of a developed emulsion, it has an extraordinarily small effect on the fundamental relationship between density and exposure.

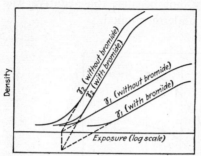

Fig. 107.—Characteristic curves showing the depression of the intersection point produced by the addition of soluble bromides to the developer. The apparent decrease in speed produced by bromide is clearly evident.

The effect of soluble bromides on development has been known for a long time, and a careful quantitative study has been made by Nietz.[1] He found that the effect is to depress the intersection point of the characteristic curves in a manner illustrated in Fig. 107. Although the exposure corresponding to the point of intersection is the same as with an unbromided developer, the effective speed of the material is less, especially for short times of development. For every developer, there is a critical amount of bromide that can be added without producing an appreciable depression of the intersection point, and this seems to restrain the development of fog without having any marked effect on the development of the image.

[1] "The Theory of Development," D. Van Nostrand Company.

It will be recalled that free bromide is liberated during development by the reduction of the silver bromide to silver. The bromide concentration is therefore higher in an old developing solution than in a fresh one. In fact, the useful life of a developer is often limited more by the gradual accumulation of bromide than by the exhaustion of the reducing agent. Of more serious consequence than this gradual accumulation of bromide are the local variations in bromide concentration over the area of the plate caused by the density variations in the image, an effect discovered by Eberhard.[1] If the image is small, the free bromide diffuses away, so the density of such an image is higher than that of a large area that received the same exposure. This *Eberhard effect* is therefore especially annoying when one is determining the intensity of stars or spectral lines by measuring the density of their images. It tends to disappear when the development is carried to completion.

The depression of the point of intersection has been used by Nietz to measure a quantity known as the *reduction potential* of a developer. This quantity is supposed to indicate the power of a developer, much as the power of one metal to replace another is indicated by its position in the potential series of the metals. A reducing agent with too high a reduction potential reduces the silver halide whether it has been exposed or not, while one with too low a reduction potential fails to reduce even the exposed silver halide. The useful photographic developers lie between these two extremes. Using as a criterion the bromide concentration required to produce a just noticeable depression of the intersection point, Nietz found that the reduction potentials of some of the more common reducing agents[2] are in the following order:

> Amidol.
> Metol (elon).
> Pyrogallic acid.
> Adurol.
> Glycin.
> Hydroquinone.

In general, developing agents having a high reduction potential like amidol are less affected by temperature, give a slightly

---

[1] *Physik. Zeits.*, **13**, 288 (1912).

[2] For descriptions and formulae of these developers and others, see Neblette's "Photography, Its Principles and Practice," Chap. XII.

higher γ_∞-value, and require a smaller concentration of the accelerator. The speed of an emulsion seems to increase slightly with the reduction potential of the developer, but other factors may easily mask this effect.

In practice, the most noticeable difference between developing agents is in the time of the first appearance of the image. With metol, for example, the image flashes up quickly, whereas with hydroquinone it is slow in appearing. This feature has given metol the reputation of being a "soft-working" developer and hydroquinone of giving excessive contrast. The reputations of these developers are due primarily to the old method of developing by inspection, which caused the photographer involuntarily to remove the material too soon from a metol developer and leave it too long in hydroquinone. Although hydroquinone is an exception to the general rule that developers having a low reduction potential give a low value of γ_∞, this circumstance alone is hardly sufficient to account for its reputation as a contrasty developer.

Pyrogallic acid has the interesting property of staining the image a yellow color, which is due to the oxidation products formed during the progress of development. These substances may be formed by atmospheric oxidation, in which case the yellow stain is uniform; or by the reduction of silver halide, in which case the amount of stain is proportional to the amount of reduced silver. As positive materials are sensitive chiefly in the blue region of the spectrum, which is absorbed by the yellow stain, the result in the second instance is a proportional increase in the effective density and therefore in gamma. If γ_v represents the value measured visually and γ_p the effective value photographically, the *color coefficient* is γ_p/γ_v. The value of this coefficient varies from about 1.3 in a pyro developer containing the average amount of restrainer to nearly 3 in a solution containing no restrainer. This differential staining accounts for the "better printing quality" that photographers have always attributed to pyro developers. Use has been made of this effect in aerial photography to secure a greater effective contrast than can be attained by ordinary development.

The extent to which the development of the negative should be allowed to proceed depends upon the positive process that is to follow. This statement requires some explanation because the theory of tone reproduction has shown that the brightness ratios of the subject are correctly reproduced if the product of the negative and positive gammas is unity, which would indicate that practically any negative gamma could be compensated in the positive process. However, the best results are obtained when any material is developed to approximately two-thirds of its γ_∞-value. If the gamma is less than this, the development may be non-uniform; if it is greater, an excessive amount of fog may be produced. In practice, a gamma-product somewhat higher than unity is found desirable. For example, a gamma-product in the neighborhood of 1.3 seems to give the best result for lantern slides and motion pictures. This is accounted for in several ways. In the first place, a photograph in monochrome can reproduce only the brightness contrast of the subject, which, in the absence of color contrast, seems too low. Moreover, the contrast is actually reduced by flare in the camera and projection lenses and by the necessity of using a portion of the toe of both characteristic curves. The present practice in the production of motion pictures is to develop the negative to a gamma of about 0.8 and the positive to a gamma of about 1.6. This makes the gamma-product about 1.3 and, furthermore, develops each material to about two-thirds of its γ_∞-value.

The value of the development constant k is an index to the proper time of development; for, if the material is developed for a time $1/k$, substitution in Eq. (184) shows that

$$\gamma = \gamma_\infty \left(1 - \epsilon^{-1}\right)$$
$$= 0.631 \, \gamma_\infty. \tag{194}$$

This is very nearly $\frac{2}{3} \gamma_\infty$. Hence, if the value of k for some concentration and temperature of the developer is 0.10, the most satisfactory development time is 10 min. If the gamma produced in this way is too high, a material with a lower γ_∞-value should preferably be chosen.

If a negative has been inadvertently underdeveloped, its gamma can be increased by a procedure known as *intensification*. Many processes are to be found in the photographic handbooks but the mercury process is typical. This consists in bathing the film in a solution of mercuric chloride, which transforms the silver of the image into silver chloride. At the same time, mercuric chloride is precipitated as mercurous chloride. After the excess mercuric chloride has been washed out, the film can be redeveloped, whereupon the silver chloride is reduced to metallic silver again and the mercurous chloride to mercury. Since the amount of mercury present is proportional to the original amount of silver, the result is a proportional increase in density and, therefore, in gamma. Contrary to the claims that are often made, intensification is not a remedy for under-exposure unless the subject has such a short brightness range that more development would also have brought about an improvement in the reproduction.

The converse of intensification is reduction. It is accomplished by dissolving part of the silver in the image, but the various solvents behave somewhat differently. Potassium ferricyanide has a somewhat greater effect on the low densities and tends, therefore, to increase the contrast, whereas ammonium persulphate behaves in just the opposite manner. Potassium permanganate leaves the gamma very nearly unaltered. In any case, the variation in gamma is relatively slight, so reduction is used chiefly for negatives which are so dense that the printing time would be inconveniently long otherwise. It is not a remedy for overexposure in the proper sense of the term.[1]

It is unfortunate that sensitometric methods are not more generally employed in the control of the processing of photographic materials. Photographers have been slow to take advantage of new tools, and development is still a hit-or-miss affair that is not at all in keeping with the spirit of modern manufacturing methods. The indications are that this condition cannot continue indefinitely, especially in the motion-picture industry. In silent pictures, a variation of 15 per cent in the gamma-product, although noticeable when two films are compared side by side, is unrecognizable otherwise. But in sound pictures, a variation of 15 per cent in the gamma-product often accounts for a difference between good quality in the sound reproduction and very mediocre quality. Already sensitometric methods are beginning to be used to a limited extent by some of the motion-picture laboratories, and it seems reasonable to suppose that such methods will eventually be used by all laboratories having any considerable quantity of material to process. In scientific work involving quantitative determinations, as in

---

[1] Crabtree and Muehler have made an extensive investigation into the sensitometry of intensification and reduction. See *Jour. Soc. Motion Picture Eng.*, **17**, 1001 (1931).

astronomy or spectroscopy, the determination of the density-exposure relationship is imperative.

The photographer whose work does not justify the use of sensitometric methods has several ways at his disposal of keeping the development within bounds. One method in common use is to calculate the time of development from the time of first appearance of the image, a procedure suggested by Alfred Watkins. This method is based on the circumstance that the time of first appearance of the image, although little affected by exposure, varies with the temperature and concentration of the developer in the same way as the time required for development to a given contrast. The procedure is to multiply the time of first appearance by a constant, known as the *Watkins factor*, which is determined once and for all for a given material and developer. This factor usually lies between 4 and 30.[1] The method is quite successful when the developer contains a single reducing agent. If it contains two reducing agents having different temperature coefficients, like metol and hydroquinone, the factor varies considerably with the temperature.

93. Spectral Sensitivity.—It is almost axiomatic that only the light that is absorbed by a photographic emulsion can be effective. Since the color of an ordinary emulsion is pale yellow, indicating absorption in the blue and violet, it is to be expected that the spectral sensitivity would be confined to these regions. Such is the case, and these emulsions are therefore "color-blind." In 1873, Vogel discovered that plates bathed in a dilute solution of certain dyes have a sensitivity extending into the green and yellow regions of the spectrum. His dyes were not stable, however, and it was nine years before a practical color-sensitive material was prepared. The dye that made this possible was eosin, but many other dyes were quickly discovered to have a similar effect. The reproduction of colored objects with color-sensitive materials prepared with these dyes was so much superior that such materials were called either *orthochromatic*, to indicate that the color rendition based on visual standards is correct, or *isochromatic*, to indicate that the materials are equally sensitive in all regions of the spectrum. Both terms are misnomers, however, because the materials to which these names were applied are predominantly sensitive in the blue and have almost no sensitivity at all in the red. This deficiency was overcome about

[1] See table in Chap. XIII, Neblette's "Photography."

1905 with the discovery of new dyes, principally pinacyanol. Materials sensitized with these dyes came to be known as *panchromatic*, being sensitive to all colors.[1]   These materials will yield truly orthochromatic results with appropriate filters, and the only reason they have not supplanted all other materials is the difficulty of handling them in the dark room.   No safelight can be really safe with panchromatic materials, and the best procedure is to develop for the proper length of time in total darkness.   If any light is needed in the dark room, the special

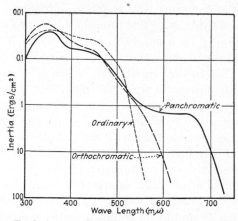

FIG. 108.—Typical spectral-sensitivity curves of negative materials.

green safelight that transmits only the rays to which the eye is most sensitive should be selected because it is the least harmful.

The spectral sensitivity of photographic materials has been measured by many investigators, but the best direct results are those of Jones and Sandvik.[2]   These investigators used a sensitometer in combination with a monochromator to furnish substantially monochromatic light.   A typical set of their results is shown graphically in Fig. 108.

It is clear that the type of color rendition that can be achieved with panchromatic materials depends only upon the possibility

[1] Panchromatic materials have been enormously improved within the last few years.   Several types are now produced and new types are being constantly developed.   For an excellent description of the types of color-sensitive materials that are commercially available, see a recent paper by Mees, *Jour. Optical Soc. Amer.*, **21**, 753 (1931).

[2] *Jour. Optical Soc. Amer. and Rev. Sci. Instruments*, **12**, 401 (1926).

of preparing suitable filters. Orthochromatic results are most frequently desired, which means that the filter should be green to absorb the surplus energy in the violet and red ends of the spectrum. The excess red sensitivity is of little importance, however, and the filters that are advertised for the purpose are usually yellow. The absorption of the Wratten K series, for example, begins at about 540 mμ. In the case of the K-3 filter, which is the deepest, the absorption is almost complete at 460 mμ. With a good panchromatic material, the increase in exposure required when using this filter is approximately four times (for white light). The filter factor varies, of course, with the quality of the exposing light and the type of the emulsion.

Occasionally a truly orthochromatic color rendition is quite misleading. A red apple amongst green leaves, for instance, may be conspicuous to the eye because of the color contrast, but if the brightness of both the apple and the leaves is the same, a strictly orthochromatic reproduction would fail to show how conspicuous the apple appears to the eye. The remedy is to use a filter that will enhance the brightness contrast in the photograph at the expense of faithful reproduction. This sort of procedure is particularly useful in photomicrography.

Since the spectral sensitivity of photographic materials is so different from that of the eye, the visual estimate of the intensity of a light source gives a very inadequate measurement of its photographic effectiveness. The relative visual and photographic effectiveness of illuminants has been studied by the staff of the Kodak Research Laboratories.[1] Their results are summarized in Table XV, the relative effectiveness of sunlight being arbitrarily taken as 100. Thus, a given illumination produced by a mercury arc has more than three times as great an effect on an ordinary plate as the same amount of illumination produced by sunlight.

The sensitivity of photographic materials extends far into the ultraviolet. The limit is set by the absorption of the gelatin, which begins at about 280 mμ and is practically complete below 200 mμ unless the gelatin is very thin. Schumann, who was the first to study the spectrum of the extreme ultraviolet, devised a method of preparing emulsions containing only a trace of gelatin to bind the silver bromide grains together.[2] In 1921, Duclaux

[1] *Trans. Illum. Eng. Soc.*, **10**, 963 (1915).

[2] Schumann plates are now available commercially from Adam Hilger, Ltd., of London.

TABLE XV.—RELATIVE PHOTOGRAPHIC EFFECTIVENESS OF VARIOUS ILLUMINANTS

Source	Ordinary	Ortho-chromatic	Pan-chromatic
Sun	100	100	100
Sky	180	160	130
Acetylene	30	40	50
Mercury arc, ordinary	320	350	270
Mercury arc, quartz	600	500	370
Carbon arc, ordinary	130	110	100
Carbon arc, white flame	260	230	220
Carbon arc, high intensity	100	100	100
Tungsten lamp, vacuum	35	40	50
Tungsten lamp, gas filled	60	65	70
Tungsten lamp, blue bulb	100	90	110

and Jeantet described a method of sensitizing plates by bathing them in fluorescent mineral oils. After exposure, the oil is washed off with acetone and the plate is then developed in the ordinary way. The characteristics of oiled plates have been studied by Harrison[1] in the region from 200 to 380 Ångström units. He found that the form of the relationship between density and exposure is the same as when visible light is used, and that the oiled plates are sufficiently reliable to be used for photographic photometry. Under certain conditions, the increase in sensitivity produced by oiling a plate may be as much as four-hundred fold.

Burroughs of the Kodak Research Laboratories has investigated the fluorescence of a large number of organic substances in the ultraviolet and has found that the carboxylic ester of dihydrocollidine can be used to advantage in the preparation of plates for use in this region. This substance is insoluble in water but can be dissolved in certain organic solvents. When a plate is bathed in a solution of this material and allowed to dry, its surface becomes covered with crystals which fluoresce strongly under ultraviolet light and which are so small that good photographic images are obtained.

Photographs of ordinary objects have been taken by ultraviolet light using quartz lenses and a filter to screen off the visible light.

[1] *Jour. Optical Soc. Amer. and Rev. Sci. Instruments*, **11**, 113 (1925).

R. W. Wood has experimented in this direction to a considerable extent. His filter consisted of a quartz plate coated with a thin layer of silver, which has a transmission band in the neighborhood of 310 mμ. Ultraviolet photographs of landscapes are striking because the sun casts practically no shadow. In other words, the ultraviolet is so scattered by the atmosphere that, to an observer sensitive only to the ultraviolet, every day would appear to be overcast.

Photographic materials are, of course, sensitive to X-rays; and Wilsey and Pritchard[1] have found that their behavior to these rays is little different from their behavior to white light. This is somewhat surprising because the X-rays penetrate the emulsion and affect all layers uniformly instead of acting more strongly on the upper layers. X-ray films are commonly made with an emulsion on both sides of the support to utilize as much of the radiation as possible; and fluorescent screens are frequently placed against the film to intensify the effect by transforming the X-rays into radiations of longer wave length, which are absorbed by the emulsion. X-ray films are usually developed for maximum contrast because, in the absence of any requirements with respect to the reproduction of tone values, it is desirable to show as much faint detail as possible.

Although photographic materials are not ordinarily sensitive in the infrared, the latent image is affected by exposure to infrared light. Herschel discovered, as long ago as 1840, that photographic materials which had been exposed to blue light gave a positive instead of a negative when they were exposed to infrared light before development. In other words, the latent image is destroyed by infrared light. This *Herschel effect* has a very important significance in connection with theories of the latent image but has not been found very useful as a technique for infrared photography. However, within recent years, dyes have been found that will extend the sensitivity into the infrared region. With the introduction of dicyanine, which has its maximum sensitizing action at 710 mμ, spectrographic investigations out to 1000 mμ became possible. Dicyanine is unsatisfactory, however, because it does not keep well nor do plates sensitized with it. This means that the plates must be bathed just before being used, and the results at best are not too certain. Kryptocyanine, discovered in 1919, has a very strong sensitizing

[1] *Jour. Optical Soc. Amer. and Rev. Sci. Instruments*, **12**, 661 (1926).

band between 700 mμ and 800 mμ. This dye is comparatively stable and so are plates sensitized with it. Its action is so powerful that only 1 part of dye in 500,000 is required. The spectral sensitivity of plates bathed in it drops off so sharply that, beyond 900 mμ, dicyanine is again more sensitive. In 1925 a modification of kryptocyanine, known as neocyanine, was found which sensitizes far into the infrared when the plates are "hypersensitized" by bathing in ammonia. With such plates, the spectrum can be photographed easily as far as 900 mμ and, by using long exposures, as far as 1200 mμ.

Photographs of landscapes taken by infrared light have the general appearance of night scenes because the sky appears dark and the high reflectance of chlorophyl gives foliage the appearance of intense local lighting. Such photographs were made some years ago by Wood and have been used to some extent by the motion-picture industry. Motion pictures of night scenes that would otherwise be very expensive to obtain can be produced in this way as cheaply as ordinary scenes. Photographs of extremely distant objects are made possible by infrared light because of its greater penetration through atmospheric haze. Views showing mountains several hundred miles away are not uncommon to-day. Figure 77 in Chap. IX indicates how the scattering by the atmosphere varies with wave length and gives ample reason for the comparatively great penetrating power of infrared light. It is not impossible for an aerial photographer to record details that are totally invisible to him beyond the blanket of haze.

94. Miscellaneous Characteristics.—The H and D curves of a photographic material show its gross behavior when acted upon by light, but they do not indicate the perfection of the photographic image. The ability of a photographic material to record fine detail—its *resolving power*—is limited by its granular structure. If the fan test object shown at A in Fig. 109 is photographed in a camera that reduces the image to microscopic dimensions, the photograph will appear as shown at B. This will occur even if the lens is sufficiently well corrected to produce a sharp image. By a test like this, the resolving power of photographic materials can be evaluated in terms of the maximum number of lines per millimeter that can just be distinguished individually. The resolving power of gelatino-bromide emulsions under the most favorable conditions of exposure and development varies from approximately 25 lines per millimeter for a coarse-grained, high-speed plate to 60 or more for a process or lantern-slide plate. Some of the slower materials, like wet collodion and albumin, give even higher resolution. The criterion by which these values are determined is so indefinite that the values alone are of less significance than the relative values for the different materials. Moreover, the character of the object affects the photographic resolving power enormously, just as it does the visual resolving power. The ability of the material to resolve double stars, for example, could be inferred only in a rough sort of way from the results of tests with

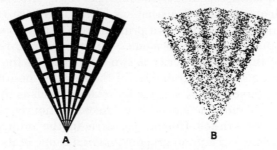

A **B**

Fig. 109.—Test of photographic resolving power. *A*, photograph of a fan test object; *B*, photomicrograph of a greatly reduced image of the test object. At the outer end of the fan, each sector had a width of 0.04 mm on the plate from which the photomicrograph was made.

the fan test object. Many types of test objects have been used by Sandvik, and the reader is referred to his papers for data more nearly applicable to special problems. It should be remembered, however, that lack of photographic resolving power is rarely the cause of poor definition in ordinary photographs. Aberrations in the lens, inaccurate focusing, and unsteadiness of the camera are more often responsible.

The granular structure of an emulsion also limits the extent to which a photograph can be enlarged. As everyone who has made enlargements from small negatives knows, areas of the image that should be of uniform density take on a mottled appearance when the degree of enlargement exceeds four or five times. The effect is much more pronounced than the size of the grains would indicate and is attributable to the tendency of the grains to clump together, probably in some sort of statistical distribution. This *graininess* cannot be measured objectively, but it has been measured subjectively by Hardy and Jones.[1]   The procedure consisted, in effect, of viewing the negative under variable magnification and noting the point where the inhomogeneities were first apparent.   To eliminate the personal equation of the observer, a crossed half-tone screen having a known number of lines per inch was used for calibration.   As might be expected, the graininess of an emulsion is low at very high and very low densities.   For cine negative film, the graininess is a maximum where the density is approximately 0.7, in which case about 80 per cent of the total area is occupied by the grains. For this density, the graininess is equivalent to a crossed half-tone screen of approximately 200 lines per inch.   At 0.2 and 1.4, the graininess is only about half as great.   Positive emulsions are less grainy, but a positive printed from a negative is more grainy than either material alone.   In other words, the superposition of the grain patterns of two materials has the effect of increasing the apparent graininess of the resulting positive.   For this reason, direct positives made by reversal, such as the 16-mm cine films, will stand a much higher magnification in projection than positives printed from a negative in the ordinary way.

The graininess of a photographic material is one of its intrinsic properties, at least to a first approximation, and is only slightly affected by the development procedure.   For motion-picture work, however, it pays to take advantage of even slight improvements in the technique, and the following formula is recommended by the Eastman Kodak Company for developing the negative because it tends to minimize the graininess:

Metol (elon)...............................	2 grams
Sodium sulphite (dry)......................	100 grams
Hydroquinone..............................	5 grams
Borax.....................................	2 grams
Water, to make...........................	1 liter

Directions for Mixing: Dissolve the metol in a small volume of water at about 125°F. (52°C.), and pour the solution into the tank.   Then dissolve approximately one-quarter of the sulphite separately in hot water at about 160°F. (71°C.), and add the hydroquinone while stirring until completely dissolved.   Then add this solution to the tank.   Now dissolve the remainder of the sulphite in hot water at about 160°F. (71°C.), add the borax, and when dissolved, pour the entire solution into the tank.   Dilute to the required volume with cold water.

[1] *Trans. Soc. Motion Picture Eng.*, No. 14, 107 (1922).

It should be added in passing that the graininess of a negative should not be judged of itself but only the graininess of the resulting positive. The reason for this is obvious enough when it is remembered that the dense portions of the negative, in which the graininess is invisible, are the very portions that, when printed, produce positive densities where the graininess is most apparent.

Another phenomenon that may be noted here, although its cause is optical rather than photographic, is *halation*. During the exposure, the light incident on the emulsion behaves in the manner shown by Fig. 110, which is a cross section of a plate on which a small bright image is formed at A. Of the light diffused by the emulsion, part strikes the back of the plate within the critical angle and is largely transmitted. The rest is totally reflected to strike the emulsion again at B and B'. If the figure

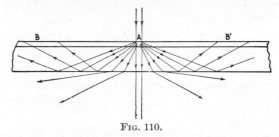

Fig. 110.

were drawn in three dimensions, it would be evident that the secondary images formed at B and B' are in reality parts of a single ring or halo surrounding the primary image at A. Halation in its pure form as described is exhibited only by small images of very bright objects, such as the sun or a lamp, but it is also exhibited in a modified form by the images of large objects that are considerably brighter than the background. For example, it is the cause of the hazy border that frequently surrounds the windows in interior scenes.

One way to prevent halation is to coat the back of the plate with an absorbing material to make what is known as a *backed* plate. Another way is to use a plate having a slow emulsion under the regular emulsion (a *double-coated* plate). The emulsion next to the glass is so insensitive that the comparatively small amount of light reflected from the back does not affect it. Halation can be reduced in a single-coated plate by using a developer which is so concentrated that the image is confined principally to the upper layers of the emulsion. Halation is more pronounced with plates than with film because the latter is so thin that the reflected light strikes the emulsion close to the primary image.

A feature of photographic emulsions that is of special importance to astronomers is a spreading of the image with increasing exposure, an effect that has been called *irradiation*. In 1889, Scheiner found that the diameter of the image of a geometrical point is given by

$$d = a + \Gamma \log_{10} \Sigma, \qquad (195)$$

where a and Γ are constants. The similarity of this equation to the characteristic density-exposure relation has led F. E. Ross to coin the term *astrogamma* for the quantity Γ. Scheiner's equation has never been entirely satisfactory, however, and various workers have proposed substitutes. One of the best is due to Ross. It is

$$\sqrt{d + h} = a + \Gamma \log_{10} \Sigma, \qquad (196)$$

where h is an additional constant. A large amount of stellar photometry has been done by measuring the diameters of the images of the stars on photographic plates and computing the magnitudes therefrom.

Many agents besides light are capable of affecting photographic materials, and occasionally they cause markings whose source is difficult to locate. If a box of film that has been stored in the laboratory for some time exhibits an unusual amount of fog, the possibility of an X-ray machine in a neighboring room should not be overlooked. Radioactive substances also affect photographic materials powerfully. Even such common substances as linseed oil and turpentine may affect them in time,[1] so photographic materials should not be stored in a freshly painted cabinet nor loaded into the camera much before they are to be used. Friction, too, will produce a developable image. For example, a plate can be marked by means of the rounded end of a glass rod even when the force exerted is comparatively light. In cold, dry weather, motion-picture photographers encounter difficulty with static electricity. The unrolling of the film generates electrostatic charges that are unable to leak away.

---

[1] This effect can be utilized for deciphering charred paper records. See *Bur. Standards Sci. Paper* 454.

Electrical discharges therefore take place, which cause characteristic markings on the film.

Occasionally there appear foreign markings that are traceable to faulty dark-room technique. Particles of chemicals that settle on the film may produce spots. Bubbles of air in the water used for diluting the developer will cause pinholes. Failure to immerse the entire film at once or to agitate the developer will result in uneven development. Grease on the film, coming either from the tap water or from the fingers, also results in uneven development. In the case of papers, contamination of the developer with hypo is a fruitful cause of yellow stains.

Even if the film is properly developed, it is still susceptible to injury. If it is removed from one solution to another of greatly different concentration, the osmotic pressure within the emulsion may cause blisters. Similarly, a sudden change in temperature may cause the emulsion to leave the support; and, if the solutions are too hot, the emulsion may soften and run. Sometimes it softens locally and in drying acquires a surface having the appearance of a file, an effect known as *reticulation*. All these effects and many others must be familiar to a photographer. They are discussed at length in the handbooks on practical photography.

95. The Sensitometry of Positive Materials.—Positive materials may be either transparent or opaque. Transparent materials—motion-picture film and lantern slides—require little comment. They closely resemble negative materials except that their speeds and fog densities are lower and their γ_{∞}-values higher. On the other hand, opaque materials—papers—are quite different.[1]

In discussing papers, the quantity "density" must be redefined, preferably so as to make the laws of blackening similar to those for emulsions on a transparent base. This is accomplished by defining density as

$$D = \log_{10} \frac{1}{R}, \tag{197}$$

where R is the reflecting power of the developed paper. A white diffusing surface like magnesium carbonate is taken as a standard and is assumed to have a reflecting power of unity. Its density is therefore zero. On this basis, the minimum reflecting

---

[1] Many different processes are in use for making positives on paper. See the standard works on photography, such as Neblette's "Photography."

power (maximum black) exhibited by photographic papers is about 1 per cent, which corresponds to a density of 2. The useful density range for photographic papers is therefore between 0 and 2, a much smaller range than in the case of negative materials.

As was stated in Sec. 12, Chap. I, the reflection of ordinary materials, such as photographic papers, is neither perfectly specular nor perfectly diffuse. It partakes of both characteristics, as shown in Fig. 111, which is a copy of Fig. 7 in Chap. I. Obviously, no value of reflecting power can be assigned without specifying the angles of illumination and observation. The

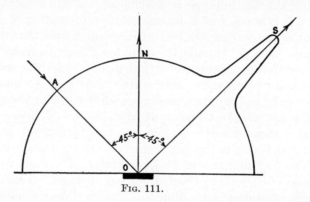

Fig. 111.

custom in photographic laboratories is to illuminate the surface at an angle of 45° and to view it normally. Although this procedure is quite arbitrary, it corresponds roughly, at least, to the conditions under which photographs are ordinarily viewed. The gloss of a surface can be specified in a number of ways, but a definition suggested by L. A. Jones[1] is very convenient in this case. According to this definition, if B_n is the brightness of the surface in Fig. 111 when viewed normally, and B_s is the brightness when viewed in the direction OS, the gloss is

$$G = \frac{B_s - B_n}{B_n}. \tag{198}$$

On this basis, magnesium carbonate has a gloss of 0.1, matte papers approximately 0.4, and glossy papers as high as 30. For obvious reasons, the maximum density of a glossy paper is higher than that of a matte paper.

[1] *Jour. Optical Soc. Amer. and Rev. Sci. Instruments*, **6**, 140 (1922).

The bromide papers, designed for making enlargements and projection prints, have emulsions that closely resemble those of negative materials. To be sure, the sensitivity of these emulsions is lower and the grains are finer, but otherwise the materials behave like negative materials. The gamma increases with the time of development in much the same way, as is shown by Fig. 112. The choice of development conditions requires special consideration, however, because the color of the image depends to a considerable extent on the composition of the developer. Also, the color is likely to be unsatisfactory if the development time is too short; and fog or stain may appear if it

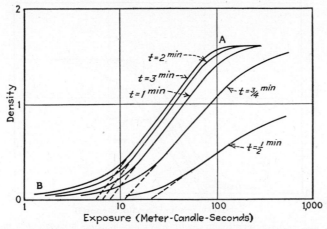

Fig. 112.—Characteristic curves of a typical bromide paper. The times of development are indicated on the curves. The points A and B define the exposure scale of the paper for a development time of 3 min.

is too long. Within these limits, however, the contrast of a bromide print can be adjusted to produce, in combination with the negative, the desired over-all contrast.

The most striking characteristic of papers is the short length of the straight portion of the characteristic curve, which might be expected from the short density range of paper emulsions. In practice, both the toe and the shoulder portions of the curve must ordinarily be utilized. For this reason, the latitude of a paper is not so useful a quantity as the *exposure scale*, which is defined as the ratio of the exposure at the point A to that at the point B in Fig. 112. A *full-scale* print is, by definition, one that utilizes the entire exposure scale of the paper. This means that the high light of the subject will be represented by a density corresponding to point B on the curve, and the deepest shadow will be represented by the point A.   It is usually found that a full-scale print is more pleasing than one for which the requirements of faithful tone reproduction are satisfied over the straight portion of the curve.   In other words, for a subject with a given brightness range, it is often better to adjust the development of the negative to fit the scale of the paper than to adhere more rigidly to the requirements of faithful tone reproduction.[1]   The scale of bromide papers when developed in the ordinary way varies from about 20 to 60.

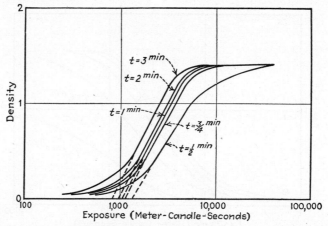

Fig. 113.—Characteristic curves for a typical chloride ("gas-light") paper.

The characteristics of chloride papers, which are commonly used in making contact prints, differ considerably from those of bromide papers, as is illustrated in Fig. 113.   It will be seen that the gamma increases rapidly with the time of development to nearly its limiting value, and that further development then changes the effective speed of the paper rather than its contrast. For this reason, these papers are supplied in several grades of contrast; the papers with a long exposure scale being used for contrasty negatives, and conversely.   The scale of chloride papers varies from about 10 for a very "hard" paper to 80 for a very "soft" paper.   Since they are designed for contact printing,

[1] For a very extensive treatment of the general subject of tone reproduction with photographic papers, the reader should consult a series of articles by Jones in *Jour. Franklin Inst.* for 1926 and 1927.

they are made with a shorter scale than bromide papers because, as was shown in Sec. 88, the effective contrast of a negative is greater when it is printed by projection than when it is printed by contact.

In general, the best results are obtained by developing the negative to such a contrast that it can be printed on a soft paper—that is, one having a long exposure scale. This is due to the fact that, with a soft paper, the slope of the straight portion of the curve differs less from that of the toe and the shoulder than with a hard paper.

NOTE: Since this chapter was written, the larger manufacturers have begun to publish representative data and characteristics of some materials under typical conditions of exposure and processing. It should be mentioned also that the Hurter and Driffield criterion of speed is often replaced by a factor empirically determined for use with photoelectric exposure meters.

CHAPTER XII

LIGHT-SENSITIVE CELLS

A light-sensitive cell is a device by means of which light energy can be used to control electrical energy; it is the optical analogue of the microphone. There are two broad classes of light-sensitive cells: those which merely change their electrical resistance when illuminated, and those whose action depends upon what has come to be known as the photoelectric effect. The first class is said to be photoconductive and the second, photoemissive.

96. Selenium Cells.—The selenium cell is the outstanding member of the photoconductive class. The action of light on selenium was first described in 1873 by Willoughby Smith, but the fifty-eight years that have elapsed since this discovery have not brought forth any satisfactory explanation of the phenomenon. To be sure, many inventors have experimented with selenium cells, but usually with the idea of employing them for some practical purpose. The truly scientific investigations are relatively few.[1]

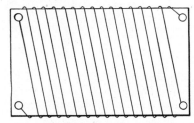

Fig. 114.—Grid construction of the Siemens selenium cell.

The first actual selenium cell was constructed by Werner Siemens in 1876. It consisted of two platinum wires wound in a double spiral around a rectangular-shaped piece of mica to form a grid, as shown in Fig. 114. This grid was coated with molten selenium, which was then annealed for some hours at a temperature of about 200°C. Although selenium cells have been constructed in a wide variety of forms, the essential features of modern cells are the same as those of this early type.

---

[1] Most of the available information has been collected recently by George P. Barnard and published under the title, "The Selenium Cell, Its Properties and Applications."

The "dark resistance" of a selenium cell is usually of the order of a few megohms. When the cell is illuminated, its resistance drops to a fraction of its former value, the size of the fraction depending in general on the magnitude of the dark resistance. The relationship between the illumination and the electrical properties of a cell can be illustrated by plotting the resistance of the cell as a function of the illumination. It is more convenient, however, to plot the current through the cell for a constant value of impressed voltage, as is done in Fig. 115 for a

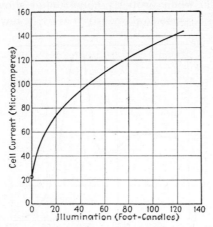

Fig. 115.—Characteristic curve of a typical selenium cell (General Electric type FJ-31) for an impressed voltage of 100 volts. The dark current of 22 microamperes corresponds to a resistance of 4.5 megohms. The resistance drops to one-sixth of the dark resistance at an illumination of 100 foot-candles. The increase in current due to the action of light is very nearly proportional to the square root of the illumination.

typical modern cell.[1] The characteristic curve shown in this figure was determined under static conditions and, due to the lag in the response of the cell, the effective sensitivity for rapid variations in light intensity is less. Although this cell is especially designed to have a rapid response, the current rises to only 50 per cent of its final value in 0.01 sec. and requires 0.2 sec.

[1] This curve indicates the amount of current passing through the cell when the entire area of the sensitive element is illuminated. The characteristics of selenium cells are such that a given amount of light flux is less effective when concentrated on a small area than when distributed over the entire surface. The sensitive area of the cell described above is approximately 17 mm wide and 40 mm long; and an optical system in which this cell is to be used should be designed so that the emergent beam has approximately these dimensions at the point where the cell is located.

to attain 95 per cent of its final value. This lag in response is characteristic of selenium cells in general and is one of their chief disadvantages. It depends to a great extent on the thickness of the selenium layer.

The spectral sensitivity of selenium cells varies widely with the form and manner of construction. In general, however, these cells are most sensitive to red light at about the long wave-length limit of visibility. A typical curve showing the relative sensitivity as a function of wave length is shown in Fig. 116.

Selenium cells when properly constructed show little loss of sensitivity over a period of several years if a few rather simple

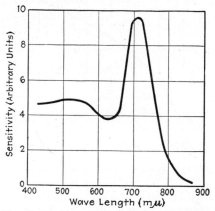

Fig. 116.—Spectral sensitivity of a typical selenium cell.

precautions are taken in their use. Because of the hygroscopic nature of selenium, cells should always be protected from moisture. Modern cells are generally sealed in a glass bulb for this reason. Selenium cells should also be protected from violent shocks because the connection between the selenium and the supporting grid is easily destroyed; and they should not be subjected to high values of illumination or impressed voltage. They may be safely used at any temperature up to about 60°C., although they are most sensitive at low temperatures.

Many substances, especially the sulphides of the heavy metals, have been found to possess light-sensitive properties similar to those of selenium. The best known of these is thallium oxysulphide, which is the active substance in the "thalofide" cell described by Case.[1] This substance, like most of the others, has

[1] *Jour. Optical Soc. Amer. and Rev. Sci. Instruments*, **6**, 398 (1922).

its greatest sensitivity in the red and infrared. None of these substances is of much use in direct quantitative measurements of light intensity because of their time lag and because their resistance varies so greatly with temperature. They are useful in null methods of photometry, however, as will be seen later.

97. The Photovoltaic Cell.—This cell utilizes an effect discovered in 1865 by Becquerel. In the most common type of cell, the electrodes are copper plates coated with cuprous oxide and immersed in a solution of some copper salt. When one of the electrodes is illuminated, a potential difference is generated which, for low values of illumination, is approximately proportional to the intensity of the illumination. These potentials are always a small fraction of a volt. The photovoltaic cell is even more sluggish than selenium, and it therefore does not lend itself to use with rapidly varying light sources.

A new type of cell which depends on the photosensitive properties of cuprous oxide has recently been developed.[1] This cell has no electrolyte and consists merely of a copper plate coated with cuprous oxide on which is superposed a metal grid or a transparent metallic film. When the cell is illuminated, electrons stream from the copper to the cuprous oxide without the application of an external electromotive force. The Weston "Photronic" cell is of this general type. It has a dark resistance of about 1500 ohms, which decreases to about 300 ohms under an illumination of 250 foot-candles. Its sensitivity is approximately 80 microamperes per lumen when inserted in a circuit of negligible resistance.

98. The Photoelectric Effect.—The first evidence of what is now known as the photoelectric effect was discovered quite accidentally in 1887 by Hertz,[2] who observed that a spark jumps more readily between two electrodes when they are illuminated than when they are in the dark. He was quick to sense the importance of this discovery and to trace the cause to the ultraviolet component of the light. A year later, Hallwachs[3] found that a zinc sphere attached to an electroscope acquires a small positive charge when illuminated by ultraviolet light. If the sphere is originally charged positively, the illumination has no appreciable effect; if it is originally charged negatively, the

[1] *Physik. Zeits.*, **31**, 139 and 913 (1930).
[2] *Wiedemann's Ann. Physik*, **31**, 983 (1887).
[3] *Ibid.*, **33**, 301 (1888).

charge leaks off until the final potential is slightly positive, usually a matter of a volt or less. This phenomenon was explained by assuming that electrons are ejected from the metallic surface as a result of the action of light, and the extensive investigations of Elster and Geitel confirmed this explanation.

In 1890, Stoletow[1] connected two electrodes in series with a battery and a galvanometer and observed a continuous current in the circuit when the negatively charged electrode (cathode) was illuminated. It was very quickly established that the number of electrons emitted per unit time is proportional to

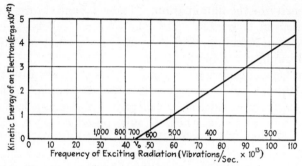

Fig. 117.—Kinetic energy of a photoelectron from sodium as a function of the frequency of the exciting radiation (from Millikan's data). For convenience, the wave lengths in millimicrons are indicated along the axis of abscissae.

the amount of light flux incident on the photoelectric surface. This result seemed reasonable enough, and it was anticipated that the velocity of the ejected electrons would depend on the intensity of the illumination. But experiment proved the contrary; for, under comparable conditions, the distribution of electronic velocities was found to be quite independent of the illumination. The velocities were found to range from zero to a definite maximum, which was explained later by assuming that all the electrons are released from their atoms with the same velocity but that those originating in the lower layers lose a part of their velocity before they reach the surface.

The kinetic energy corresponding to the maximum velocity of the photoelectrons was subsequently shown to be a linear function of the frequency of the exposing light. This is illustrated by Fig. 117, which is plotted from data obtained by Milli-

[1] *Jour. Physique,* **9,** 468 (1890).

kan[1] for sodium. The slope of this curve is found to be the same for all elements but the limiting frequency ν_0 is different. This result was interpreted by Einstein[2] on the basis of the quantum theory. He reasoned that the absorption of light in the photoelectric process should take place by quanta of energy, just as Planck had found that thermal radiation is apparently emitted by quanta. Assuming that the ejection of a single photoelectron requires the absorption of an amount of energy $h\nu$, the kinetic energy of the electron should be given by

$$\tfrac{1}{2}mv^2 = h(\nu - \nu_0) = h\nu - W, \qquad (199)$$

where h is Planck's constant and W represents the amount of energy given up by the electron in escaping from the photoelectric surface. This is Einstein's famous *photoelectric equation*, and the evidence supporting this interpretation of the photoelectric effect is most convincing. In fact, Millikan has stated that the photoelectric effect provides the most accurate method for determining Planck's constant.

The value of the quantity W, which is known as the *work function*, can be determined experimentally for a given substance from measurements of contact potentials or thermionic emission. Since $W = h\nu_0$, the limiting frequency below which the photoelectric effect does not take place can be readily computed. The limiting frequencies of a few common metals are given in the first column of Table XVI. The second column gives the corresponding values of wave length in millimicrons. These values are greatly affected by impurities, and some of the limiting frequencies would almost certainly be higher if the metals could be made absolutely pure.

99. Photoelectric Cells.—The photoelectric effect has been studied extensively almost from the moment of its discovery, but for many years few attempts were made to utilize it for practical purposes. This was largely because selenium cells were already available and gave more current for the same amount of light flux. It was only after vacuum-tube amplifiers were perfected that advantage could be taken of the superior properties of the photoelectric cell.

---

[1] *Phys. Rev.*, **7**, 355 (1916). Other investigators had previously obtained similar but less exact results.

[2] *Ann. Physik*, **17**, 132 (1905).

TABLE XVI.—LIMITING FREQUENCIES OF CERTAIN METALS

Element	ν_0, vibrations per second	λ_0, millimicrons
Caesium	44.1×10^{13}	681
Sodium	51.6	583
Lithium	51.7	580
Aluminum	62.9	477
Potassium	68.8	436
Magnesium	78.5	382
Calcium	81.1	370
Silver	92.3	325
Cadmium	95.5	314
Iron	98.4	305
Zinc	99.3	302
Copper	100.0	300
Platinum	107.0	280
Tungsten	130.5	230

One type of cell that is particularly useful for general laboratory purposes is shown in Fig. 118. This cell is approximately as large as a 100-watt lamp and has a window 1½ in. in diameter. The anode is a wire projecting through the base into the center of the bulb and connected to one of the prongs in the base. The cathode is a coating deposited on the inside of the bulb, the connection being made through the side of the bulb by means of a flush seal. The active material in this cell is caesium, which is selected because of its spectral sensitivity. Since caesium melts at approximately room temperature, a special method of preparing the cathode is adopted. The procedure is to silver the inside of the bulb and then oxidize the silver by filling the bulb with oxygen and causing a glow discharge to pass.

FIG. 118.—Caesium photoelectric cell for general laboratory use. (General Electric types PJ-14 and PJ-15.)

The oxygen is then pumped out and the proper amount of caesium is introduced. On being heated, this combines with silver oxide to form oxides of caesium and leaves a layer of metallic caesium

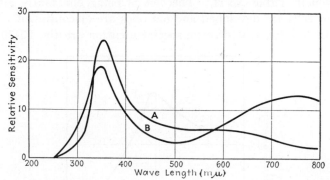

Fig. 119.—Spectral sensitivity of typical caesium cells. Curve *A*, for General Electric types PJ-14 and PJ-15; curve *B*, for types PJ-22 and PJ-23.

approximately one atom deep. This layer does not distill off at any ordinary temperature and is as satisfactory as a thicker layer would be. The spectral sensitivity of this cell extends throughout the visible region, as shown by curve *A* in Fig. 119. Its response can therefore be made similar to that of the eye by means of suitable filters, a necessary procedure when the cell is to be used for photometric purposes. This cell is either completely evacuated (type PJ-14) or filled with argon (type PJ-15), the function of the argon being to increase the sensitivity in a manner that will be described later.

Fig. 120.—Caesium photoelectric cell used in sound reproduction. (General Electric types PJ-22 and PJ-23).

The small cell shown in Fig. 120 has been developed for the reproduction of sound from motion-picture film. The vacuum type is known as the PJ-22 and the gas-filled type as the PJ-23. The sensitivity of both types is somewhat greater than that of the corresponding types just described. Their spectral sensitivity is higher in the infrared, due to oxides of caesium, as is shown by curve *B* in Fig. 119.

Many other cells have been developed for various purposes,[1] and a list of those made by one of the leading manufacturers is given in Table XVII. This list is being constantly altered as new cells are developed and old ones are discontinued. Two cells in this list that deserve special mention are the FJ-76 and

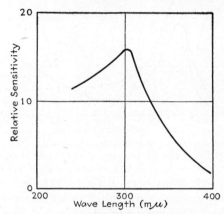

Fig. 121.—Spectral sensitivity of a sodium cell in a quartz bulb designed for experimental work in the ultraviolet. (General Electric types FJ-76 and FJ-77.)

the FJ-77, which are designed for experimental work in the ultraviolet. The active material of these cells is sodium and the bulbs are made of quartz. A representative spectral sensitivity curve is shown in Fig. 121.

If a photoelectric cell of the vacuum type is connected in a circuit like that shown in Fig. 122, the relationship between the

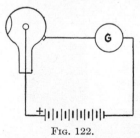

Fig. 122.

current and the impressed voltage for various values of light flux is as shown in Fig 123. It is evident that, for a given value of light flux, the current approaches a limiting value as the voltage is increased. This is to be expected because, when the voltage between the electrodes is sufficient to attract to the anode all the electrons that are released by the light, no further increase in current can be obtained. In other words, the vacuum cell has a definite *saturation current* for every value of light flux. This feature makes this type of

[1] The construction, operation, and characteristics of photoelectric cells have been described by Koller, *Jour. Optical Soc. Amer. and Rev. Sci. Instruments.* **19**, 135 (1929), and *Jour. Western Soc. Eng.*, **36**, 15 (1931).

TABLE XVII.—CHARACTERISTICS OF PHOTOELECTRIC CELLS MADE BY THE GENERAL ELECTRIC COMPANY

The sensitivity is expressed in microamperes per lumen for light from a Mazda C lamp at 2870°K.

Type	Cathode	Gas	Sensitivity	Maximum voltage	Type of bulb	Maximum diameter, inches	Maximum length, inches	Designed for
PJ-14	Caesium	Vacuum	3	150	G-20	2½	6³⁄₁₆	Photometry
PJ-15	Caesium	Argon	14	150	G-20	2½	6³⁄₁₆	General purposes
PJ-16	Caesium	Vacuum	3	150	G-40	5	9½	Experimental purposes
PJ-17	Caesium	Argon	14	80	G-40	5	9½	Experimental purposes
PJ-18	Caesium	Vacuum	3	150	G-56	7	12½	Experimental purposes
PJ-19	Caesium	Argon	14	80	G-56	7	12½	Television
PJ-22	Caesium	Vacuum	5	150	T-8	1³⁄₁₆	4⅛	Picture transmission
PJ-23	Caesium	Argon	50	90	T-8	1³⁄₁₆	4⅛	Sound reproduction
FJ-76	Sodium	Vacuum	..	90	Quartz	1½	4¾	Ultraviolet
FJ-77	Sodium	Argon	..	90	Quartz	1½	4¾	Ultraviolet

cell ideal for photometric use because, by impressing a sufficiently high voltage, the current becomes sensibly independent of the voltage and depends only on the total amount of light incident on the cathode.

The variation in current with light flux for 50 volts on the cell is shown in Fig. 124, which is replotted from the curves in Fig.

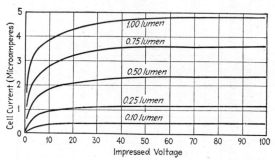

FIG. 123.—Current-voltage relationship of a typical photoelectric cell of the vacuum type (PJ-22).

123. In a well-constructed cell, this relationship is very nearly linear. The most frequent cause for non-linearity is leakage within the cell, which becomes important when the current is small. Cells like the one shown in Fig. 120, in which the connection to the cathode is made through the base, have a relatively

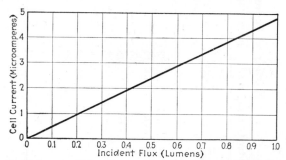

FIG. 124.—Variation of cell current with light flux in a cell of the vacuum type when 50 volts are applied to the cell.

large leakage current. Even in a cell of the form shown in Fig. 118, where the leakage is ordinarily small, the condensation of moisture on the outside of the bulb in damp weather may give rise to a leakage current as great as 10^{-9} amp. This current can be reduced materially by equipping the cell with a guard ring as shown in Fig. 127. The guard ring need only be a piece of wire wrapped around the stem of the tube and attached to a constant source having approximately the same potential as the cathode.

Cells of the gas-filled type are more sensitive than those of the vacuum type because the ionization of the gas by collision can be utilized to increase the number of electrons reaching the anode for a given amount of light. Each electron that is released from the cathode collides with many gas molecules on its way to the anode; and, if the potential difference across the cell is sufficiently high, the force of the collision will ionize these molecules. The sensitivity of a gas-filled cell depends, therefore, on the impressed voltage, and the limit is reached when the volt-

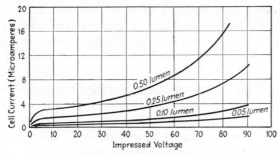

Fig. 125.—Current-voltage relationship of a typical photoelectric cell of the gas-filled type (PJ-23).

age is so high that the ionization becomes cumulative and a continuous glow discharge takes place.[1] For stability of operation, the cell should be operated well below the glow voltage. The limit thus imposed on the amplification produced by the gas is about ten-fold.

The characteristic current-voltage relationship for a typical gas-filled cell is shown by the curves in Fig. 125. The lower portions of these curves are similar to the corresponding portions of the curves in Fig. 123, but the increase in sensitivity due to the presence of the gas makes itself evident above about 15 volts. This increase in sensitivity is obtained at some sacrifice of linearity of response, however, especially at high values of impressed voltage or illumination. As the increase in sensitivity

[1] To prevent damage in case this accidentally occurs, a gas-filled cell should always be connected in series with a resistance of approximately one megohm to limit the current.

is the only point of superiority of the gas-filled type of cell, the vacuum type should always be used when possible.

Photoelectric cells respond almost instantaneously to variations in the exposing light. In fact, the response of a cell of the vacuum type is so rapid that, in practice, it is limited more by the electrostatic capacity of the cell and associated elements than by any inherent lag in the cell itself. The response of a cell of the gas-filled type is limited by the rate of decay of the ionization of the gas, but it is usually so rapid that gas-filled cells can be used without appreciable attenuation throughout the entire range of audible frequencies. In this respect, photoelectric cells are distinctly superior to selenium or other photoconductive substances. They are also superior because of the almost linear nature of. their response. This is so nearly linear that many investigators have attempted to use photoelectric cells as a substitute for radiometers in the direct measurement of the intensity of a beam of light. The results of such a procedure are likely to be disappointing unless the precision required is low, since all the cells that have thus far been produced exhibit marked changes in both their spectral sensitivity and their total sensitivity with time.[1] One remedy is to calibrate the cell frequently. A more elegant procedure is to use a null method in which the unknown source and a standard source are compared in rapid succession, the two being adjudged equal when there is no variation in the cell current. This method will be described in more detail in the next chapter.

100. The Amplification of Photoelectric Currents.—The most common use of photoelectric cells to-day is in connection with the reproduction of sound from motion-picture film. The amount of light flux incident on the cell in such apparatus is usually about 0.1 lumen, and the current that is obtainable with the best of photoelectric cells is only a few microamperes. Even this is a relatively large amount of current, and some photoelectric devices have been satisfactorily operated with currents as small as 10^{-12} amp. Although currents of this order of magnitude can be measured with a good galvanometer, it is fair to say that photoelectric currents would ordinarily be of little use without amplification.

---

[1] The applicability of photoelectric cells to photometry and colorimetry has been discussed extensively by Ives and Kingsbury, *Jour. Optical Soc. Amer.*, **21**, 541 (1931).

If the output of a light-sensitive cell of the photoconductive type is to be amplified, its effective sensitivity may be very different from that indicated by the curves showing the variation of cell current with light flux. This is because these curves are determined with a current-measuring instrument, such as a galvanometer, whose resistance can be neglected in comparison with that of the cell itself. The thermionic tube, on the other hand, is essentially a voltage-operated device; and a high resistance must therefore be inserted in the cell circuit to transform the variations in current into variations in voltage. A typical circuit is shown in Fig. 126, where a cell having a resistance r is connected in series with an external resistance R and a source of electromotive force E. The thermionic tube, assumed to draw no current from the circuit, is connected between the points A and B. When the resistance of the cell changes as a result of variations in the light flux, the voltage across AB varies in a manner that will now be investigated.

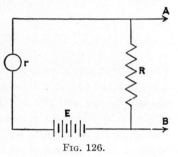

FIG. 126.

Let the voltage across the cell be represented by e. Then

$$e = ir,$$

where i is the current in the circuit. If now the resistance of the cell changes by an amount dr as a result of a change dF in the incident flux, the corresponding change in e is

$$de = r\,di + i\,dr. \tag{200}$$

The change in voltage across AB is, of course, the same as that across the cell. Hence the effective sensitivity of a light-sensitive cell is measured by the ratio of de to dF when it is to be used in conjunction with an amplifier or other voltage-operated device.

The value of de can be found in terms of the circuit constants by noting that

$$i = \frac{E}{R + r}.$$

Then, since E and R are constant,

$$di = \frac{-E\,dr}{(R + r)^2}. \tag{201}$$

By combining these equations, it is found that

$$de = \frac{Re}{r(R + r)}dr.\qquad(202)$$

In the limit, if R is very large, the ratio $\frac{R}{R + r}$ approaches unity.
For this case, the change in voltage across AB produced by a change dr in the cell resistance is

$$de = -\frac{e}{r}dr.\qquad(203)$$

Under these conditions, the voltage change across AB is obviously a maximum; and it will be seen to depend only on the fractional change in the cell resistance and the highest voltage that can safely be applied to the cell.

A numerical example will make the above relationships clear. Suppose that the selenium cell whose characteristics are shown in Fig. 115 receives 0.1 lumen of light flux. This flux is distributed over an area of 7.0 cm², so the illumination is 13.3 foot-candles. By referring to the curve, it is easy to compute that, for this amount of illumination, the resistance of the cell is approximately 1.5 megohms. The slope of the curve at this point indicates that, if the illumination were reduced by 1 per cent, the resistance would be increased by 5500 ohms. Substitution of these values in Eq. (203) indicates that, under the most favorable conditions, this change in illumination will produce a voltage change across AB of 0.35 volt.

It is evident from Eq. (202) that the external resistance R should be as large as possible, but this condition is usually not attainable in practice because the voltage E of the battery would have to be unduly large to maintain the desired voltage drop e across the cell. It is easily shown that, if the voltage of the battery is less than twice the voltage that can safely be applied to the cell, the maximum signal voltage across AB occurs when R is equal to r. It can also be shown that the signal voltage under these conditions is directly proportional to E. There is little to be gained by using a value of E greater than twice the maximum cell voltage because, even if E is infinite, the signal voltage is only doubled.[1]

---

[1] It goes without saying that the value of R should be such that the potential across the cell will be the highest that is safe.

The foregoing considerations do not apply to a cell of the photoemissive type for the reason that the resistance is ordinarily so high that it would be impracticable to attempt to match it with an external resistor. For example, when 50 volts are applied to the photoelectric cell whose characteristics are shown in Fig. 123, the current for an incident flux of 0.1 lumen is approximately 0.5 microampere. The resistance of the cell under these conditions is therefore 100 megohms, and the resistance is even greater when the amount of light flux is less. A stable resistor of this size is difficult to obtain, and, furthermore, it is usually undesirable because it would make the circuit sluggish in responding to changes in light flux.[1] For this reason, the practical limit to the value of R is frequently one megohm or less. This means that the resistance of the cell is ordinarily infinite in comparison, and, therefore, the change in voltage across AB in Fig. 126 is

$$de = R \, di.$$

The change in current corresponding to a given change in light flux can in this case be read directly from a curve of the type shown in Fig. 124.

It is of some interest to compare the signal voltage obtainable from a photoelectric cell with that computed above for the selenium cell. If 0.1 lumen is incident on the cell whose characteristics are shown in Fig. 124, the current is approximately 0.5 microampere. A change of 1 per cent in the light flux would produce a change in current of 0.005 microampere and, hence, if R equals 1 megohm, the signal voltage is 0.005 volt. This is in contrast to the 0.35-volt signal obtained with the selenium cell; but it is only fair to add that, because of the sluggishness of the selenium cell, the conditions are not strictly comparable. If the photoelectric cell is used with such a large series resistance that its response is as slow as that of the selenium cell, the photoelectric cell is the more sensitive.

One method of connecting a photoelectric cell to a vacuum-tube amplifier is shown in Fig. 127. The grid is given the proper negative bias by connecting the filament to a point of the battery

[1] This is because of the inevitable electrostatic capacity of the grid of the vacuum tube, the photoelectric cell itself, and the connecting wires. The time constant of the circuit is RC. Hence if R is 100 megohms and C is 10^{-11} farad, the voltage applied to the grid will require approximately one-thousandth of a second to rise to two-thirds of its final value.

that is slightly more positive than the low-potential end of the resistance.   The guard ring, which should be used if the currents to be amplified are small, is so connected that its potential is approximately the same as that of the cathode when the normal cell current is flowing.   It has already been mentioned that the resistance R must be low if the cell is to respond rapidly to variations in the light flux.   Quite often these variations are cyclical in character, and it is therefore desirable to express the limiting value for R in terms of the frequency of the signal.   The grid-filament capacity of a tube of the screen-grid type[1] is about

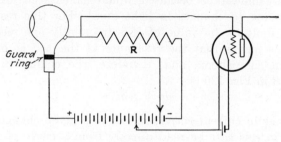

FIG. 127.

6×10^{-12} farad, and the capacity of the photoelectric cell and connecting wires is at least of the same order of magnitude. Taking the capacity of the entire grid circuit in round numbers as 10^{-11} farad, the capacity reactance $1/2\pi fC$ is given in the table below for various values of frequency:

Frequency, Cycles per Second	Capacity Reactance, Megohms
1	15,900
10	1,590
60	265
100	159
1,000	15.9
10,000	1.59
100,000	0.159
1,000,000	0.0159

[1] Unless a tube is of the screen-grid type, the effective electrostatic capacity of the grid is increased approximately in proportion to the voltage amplification.   Another important advantage of the screen-grid tube is that the connection with the grid is made through the top of the tube, so the leakage is much less than when the connection is made through the base.

It will be seen that the capacity reactance decreases with increasing frequency. If the amplification is to be approximately constant over a range of frequencies, it is easily shown that R must be no greater than the capacity reactance at the highest frequency. For example, in using a photoelectric cell for the reproduction of sound, the highest frequency that must be amplified can be set at approximately 10,000 cycles/sec.; and referring to the table, it is clear that in this case R must not exceed about one megohm.

The operating conditions of the vacuum tube into which the cell works must be quite different from those recommended

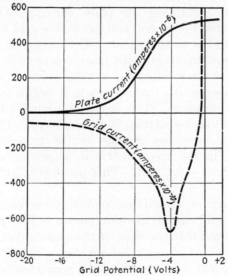

Fig. 128.—Relation of grid and plate currents to the grid potential of a typical four-element vacuum tube (UY-224) under normal operating conditions.

for radio purposes. In radio circuits, although the voltages are small, the resistances of the circuits are small also, and consequently the currents are fairly large. Under these conditions, it is possible to neglect the grid current within the vacuum tube. When amplifying photoelectric currents, on the other hand, the grid current may become appreciable unless special precautions are taken. This will be clear from Fig. 128, which shows the plate- and grid-current curves for a typical tube of the UY-224 type operated under the following conditions, which are substantially the same as are recommended for radio purposes:

Filament voltage........................	2.5 volts
Plate voltage............................	180 volts
Screen-grid voltage......................	60 volts
Plate-circuit resistance..................	250,000 ohms

When the grid is at a high negative potential, the grid current is due to electrons emitted by the grid itself resulting from its heating by the filament. The remedy is to operate the filament at a low temperature, a procedure that is quite satisfactory because the plate current in the first stage of the amplifier need not be large. In the region from -14 to -4 volts in the case illustrated, the grid current is due primarily to positive ions formed by the bombardment of the residual gas molecules by the electrons constituting the plate current. These positive ions are attracted to the grid and produce a grid current nearly proportional to the plate current. The formation of these ions can be prevented by keeping the plate voltage below the ionization potential of the residual gas, usually about 12 volts. When the grid is more positive than -4 volts, it begins to attract electrons from the filament. This produces a current in a direction opposite to that of the currents just considered. The magnitude of this current increases rapidly as the grid becomes more positive; and, in the case illustrated, it neutralizes the other currents at about -0.4 volt. This point is therefore the free-grid potential.

The difficulty of amplifying photoelectric currents with a tube having a grid current like that shown in Fig. 128 is obvious when it is realized that the slope of the grid-current curve represents the reciprocal of a virtual resistance in parallel with R. If the grid-current curve is steep, the resistance is low and the signal voltage is correspondingly reduced. The portion of the grid-current curve that causes the most difficulty can be eliminated by decreasing the voltages applied to both the plate and the filament. For example, the above tube can be operated under the following conditions:

Filament voltage...........................	1.5 volts
Plate voltage..............................	15.0 volts
Screen-grid voltage........................	7.5 volts
Plate-circuit resistance....................	250,000 ohms

Then the grid current is sensibly zero for all grid voltages more negative than -0.4 volt, as is shown in Fig. 129. The mutual conductance of the tube when operated in this way is low and the amplification is therefore small. This feature, however, is of little moment because the first stage may be followed by others of orthodox design to build up the signal to the required strength.

A new tube that is particularly well adapted to the amplification of small photoelectric currents has been recently placed on the market by the General Electric Company. This tube is

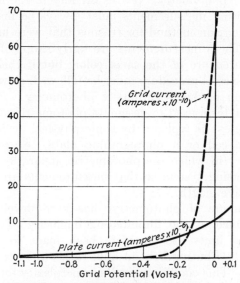

Fig. 129.—Relation of grid and plate currents to the grid potential of the UY-224 tube with reduced filament and plate potentials.

known as the FP-54 and has been described by Metcalf and Thompson.[1] It is designed to have a relatively high mutual conductance even when operated at a plate voltage as low as 6 volts. The insulation of the grid is unusually high, the grid current being less than 10^{-15} amp.[2]

[1] *Phys. Rev.*, **36**, 1489 (1930).

[2] For details concerning some of the special precautions that must be taken in the amplification of photoelectric currents, the reader should consult the literature of the subject, notably a paper by Nottingham in *Jour. Franklin Inst.*, **209**, 287 (1930). See also "Photoelectric Phenomena" by Hughes and DuBridge and Chapter X of "Procedures in Experimental Physics" by Strong.

CHAPTER XIII

PHOTOMETRY

The term "photometry" relates broadly to the measurement of light. Visual measurements must always be made by some sort of comparison method for reasons that were made clear in Chap. X. These measurements are fairly simple if the sources to be compared are of the same color; but if their colors are different, a special procedure must be followed, as will be shown in the section on heterochromatic photometry. *Physical photometry* is the term used to designate photometric measurements in which the eye is replaced by some physical device such as a photoelectric cell or a photographic plate. *Spectrophotometry* is photometry in which the photometric apparatus is combined with a dispersing system so that measurements are made wave length by wave length.

The technique of photometry[1] has been developed largely at the instance of the illuminating engineer. The choice of concepts and units has therefore been made to expedite the problem of distributing light in bulk rather than to systematize the subject. This condition results in perplexity for the student of physics, who is accustomed to concepts that were rationalized long before they found an engineering application. The term "foot-candle" is a case in point. From the very nature of things, illumination must be evaluated in terms of flux per unit area; in the English system, the logical unit is the lumen per square foot. To call this unit a foot-candle is not in keeping with the exactitude that characterizes scientific nomenclature.

There are really only four fundamental photometric quantities, and these are so related geometrically that only one is an independent entity. These quantities, which were discussed in Sec. 11 (p. 18), are listed on the next page. It is a matter of indifference which is accepted as fundamental and which as derived, although it is most logical to consider the lumen as the funda-

---

[1] Walsh's "Photometry" is an excellent treatise on the subject. It contains an unusually extensive bibliography.

Quantity	Dimensions	Unit	Symbol
Flux......................	Lumens	Lumen	F
Intensity (point source)......	Lumens per unit solid angle	Candle	I
Brightness (extended source)..	Lumens per unit solid angle per unit area	Candle per unit area	B
Illumination................	Lumens per unit area	Lumen per unit area	E

mental unit. The candle is an easier standard to maintain, however, because measurements of intensity are simpler than those of total flux.

The present standard of luminous intensity is the international candle. This has been maintained since 1909, when it was established by agreement between the national standardizing laboratories of France, Great Britain, and the United States.[1] In this country, the Bureau of Standards maintains the standard by means of 45 carbon filament lamps, which are operated at a temperature corresponding to 4 watts/candle. These lamps constitute the primary standard, and reference and working standards are derived from them.

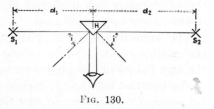

FIG. 130.

101. The Measurement of Luminous Intensity.—Since the concept of luminous intensity applies only in the case of a point source, measurements of luminous intensity are generally based on the inverse-square law. The method is illustrated in Fig. 130. If I_1 is the intensity of a standard source S_1, the illumination produced on the diffusely reflecting surface of the photometer head H will be

$$E_1 = \frac{I_1}{d_1{}^2} \cos i.$$

In similar fashion, the source of unknown intensity S_2 will produce an illumination

$$E_2 = \frac{I_2}{d_2{}^2} \cos i.$$

[1] In Germany and some other countries, the Hefner lamp is still the legal standard. Its intensity is 0.90 candle.

The procedure for determining the intensity of the unknown source is to move the photometer head along the line joining the two sources until the two halves of the photometric field appear to have the same brightness. If the head is properly constructed, E_1 is then equal to E_2, and the above equations can be combined to give

$$\frac{I_1}{d_1{}^2} = \frac{I_2}{d_2{}^2}.$$
(204)

Thus the intensity of the unknown source can be computed in terms of that of the standard source from a simple measurement of the two distances.

In practice, no source can be a true point, but any source can be treated as a point if it is so small compared with the distances involved that, if it were smaller, the same result would be obtained within the limits of experimental error. The precision of measurements of luminous intensity is such that, provided the greatest dimension of the source is less than one-twentieth of its distance from the photometer head, the assumption that it is a point is usually justified. This means that the length of the photometer bench should be made to suit the dimensions of the source to be measured.

The accuracy of visual photometric methods depends upon the ability of the eye to estimate the relative brightness of the two halves of the photometric field. This ability is related to the contrast sensitivity, which, as shown in Chap. X, is about 1.8 per cent. Photometric measurements are more accurate than this value would indicate because the procedure is to adjust the photometer head until first one half of the field and then the other appears just noticeably too bright. This operation is repeated several times and a final setting is made at an estimated midpoint.

The accuracy of photometric settings depends to some extent upon the brightness of the field and is a maximum for a field brightness of approximately 10 candles/meter^2. To attain high precision, the dividing line between the two halves of the field must be as fine as possible. The form of photometer head shown in Fig. 130 is not used for serious work because it has a dark line down the center of the field that seriously affects the accuracy of the settings. Although photometer heads of many forms have been devised, the types in common use are based on one originated by Lummer and Brodhun. This is shown

schematically in Fig. 131. Light from the two sources S_1 and S_2
falls on the opposite sides of the photometric surface P, which
is made of some white diffusing substance, usually plaster of
Paris. The essential feature of the Lummer-Brodhun head is
the photometric "cube" C. This consists essentially of two
right-angle prisms, the outer portion of the hypotenuse of one
being ground away before they are cemented together. Where
the two prisms are in optical contact, light reaches the eye from
the side of P that is illuminated by S_2. Where they are not in
contact, total reflection takes place and the side of the surface
illuminated by S_1 is seen. The appearance of the field is shown
at A. When the field is balanced, the dividing line practically
disappears. Like all subjective observations, the accuracy

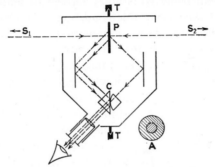

Fig. 131.—Sketch showing the principle of Lummer-Brodhun photometer head.
A, the appearance of the field.

depends to a great extent on the comfort and physiological
condition of the observer, but, under the most favorable conditions, an experienced observer can attain an accuracy of 0.2
per cent in the mean of a large number of settings.

It should be noted that the eye compares the brightness
of the two halves of the field, whereas the assumption underlying
Eq. (204) was that the illumination produced by the two sources
is the same. To avoid errors within the photometer head itself,
such as might be due to a difference in reflectance between the
two sides of the surface P, the customary procedure is to rotate
the head on the trunnions T and to make half of the settings in
the reversed position. This procedure is similar to double
weighing on a balance whose arms are not of equal length.
Averaging the two sets of readings very nearly eliminates the
error caused by any dissimilarities in the photometer head.

Sometimes a substitution method is used, the unknown and the standard being compared successively with an auxiliary source. It need scarcely be mentioned that any stray light reaching the photometric surface P will affect the reading. This is avoided by means of baffles suitably located between the sources and the head.

A very slight difference in the color of two sources is easily perceptible in a photometric field, and this circumstance makes it possible to match the color temperature of two sources with considerable precision. In incandescent-lamp practice, for example, the color temperature of one lamp can be made equal to that of a standard lamp by adjusting the applied voltage until there is no color difference in the photometric field, the photometer head being constantly moved to maintain a brightness match. Under favorable conditions, the error in matching the color temperature of two sources is about 3°C. at the operating temperatures of incandescent lamps.

102. The Measurement of Luminous Flux.

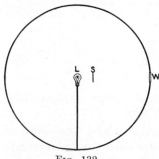

Fig. 132.

—The fact that a source may be small enough to make the concept of intensity applicable does not imply that the intensity is the same in all directions. Since most light sources nowadays are used in some sort of diffusing globe or its equivalent, the total flux emitted by the source is of more significance than the intensity in a single direction. The total flux can be found indirectly by measuring the intensity in a large number of directions and computing the amount of flux emanating in each. Because of the laborious nature of this procedure, it is seldom used, however.[1]

The apparatus in common use at the present time for the measurement of total flux depends on a principle first recognized by Sumpner in 1892. In connection with an investigation of the reflection factors of various materials, he showed that, if a source of light is placed within a hollow sphere whose wall is perfectly diffusing, the brightness of every portion of the sphere

---

[1] Many methods of facilitating the computations have been devised. They are described in the standard texts on photometry and illuminating engineering.

wall due to light reflected from the remainder of the wall is the same. The proposal to use the sphere in photometry was first made by Ulbricht in 1900, and the theory and technique of photometry by the use of the integrating sphere have been studied extensively since that time.[1]

The procedure most commonly used to-day is illustrated in Fig. 132. The light source is introduced at L within a sphere whose wall is coated with a diffusely reflecting white paint.[2] The screen S prevents the direct light from striking the window W, which is made of opal glass. Then, by Sumpner's principle, a given amount of flux from the lamp produces the same illumination on the window regardless of the direction in which it is emitted from the lamp. The illumination on the window is therefore proportional to the total flux emitted by the lamp, which can be readily evaluated in terms of the intensity of an auxiliary source by means of an external photometer bench. A standard lamp whose mean spherical candlepower has been previously measured by the point-by-point method is then substituted at L

[1] See, for instance, *Bur. Standards Sci. Paper* 447.

[2] It is important that the paint with which the interior of the sphere is coated should be not only perfectly diffusing but also non-selective, so that the repeated reflections within the sphere will not appreciably alter the color of the light. The paint used at the Bureau of Standards contains zinc oxide for the pigment and is made by first preparing a lacquer as follows:

	Parts by Weight
Denatured alcohol	100
Camphor	15
Celluloid (colorless, small pieces)	10

The camphor is first dissolved in the alcohol, after which the pieces of celluloid are added. The mixture is stirred occasionally until the celluloid is dissolved, which usually requires about 10 hr. The alcohol lost by evaporation is then replaced and the paint is made up as follows:

	Parts by Weight
Cellulose lacquer	4
Alcohol	1
Zinc oxide	4

This mixture is stirred until a smooth, thick paste results, which may require an hour or more. Then approximately 2 parts of alcohol and 1 or 2 parts of water-white turpentine are added, the alcohol to thin the mixture and the turpentine to retard the drying.

for the unknown lamp; and the total luminous output of the latter is computed from the ratio of the values of the intensity of the window in the two cases.

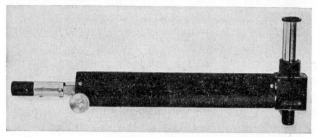

Fig. 133.—The Macbeth illuminometer. (*By courtesy of Leeds and Northrup Instrument Company.*)

103. The Measurement of Brightness.—Brightness is the only one of the four fundamental photometric quantities that

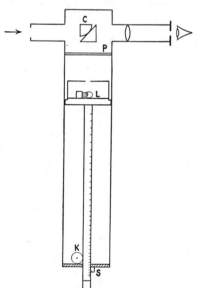

the eye is capable of comparing directly.[1] To make a brightness photometer it is, therefore, only necessary to replace the surface comprising one half of the photometric field by the surface whose brightness is to be measured. This could be done with the Lummer-Brodhun photometer head shown in Fig. 131 by placing a mirror over one surface of the plaster screen, the surface to be measured being so placed that its image is visible on looking through the cube. Where an accuracy of 2 to 3 per cent is sufficient, a portable photometer is more convenient. A

Fig. 134.—Diagrammatic sketch of the Macbeth illuminometer.

photograph of such an instrument is shown in Fig. 133 and a diagrammatic sketch of its construction in Fig. 134. Light from

[1] Although the intensity of a point source can be estimated roughly, precise measurements require a photometer head in which the eye estimates the brightness of an extended surface illuminated by the source.

the small lamp L illuminates the photometric surface P, which is usually a piece of ground glass. This surface is seen through the outer portion of the photometric cube C, the center of the field being illuminated by light entering the front of the cube from the surface under test. The photometric setting is made by turning the knob K to vary the distance of the lamp from the ground glass, after which the reading is taken from the scale S on the rod supporting the lamp.

Objects that are very bright can be measured by means of an instrument in which one of the photometric surfaces is the filament of a small lamp. This is the principle of the optical pyrometer, which is used to determine the temperature of incandescent liquids and solids. The optical system of this instrument is shown in Fig. 135. The surface being measured is imaged by

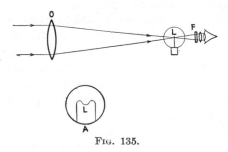

Fig. 135.

the objective O in the plane of the lamp filament L. On looking through the instrument, the observer sees the filament outlined against this surface, the field appearing as shown at A. In making a setting, the current through the filament is adjusted until the downward-curving tip disappears against the background. The instrument is calibrated to read temperature by noting the extinction point for a surface whose temperature is known, such as a metal at its melting point. To avoid any color difference between the filament and the surface under observation, a red filter is introduced at F.

The unit of brightness was stated in Sec. 11, Chap. I, to be the candle per unit of area, the area being projected on a plane normal to the direction in which the surface is observed. The brightness of a diffusely reflecting surface is the same for every angle of observation; and another unit, called the *lambert*, is designed to take advantage of this circumstance. By definition, one lambert is the brightness of a perfectly diffusing surface emitting or reflecting one lumen per square centimeter. The advantage of this unit is that the brightness of the surface in lamberts is simply the product of the illumination in lumens per square centimeter and the reflecting power of the surface. In other words, if a diffusing surface reflects all the light incident upon it, its brightness in lamberts is equal to its illumination in lumens per square centimeter. When the surface does not obey Lambert's law, its brightness depends upon the angle of observation, and the chief advantage of the lambert disappears. In fact, the meaning of the term is difficult to interpret in this case. One is compelled to represent the brightness of such a surface in a particular direction by the number of lumens per square centimeter that a perfectly diffusing surface of the same brightness would radiate.

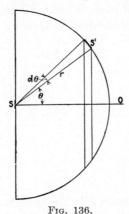

The relationship between a given brightness expressed in candles per square centimeter and in lamberts is not immediately apparent. It might be assumed at first glance that, since there are 2π solid angles in a complete hemisphere, a given brightness measured in candles per square centimeter should be 2π times as great as when measured in lamberts. A more careful analysis shows that this is not the case.

Fig. 136.

In Fig. 136, let the small source of area S radiate according to Lambert's law. Let its brightness in candles per square centimeter be represented by B. The brightness is the same from every angle of observation, of course, but the intensity varies with the angle θ in accordance with the equation

$$I = BS \cos \theta.$$

The illumination at a point S' on the surface of a hemisphere of radius r is I/r^2. The total flux radiated by the area S can be found by integrating the illumination over the area of the entire hemisphere. This is accomplished most conveniently by dividing the latter into zones generated by revolving the surface element at S' about an axis SO normal to S. The area of such a zone is

$$2\pi r \sin \theta \cdot r \, d\theta.$$

Therefore, the flux intercepted by the zone is

$$dF = \frac{I}{r^2} \cdot 2\pi r^2 \sin \theta \ d\theta$$

$$= 2\pi BS \sin \theta \ \cos \theta \ d\theta.$$

The total flux

$$F = 2\pi BS \int_0^{\frac{\pi}{2}} \sin \theta \cos \theta \ d\theta$$

$$= 2\pi BS \left[\frac{\sin^2 \theta}{2} \right]_0^{\frac{\pi}{2}}$$

$$= \pi \cdot B \cdot S. \tag{205}$$

It is seen, therefore, that a source having an area of 1 cm² will radiate πB lumens; and consequently 1 candle/cm² is equivalent to π lamberts.

104. The Measurement of Illumination.—The illuminating engineer is more frequently concerned with the measurement of illumination than any other photo-metric quantity. Since the precision required in such measurements is not high, they are usually made by means of a portable photometer like that illustrated in Fig. 133. This instrument really measures brightness, but it is calibrated to read directly in foot-candles when used with a standard test plate. The procedure is first to place an auxiliary unit, shown in Fig. 137, on the test plate P. This unit contains a small lamp that produces a known illumination on the plate for a given current. The photometer is sighted at the plate through the hole H and is set for the proper value of illumination. The current through its own lamp is then varied until a brightness match is produced. In this way, the photometer and test plate are calibrated together. The illumination at any given point can then be found by placing the test plate at the point in question and sighting on it with the photometer.

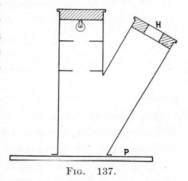

Fig. 137.

The unit of illumination that is used most frequently in this country is the foot-candle, which is numerically equivalent to one lumen per square foot.　An illumination of one lumen per square meter is sometimes called a *lux*, and one lumen per square centimeter has been called by Blondel a *phot*.　The *milliphot*, which is about the size of a foot-candle, is also sometimes used. For convenience, a table of conversion factors is presented below.

Table XVIII.—Conversion Factors

Quantity	To convert m	Into n	Multiply m by
Brightness			
	Candles/centimeter^2	Candles/meter^2	10,000.
	Candles/centimeter^2	Millilamberts	3,142.
	Candles/centimeter^2	Lamberts	3.142
	Lamberts	Candles/meter^2	3,183.
	Candles/foot^2	Candles/meter^2	10.764
	Candles/foot^2	Millilamberts	3.382
	Millilamberts	Candles/meter^2	3.183
	Candles/meter^2	Candles/foot^2	0.0929
Illumination			
	Lumens/meter^2 (meter-candles, lux)	Lumens/foot^2	0.0929
	Milliphot	Lumens/meter^2	10.
	Milliphot	Lumens/foot^2	0.929
	Lumens/foot^2 (foot-candles)	Lumens/meter^2	10.764
	Lumens/centimeter^2 (phot)	Lumens/meter^2	10,000.

105. Special Methods.—When the intensity of a very weak or a very distant source is to be measured, the ordinary method of measuring the brightness of a diffusing surface illuminated by it is impractical.　For example, in measuring stellar magnitudes, one is forced to compare the intensity of the star under consideration with that of a star whose magnitude is known.　To narrow the space between the two images, a prism that deviates one image is sometimes used.　A more refined method is to use an artificial star for comparison, but this procedure takes no account of atmospheric absorption.　The need of a comparison star is eliminated in the extinction method, in which an absorbing wedge is moved in the plane of the image until the star becomes invisible.　None of these methods are very precise.

A method devised by Maxwell is sometimes used in portable photometers for measuring the intensity of point sources that are very faint or very distant.　An instrument on this principle is shown diagrammatically in Fig. 138. An image of the source in question is formed on the pupil of the observer's eye by the lens L, which consequently appears equally bright over its entire surface. The lens occupies one half of the photometric field and the other half is occupied by a mirror R, which reflects light from a piece of opal glass G. The comparison source S illuminates the opal glass, and the setting is made by adjusting the distance between the two. In this type of instrument, a sharp dividing line between the two halves of the field is obtained without the great sacrifice of light that would result if the light were allowed to fall on a diffusely reflecting surface, as it is in the conventional type of photometer head.

Special instruments, known as exposure meters, have been developed for determining the proper time of exposure in photography. This can be done with a brightness photometer like that shown in Fig. 133. The procedure is to determine the brightness of the deepest shadow within the scene to be photographed and then to calculate the illumination in the image on the plate from Eq. (223) of Chapter XIX. This equation

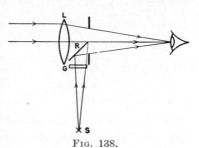

Fig. 138.

indicates that the illumination for a relative aperture of $f/8$ is very nearly $\frac{1}{100}$th of the brightness of the surface toward which the camera is directed. Given the lens opening, it is a simple matter to compute the shutter speed that will produce an exposure in the deepest shadow that is just slightly greater than the inertia of the photographic material. The principal difficulty in the application of this method is that the deepest shadow is sometimes hard to recognize. An alternative procedure is to measure the brightness of the high light of the scene. Then, since few subjects having a brightness range greater than 100 are encountered, an exposure for the high light area equal to 100 times the inertia of the film is usually adequate. This method tends to make the density of the high light the same for all negatives and thus keeps the printing time approximately constant. Of course, the readings of the photometer must be corrected to take account of the difference between the spectral sensitivity of the eye and that of the photographic material.

Unfortunately, there is no compact instrument that measures brightness directly. A close approach to the ideal is realized in one developed by F. H. Norton,[1] which is shown schematically in Fig. 139. A glass plate G reflects light from the comparison lamp S into the field of view. This plate is made of a light smoke glass so that the two reflected images of the filament are not of equal brightness. These images are placed at infinity by the lens L and are seen superposed on the scene being examined. In making a measurement, the current through the lamp is reduced by a rheostat until one of the reflected images can be just seen against the field while the other is just invisible. The calibration of the instrument is in terms of the lamp current, as in an optical pyrometer, but in this case the current is indicated by the setting of the rheostat. It should be noted that the instrument is neither a photometer nor an optical pyrometer, but that the quantity measured is really the adaptation level of the observer. Care should be taken, therefore, to exclude all stray light from the eye.

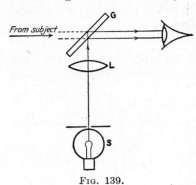

Fig. 139.

A rather extensive class of exposure meters depends upon the variation of visual acuity with the level of illumination. This variation is great enough to lead to results that are sufficiently precise for photographic purposes. In most of these instruments, however, the field seen by the observer is illuminated by light from the entire subject rather than from a selected portion of it. Such exposure meters, therefore, measure the average brightness of the entire scene. They are reliable when the brightness distribution in the subject is normal, but they should be used with caution for subjects of an unusual character.

A quite different class of exposure meters depends upon the action of light on sensitized paper. Usually the procedure is to find the time required for the paper to darken to a predetermined tint. These instruments, while sufficiently accurate for determining the proper exposure, are subject to large errors owing to the failure of the reciprocity law and the difference

[1] *Jour. Optical Soc. Amer. and Rev. Sci. Instruments,* **14,** 435 (1927).

in color sensitivity between the sensitized paper and the material used in the camera. They can be calibrated to determine the exposure by measuring either the light falling on the subject or the light reflected from it.

106. Reflectometry.—In general, when light falls on a substance, part of it is transmitted, part is reflected, and the remainder is absorbed. Most substances of ordinary thickness are so opaque that the proportion of the light transmitted can be neglected. The proportion of light absorbed cannot be measured

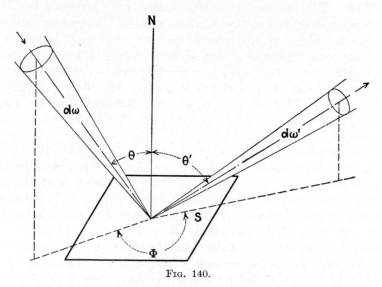

Fɪɢ. 140.

directly, but it can be inferred from measurements of the proportion reflected. The ratio of the luminous flux that is reflected to the flux that is incident is known as the *reflectance*[1] of the substance, but the term is meaningless unless the conditions of illumination and observation are specified. This will be clear from Fig. 140. If the beam of light contained within the small solid angle $d\omega$ is incident on the surface at an angle θ with the normal, the amount of light reflected within another small solid angle $d\omega'$ at an angle θ' with the normal and an azimuth angle Φ depends upon the character of the surface. When the surface

[1] In lieu of any general agreement on the use of the terms "reflectivity" and "reflectance," the former is used in Chap. VIII in connection with the total amount of energy reflected by a surface, and the latter in the present chapter to indicate the amount of visible light that is reflected.

is smooth like a mirror, the reflected flux is zero except when $\theta' = \theta$ and $\Phi = 180°$. To measure the reflectance in such a case, therefore, one has only to compare the intensity of a point source viewed directly with that of its reflected image.

When the surface is rough in comparison with the wave length of light, the phase relationship between the elementary wavelets that is necessary for specular reflection is destroyed. In the limiting case, every element of the surface acts as an independent source, and the reflection is said to be completely diffuse. This is the case represented by Lambert's law of reflection discussed in Sec. 67, Chap. VIII. According to this law, the amount of flux reflected per unit solid angle is proportional to the cosine of θ' and is independent of θ and Φ. No substance obeys Lambert's law exactly, and the consequence is that, in general, the proportion of the flux reflected in any given direction is a function of θ, θ', and Φ. It usually depends also upon the wave length of the light, but this is ignored for the present.

It is impossible, of course, to find a single constant that will give complete information about the reflection characteristics of a material. For this reason, certain standard methods of illumination and observation have been adopted in the determination of reflectance. The results obtained by these methods are significant if the conditions are representative of the usual modes of illuminating and observing the materials. For example, in measuring the reflectance of photographic papers,[1] the standard method is to illuminate the sample by a small solid angle of incident flux at 45° from the normal, and to observe it through a small solid angle along the normal. This method is chosen because it corresponds closely to the conditions under which photographic prints are ordinarily viewed. Such a method is not applicable to very rough surfaces, like textile fabrics, because the reflectance depends to such a marked extent on the azimuth angle. An average value can be obtained in such cases, however, by rotating the specimen in its own plane while the measurements are being made. A still greater averaging effect may be produced without rotating the sample by using diffuse illumination, which can be provided by means of an integrating sphere, such as is shown diagrammatically in Fig. 141. Light enters the sphere through the hole X and strikes the inner

[1] See Sec. 95, Chap. XI.

wall at Y. This wall is coated with a white, diffusely reflecting material having as high a reflectance as possible.[1] Because of this high reflectance, the multiple reflections within the sphere produce an almost perfectly diffuse illumination on the sample. There is, of course, a slight excess of illumination from the direction of the bright spot Y and a deficiency from the directions of the holes at X and Z, but this is ordinarily of slight importance. An incidental advantage of using a paint of high reflectance for

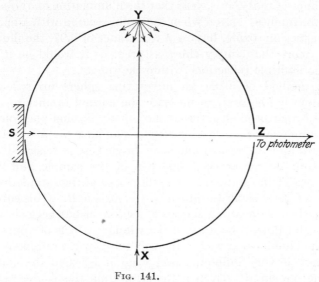

FIG. 141.

coating the inside of the sphere is the very great increase in illumination on the sample. Suppose that an amount of flux F enters the sphere. If the reflectance of the sphere wall is R, an amount of flux FR is diffusely reflected from the bright spot. This flux is finally absorbed on the area A of the sphere wall after a series of multiple reflections. Assuming that the area of the sample and the holes together is negligible,

[1] A procedure that has been recommended is to paint the wall white and then "smoke" it with magnesium oxide. The smoking is done by placing a small pile of magnesium shavings on a refractory plate and igniting them with a blow torch, the surface to be coated being held a few centimeters above the pile. This operation should be repeated until the entire surface is well coated. The pile of shavings should not be too large because of the danger of forming magnesium nitride, which is yellow. The work should be done under a ventilated hood, and the operator should protect his eyes from the large amount of ultraviolet light emitted during the combustion.

$$FR = EA(1 - R),$$

where E is the illumination of the sphere wall. By Sumpner's principle, E is the same everywhere except at the bright spot Y, and its value is

$$E = \frac{FR}{A(1 - R)} \tag{206}$$

from the equation above. If a material could be found having a reflectance of unity, it is clear that the illumination on the sample would be infinite. Even when the wall is coated with a material like magnesium oxide, having a reflectance of 0.97, the illumination is more than thirty times as great as it would be if there were no multiple reflections within the sphere.

One method of using an integrating sphere for reflectance measurements is, first, to measure the normal brightness of the sample by means of an external photometer through the hole at Z. The sample is then replaced by a standard whose reflectance is known and the measurement of brightness is repeated. If b represents the observed brightness of the sample and B the brightness of the standard, the reflectance of the sample relative to that of the standard is given by the ratio b/B. This substitution method is open to a serious objection, as has been shown by Hardy and Pineo;[1] because, if the window at S is of appreciable size, the illumination within the sphere when the sample is being measured is very different from what it is when the standard is being measured. Even if the error from this source is negligible, there remains the difficulty of finding a suitable standard. The most satisfactory one known at present is magnesium carbonate in the form of a block. It is readily available, and a fresh surface is easily prepared by scraping with a straightedge. For diffuse illumination, its normal unidirectional reflectance is about 98 per cent.

The need of a reference standard is avoided in the so-called absolute methods of reflectometry. Such a method is illustrated diagrammatically in Fig. 142. The bright spot Y is again the source of illumination but a small screen K is placed between it and the sample. This screen should be so constructed that its brightness, as seen from the sample, is the same as that of the remainder of the sphere wall. The reflectance of the sample is determined in this case by comparing its brightness with that

[1] *Jour. Optical Soc. Amer.*, **21**, 502 (1931).

of an unscreened portion of the sphere wall such as W. Let the absolute reflectance of the sample be r. Its brightness b is given by

$$b = re,$$

where e is the illumination on the sample. Similarly, the brightness B of the sphere wall at W is given by

$$B = RE,$$

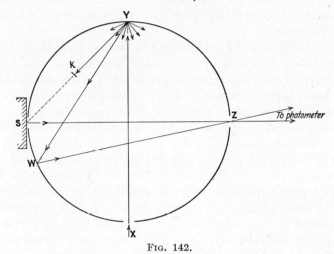

Fig. 142.

where E is its illumination. A photometer situated outside the sphere measures the ratio b/B, which is

$$\frac{b}{B} = \frac{re}{RE}.$$

The illumination E at W is given by Eq. (206). The illumination e of the sample is less than this by an amount corresponding to the illumination produced by light that is once reflected from the bright spot, whence

$$e = \frac{FR}{A(1-R)} - \frac{FR}{A}. \tag{207}$$

From Eqs. (206) and (207), the ratio $e/E = R$. Therefore, $b/B = r$. In other words, this method of comparing the brightness of the screened sample with that of the unscreened sphere wall gives the *absolute reflectance* of the sample for diffuse illumination and normal observation. By the principle of reversibility of the light path, this quantity also represents the proportion of light diffusely reflected when the incident light is a unidirectional beam normal to the surface.

The method here described is only one of a number that have been used, and the reader should consult a paper by McNicholas[1] for a comprehensive treatment of the subject of reflectance measurements. It may be worth while to mention, however, that the above method is often modified by substituting one or more small lamps for the bright spot. The results are substantially the same if the direct light from the lamps is screened from the sample.

A single value of the reflectance of a surface gives no indication of its gloss.[2] There is probably no other term in common use that conveys such a concrete idea and yet is so difficult to define. The reason is that a definition which is satisfactory for one type of material may be quite misleading when applied to some other. Thus the definition of gloss used in connection with photographic papers is inadequate to express what the painter means by the gloss of a painted surface. In the painter's mind, gloss is an intrinsic property of the paint and it should therefore be independent of the pigment, which is added merely to produce the desired color. Since the pigment affects the diffusely reflected component to a pronounced degree and the specularly reflected component but slightly, it is clear that any definition that involves the diffuse reflectance is unsatisfactory. Possibly the best procedure in specifying the gloss of a painted surface is to measure merely the intensity of the specular component. An instrument devised by Pfund[3] that operates on this principle has been found to yield results in keeping with the common conception of gloss in this connection.

When a complete specification of the gloss of a surface is desired, one is compelled to use a gonio-photometer. In principle, this instrument consists simply of a photometer arranged to measure the brightness of the surface for any angle of incidence and observation. A simple apparatus was used by Jones[4] in the measurement of the reflection characteristics of photographic papers and motion-picture projection screens. It

---

[1] *Bur. Standards Jour. Research,* **1,** 29 (1928) (*Research Paper* 3).

[2] The subject of gloss was discussed briefly in Sec. 12, Chap. 1, and again in connection with photographic papers in Chap. XI.

[3] *Jour. Optical Soc. Amer.,* **20,** 23 (1930).

[4] *Jour. Optical Soc. Amer. and Rev. Sci. Instruments,* **6,** 140 (1922)

will be obvious that, if the unidirectional reflectance is known for all angles of illumination and observation, the reflectance under any set of assigned conditions can be computed.

107. The Measurement of Transmission.—The general principles discussed in connection with reflectometry hold also in the measurement of transmission.[1] An optically homogeneous material, such as a piece of glass or a solution of copper sulphate, corresponds to a plane mirror; and its transmission can be measured by comparing the intensity of any convenient source of light with the apparent intensity as seen through the material in question. The procedure can be carried out on an ordinary bar photometer, but this instrument has the disadvantage of requiring two sources that must be maintained at a constant intensity. Instruments designed primarily for transmission measurements therefore usually contain a single source. Two

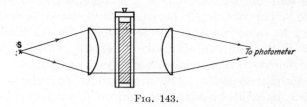

Fig. 143.

beams are derived from this source, one passing through the specimen and the other around it, so that fluctuations in the intensity of the source do not affect the results.

Since the proportion of light transmitted by an absorbing material depends upon its thickness, the beam should ordinarily be collimated at the point where the specimen is introduced, as shown in Fig. 143. For the same reason, the dimensions of the source should be small compared with the distance from the collimator. It is clear that the value of the transmission obtained in this way is a maximum because the light path within the specimen is a minimum. In the case represented, the material is a liquid contained in a cell having plane-parallel faces. A solid material is prepared for measurement by grinding the opposite faces plane and parallel.

[1] The ratio of the amount of light transmitted by a material to the amount incident upon it was defined in Chap. I as "transparency." Although this term is used as a measure of the blackening of photographic materials, the term "transmission" is more common in other connections.

A material that is non-homogeneous, such as a piece of ground glass or a photographic plate, corresponds to a diffuse reflector, and its transmission obviously depends to a great extent upon the conditions of illumination and observation. The most generally useful single value for the transmission of such a material is that obtained by illuminating the sample by completely diffuse light and measuring the transmission in a direction normal to the surface. This is equivalent, of course, to allowing a collimated beam of light to strike the material normally and measuring all the flux transmitted. An integrating sphere can be used to obtain the diffuse light, but a simpler procedure is to place a piece of opal glass in contact with the specimen on the side toward the source. A simple test for the completeness of the diffusion is to determine whether adding a second piece of opal glass alters the results. It cannot be emphasized too strongly that the transmission of a non-homogeneous material that is to be part of an optical system should always be measured *in situ* or in some manner that is optically equivalent.

The advantage of expressing the absorption of a material in terms of density rather than transmission is obvious in the case of photographic deposits. This procedure is also advantageous with other materials because of the nature of the laws governing the variation of transmission with thickness (Bouguer's law) and with concentration (Beer's law). It will be seen that the density of absorbing materials is directly proportional to both the thickness and the concentration of the absorbing substance. Furthermore, if two absorbing substances are inserted in the same beam, the resultant density is simply the sum of the individual densities, whereas the resultant transmission is the product of the individual transmissions.[1]

The problem of measuring the density of photographic deposits occurs so frequently that special instruments have been developed for the purpose. As a class they are known as densitometers, but it is clear that there is no essential difference between them and other types of photometers. Since compactness is desirable, these instruments rarely operate on the inverse-square principle. Instead, diaphragms or wedges are sometimes used for varying the intensity of the comparison beam; but most of the commercial

---

[1] This statement is subject to the qualification that, when two substances are inserted together, the inter-reflections between their faces may slightly modify the results.

instruments operate on a polarization principle devised by Martens. He developed his original instrument for determining the polarization of sky light, but it has proved to be extremely useful as a photometer. A photograph of a modern type is shown in Fig. 144. The essential elements of the optical system are a Wollaston prism and a Nicol prism, the rotation of one with respect to the other producing a known variation in the relative intensities of the two beams. The transmission can be computed from the azimuth of the Nicol prism before and after the specimen is introduced.[1]

108. Spectrophotometry.—It has been assumed up to this point that the two beams of light involved in the photometric

Fig. 144.—The Martens photometer as made by Franz Schmidt and Haensch.

comparison have the same color. The comparison of two beams of different color is called *heterochromatic photometry*. This particular branch of photometry will be treated in the next section, and it will suffice to state here that the difficulties involved are formidable. They are avoided, however, in spectrophotometry,[2] wherein the two beams are dispersed into spectra and compared wave length by wave length, the photometric field being homochromatic, of course. Spectrophotometry may nevertheless be considered as a type of heterochromatic photometry in the sense that it accomplishes the same result.

Spectrophotometry bears the same relationship to photometry that spectroradiometry bears to radiometry; it is distinguished from spectroradiometry by giving results that are relative instead

---

[1] This instrument is described more fully in Sec. 215, Chap. XXIX.

[2] The subject of spectrophotometry is treated at length in a report of the Committee on Spectrophotometry of the Optical Society of America, *Jour. Optical Soc. Amer. and Rev. Sci. Instruments*, **10**, 169 (1925). See also a paper by Gibson, *Jour. Optical Soc. Amer.*, **21**, 564 (1931).

of absolute.   Thus a spectrophotometric comparison of two light sources gives the energy distribution of one source relative to that of the other, whereas a spectroradiometric analysis can be made of either source without reference to the other.   A spectrophotometer is therefore more useful in connection with the measurement of transmission or reflection characteristics of materials than in the examination of light sources.   The first spectrophotometers were visual instruments, but nowadays they

Fig. 145.—The König-Martens spectrophotometer as made by Franz Schmidt and Haensch.

are more likely to depend upon some physical detector of radiation, such as the photoelectric cell or the photographic plate. Inasmuch as the observations are always made with light of a single wave length, it is clear that this method gives results that are independent of the spectral sensitivity of the particular detector of radiation that is employed.

A typical spectrophotometer for visual use is shown in Fig. 145. This instrument was devised by König, who combined a prismatic dispersing system with the Martens polarizing photometer.   The dispersing prism forms two adjacent spectra at the eye point, one from the source under investigation and the other from the comparison source. The instrument is so constructed that the observer views a homochromatic field in monochromatic light of the wave length to which the instrument is adjusted. The field is balanced by rotating the Nicol prism, as with the Martens photometer.[1] When the König-Martens spectrophotometer is used for the examination of opaque materials, it is customary to mount the sample and the standard side by side and illuminate them by means of an integrating sphere. Light reflected from the sample enters one end of the slit and fills one half of the photometric field; light from the standard fills the other half of the field. In the case of liquid specimens, such as dye solutions, a dummy cell containing the solvent is often placed in the comparison beam.[2]

The difficulties in visual spectrophotometry are many. In the first place, the optical system contains a large number of air-glass surfaces that are likely to cause the field of view to be filled with stray light. In the König-Martens instrument, thin prisms are cemented to the collimator and telescope lenses to deflect the stray light originating at these surfaces. An unavoidable difficulty in visual spectrophotometry results from the low visibility of radiation near the ends of the spectrum. This difficulty is especially pronounced in the violet because the incandescent lamps that are commonly used as a source of illumination emit so feebly in this region. Visual spectrophotometers have not been widely used, partly because of the difficulty just mentioned but more because of the time required for the complete analysis of a single specimen. Ordinarily, observations should be made at no fewer than 30 points throughout the spectrum, and at least four settings should be made at each point. Even an experienced observer requires upwards of half an hour to make all these settings.

A photoelectric spectrophotometer that aims to expedite the determination of spectrophotometric data has been described by one of the present authors.[3] The instrument is designed

---

[1] A more extensive description of the instrument is to be found in Chap. XXIX.

[2] For an extensive description of the use of the König-Martens spectrophotometer, the reader should consult a paper by McNicholas, *Bur. Standards Jour. Research*, **1**, 793 (1928) (*Research Paper* 30).

[3] *Jour. Optical Soc. Amer. and Rev. Sci. Instruments*, **18**, 96 (1929).

primarily for use with opaque materials, but transparent homogeneous materials can also be accommodated, and a modified form of the instrument could be used for light sources. The optical system is shown in Fig. 146. The sample to be measured and a standard surface of magnesium carbonate are illuminated normally from opposite sides of a ribbon-filament tungsten lamp. Beams of light reflected at 45° from the sample and the standard are admitted alternately to the entrance slit of a pris-

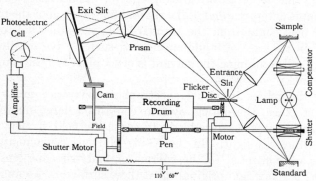

Fig. 146.—The principle of operation of a photoelectric spectrophotometer employing the null method.

matic dispersing system by means of a glass flicker disk, the alternate sectors of which are silvered. The exit slit isolates a 10-mμ band of the spectrum formed by the prism, and this band is allowed to fall on the photoelectric cell. When the amount of light reflected from the sample is different from that reflected by the standard, a pulsating photoelectric current is produced. This current is amplified, and the alternating component is applied to the field coils of a small motor. The frequency of the pulsation is 60 cycles/sec., and, hence, when the armature is supplied also from a 60-cycle source, the motor is caused to rotate. This motor operates a shutter placed between the lamp and the standard, and the direction of rotation is always such as to balance the two beams. When the balance point is reached, the pulsations in the light cease and the motor stops. A pen moving on a rotating drum records the position of the shutter, while the rotation of the drum changes the wave length. In this way, a complete spectrophotometric curve for the entire visible spectrum is traced in about two minutes. Figure 147 is a photograph of the commercial model of this instrument.

A photographic method of spectrophotometry is generally used in the ultraviolet or whenever the light is weak. The laws connecting the density of the photographic deposit with the intensity of the exposing light depend on so many factors that, unless a null method is used, the precautions to be observed are very formidable. The assumption underlying the null method of photographic photometry is that, if two small contiguous areas of an emulsion are exposed for the same length of time to light of the same wave length from two different light sources, the sources may be judged equal if the resulting densities are equal. If these conditions are fulfilled, errors due to the failure

FIG. 147.—A commercial photoelectric color analyzer employing the null method. (*By courtesy of General Electric Company.*)

of the reciprocity law, variations of gamma with wave length, or variations in sensitivity from point to point in the emulsion are avoided. An instrument that fulfills these conditions has been proposed by L. A. Jones.[1]

A rough but simple method of photographic spectrophotometry consists in placing an optical wedge over the slit of an ordinary spectrograph in such a manner that the intensity of the light transmitted by the slit varies according to a known law from top to bottom. The wedge can be made of gelatin dyed with a neutral dye or it can be a piece of black glass ground into the form of a prism.[2] The method will be obvious from the wedge spectrograms shown in Fig. 148. The upper spectrogram was

---

[1] *Jour. Optical Soc. Amer. and Rev. Sci. Instruments*, **10**, 561 (1925).

[2] Neither type of wedge is ever truly non-selective in its absorption, and to overcome this fault, O. E Miller has devised an instrument in which a template is used instead. See *Rev. Sci. Instruments*, **3**, 30 (1932).

made with a panchromatic plate without a filter, and the lower was made with a Wratten K-2 filter in the beam, the time of exposure being the same in both cases. The steepness of the wedge can be measured optically and an intensity scale can be placed on the spectrograms to indicate the approximate value of the absorption characteristics of the filter. Such an instrument is known as a wedge spectrograph.

It was tacitly assumed in the two preceding sections on the measurement of reflectance and transmission that the specimens

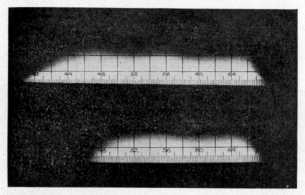

Fig. 148.—Wedge spectrograms of Eastman supersensitive panchromatic cine film showing its spectral sensitivity without a filter and with a Wratten K-2 filter.

were non-selective as to wave length. Now it is clear that the results of a spectrophotometric analysis are expressible in terms of the reflectance at each wave length in the case of an opaque material, or in terms of the transmission at each wave length in the case of a transparent material. Whether the sample is selective or non-selective is obviously of no consequence. Some consideration must be given, however, to the method of computing the total reflectance or total transmission from spectrophotometric data. For convenience, the case of a transparent material will be selected for illustration, but the same procedure is applicable in the case of an opaque material. Let the function expressing the variation of the transmission of the specimen through the spectrum be T_λ. Then if E_λ represents the energy distribution of the source, and S_λ the spectral sensitivity of the radiation detector, the total transmission of the specimen in the language of the integral calculus is

$$T = \frac{\int_0^\infty T_\lambda E_\lambda S_\lambda d\lambda}{\int_0^\infty E_\lambda S_\lambda d\lambda}. \qquad (208)$$

Ordinarily the radiation detector is the human eye, and the quantity S_λ is then the visibility function. It cannot be emphasized too strongly that a mere statement of the transmission of a material is meaningless unless both functions E_λ and S_λ are specified. This probably causes the most confusion in connection with the so-called "filter factors" of the filters used in photography. The factor of a filter depends, of course, on the type of photographic material, the spectral quality of the illuminant, and even the color of the object.

109. Heterochromatic Photometry.—Although the meaning of this term refers broadly to the comparison of two beams of light of different color, it is generally used in a somewhat restricted sense to mean the direct comparison of the two beams without resorting to the wave-length-by-wave-length comparisons that are characteristic of spectrophotometry. If the two halves of a photometric field are illuminated by light of different color, the eye is seriously embarrassed in making an equality-of-brightness match. For example, if one half of the field is red and the other green, there is no point at which the two halves can definitely be said to have the same brightness. Settings can be made which appear to be fairly reproducible when judged by the average deviation from the mean; but if the experiment is repeated by another observer, or even by the same observer at a subsequent time, a very different result may be obtained. In other words, during the course of a single experiment an observer adopts an artificial criterion for equality of brightness.

One method of avoiding the difficulties of making a heterochromatic setting is to employ a color filter to produce a color match in the photometer. Gelatin filters for this purpose are available from the Eastman Kodak Company for use in the inter-comparison of light sources, but glass and liquid filters have also been used advantageously.[1] In every case, the transmission of the filter must of course be known. It can be computed from the spectrophotometric curve of the filter by the method outlined in the preceding section, or it can be found experimentally by

[1] A series of liquid filters especially designed for this purpose is described in *Bur. Standards Misc. Pub.* 114.

measuring the intensity of a source both with and without the filter in the beam.   The latter method involves all the difficulties of comparing the two sources directly, but it has the advantage that the transmission of the filter can be determined once and for all by several observers.   Subsequent comparisons of the two light sources by a single observer are, therefore, nearly as precise as though many observers had cooperated.

A procedure that is sometimes used in the photometry of incandescent lamps operating at different color temperatures is to divide the color difference into small steps by means of auxiliary sources.   This is the so-called step-by-step or cascade method.   For a single observer, the end result of this procedure is no more accurate than a direct comparison in the presence of the whole color difference, but the day-to-day consistency is found to be better.   The ideal procedure, of course, is to calibrate a series of standard sources operating at various color temperatures, so that an unknown source can be compared directly with one approximating it in color; but this method is applicable in general only to incandescent sources.

The flicker method of heterochromatic photometry is ordinarily used when the color difference is large, the procedure being to expose the eye to light from the two sources in rapid succession. This method depends upon the experimental fact that a frequency can be found at which the color difference disappears, but the flicker due to the brightness difference remains.   The photometer head is then adjusted until the brightness flicker disappears altogether or is a minimum.   There is no *a priori* justification for this method, and at first the experimental results obtained by it did not agree with those found by the direct-comparison methods.   The discrepancies led Ives[1] to study the flicker photometer extensively, and he formulated certain conditions for its use.   Chief among these is that the photometric field should subtend an angle of not more than 2° to insure that its image will lie entirely on the macula.   When the flicker photometer is used under the prescribed conditions, the reproducibility of the readings is high and the results are in good agreement with those obtained by other methods.   In addition, it is found that inexperienced observers have considerably less difficulty with the flicker method than with direct-comparison methods when a large color difference is involved.

[1] *Phil. Mag.*, **24**, 149, 352, 744, 845, 853 (1912).

110. Physical Photometry.—Since most photometric measurements are designed to evaluate the effect of light on the human retina, it follows that the light-sensitive detector in a physical photometer should have the same effective sensitivity as the human eye. Ives and Kingsbury[1] attacked the problem by using a thermopile and a galvanometer in conjunction with a suitable filter. This filter consisted of a 2-cm thickness of a solution made up according to the following formula:

Cupric chloride ($CuCl_2$)	60.0	grams
Cobalt ammonium sulphate $[Co(NH_4)_2(SO_4)_2]$	14.5	grams
Potassium chromate (K_2CrO_4)	1.9	grams
Water, to make	1.0	liter

In addition, at least 4 cm of water should be used to absorb the infrared. Instead of using a filter, the light to be measured could have been dispersed into a spectrum and then passed through a template so fashioned that the amount transmitted at any wave length is proportional to the visibility of the eye at that wave length.

The chief difficulty with the thermopile and similar instruments is the necessity of measuring very small electric currents. A galvanometer of suitable sensitivity is subject to mechanical disturbances, drift of the zero, and lack of proportionality between the deflection and the current producing it. These difficulties make it seem unlikely that the thermopile can ever replace the eye in photometric determinations.

The selenium cell has been used in photometry, but it suffers from a disadvantage common to all selective detectors of radiation—namely, that the spectral sensitivity varies so much from one cell to another that the amount of labor necessary to find a suitable filter is unjustified. Furthermore, the sensitivity of even a single cell is far from constant. Although the photoelectric cell is vastly superior to the selenium cell for photometric purposes, it suffers to a considerable extent from the same faults. If devices of this character are to compete successfully with the trained human eye, it appears that a null method must be adopted.[2] The conditions that must be fulfilled by the optical system of a photometer based on the null method are as follows:

[1] *Phys. Rev.*, **6**, 319 (1915).

[2] A null method for the photometry of incandescent lamps has been described by Sharp, *Trans. Illum. Eng. Soc.*, **23**, 428 (1928). A null method for spectrophotometry is described in Sec. 108.

1. The two beams under comparison must have the same spectral quality and state of polarization.

2. The same area of the active surface of the cell must be illuminated at the same angle by both beams in rapid succession.

3. The transition from one beam to the other must take place without an intervening dark period.

If these conditions are satisfied, the beams are obviously of equal intensity when there is no variation in the cell current.

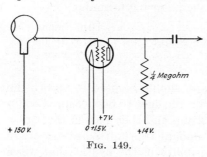

The null method is simple of application because of the ease with which rapid variations in the cell current can be amplified. Furthermore, there is no limit to the precision of the method that corresponds to the limit set for visual methods by the contrast sensitivity of the eye.

Fig. 149.

The ultimate limit to the precision is set only by the "shot" effect in the cell and the associated circuit, but this limit is far beyond the most exacting requirements of present-day photometry.

A special method of connecting a photoelectric cell to a vacuum tube has been found useful in connection with the null method of photoelectric photometry. This is shown in Fig. 149, where the cathode of the cell is connected directly to the grid of the vacuum tube. If precautions are taken in operating the tube so that the reverse grid current is negligible,[1] a given fractional change in the cell current

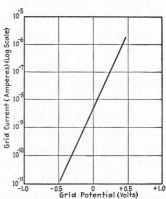

Fig. 150.—Grid current of the UY-224 tube as a function of the grid potential. The data are the same as for Fig. 129.

produces the same change in grid potential regardless of the magnitude of the cell current. This is shown in Fig. 150, which is plotted from the same data as Fig. 129. When this method of connection is used, the precision of a setting is almost independent of the level of illumination within wide limits, a characteristic also possessed by the human eye (Fechner's law).

[1] See Sec. 100 of the preceding chapter.

The chemical action of light has been suggested many times as a basis of physical photometry. The only practical methods of this type involve the use of a photographic plate, which suffers from faults analogous to those of light-sensitive cells and from many others in addition, as shown in Chap. XI. The only merit of photographic methods is that they can be used in some cases where others cannot. In the photometry of weakly fluorescent materials, for example, the ability of a photographic plate to accumulate exposure over long periods of time makes it decidedly superior to other types of photometers.

CHAPTER XIV

COLOR

The term "color" is used in three different senses. To the chemist, a color is simply a material such as a dyestuff. To the physicist, "color" is practically synonymous with "light," and both are described in objective terms by the spectral distribution of energy in the radiation in question. To the psychologist, on the other hand, the term "color" denotes the subjective sensation produced in the brain of a human observer, generally the result of a physical stimulus. This triple meaning of the term may easily be the cause of confusion because it may be used in all three senses in even a single sentence. One might properly say, for example, that the *sensation of color* is generally the result of the *color stimulus* produced when white light is reflected from a *colored object*. Such an ambiguous use of a term is inconsistent with the exactitude that characterizes science, but it is typical of the whole body of color terminology. Most of the terms used by color technologists are household words which, for want of suitable substitutes, have been given a restricted technical significance. This has happened so recently that even technical workers in the field do not always agree among themselves; and it will probably take some time to evolve a systematic nomenclature that will win universal recognition. For a striking illustration of the chaotic condition of color nomenclature, the reader should examine the replies to a questionnaire that was distributed by the Optical Society of America to a large number of workers in the field of color.[1]

During the past decade, the problem of measuring and specifying color has become one of extraordinary importance. This has been due in part to the more liberal use of color that has come into vogue since the war. A more cogent reason, however, is the rapid spread of methods of quantity production, which require a uniformity in the product that would otherwise be unnecessary. Hence the subject of color, instead of being of

[1] *Jour. Optical Soc. Amer. and Rev. Sci. Instruments*, **13**, 43 (1926).

interest only to those who manufacture or use dyes, paints, inks, and other coloring materials, is of great significance in connection with practically every article of commerce. Indeed, there is every indication that the subject of color will become one of the most important branches of applied optics.

The measurement of a color in the objective sense is accomplished by means of either a spectroradiometer or a spectrophotometer. The former is more convenient for measuring the color of light sources, and the latter for measuring the color of transparent and opaque materials. Some typical spectrophotometric curves for objects whose colors are well known are shown in Fig. 151. If these curves, or the data from which they are

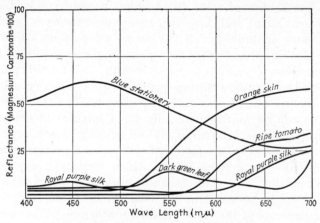

Fig. 151.—Spectrophotometric curves of certain well-known objects when illuminated at 45° and viewed normally.

plotted, are determined with sufficient precision, the color of the object in question is adequately specified in the objective sense. Of course, unless the material reflects diffusely, the color depends to a great extent upon the angle of illumination and observation. In other words, a glossy surface exhibits, in general, an infinite number of colors. This means that a single spectrophotometric curve can represent the color of a surface only under a single set of specified conditions.

111. The Sensation of Color.—It is a fact of common experience that the eye is incapable of analyzing a complex stimulus into its spectral components.[1] Those whose business it is to mix

[1] In this respect there is a fundamental difference between the response of the eye and that of the ear, because the latter can, with proper training,

colors sometimes believe they can see in the resulting mixture the components which they have added, but this effect is due simply to judgment based on experience and not to any analytical powers possessed by the eye. Because of this lack of ability to analyze radiation, there are in general an infinite number of color stimuli that will evoke the same sensation. Thus the objective method of specifying colors by means of spectrophotometric curves may be misleading in the sense that it fails to indicate whether two colors having different curves will appear alike or to what extent they will appear unlike. It is necessary, therefore, to investigate the effect produced by a complex color stimulus on the visual apparatus of a normal human observer.

The mechanism of color vision is but partially understood at the present time; and, although many theories have been proposed, none accounts for all the known phenomena. From the standpoint of applied optics, the most important problem is the interpretation of spectrophotometric data, and, for this purpose, the Young-Helmholtz theory provides a satisfactory solution. This theory is founded upon the experimental fact that any color stimulus can be matched visually by a mixture of the proper amounts of three arbitrarily chosen stimuli, which are called *primaries*. Let it be assumed that one half of a photometric field is illuminated by a stimulus E_λ, which may have any desired energy distribution. This stimulus produces a sensation that can be exactly matched in the other half of the field by the proper amounts of the three primaries, which may likewise be of any arbitrary spectral quality or may even be monochromatic. Let the amount of each primary required for a color match be represented by A, B, and C respectively. Then, regardless of the manner of choosing the primaries, a unique set of values for A, B, and C can always be found to satisfy the relation[1]

$$E_\lambda = A + B + C.$$

These quantities may have negative values, in which case the primary in question must be added to the half of the field that is illuminated by the unknown stimulus instead of the comparison field.

analyze as complex a stimulus as the music of a symphony orchestra into the components produced by the various instruments.

[1] The sign of equality is used here to indicate that the sensations are equal rather than that the stimuli are equal.

All the basic facts of color mixture can be determined from one simple experiment. Such an experiment will now be described, not in the form in which it is usually conducted, but in a slight modification that is more easily comprehended. One half of a photometric field is illuminated by monochromatic light, the energy of which is held constant as the wave length is varied. The other half of the field is illuminated by measurable amounts

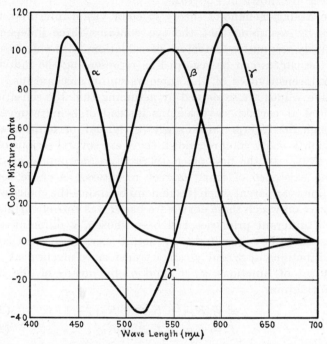

Fig. 152.—Color mixture data for monochromatic primaries of wave length 450 mμ, 550 mμ, and 620 mμ.

of three monochromatic primaries, which, for the sake of concreteness, will be assumed to be at 450 mμ, 550 mμ, and 620 mμ. The apparatus is assumed to be so designed that these primaries can be transferred when necessary to the opposite side of the photometric field. The first step in the experiment is to make the wave length of the monochromatic stimulus the same as that of one of the primaries, say the one at 450 mμ. To match this stimulus, only the 450-mμ primary is required, and the scale on which this one is measured can be set arbitrarily at 100 as a matter of convenience. By repeating this operation with the

monochromatic field set at 550 mµ and 620 mµ in turn, the scales
on which the other primaries are read can be arbitrarily set at 100
likewise. With these preliminary adjustments made, the
monochromatic field is set at other wave lengths throughout the
spectrum in turn, and the values of α, β, and γ required to produce a color match are determined. The values that would be
obtained if such an experiment were performed by a normal
observer are shown in Fig. 152.

The Young-Helmholtz theory of color vision interprets these
curves by assuming that the eye contains three independent
selectively-responsive detectors of radiation. On this assumption, the curves can be regarded as representing the individual
spectral sensitivities of the three receptor mechanisms. The
negative values are explained by assuming that the sensation is
inhibited at certain wave lengths instead of being stimulated.
Although this interpretation suggests a visual mechanism whose
behavior is easily comprehended, there are several serious objections to it. In the first place, there is no anatomical evidence
for the existence of three sets of receptors. A more serious
objection is apparent when it is remembered that the choice of the
primaries on which these curves are based was entirely arbitrary;
thus, if different primaries had been chosen, a different set of
curves would have resulted. In fact, it is easily shown that the
three functions α, β, and γ can be transformed algebraically into
a new set of functions α', β', and γ' by means of the linear
transformation:

$$\alpha' = K_1\alpha + K_2\beta + K_3\gamma, \qquad (209a)$$
$$\beta' = K_4\alpha + K_5\beta + K_6\gamma, \qquad (209b)$$

and

$$\gamma' = K_7\alpha + K_8\beta + K_9\gamma. \qquad (209c)$$

The quantities, $K_1, K_2, \ldots K_9$, are constants whose values may
be chosen quite at random.[1] By substituting the values of α, β,
and γ at each wave length in the above equations, the new set
of functions thus derived is as adequate an expression of the facts
of color mixture as any other. If the eye does contain three
sets of receptor mechanisms, it is clear that color-mixture data

[1] Subject only to the restriction that the determinant $\begin{Bmatrix} K_1K_2K_3 \\ K_4K_5K_6 \\ K_7K_8K_9 \end{Bmatrix}$ must
not equal zero.

alone are insufficient to determine explicitly the form of their sensitivity curves.

König and Dieterici experimented with dichromats—that is, observers with abnormal color vision whose mixture data can be interpreted on the basis of two excitation functions instead of three. It seemed natural to assume that such observers lacked one of the three receptor mechanisms possessed by normal trichromats and that the missing function should represent the sensitivity of one of the normal receptor mechanisms. Although

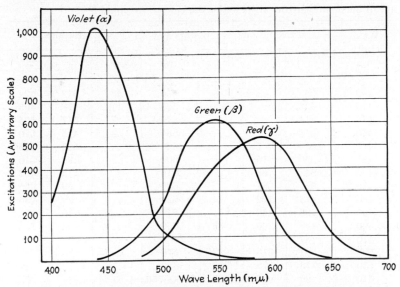

Fig. 153.—The excitation functions recommended by the 1920 Optical Society of America Committee on Colorimetry. The values are for an equal-energy spectrum, but the relative magnitudes of the three functions have been chosen so that the areas under the curves are equal for mean noon sunlight. The data for the curves are given in Table XIX.

these experiments are of interest in the understanding of the mechanism of vision, the present tendency in colorimetry is to regard the mixture curves for no more than they are worth and to select them purely with reference to their convenience in reducing spectrophotometric data.

One set of excitation functions that has been used more widely than any other was given in a report of the Colorimetry Committee of the Optical Society of America.[1] These curves are repro-

[1] *Jour. Optical Soc. Amer. and Rev. Sci. Instruments,* **6,** 527 (1922).

duced in Fig. 153 and the data from which they are plotted are given in Table XIX. The curves are for an equal-energy spectrum, but the relative magnitudes of the functions have been chosen so that a stimulus having the quality of average noon sunlight excites the three receptor mechanisms equally. This

TABLE XIX.—EXCITATION FUNCTIONS RECOMMENDED BY THE 1920 COM-
MITTEE ON COLORIMETRY OF THE OPTICAL SOCIETY OF AMERICA

The values, which are in arbitrary units, are for an equal-energy spectrum. The relative magnitudes of the three functions have been chosen so that for mean noon sunlight the areas under the curves are equal.[*]

Wave length, $m\mu$	Excitations			Wave length, $m\mu$	Excitations		
	α	β	γ		α	β	γ
400	253	...	...	550	18	612	424
410	433	...	...	560	11	578	466
420	614	...	...	570	7	517	505
430	915	...	...	580	4	415	520
440	1019	7	...	590	..	296	535
450	950	16	...	600	..	196	510
460	842	38	...	610	..	113	462
470	697	81	...	620	..	59	375
480	473	122	14	630	..	29	285
490	220	169	41	640	..	10	195
500	123	260	83	650	..	3	118
510	87	391	151	660	..	...	68
520	61	510	233	670	..	...	40
530	43	572	307	680	..	...	22
540	29	603	373	Σ690–750	..	...	27

[*] *Jour. Optical Soc. Amer. and Rev. Sci. Instruments*, **6**, 549 (1922).

NOTE.—$\Sigma\alpha = 6799$; $\Sigma\beta = 5597$; $\Sigma\gamma = 5754$.

choice is merely a matter of convenience because it places sunlight in the center of the color triangle, which will be discussed presently. Unfortunately these curves are based on old data, obtained by König and Abney, and recent investigations by W. D. Wright[1] and J. Guild[2] with more refined apparatus indicate that some of the values may have to be revised. In view of the importance that this subject has assumed, it is desirable that

[1] *Trans. Optical Soc. (London)*, **30**, 141 (1928–1929); *idem*, **31**, 201 (1929–1930).

[2] *Phil. Trans. Roy. Soc. London*, **230**, 149 (1931).

an international agreement be reached on a specific form of the excitation functions.[1]

For the interpretation of spectrophotometric data, it is unnecessary to make any speculations whatever concerning the mechanism of the visual process. Curves like those of Fig. 153 indicate directly the amount of each of the three arbitrarily selected primaries that must be added together to match a given monochromatic stimulus of any wave length. If the unknown stimulus is not monochromatic, the computations can still be made on the basis of these curves. By representing the energy distribution in the stimulus by E_λ, it is clear that the amount of each primary required for a color match can be found by multiplying the value of E_λ at each wave length by the corresponding values of α, β, and γ, and summing the results. In mathematical symbols, these operations are represented by

$$A = \int_0^\infty \alpha E_\lambda d\lambda, \qquad (210a)$$

$$B = \int_0^\infty \beta E_\lambda d\lambda, \qquad (210b)$$

and

$$C = \int_0^\infty \gamma E_\lambda d\lambda. \qquad (210c)$$

Any other stimulus E_λ' will obviously evoke the same sensation as E_λ if

$$\int_0^\infty \alpha E_\lambda' d\lambda = A = \int_0^\infty \alpha E_\lambda d\lambda,$$

$$\int_0^\infty \beta E_\lambda' d\lambda = B = \int_0^\infty \beta E_\lambda d\lambda,$$

and

$$\int_0^\infty \gamma E_\lambda' d\lambda = C = \int_0^\infty \gamma E_\lambda d\lambda.$$

It is evident, therefore, that the quantities A, B, and C, although not necessarily a measure of the visual sensation, are sufficient to indicate the conditions under which two stimuli that are different in the objective sense will evoke the same sensation.

The stimuli E_λ and E_λ' may represent the direct radiation from primary sources of light, but more frequently they represent radiation that is reflected or transmitted by a material whose

[1] Since this chapter was written, the International Commission on Illumination, meeting at Cambridge, England, has adopted a standard set of excitation functions. A comprehensive treatment of this subject will be found in an article by Judd in *Jour. Optical Soc. Amer.*, **23**, 359 (1933).

color is to be measured.   Taking the case of reflected light as an example because it is more common, let R_λ represent the reflectance of the material as a function of wave length, and E_λ the energy distribution of the source by which the material is illuminated.   The excitation values in this case are evidently

$$A = \int_0^\infty \alpha R_\lambda E_\lambda d\lambda, \tag{211a}$$

$$B = \int_0^\infty \beta R_\lambda E_\lambda d\lambda, \tag{211b}$$

and

$$C = \int_0^\infty \gamma R_\lambda E_\lambda d\lambda. \tag{211c}$$

It appears from this that a material whose color is specified objectively by $R_\lambda = f(\lambda)$ (that is, in terms of spectrophotometric data) evokes a sensation that is adequately specified by A, B, and C.   The values of these quantities obviously depend upon the quality of the illumination E_λ.   Two materials specified objectively by different functions R_λ may therefore appear of the same color under one particular kind of illumination.   If the quality of the illumination is changed, the colors will, in general, no longer match.   This fact hardly requires comment for it is well known that many materials that match well under daylight fail to match at all under artificial light, although the difference in spectral quality is relatively small.   This may be summarized by stating that if two materials are to match in the objective sense, their spectrophotometric curves must be identical; and, in this case, they will always match regardless of the spectral quality of the source by which they are illuminated or the peculiarities of the observer's visual apparatus.   Two materials having different spectrophotometric curves may match in the subjective sense for one observer and one type of source, but they will, in general, fail to match for an observer with a different color sense or a source of different spectral quality.

112. The Representation of Colorimetric Data.—One of the commonest complaints among the industrial users of color is the difficulty of keeping color records in a systematic manner. For example, a paint manufacturer may easily have fifty thousand or more formulae in his file.   If this file is to be useful, the colors must be arranged by some sort of system, preferably with a number assigned to each.   One obvious method of assigning such a number is to decide arbitrarily that the color of a white standard, such as magnesium carbonate, when illuminated by a source having an equal-energy spectrum shall be represented by $A = 100$, $B = 100$, and $C = 100$. On this basis, a light neutral gray under the same illumination might be represented by 40-40-40, and a light green by 13.1-51.4-35.3. By arranging the file according to these numbers, it is evident that all colors that look alike will be filed together. When a new sample is to be matched, its color can be measured with a spectrophotometer and the values A, B, and C computed. With this information, one can quickly turn to the formula producing the closest approximation to a color match. That such a practice has not been already universally adopted is due simply to the lack of suitable color-measuring instruments.

A graphical representation of colors is obtained by plotting the values of A, B, and C in some three-dimensional system of coordinates. This procedure is not very convenient, and it is therefore desirable to find a method of representing the maximum amount of information about a color on a two-dimensional plot. Suppose that, instead of taking A, B, and C as the parameters, the following ratios are used:

$$\frac{A}{A + B + C},$$

$$\frac{B}{A + B + C},$$

and

$$\frac{C}{A + B + C}.$$

Only two of these quantities are independent since the sum of the three is always equal to unity. By plotting these three fractions in trilinear coordinates—that is, as distances from the three sides of some arbitrary triangle—one obtains what is known as a *color triangle*. It is usually more convenient to select a right-angle triangle and to plot two of the ratios, such as $\frac{A}{A + B + C}$ and $\frac{C}{A + B + C}$, in ordinary Cartesian coordinates. A color triangle of this type is shown in Fig. 154, and the usefulness of such a triangle will be discussed later.

It is clear that the above procedure of dividing each of the excitation values by the sum of the three eliminates as a parameter the total amount of light present in the stimulus. In other words, if the stimulus is a primary source of light, the above ratios give no indication of its intensity but merely indicate what we may call its *chromaticity*. To specify the color of a material completely, it is necessary to give not only the chromaticity but also the luminosity. As was shown in Sec. 11, Chap. I, the luminosity of a primary source is obtained by determining the

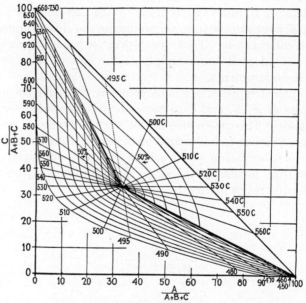

Fig. 154.—The color triangle recommended by the 1920 Optical Society of America Committee on Colorimetry. The white point at the center represents mean noon sunlight.

integral of the product of its energy distribution and the visibility function. The luminosity of a transparent material is generally expressed in relative terms by its transmission, which can be computed by means of Eq. (208) in the preceding chapter. In the same way, the luminosity of an opaque material relative to that of a perfectly white material is expressed by a similar equation in which R_λ is substituted for T_λ.

In general, the specification of a color sensation requires four integrations—three for the determination of the excitation values and one for the determination of luminosity. The chromaticity can be obtained directly from the excitation values.

If the primaries are monochromatic, their luminosities are given by the ordinates of the visibility function at the wave lengths of the primaries. If the primaries are not monochromatic, their relative luminosities can be obtained by integrating the energy-distribution curve of each primary by the visibility function. In this way, it is possible to find coefficients by which each excitation value can be multiplied to yield its contribution to the luminosity of the stimulus. For the O.S.A. curves given in Fig. 153, Judd[1] has found the values to be respectively 0.01,[2] 0.54, and 0.45. The luminosity of a given stimulus is therefore

$$L = 0.01\,A + 0.54\,B + 0.45\,C. \qquad (212)$$

Judd[3] has also shown that the excitation functions can be so transformed that the luminosity coefficients of A and C are zero. The β-function then has the form of the visibility function, and the value of B indicates the luminosity directly.

One shortcoming of the method of representing colors by their excitation values is that the parameters do not correspond to the fundamental psychological attributes of a color—*hue*, *saturation*, and *brilliance*. The meaning of these terms will be made clear by attempting to arrange a collection of colored objects—cards, for example—in some sort of orderly classification. The first step, after segregating the gray cards, is naturally to arrange the remainder in groups according to hue, in terms of which they may be described as being red, orange, yellow, green, blue, violet, or the non-spectral hue, purple. These hues can be arranged most conveniently in a circle, purple being placed between the red and the violet. The gray cards can be arranged on a brilliance scale headed by white at one end and black at the other. The cards of any one hue can also be arranged according

---

[1] *Jour. Optical Soc. Amer. and Rev. Sci. Instruments*, **10**, 635 (1925).

[2] It is worth while to note that, although radiation in the violet region contributes very little to the luminous sensation, Fig. 153 shows that it contributes greatly to the color sensation. This paradox is the cause of a fundamental difficulty in visual spectrophotometry. The visibility of radiation below 440 mμ is so low that one is tempted to assume that spectrophotometric observations at shorter wave lengths are of little importance. The point is that an amount of violet radiation that would be almost invisible alone has a pronounced effect on the color of a stimulus to which it is added. One of the chief advantages of photoelectric spectrophotometry is that readings can be continued as far as may be necessary into the violet end of the spectrum.

[3] *Bur. Standards Jour. Research*, **4**, 540 (1930) (*Research Paper* 163).

to brilliance, in respect to which they may be classed as equivalent to some member of the gray scale.   When this is accomplished, it will be seen that cards having the same hue and brilliance vary in the degree of their difference from gray.   This attribute is called saturation, the cards having a pronounced hue being called saturated and those approaching gray, unsaturated.

It is impossible, of course, to identify radiant energy with the sensation that it produces, and hence there are no objective parameters that truly correspond to these psychological attributes

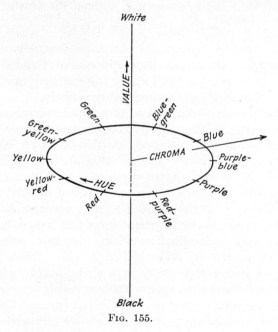

Fig. 155.

of color.   For example, it will be recalled that the parameters *A, B,* and *C* previously discussed represent merely the amounts of three arbitrarily selected physical primaries that produce the same sensation as the stimulus in question and do not furnish any information about the sensation.   Nevertheless, there are three objective parameters that correspond in a general sort of way to the psychological attributes.   These are known as *dominant wave length, colorimetric purity,* and *luminosity* (or brightness). The meaning of these terms will be clear from a consideration of the so-called monochromatic method of colorimetry.   In the instruments that measure color by this method, one half of the photometric field is illuminated by the color to be matched and the other half by a mixture of controllable amounts of monochromatic light of adjustable wave length and white light of some definite spectral quality. The three adjustments—namely, the wave length of the monochromatic light, its intensity, and the intensity of the white light—provide the means for matching every color except purple.[1] The dominant wave length is, of course, read directly from the instrument in terms of the wave length of the monochromatic radiation. The luminosity is simply the sum of the luminosities of the monochromatic radiation and the white radiation. The colorimetric purity is the ratio of the luminosity of the monochromatic radiation to the total luminosity.

A color specification in terms of three excitation values, A, B, and C, can be converted into terms of dominant wave length, purity, and luminosity. The most obvious method is to construct a color triangle, which has been done in Fig. 154 from the data of Table XIX. Some of the details of this procedure would be out of place here, but it will be apparent at once that the line representing spectral colors can be constructed by simply assuming monochromatic light of various wave lengths and determining the values of $\dfrac{A}{A+B+C}$ and $\dfrac{C}{A+B+C}$ from Table XIX. Likewise, the white point corresponding to radiation of some assumed quality can be located. In this particular case, the excitation functions were so chosen that equal amounts of the primaries produce the same sensation as mean noon sunlight, and hence the white point occupies the position where

$$\frac{A}{A+B+C} = \frac{B}{A+B+C} = \frac{C}{A+B+C} = 33.3 .$$

Between the line representing the spectral colors and the white point at the center lie all the colors whose purity is between zero (white) and 100 per cent. The purples are represented on the opposite side of the white point from the spectral colors in accordance with the artifice previously described. It is

---

[1] Since purple cannot be matched by a mixture of any single monochromatic radiation and white light, the converse procedure is adopted, monochromatic green of the proper wave length being added to the purple to be matched. The intensity and wave length of the green are adjusted until the green-purple mixture matches the white in the comparison field. In other words, the purple is specified in terms of its complementary.

clear that once the triangle has been constructed, the dominant wave length and the colorimetric purity of any stimulus can be determined from the values of A, B, and C by locating the points $\dfrac{A}{A+B+C}$ and $\dfrac{C}{A+B+C}$. The color triangle is, of course, incapable of showing the luminosity, but this can be found readily by means of Eq. (212).

The monochromatic method of colorimetry can be further elucidated by an examination of the Munsell system of color specification. This system is based upon ten hues and nine degrees of brilliance (*value* in the Munsell notation). Each of the hues is represented by as many different degrees of saturation (*chroma* in the Munsell notation) as is feasible. These quantities are represented in cylindrical coordinates as shown in Fig. 155. The vertical axis is taken to represent brilliance. The hue is then represented by the azimuth of a radius vector normal to the vertical axis, and the saturation is represented by the length of the vector.

113. Colorimeters.—The difficulties associated with the use of spectrophotometers and the interpretation of their results have led to many attempts to devise instruments, called colorimeters,[1] for measuring colors subjectively. Various instruments have been described from time to time in which the color to be measured is matched by a mixture of three arbitrarily chosen primaries. One early form was the "color-patch" apparatus used by Abney[2] in his researches on color vision. In this instrument, the primaries were spectral colors isolated by means of three slits in the plane of the spectrum, the relative proportions in the mixture being varied by altering the width of the slits. Other instruments have made use of primaries obtained with color filters, a well-known instrument of this type being due to Frederick E. Ives.[3]

An instrument of the monochromatic type has been described by Nutting[4] and an improved model of it has been described by

---

[1] Instruments called colorimeters are used by chemists to determine when two solutions have the same color. As these instruments usually have only a single adjustment, generally the depth of one of the liquids, they are not properly termed "colorimeters" but should be called color comparators instead.

[2] "Color Measurement and Mixture," London, 1891.

[3] *Trans. Illum. Eng. Soc.*, **3**, 627 (1908).

[4] *Bur. Standards Bull.*, **9**, 1 (1913) (*Sci. Paper* 187).

Priest.[1] This instrument matches the color under test by a mixture of white light with monochromatic light produced by a dispersing system.

An instrument operating on the so-called subtractive principle has been described by L. A. Jones.[2] This instrument contains red, yellow, and blue filters in the form of long wedges whose density increases uniformly from one end to the other. By inserting different thicknesses of the various wedges in the path of the comparison light, the color of the latter can be made to match the color under test. Obviously, colors of high saturation cannot be matched on such an instrument, and it suffers from a further drawback because of the doubtful reproducibility of the wedges and the complexity of the process of converting the arbitrary scale of the instrument to any fundamental basis.

The inherent disadvantages of all colorimeters are not apparent until one actually proceeds to use them. It must be remembered that in all these instruments, the quality of the light used as a source must be carefully maintained. If the source is a tungsten lamp, not only must careful control be applied to the voltage at which it is operated but frequent tests must be made to insure that it has not aged perceptibly. This difficulty is perhaps not so serious as that of obtaining an observer having what may be called normal color vision. In fact, even if an observer has normal vision in the sense that his mixture data are normal, it does not follow that his visibility curve is normal. Since both conditions are necessary, a truly normal observer is well-nigh nonexistent. In view of these facts, it seems likely that the measurement of color will be effected not by means of these colorimeters, simple as they are in theory, but by the more indirect method of spectrophotometric analysis and the subsequent computation of the sensation values based upon data to be universally agreed upon as representing a normal observer. It has been proposed by one of the present authors[3] to combine an integrating attachment, shown in Fig. 156, with the recording spectrophotometer shown in Fig. 147. By means of this attachment, the sensation values are computed while the spectrophotometric curve is being traced, the cams that operate the attachment being so fashioned as to represent the excitation functions of a normal observer for light of a given quality.

[1] *Jour. Optical Soc. Amer. and Rev. Sci. Instruments*, **8**, 173 (1924).

[2] *Jour. Optical Soc. Amer.*, **4**, 420 (1920).

[3] *Jour. Optical Soc. Amer. and Rev. Sci. Instruments*, **18**, 116 (1929).

A vast amount of work remains to be done in the field of color, even apart from establishing an adequate theory of color vision. Assuming that spectrophotometers of sufficient precision and ease of use can be constructed and that adequate mixture data are available so that the dominant wave length, colorimetric purity, and luminosity of a color can be computed, there still remains the problem of determining the precision requirements of these quantities. For example, a given change in dominant wave length is more readily perceptible in some portions of the spectrum than in others. The method of determining the least

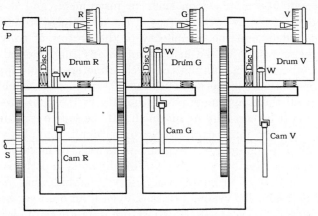

FIG. 156.—Integrating attachment for the photoelectric spectrophotometer shown in Fig. 146. The engraved drums *V*, *G*, and *R* indicate the values of *A*, *B*, and *C* for the sample whose spectrophotometric curve is being drawn. The cams are shaped in accordance with the color sense of the observer and the spectral quality of the light by which the sample is assumed to be illuminated.

perceptible change is to illuminate the two halves of a photometric field by light from neighboring regions of the spectrum and to increase the difference in wave length between the two regions until a hue difference becomes perceptible. The results can be plotted as a hue-sensitivity curve, in which the ordinates give the *difference limen* for spectral colors at each wave length. The curve obtained by Jones[1] is shown in Fig. 157. From this curve it can be found that there are about 130 steps of just distinguishable hue difference in the spectrum. The high sensitivity (small difference limen) in the yellow region (585 mμ) and in the blue-green (490 mμ) is very apparent when one merely looks at a spectrum.

[1] *Jour. Optical Soc. Amer.*, **1**, 63 (1917).

The least perceptible variation in colorimetric purity has been investigated by Jones and Lowry,[1] and curves representing their results are given in Fig. 158. In this figure, the ordinates

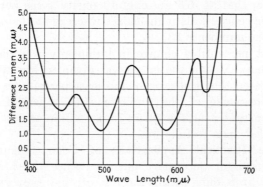

FIG. 157.—The hue-sensitivity curve of a normal observer according to Jones. This curve indicates the least perceptible difference in wave length as a function of wave length.

represent purity and the abscissae, wave length. Each curve is the locus of points representing a certain value of the least perceptible variation in purity. Although it is clear that the

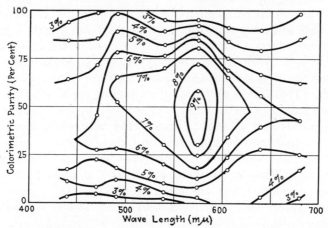

FIG. 158.—Curves showing the colorimetric purity for which the least perceptible variation has certain values. The data are from Jones and Lowry.

observational errors are considerable, as might be expected in the determination of such a quantity, the more pronounced trends are unmistakable. When more data are collected, the

[1] *Jour. Optical Soc. Amer. and Rev. Sci. Instruments,* **13,** 25 (1926).

details of the curves may be expected to become more systematic in nature. The difference in sensitivity between one part of the spectrum and another is noticeable. Jones and Lowry found, for example, that at 575 mμ only 16 purity steps between zero and 100 per cent are distinguishable, whereas at the ends of the spectrum the number is 23.

The least perceptible change in luminosity was discussed in Sec. 82, Chap. X, and the curve was given in Fig. 91. It will be remembered that the ratio of the least perceptible change to the absolute value of the luminosity (Fechner's fraction) is sensibly constant over the entire range within which the eye is usually called upon to function.

114. The Practical Applications of Color Science.—Color has been used for decorative purposes since the Magdalenian period, but it is only within the last century that its scientific basis has been investigated and still more recently that color-measuring instruments have become available. As would be expected, the information possessed by those who deal with the practical applications of color consists largely of empirical "laws" concerning the behavior of mixtures of coloring materials. For example, the artist's dictum that "blue and yellow produce green" is true for pigments and dyes, although the color triangle (Fig. 154) indicates that mixing a blue stimulus with a yellow stimulus produces a combination[1] that approximates white. The color of a mixture of pigments is evidently determined by a different set of principles from those that apply to a mixture of stimuli. This fact is emphasized even more forcibly by coloring the two halves of a disk with a blue and a yellow pigment and spinning the disk at such a speed that the colors fuse. The disk then appears to be approximately white, showing that colors combined in this manner obey the laws governing the addition of stimuli. This is therefore called the *additive* method of combining colors, while the ordinary procedure of mixing pigments produces colors by the *subtractive* method, as will be clear presently.

The simplest example of the production of color by the subtractive method is represented in Fig. 159. These curves indicate the transmission of a dye solution as a function of the wave length, each curve being for a different concentration of the dye.

---

[1] The point in the color triangle indicating the resultant stimulus obviously lies on the line joining the points representing the individual stimuli.

This particular dye has marked absorption bands at about 400 mμ and 655 mμ. With increasing concentration, the transmission in these regions decreases more in proportion than it does in regions where the transmission is higher. As a consequence, the dye appears a pale blue-green in dilute solution and becomes darker and more saturated in color as the concentration is increased. The variation in the chromaticity of the solution can be determined quantitatively by computing the values of *A, B,* and *C* and then finding the dominant wave length and colorimetric purity as described in Sec. 112. The luminosity

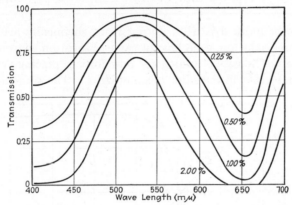

Fɪɢ. 159.—Spectrophotometric curves of a green dye showing the effect of increasing the concentration.

factor is best represented in this case by the transmission, which can be computed by means of Eq. (212), with a clear solution as the standard. These data specify the color of the solution under the conditions assumed in establishing the excitation curves —namely, that the observer has normal color sense and that the source of light is an equal-energy spectrum.[1] Under these conditions, the color of the dye in the various concentrations is as shown on the next page.

The behavior of this dye is typical in that the transmission decreases with increasing concentration. At the same time, there is a decided increase in the purity and a slight shift in the dominant wave length. However, there are some dyes whose charac-

[1] The values for any other type of source can be obtained by multiplying the excitation curves by the spectral-distribution curve of the source before computing *A, B,* and *C.*

teristics are such that changing the concentration produces a pronounced change in the dominant wave length. For example, a dilute solution of cyanine appears blue and a concentrated solution, red. This effect is known as *dichroism*.

Concentration of dye, per cent	Dominant wave length, mμ	Colorimetric purity, per cent	Transmission
0.25	503	33	0.90
0.50	510	48	0.79
1.00	514	65	0.64
2.00	520	85	0.44

If two or more dyes that do not react chemically are present in the same solution, each has the same absorption characteristics as before. The case is analogous, therefore, to placing two pieces of colored glass in the same beam of light. The transmission of

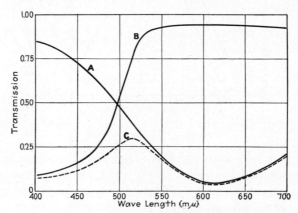

Fig. 160.—Spectrophotometric curves showing how a blue dye (*A*) and a yellow dye (*B*) produce a green dye (*C*) when mixed together.

the combination is found by multiplying together the values of the transmission[1] of each of the components, wave length by wave length. By following this procedure, we can readily understand why the mixture of a blue and a yellow dye usually produces green. In Fig. 160, curve *A* represents the spectral

[1] The absorption curves for light filters are usually represented in terms of optical density instead of transmission. The advantage of this procedure is that the curve for a combination of filters can be determined by simply adding the ordinates of the curves of the components instead of multiplying them.

transmission of a typical blue dye and curve B that of a typical
yellow dye. The mixture of the two dyes, represented by curve
C, is obviously green, the rise at the red end of the curve lying
in a region of the spectrum where the eye is relatively insensitive.

The behavior of mixed coloring materials when applied to
opaque objects is more complex, and one must first form a mental
picture of the behavior of light when it is
reflected by an aggregate of transparent
particles. To do so, consider what happens when light falls upon a layer of
freshly fallen snow. From the fact that
large ice crystals are almost perfectly
transparent, one can assume that this is
also true of the small crystals of which
snow is composed. When light strikes

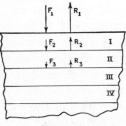

Fig. 161.

these crystals, some is reflected, some is refracted, and some
is totally reflected within the crystals. It would, of course,
be quite impossible to determine precisely what takes place
at each individual crystal, but it is fairly simple to determine the combined effect produced by a very large number
of crystals. In Fig. 161, let a beam of light containing F_1
lumens be incident on the upper surface of the snow, and let the
snow be divided into n imaginary layers of arbitrary thickness
as shown. In a similar manner, let F_2 represent the flux entering
the second layer, F_3 that entering the third, etc. Without making any assumption regarding the cause of the reflection, let
R_1, R_2, R_3, etc., represent the amount of flux reflected by the
layers I, II, III, etc. If no light is absorbed by the crystals,
the amount of light entering the first layer from both directions
is equal to the amount that leaves, or
$$F_1 + R_2 = F_2 + R_1.$$
For the second layer
$$F_2 + R_3 = F_3 + R_2.$$
Now R_1 clearly represents the amount of flux reflected by the
entire thickness of the material. From the first equation,
$$R_1 = F_1 + R_2 - F_2,$$
but from the second,
$$R_2 - F_2 = R_3 - F_3.$$
Setting up similar equations for all n layers and adding them,
one finds that

$$R_1 = F_1 + R_n - F_n.$$

But R_n and F_n approach zero as a limit for large values of n, and hence it follows that, if the material is thick enough, all the incident flux is eventually reflected back into the original medium.

The same argument applies to all white materials because they consist of an aggregate of minute transparent particles surrounded by a medium having a different refractive index. In the case of a white cloth, the white color is due to the reflection from the transparent fibers. A white paint behaves similarly because it consists of minute transparent particles of pigment suspended in some sort of vehicle having a different index. If the index of the vehicle were the same as that of the particles, the paint would be transparent like ice instead of white like snow.

Similar considerations apply to a colored paint, since the pigment in this case is merely a finely divided substance that absorbs selectively in the visible region. As a consequence, the only part of the incident light that is not altered in spectral composition is the relatively small fraction that is reflected at the first surface. The strength of the color depends upon the depth to which the light penetrates before being reflected, and thus the color can be enhanced either by using a vehicle having an index similar to that of the pigment or by using a coarse pigment. In any case, the greatest proportion of light is reflected from below the surface of the paint, and it is therefore evident that a mixture of pigments should act upon the light like a series of filters. The fact that a mixture of blue and yellow pigments appears green shows that this conclusion is warranted qualitatively, and a quantitative investigation by F. F. Rupert[1] shows that mixed pigments do indeed obey the laws governing the subtractive process. The same is true, of course, for fabrics colored with mixed dyes, provided the dyeing process is properly conducted.

The utilization of color-measuring instruments by industry is in its infancy. With the present tendency of industrial leaders to discard rule-of-thumb methods, it seems inevitable that the control of color processes will eventually be taken over by men possessed of an accurate knowledge of the subject of color and equipped with suitable instruments. Most of the practical applications of color involve the mixing of pigments or dyes,

---

[1] *Jour. Optical Soc. Amer.*, **20**, 661 (1930).

and consequently the spectrophotometer is the fundamental instrument. The interpretation of the behavior of coloring materials on any basis except that provided by the spectrophotometer is so complex that, as soon as one becomes familiar with the spectrophotometric method, he finds it well-nigh impossible to think in any other terms.

CHAPTER XV

OPTICAL GLASS

The materials used for lenses, prisms, and other optical parts must possess five characteristics—transparency, homogeneity, reproducibility, durability, and workability—and this combination is possessed by a remarkably small number of substances. Most of them are natural crystals like quartz, but an artificial mixture, called glass, is the one most commonly used. Many kinds of glass are manufactured but almost all of them are essentially mixtures of silicates in supercooled solution. Optical glass differs from ordinary window glass both in its composition and in its freedom from small amounts of impurities that would impart undesirable characteristics. It also requires a very different treatment throughout its manufacture—from the mixing of the batch to the preparation of the final blank that is put on the grinding machine.

The demand for glass of optical quality was created by the invention of the achromatic lens in the middle of the eighteenth century. The father of the optical glass industry was Guinand, a Swiss. It was he who first overcame the chief defect of ordinary glass—namely, streaks of varying index produced by improper mixing. He later moved to Germany and became associated with Fraunhofer, with whom he made lenses as large as 11 in. in diameter. His sons established the industry in France, whence it was introduced into England in 1848.

All the optical glass used in the United States was imported until about 1912, when certain firms made desultory attempts to manufacture some of their own. No earnest endeavor to establish the industry was made until 1917, when the entry of the country into the war made a domestic supply of glass imperative. Then the problem was attacked so vigorously that, despite the secrecy that had traditionally surrounded the process of glass making, over 300 tons of usable glass had been produced by the time the armistice was signed, 19 months later. This achievement was made possible by a systematic investigation, as a result of which the manufacture of optical glass has become a matter of factory routine instead of a jealously guarded art [1]

115. The Manufacture of Optical Glass.—The basic component of the mixture or batch that is melted together to make optical glass is almost always silica in the form of sand. To this is added either sodium or potassium carbonate and nitrate, or a mixture of the two. Salts of other elements, such as calcium, barium, lead, and boron, are often added to impart special properties. These raw materials must be exceedingly pure, because a trace of impurity often has a pronounced effect on the transparency. Ferrous iron is the commonest impurity and imparts a green coloration to the glass. The best optical glass contains less than 0.02 per cent of Fe_2O_3; as little as 0.05 per cent produces a noticeable color in layers of moderate thickness. [2]

The first step in manufacture is to weigh out the proper amounts of the raw materials of a previously tested degree of purity. These are thoroughly mixed, either by hand or by machine, and are then ready for the melting pot.

The quality of the finished product depends quite as much on the excellence of the pot as on the care taken in preparing the glass itself. Since an appreciable amount of the pot goes into solution at the high temperatures to which it is subjected, it is made of a clay that is as nearly pure kaolin as can be found. Pots are commonly made to hold either half a ton or a ton of the raw materials. A half-ton pot is about 36 in. in outside diameter and 36 in. high, the inside diameter and depth being about 27 in. each. The wall of the pot is thus about $4\frac{1}{2}$ in. thick and, although the pot looks strong, it is extremely fragile and must be handled with care. Formerly, pots were laboriously built up by hand, but methods of casting them have been developed within recent years. After a pot is made, it must be dried very slowly to avoid forming cracks. From two to six months are required for this process.

[1] The information gathered during this investigation has been published in a comprehensive monograph, "The Manufacture of Optical Glass and Optical Systems," *Ordnance Dept. Doc.* 2037. See also papers by J. W. French, *Trans. Optical Soc.* (*London*), **17** (1915–1916), **18** (1917–1918).

[2] For cheap glasses, manganese salts are sometimes added to oxidize the ferrous iron to the ferric state. The ferric iron alone imparts a pale yellow color, which is largely neutralized by the purple color produced by the manganese. This procedure reduces the transparency, however, and therefore is not permissible in the manufacture of optical glass.

When a pot is to be used, it is placed in a small furnace called a pot arch in which it is preheated for three to five days. At the end of this time, it attains a temperature of about 1000°C. It is then removed by means of a pot wagon, which consists of a mammoth pair of tongs mounted on wheels, and is placed in the furnace.

The type of furnace commonly used is large enough for but a single pot, which is heated by the hot gases passing up from the furnace chamber below. The floor, or siege, on which the pot is to be placed is made as smooth as possible and then covered with sand to form a level base. The pot is inserted and heated slowly until it attains a temperature of approximately 1450°C., which causes the clay to sinter together. The pot is then allowed to cool to 1300°C. before it is charged.

The first step in charging a pot is to add waste glass from previous melts in 50-lb. lots at intervals of half an hour. It will be seen shortly that only about 20 per cent of the contents of a pot is of usable quality, but the waste glass, called *cullet*, can be salvaged in this manner.   In addition, this cullet serves to protect the walls of the pot from the action of the fused alkali. Sometimes as much as 50 per cent of a melt may consist of cullet although good glass can be made without any.

As soon as the pot is charged, the temperature is raised to 1400°C. This causes chemical reactions to take place in which carbon dioxide and nitrogen pentoxide are expelled, leaving a solution of silicates. The bubbles of gas given off at this stage must be entirely removed, a procedure known as fining. It is accomplished by stirring the melt with a clay rod fastened to the end of a long iron bar. This stirring rod is always kept at least 2 in. from the wall of the pot because the melt adjacent to the wall dissolves material from the pot which would introduce streaks of varying refractive index if stirred into the melt.   The pot is stirred rapidly while being charged and more slowly after all the material is melted. Sometimes the removal of bubbles is accelerated by blocking, which consists of introducing into the melt either water, arsenious oxide, or ammonium nitrate. These materials evolve large quantities of gases which rise through the melt and carry the bubbles with them.

At the end of the fining operation, which may require from 24 to 48 hr., the impurities floating on the melt are skimmed off and the furnace is allowed to cool to about 1000°C. The pot is then pried loose from the siege and is removed from the furnace with the pot wagon. Any material that has slopped over the outside of the pot is blown off with a blast of air.

The ensuing operations depend upon the quality of the glass required. The best optical glass is obtained by allowing it to solidify within the pot. This procedure is expensive and requires much care, but it must be adopted when the glass is to be used in instruments of the highest quality. The pot is first allowed to cool in the open for about half an hour since there is no danger of introducing strains while the melt is still liquid.

Fig. 162.—A pot of optical glass partly broken up. (*By courtesy of Bausch and Lomb Optical Company.*)

Infusorial earth is thrown on the surface of the melt and a blast of air is played on the bottom of the pot during this period to make the rate of cooling uniform. The bottom of the pot is much hotter than the top when the pot is removed from the furnace, and, if this temperature difference were allowed to continue, the convection currents within the melt would produce streaks of varying index. The pot is then placed in a pot arch and cooled to about 600°C. in a period of approximately 24 hr. From this temperature, it is gradually cooled to room temperature in about a week. This is the crucial period because the temperature differences within the pot are greatest and, since the glass is on the point of becoming solid, strains are readily produced.

Nevertheless, it has been found possible to dispense with the pot arch by placing a large heat-insulating cover over the pot until it attains room temperature.

When the pot is cool, it is broken open as shown in Fig. 162. As can be seen in this figure, the glass is found in chunks of assorted sizes having approximately plane faces. These chunks are broken up further if necessary and are then either sawed into pieces of the right size for the grinding and polishing operations or molded into plates about 1 in. thick to facilitate inspection and handling.

FIG. 163.—Rolling optical glass. (*By courtesy of Bausch and Lomb Optical Company.*)

For many purposes, glass prepared by a process of rolling is satisfactory. This process consists in pouring the melt on a metal plate as soon as it comes from the furnace and flattening it with a roller as shown in Fig. 163. The sheet is rolled to about $5/16$ in. thick for spectacle lenses and about $1/2$ in. for photographic lenses. After being rolled, the sheet is passed through an oven, called a lehr, which is hot at the entrance and at room temperature at the exit. The glass is annealed for about two days in this lehr, and is then cut into pieces of the proper size.

Rolled glass is much cheaper than pot glass because the pot can be used over and over, as many as twenty times, and also because most of the melt is usable. However, as rolled glass is composed of material from all parts of the melt, it is not of uniform index of refraction. The streaks of different index are called *striae*, and the rolling flattens these striae so that they are parallel to the surface, in which shape they are known as *ream*. This defect makes rolled glass unsuitable for lenses having steep curves and lenses of which sharp definition is required. Rolled glass is perfectly satisfactory for spectacle lenses, however, and is often used for photographic objectives. It is entirely unsuitable for prisms because, in this case, the light does not traverse the layers of ream in a direction even approximately normal and hence the injury to the definition of the image is pronounced.

Lenses and prisms are commonly ground from blanks that are made by pressing the glass into approximately the finished form. If the glass has been rolled, a sheet of suitable thickness is cut into squares of the proper weight; if the glass has been allowed to cool in the pot, the pieces are cracked or sawed out of the large chunks. In either case, the pieces are softened in a small furnace and then placed one at a time in a hot mold into which they are squeezed by means of a die. The surface produced in this way is fairly smooth but is pitted with the clay blown up from the floor of the furnace by the hot gases. Nevertheless, the amount of material to be ground away after this operation is much less than it would be otherwise. The pressings, as the blanks thus prepared are called, are annealed for a length of time depending upon the size—condenser blanks, for example, requiring about a week. The subsequent operations of grinding and polishing will be described in the next chapter.

116. Types of Optical Glass.—Since the time of Fraunhofer, optical glass has been specified according to its index for the sodium line (n_D) and the value of the ratio

$$\nu = \frac{n_D - 1}{n_F - n_C},\tag{213}$$

which is a restatement of Eq. (154) in Chap. VI. It is the custom nowadays to furnish also the partial dispersions $n_D - n_{A'}$, etc., and the partial dispersion ratios $\dfrac{n_D - n_{A'}}{n_F - n_C}$, etc., to allow the amount of secondary spectrum to be estimated.

Prior to 1886, only two types of glass were known—ordinary crown and ordinary flint. The basis of both is a mixture of sodium and potassium silicates, but the former contains calcium in addition and the latter contains lead. With so little variety in the choice of optical glass, it was impossible to satisfy all the conditions of achromatism discussed in Sec. 56, Chap. VI. The need for new optical materials was recognized by Abbe in

1880. In that year he and Schott,[1] aided financially by the Prussian government, began experimenting at Jena. They tried the effect of adding compounds of boron, barium, fluorine, phosphorus, and other elements. Some elements did not impart new properties and others made the glass soft or cloudy, but a few were found to impart desirable optical properties to the glass without injuring it. After six years of research, they placed on the market optical glasses in which the ν-values did not go hand in hand with the index and in which the dispersion varied with wave length in such a manner that something approximating complete achromatism could be achieved.

The designer has now a wide choice in the selection of optical glasses, which can be conveniently divided into series named from their characteristic constituent. Other constituents having little effect on the index or dispersion may, of course, also be present. For example, arsenic may be used to clear the glass from bubbles and make it transparent, while aluminum and zinc are sometimes added to reduce the likelihood of crystallization. Aluminum also makes the glass tough, and zinc makes it easier to work in the furnace. The important series of optical glass are: (1) ordinary crown; (2) borosilicate crown; (3) fluor crown; (4) barium crown; (5) ordinary flint; (6) baryta flint; (7) borate glass; and (8) phosphate glass. These will be described in order.

1. *Ordinary Crowns.*—Calcium is the characteristic constituent of these glasses. They all have an index for the *D*-line of about 1.52 and a ν-value of about 60.

2. *Borosilicate Crowns.*—These resemble the ordinary crowns with the exception that some or all of the calcium is replaced by boron. The index varies from about 1.50 ($\nu = 65$) to about 1.52 ($\nu = 60$), and the ν-value varies from about 54 ($n_D = 1.52$) to 65 ($n_D = 1.50$). Hence they are not very different optically from the ordinary crowns, the greatest difference being that the dispersion in the red end of the spectrum is relatively greater for the same total dispersion.

3. *Fluor Crowns.*—These glasses are characterized optically by very low indices and ν-values. They are but little used.

4. *Barium Crowns.*—This series contains relatively large amounts of barium and a little boron at the expense of the silica.

[1] The significance of the work of these men can be understood better from Hovestadt's "Jena Glass," which has been translated into English by J. D. and A. Everett.

The indices are slightly higher and the ν-values slightly lower than for ordinary crowns, although the rate of change of dispersion through the spectrum is about the same. The indices range from about 1.54 ($\nu = 60$) to 1.61 ($\nu = 59$), and the ν-values range from about 54 ($n_D = 1.58$) to about 61 ($n_D = 1.59$).

5. *Ordinary Flints.*—The characteristic constituent of this series is lead, which raises the index and lowers the ν-value. The dispersion in the blue end of the spectrum relative to that at the red end is much greater for this series than for crowns. It will be recalled from Eq. (150) in Chap. VI that to achieve complete achromatism in a thin cemented doublet, the ratio of the dispersions of the two elements must be constant throughout the spectrum. The variation in the ratio is the reason for the imperfect achromatism of an ordinary crown with an ordinary flint. The optical properties of the ordinary flints range from about $n_D = 1.52$ ($\nu = 57$) to $n_D = 1.96$ ($\nu = 20$).

6. *Baryta Flints.*—In this series, barium is added at the expense of the lead. These glasses have a higher index for the same ν-value than the ordinary flints and a relatively greater dispersion in the red. They range from $n_D = 1.55$ ($\nu = 53$) to $n_D = 1.63$ ($\nu = 39$).

7. *Borate Glasses.*—In these glasses, the silica is replaced by boric acid. Aluminum and sometimes lead may also be added. They range from $n_D = 1.51$ ($\nu = 60$) to $n_D = 1.67$ ($\nu = 39$).

8. *Phosphate Glasses.*—In these glasses, the silica is replaced by a phosphate, and some barium and a little boron are added. They range from $n_D = 1.52$ ($\nu = 70$) to $n_D = 1.59$ ($\nu = 64$). In spite of their desirable dispersion relations, they have been almost entirely discarded because of their instability.

The numerical values given above for the index and ν-values furnish merely an idea of the range covered by the various glasses of the respective series. Glass makers are constantly changing their lists of glasses, adding new ones for special purposes and dropping others because of their instability, the small demand, or the difficulty of reproducing them. European makers offer a greater variety of optical glass than American makers because the conditions in this country are such that only the types that are widely used can be produced economically. The list of the Bausch and Lomb Optical Company, the largest American maker, is reproduced by permission in Table XX. One type of crown, which is made for condensers, is not listed

TABLE XX.—Stock Types of Optical Glass Made by the Bausch & Lomb Optical Company

Number	Type	ν	n_D	Mean dispersion $n_F - n_C$	Partial dispersions and partial dispersion ratios					Specific gravity
					$n_C - n_{A'}$	$n_D - n_C$	$n_F - n_D$	$n_{G'} - n_F$	$n_h - n_{G'}$	
20–2	Borosilicate crown	64.5	1.5170	0.00801	0.00285 / 0.356	0.00240 / 0.300	0.00560 / 0.700	0.00445 / 0.555	0.00334 / 0.417	2.56
20–1	Borosilicate crown	63.5	1.5110	0.00805	0.00284 / 0.352	0.00237 / 0.295	0.00567 / 0.705	0.00449 / 0.558	0.00342 / 0.425	2.49
70	Ordinary crown	60.5	1.5125	0.00847	0.00293 / 0.346	0.00252 / 0.297	0.00596 / 0.703	0.00478 / 0.564	0.00363 / 0.429	3.21
100–1	Barium crown	59.5	1.5411	0.00909	0.00309 / 0.340	0.00274 / 0.301	0.00635 / 0.699	0.00513 / 0.564	0.00393 / 0.432	2.84
120–1	Densest barium crown	58.8	1.6110	0.01039	0.00359 / 0.345	0.00307 / 0.295	0.00733 / 0.705	0.00591 / 0.569	0.00442 / 0.425	3.48
50–1	Spectacle crown	58.4	1.5230	0.00895	0.00313 / 0.350	0.00264 / 0.295	0.00631 / 0.705	0.00510 / 0.570	0.00386 / 0.431	2.52
110–1	Dense barium crown	57.4	1.5725	0.00997	0.00342 / 0.343	0.00292 / 0.293	0.00704 / 0.705	0.00570 / 0.571	0.00436 / 0.437	3.21
110–2	Dense barium crown	56.8	1.5725	0.01008	0.00347 / 0.344	0.00294 / 0.292	0.00714 / 0.707	0.00578 / 0.573	0.00434 / 0.430	3.21
160–2	Crown flint	55.1	1.5230	0.00949	0.00326 / 0.343	0.00277 / 0.292	0.00671 / 0.707	0.00541 / 0.570	0.00420 / 0.443	2.61
120–4	Densest barium crown	55.1	1.6160	0.01118	0.00379 / 0.339	0.00328 / 0.293	0.00790 / 0.707	0.00638 / 0.571	0.00481 / 0.430	3.49
120–2	Densest barium crown	54.7	1.6150	0.01124	0.00380 / 0.338	0.00331 / 0.294	0.00794 / 0.706	0.00646 / 0.575	0.00490 / 0.436	3.49
130–1	Baryta light flint	53.4	1.5880	0.01101	0.00370 / 0.336	0.00322 / 0.292	0.00780 / 0.708	0.00632 / 0.574	0.00486 / 0.441	3.31

160–1	Telescope flint	1.5286	51.6	0.01024	0.00349 / 0.341	0.00299 / 0.292	0.00724 / 0.707	0.00596 / 0.582	0.00455 / 0.444	2.73
140–1	Baryta light flint	1.5825	46.4	0.01255	0.00413 / 0.329	0.00364 / 0.290	0.00891 / 0.710	0.00742 / 0.591	0.00575 / 0.458	3.29
190–1	Ordinary light flint	1.5585	45.5	0.01227	0.00404 / 0.329	0.00358 / 0.292	0.00869 / 0.708	0.00726 / 0.592	0.00564 / 0.460	3.08
140–2	Baryta light flint	1.6053	43.6	0.01388	0.00457 / 0.329	0.00400 / 0.288	0.00987 / 0.711	0.00822 / 0.592	0.00651 / 0.469	3.50
190–2	Ordinary light flint	1.5725	42.5	0.01347	0.00437 / 0.324	0.00389 / 0.289	0.00958 / 0.711	0.00800 / 0.594	0.00628 / 0.466	3.28
190–3	Ordinary light flint	1.5795	41.0	0.01413	0.00464 / 0.328	0.00406 / 0.287	0.01008 / 0.713	0.00850 / 0.601	0.00667 / 0.472	3.28
200–3	Ordinary flint	1.6170	38.5	0.01603	0.00508 / 0.317	0.00460 / 0.287	0.01143 / 0.713	0.00970 / 0.605	0.00769 / 0.480	3.60
200–2	Ordinary flint	1.6170	36.6	0.01686	0.00541 / 0.321	0.00481 / 0.285	0.01197 / 0.716	0.01025 / 0.608	0.00809 / 0.480	3.60
210–2	Dense flint	1.6490	33.8	0.01920	0.00606 / 0.316	0.00545 / 0.284	0.01374 / 0.716	0.01183 / 0.616	0.00942 / 0.491	3.90
210–1	Dense flint	1.6660	32.4	0.02056	0.00650 / 0.316	0.00582 / 0.283	0.01474 / 0.717	0.01273 / 0.619	0.01016 / 0.494	4.02
220–1	Extra dense flint	1.6890	30.9	0.02230	0.00694 / 0.311	0.00631 / 0.283	0.01598 / 0.717	0.01389 / 0.623	0.01115 / 0.500	4.23
220–3	Extra dense flint	1.7200	29.3	0.02457	0.00762 / 0.310	0.00691 / 0.281	0.01767 / 0.719	0.01538 / 0.626	0.01243 / 0.506	4.45

NOTE.—The Fraunhofer lines for which the indices of glass are usually specified in glass catalogues are as follows: A' (K), 768.2 mμ; C (H), 656.3 mμ; D (Na), 589.3 mμ; d (D_3) (He), 587.6 mμ; e (Hg), 546.1 mμ; F (H), 486.1 mμ; g (Hg), 435.8 mμ; G' (H), 434.1 mμ; and h (Hg), 404.7 mμ. (If this list is compared with Table VII on p. 162, it will be noticed that some of these lines are different from the lines in the solar spectrum designated by the same symbols.) In this condensed table, the values for d, e, and g have been omitted.

because it is not used when critical definition is required. Its index for the D-line is approximately 1.513 and its ν-value, 59.

117. Reproducibility.—Manufacturers of optical glass usually give indices in their catalogues to five decimal places and occasionally to six. Although the partial dispersions may remain constant from one melt to another to within a few units in the fifth place, the indices themselves vary in the fourth place or occasionally in the third place. From the standpoint of the purchaser of optical glass, the best procedure is to specify the value of n to ± 0.001 and ν to ± 0.2. Under these circumstances, the optical system cannot be finally computed until the particular lot of glass destined for it has been measured, but to specify closer tolerances may increase the cost or cause delay. If pot glass is required, pieces of the right size may not be in stock in sufficient quantity, or the manufacturer may refuse to reduce his stock of large pieces by breaking them into smaller ones. Optical glass is sold by the pound, the price ranging upwards from about \$1.50 per pound for spectacle crown to \$7.50 for types that are especially difficult to manufacture. For obvious reasons, unusually large pieces may command a higher price.

It is often desirable to have a stock of glass of identical optical characteristics so that a lot of instruments can be constructed with identical mechanical parts and scales. For example, in manufacturing spectroscopes having a wave-length scale, the amount of labor involved in preparing the wave-length scale makes it undesirable to calibrate each instrument separately. In such cases, an entire melt is often set aside for use in the construction of a particular kind of instrument.

118. Dispersion.—The variation of index with wave length is best represented by an empirical formula proposed by Hartmann. This formula[1] is

$$n = n_0 + \frac{c}{(\lambda_0 - \lambda)^{1.2}}, \tag{214}$$

where n_0, c, and λ_0 are constants for a given glass. It is to be regretted that the catalogues of the glass manufacturers do not list the values of the constants in Hartmann's formula, as undoubtedly this would lead to the discovery of simple relations that are more easily understood than the partial dispersion ratios that are commonly given.

[1] An approximate form of this relation was given by Eq. (151) in Chap. VI. For another dispersion formula, see Eq. (218) in Chap. XVIII.

119. Defects.—The possible defects of optical glass are many. Even though its index and dispersion may be correct, it may contain striae, bubbles, "seeds" (minute bubbles), or stones (undissolved material). It may also be milky, colored, or in a state of strain due to improper annealing. The harmful effect of these defects cannot be estimated without knowing the function that the completed part is to perform in the optical system. For example, a few bubbles in the elements of a photographic objective merely reduce the transmission by a negligible amount. On the other hand, the field lens of a Ramsden ocular must be free from both bubbles and seeds because it lies in the plane of the image which is seen magnified by the eye lens. For obvious reasons, glass that is cloudy (a fault that sometimes appears when chlorine or sulphur is present in the batch materials) is of little use in image-forming instruments. Mechanical stresses produced in the glass by improper annealing are especially serious in instruments employing polarized light because of the birefringence they produce. Pronounced stresses may be indirectly important also in systems requiring the formation of critically sharp images, because they may deform the piece while it is being worked, or even afterward. Stones, which are due to solid material from either the melt or the pot, are objectionable because of the stresses and the striae they introduce in the surrounding glass.

Optical glass is inspected frequently during the process of manufacture, the object being to do the minimum amount of work on pieces that must ultimately be rejected. Pot glass is inspected for bubbles, stones, and striae as soon as the pot has been broken by simply looking through the separate pieces at a diffusing glass covered with dark bands or spots. The defects can be more easily detected against the half-shadow formed by the dark areas than against a clear illuminated area. Striae are easily observed by immersing the piece in a liquid of the same refractive index, such as a mixture of carbon disulphide and benzol, but this test is not used in commercial plants because the fumes from the liquid are harmful to the workers.

After the opposite faces of a piece have been polished, striae are readily detected by a modification of Töpler's shadow method. In Fig. 164, *S* is a source of light; *D*, a diffusing screen of fine-ground glass or flashed opal; and *H*, a pinhole in the first focal plane of the achromatic collimator L_1, whose focal length is 300 mm to 750 mm and whose diameter is 50 mm to 130 mm.

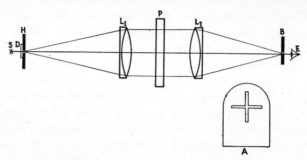

Fig. 164.—Sketch of apparatus for detecting striae in glass.

The plate to be inspected is placed at P; behind it is the achromatic field lens L_2, which should have a focal length of about 300 mm to 400 mm. A pinhole aperture, or, better, a cross-slit

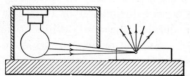

Fig. 165.—Sketch of apparatus for detecting stones, bubbles, and seeds in glass.

as shown at A is placed at B in the second focal plane of this lens. The aperture is held in clips so that it can be shifted at will. The eye E is moved until the plate to be examined appears in half-shadow; in this position, the striae are readily seen on tilting and moving the plate across the field.

Bubbles, seeds, and stones are most readily detected in a piece having polished faces by using indirect illumination in an arrangement like that shown in Fig. 165. Foreign particles in the glass reflect and deflect the impinging light rays so that they reach the eye of the observer; thus each particle appears as a bright source of light that is readily visible. To make the contrast as great as possible, the plate under examination should rest on a dull black sheet and should be shielded from light at the side. The background is then dark and the illuminated points stand out brightly.

Stresses are detected by observing the birefringence they cause. As will be described in Chap. XXIX, birefringence is the property of splitting light into an ordinary and an extraordinary ray, one traveling in the birefringent medium faster than the other. The amount of stress can be measured by determining the path difference between the two rays. This can be accomplished by placing the glass in a beam of polarized light and studying the dark patterns seen in the analyzer as the latter is rotated. The dark lines of each pattern correspond to positions of equal path difference. Specimens that are noticeably birefringent are returned to the glass plant for reannealing.

120. Transparency.—Optical glass is generally so transparent to visible light that the absorption can be neglected except when the pieces are very thick. Even in optical instruments containing a large amount of glass, such as range-finders and periscopes, the losses due to reflection at the air-glass surfaces generally exceed those due to absorption. Of course, all glasses absorb in the ultraviolet, the position of the cut-off depending upon the composition of the glass. In general, the position of the cut-off moves toward longer wave lengths as the index of the glass increases. Most dense flints are yellow for this reason, the violet and some of the blue being completely absorbed, even by relatively thin pieces.

The transmission of a slab of glass with plane-parallel faces is easily determined by the method discussed in Sec. 107, Chap. XIII. This method measures the losses due to both absorption and surface reflection. Although the latter can be calculated by means of Fresnel's formula, Eq. (16), a somewhat better method is to measure the transmission of two pieces of the same material having different thicknesses, since from these data the reflection losses can be eliminated by computation. The absorption of visible light by optical glass varies from about 0.5 per cent per centimeter in light crowns to about 3 per cent in flints.

121. Stability.—Some glasses have very desirable optical properties but are affected by air, water, and gases. For example, glasses high in alkali content are hygroscopic, and the phosphate glasses are notoriously unstable. Others, like dense barium crowns and the borate glasses, are fairly stable but tarnish if exposed. They are used, however, by cementing them between more stable glasses.

To determine the stability of a glass in the laboratory is very difficult. In use, the glass may be exposed to any one or more of such injurious agents as water vapor, carbon dioxide, finger perspiration, bacteria, and minute plant organisms; and laboratory tests of the resistance to all these agencies are impracticable. About the best that can be done is to determine the effect of the most common agent, water, and even for this one agent a suitable test must be conducted over a long period of time. Means for accelerating the reaction may be adopted, of course, but it is doubtful that this procedure really simulates the effect of protracted use.

Perhaps the best quantitative test for stability is the iodoeosin test of Mylius.[1] A freshly fractured piece of the glass under examination is immersed for 1 min. in a test solution at 18°C. consisting of a saturated solution of water in ether to which 0.5 gram of pure iodoeosin ($C_{20}H_8I_4O_5$) is added for each liter of solution. This attacks the glass, and the small quantity of alkali that is set free enters into combination with the iodoeosin to form a red alkaline salt. Since this salt is insoluble in ether, it is precipitated on the glass surface. After the specimen has been removed from the solution, it is plunged quickly into ether to wash off the excess. It is then allowed to dry, and the surfaces, except the freshly broken one, are wiped clean with a cloth. The iodoeosin salt is then dissolved in a small amount of water and its quantity is determined colorimetrically by matching it against a standard iodoeosin salt solution. The alkalinity of the fresh surface in terms of milligrams of iodoeosin thus absorbed per square meter of area is called by Mylius the *weather alkalinity*.

Mylius divides glasses into five groups on the basis of their weather alkalinity as follows:

TABLE XXI

Class	Type of glass	Weather alkalinity, mg/meter^2	Example
I	Practically insoluble	0–5	Silica glass
II	Resistant	5–10	Jena Geräte, Pyrex
III	Hard	10–20	Flints, best crowns
IV	Soft	20–40	Ordinary crowns
V	Poor	Over 40	

Optical glasses should have a weather alkalinity of less than 40 mg/meter^2.

122. The Care of Glass Parts.—Lenses and prisms are beautifully clear and polished when they leave the optician's shop, but they seldom remain so after being in the hands of the user

[1] *Ordnance Dept. Doc.* 2037, p. 220.

for any length of time. Since in most cases the function of the optical part—namely, the transmission of light—does not injure it in any way, we must conclude that its useful life depends entirely on the sort of care it receives. It is needless to state that a cemented lens may be ruined by heat because, even if it is mounted so that it will not fall apart when the cement softens, bubbles may form in the cement and ruin the definition of the image. But there are more insidious causes of damage. If the part is not protected, dust containing deleterious chemical agents may collect upon it, or fumes in the atmosphere may attack it. In the tropics, bacteria may collect and grow, thus covering the surface with a scum. The simplest (but all too uncommon) method of protecting glass parts when not in use is by a closely fitting cap. This does not entirely prevent damage because fumes from the lacquer and grease within the instrument may still have access to the part, but it does very greatly retard the deterioration of the polished surfaces in addition to protecting the part against mechanical injury. Unmounted parts should be wrapped in tissue paper and placed in small boxes stuffed with cotton batting.

If a polished surface is touched with the fingers, the grease that is deposited should be carefully wiped off immediately or a permanent marking may result. Dampness should also be removed as soon as possible because it accelerates crystallization and tarnishing. A clean piece of linen or lens paper is suitable for the purpose. If dust has been allowed to collect on the surface, it should be removed gently with a camel's-hair brush before the surface is wiped. The glass should never be rubbed vigorously because, if it is one of the soft varieties, it will certainly be scratched. If a surface has begun to crystallize, it may be wiped under water. The water will usually dissolve the crystals whereas, if they were removed by hard rubbing, they would surely produce scratches. A polishing agent, such as rouge, should not be used, not only because it might alter the figure of the surface but also because, unless very pure, it is likely to contain coarse particles that would scratch the glass.

CHAPTER XVI

THE MANUFACTURE OF OPTICAL PARTS

The art of working optical glass is unique. In the first place, glass is so brittle that the ordinary methods of fabricating wood or metal objects cannot be used and a special technique has, of necessity, been developed. In addition, the precision required of optical parts transcends that required of any other manufactured article. This is an inevitable consequence of the short wave length of light because, as shown in Chap. VII, the formation of images of the highest quality requires that the optical path along every ray be the same within one-fourth of a wave length.

The art of working optical glass can be acquired only by long experience. Nevertheless, some knowledge of the procedure is essential, even for those who intend to have their optical work done by others. Optical firms constantly receive orders which they are unable to fill because the specifications are either ridiculously strict, hopelessly vague, or even contradictory. The literature of the subject is meager, but much valuable information can be found in the *Ordnance Department Document* mentioned in the preceding chapter.

123. Preparing the Blank.—The first operation in the construction of any optical part is the preparation of a blank having roughly the shape of the finished part. The most economical procedure is to make a pressing as described in Sec. 115. The pressing molds are so designed that the blank is a trifle larger in every dimension than the finished part. In lenses, from 2 mm to 5 mm are added to the diameter, and about 1 mm is allowed for grinding on each surface. For prisms, from 3 mm to 8 mm are added to each dimension.

Pot glass must be used for work of the finest quality. It can be pressed as described, but a better procedure is to select a chunk of the proper size and saw a blank from it by means of a glass saw. A typical saw is illustrated in Fig. 166. It consists of a circular disk of brass, copper, or soft iron, which is charged with diamond dust mixed with thick oil. A saw 5 in. in diameter is usually about $\frac{1}{16}$ in. thick. The chunk of glass is pressed against the edge of the disk, which is rotated at a speed of about 1000 r.p.m. At this speed, a 5-in. saw will cut about $\frac{1}{2}$ in. per minute. Kerosene or some other light oil is squirted into the cut to keep the glass cool. Glass can also be milled by using as a tool a cylinder of brass, copper, or soft iron charged with diamond dust. Such a tool may be from 2 in. to 4 in. in diameter and 3 in. to 6 in. long.

In preparing lens blanks from pot glass, plates having approximately parallel faces are first sawed out. The corners are then nipped off the plates, which are stacked in a column, one on top of the other, with oil between. The column is then clamped together in a lathe and rotated against a revolving carborundum wheel. This operation grinds the plates into circular disks of the proper diameter. When only one lens is required, an alternative procedure is to fasten the plate on the bed of a drill press and cut out a disk of the required diameter by means of a hollow

FIG. 166.—A glass saw in operation. The plate of glass above the saw is to protect the workman from the flying abrasive. (*By courtesy of Spencer Lens Company.*)

cylindrical tool of copper or brass charged with diamond dust or carborundum.[1] A more primitive way is to chip the corners off the plate, mount it in a lathe, and turn the edge down with either a diamond point or a hardened-steel tool. In every case, a stream of kerosene or turpentine is constantly played on the glass.

124. Grinding and Polishing.—From a manufacturing standpoint, there are two general classes of optical goods. The first class, which includes ophthalmic lenses, goggles, and condensers, is characterized by low precision and large volume of production. To meet price competition, optical goods of this class are usually made by machines tended by unskilled workmen. The other class of goods includes such precision instruments as telescopes,

---

[1] This method is also used to drill a hole in glass. If the hole is very small, a solid drill may be used.

microscopes, photographic objectives, and projection objectives. These are usually manufactured in relatively small quantities to high standards of precision. The essential operations are the same for both classes, the principal distinction being in the method of polishing. We shall identify these classes by the terms *spectacle quality* and *precision quality* respectively.

The procedure in preparing surfaces of spectacle quality is best illustrated by describing the method of manufacturing ophthalmic lenses. When these are made individually to the customer's prescription in the shop of the local optician, the starting point is a pressed blank of rolled glass. This blank is cemented with hot pitch to what is known as a blocking tool or block, which is usually made of cast iron. The exposed surface of the blank is then ground by holding it against another tool, called a lap, which has previously been given the proper radius of curvature. The lap is rotated at a moderate speed on a vertical shaft and is fed with a mixture of coarse emery and water. The block is secured to a lever arm and is held against the lap by the optician, who moves it constantly over the lap to equalize the wear on the latter. When the surface irregularities have been removed and the blank has acquired the same curvature as the lap, it is removed and carefully washed free from the emery. A finer grade of emery is then substituted and the grinding is continued, several changes to successively finer grades being made from time to time. Frequently the fine grinding is done on a different lap because the lap used for rough grinding becomes deformed and therefore incapable of producing a satisfactory finished surface. The surface left by the fine-grinding operation has a velvety finish and is smooth by all ordinary criteria, but it is still rough in comparison with the wave length of light. The final operation—polishing—is not required to remove any substantial amount of material but rather to cause a flow of the glass that fills up the scratches left by the fine grinding. For ophthalmic lenses, the polishing is done against a felt surface charged with wet rouge (usually a very fine grade of red ferric oxide). This completes the work on the first surface, which has required perhaps half an hour.

The first surface having been finished, the blank is removed from the blocking tool. This is accomplished by directing a stream of cold water against the pitch, the sudden cooling causing it to crack away from the blank. The blank is then turned over and mounted on another tool, and then the second surface is worked in a manner similar to the first. Some little care is required in mounting the blank this time because it must be finished to a definite thickness. Consequently the film of pitch holding it to the block must be thin to enable the lens to be gauged for thickness without being removed. After the second surface is polished, the lens is cut to the proper shape and fitted to the spectacle frame. The method of cutting will be described in the next section.

It is a widespread custom among small opticians to keep in stock blanks with one surface finished, and to work only the

Fig. 167.—A view in the lens-grinding room of the Bausch and Lomb Optical Company.

second surface according to the customer's prescription.[1] At the factory, where lenses are made in quantity, the procedure is the same as has just been described except that many lenses are worked at once. This is done by mounting them on large blocking tools, called shells. The grinding and polishing operations are performed by automatic machines. These rotate the grinding or polishing tool about a vertical axis while the shell is moved over the surface of the tool in a random manner. In this way, the spherical form of the tool is maintained although wear does cause a slight change in the radius of curvature. The

[1] Sometimes the lens is obtained from the factory with both surfaces finished and ready to be cut to fit the frame.

operation is well shown in Fig. 167, which is a photograph of the lens-grinding room of a large factory.

The abrasives most commonly used for lens grinding are emery and carborundum, although crushed steel is sometimes used for the preliminary roughing. The coarse grinding is done with 90-mesh abrasive; then the surface is smoothed successively with 150-mesh, 200-mesh, and 600-mesh abrasives. Each grade is used until the scratches produced by the preceding have been entirely eliminated. As each change is made, the preceding abrasive is washed from the block very thoroughly so that no coarse grains will remain to cause grooves during the succeeding operation. For smoothing—the last fine-grinding operation— the abrasives are selected according to the length of time required for them to settle from a tank of water. For the final finishing, emery that remains in suspension for 10 min. but settles at the end of 60 min. is commonly used. This emery is selected from the emery worn down during the grinding operations. No small part of the worker's art is to keep the abrasive properly wet. If the abrasive is too wet, all the air is excluded from the working surfaces and the load is increased so much that particles of the abrasive may become embedded in the glass. If the abrasive is too dry, lumps may form that behave in the same way.

The tools used for ordinary ophthalmic lenses are known as diopter tools because they impart a certain power in diopters[1] to a lens that is plane on one side. Most ophthalmic lenses are so thin that they can be considered equivalent to two plane lenses in contact. Thus a lens made with a -6.00-diopter and a $+9.00$- diopter tool is considered to have a total power of $+3.00$ diopters. One curious feature to be remembered when curves are ordered in diopters is that the tools are named according to the power they would impart if the index of the glass were 1.530 instead of 1.523, which is the standard nowadays. Thus a $+5.00$-diopter tool has a radius of curvature of 106.0 mm and imparts a power of $+4.94$ diopters to an infinitely thin plano-convex lens made of modern spectacle crown glass. It must also be noted that diopter tools are limited in number. Below 10 diopters, the tools vary by one-eighth of a diopter; beyond that, they vary by one-quarter and finally one-half of a diopter. The 20.00-diopter tool is the strongest that is made regularly; its radius is 26.5 mm.

[1] It will be recalled that, by definition, one diopter is the power of a lens whose focal length is one meter.

While a lens is in work, its power is tested by checking the radius of curvature with a gauge, which is simply a piece of metal having a curved edge of the proper radius. When the lens is finished, its power is tested optically by means of instruments that will be described in the next chapter. The usual tolerance in power for ophthalmic lenses is one-sixteenth of a diopter except for very strong lenses. The usual tolerance in thickness is ± 0.2 mm. For condenser lenses, which are manufactured like ophthalmic lenses, the usual tolerance in thickness is ± 1 mm.

Although lenses of spectacle quality have a beautiful polish, their figure is far from perfect. This is due to a number of causes. In the first place, they are usually allowed to run hot during the grinding and polishing operations and their figure changes slightly when they become cool. Moreover, polishing on felt tends to destroy the figure. For lenses of precision quality, therefore, the operations are performed with more care, although they are the same in principle. The lapping and blocking tools are worked together with abrasive to attain exactly the correct curvature instead of being merely milled to shape. Also, the change in curvature during grinding, which is negligible for an ophthalmic lens, must be taken into account by the precision optician. In general, the upper surface tends to become more concave and the lower surface, more convex. This tendency is so pronounced that it is allowed for in preparing the tools. It can be overcome and even reversed by suitably adjusting the stroke of the blocking tool on the lap while the lens is being worked, but it demands constant attention from the operator. However, as was mentioned previously, the chief feature that distinguishes precision optical goods is the method of polishing. This operation is done on a tool coated with pitch that is charged with rouge. The pitch surface, being hard, does not tend to deform the figure of the lens as felt does. The preparation of the polishing tool is clearly described in the *Ordnance Department Document* mentioned previously:

The polishing tool is prepared by melting clean strained Norwegian pitch to which a little rosin has been added, and pouring the viscous liquid on a horizontal iron tool to a depth of one-fourth of an inch. Strips of wet paper are placed around the edge of the tool to prevent the pitch from overflowing. In cold weather, a little pine tar is added to the pitch to soften it slightly. After the layer of pitch has become cold, two series of parallel grooves, mutually perpendicular, about one-eighth of an inch wide and one inch apart, are cut into the surface.

The pitch is then reheated sufficiently to soften this surface, upon which is pressed a cold tool of the opposite curvature. This tool is moistened with a creamy mixture of water and rouge or dilute glycerin to prevent its sticking to the pitch. This imparts to the pitch surface the exact negative of the surface of the iron tool. The iron plate may be pressed against the pitch surface directly after the first heating if desired, and the grooves cut afterwards.

The amount of labor involved in producing an optical part depends upon the permissible variations in its dimensions and the perfection demanded of its various surfaces. There is almost no limit to the accuracy with which a part could be constructed by a skillful workman if he were allowed sufficient time. How-

Fig. 168.—Testing the surfaces of prisms with an optical flat. The prisms are mounted in plaster of Paris cast in a metal ring. (*By courtesy of Bausch and Lomb Optical Company.*)

ever, the cost of production rises entirely out of proportion as the tolerances are narrowed. In ordering optical parts, therefore, the tolerances should be made as liberal as the required performance of the completed instrument permits. Thus a reasonable tolerance for radius of curvature is 1 part in 10,000 if the radius is less than 200 mm, and 1 part in 3000 if the radius is greater. One method of specifying the tolerance in radius and surface quality results from the method used to test the surfaces. During the grinding, the surfaces are checked for curvature with a gauge, but, after a surface has been polished, an interference method can be used. This consists in comparing the surface with a test glass of known curvature, as shown in Fig. 168, and noting the resulting interference fringes. The method of formation of these fringes will be described more in detail in Chap. XXVIII. It must suffice here to state that, of the light passing through the test glass, some will be reflected at the lower surface of the test glass and some at the upper surface of the object being tested. Whether these two beams reinforce or annul depends upon the separation of the surfaces. If the surfaces are in contact at only one point, the familiar Newton's ring system of alternate bright and dark rings will be formed around the point of contact.[1] If the surface of the test glass is known to be accurately flat or spherical, the deformation of the rings indicates a deformation of the surface being tested. The quality of surface desired can be specified by the number of rings exhibited. The best quality is, of course, an exact fit so that no rings appear. A surface exhibiting only one or two wide rings is of high quality, and, for most purposes, a three- or four-ring surface is satisfactory. If a surface is to be cemented, as many as eight or ten rings are often permissible.

The tolerance in thickness also affects the cost to a marked extent, as might be surmised from the description of the method of grinding and polishing. A reasonable tolerance for a lens upwards of 3 in. in diameter is ± 0.1 mm. For small lenses, it is sometimes necessary to reduce this to ± 0.05 mm, and a tolerance of only ± 0.01 mm may be required in a lens for a high-power microscope objective. Occasionally a tolerance as small as ± 0.005 mm may be necessary, as in a standard filter for a photometer, although it is very expensive to work to such close limits.

125. Edging and Centering.—After the surfaces of a lens are finished, the next operation is to cut the lens to size and finish the edge. On lenses of spectacle quality, this operation is known as *centering to dot* or *edging*. The lens is placed in a rotatable holder, and the operator observes through an ocular an image of a target formed by the lens. The lens is moved in the holder until the image remains stationary, whereupon an arm is brought against the lens to make a dot on its surface at the exact center. This dot serves as a guide for placing the lens on the edging machine, which may be of either of two types. In one type, the lens is cut to size with a diamond, after which the rough edge is smoothed against a grinding wheel. In the other type, the lens is held firmly between two rotating rubber-capped spindles so that its edge is brought against a grinding wheel. A template of the size and shape—circular, oval, octagonal, or what not—to which the lens is to be edged is mounted on one of the spindles to stop the grinding when the lens has reached the proper shape. A reasonable tolerance in diameter for an edged lens is ± 0.2 mm.

[1] See pp. 574ff.

If the lens is to fit loosely in a cell, or if it is not to be mounted at all, it can be left with the edge that results from the pressing operation.   In this case, it is clear that the lens may be markedly wedge shaped, one side being thinner than the other.   Condensers for stereopticons are commonly left this way, a difference of thickness of 1 mm between one side and the other being permitted.   The variation in diameter to be expected in small lenses with pressed edges is about ±0.2 mm, and in condensers about ±0.5 mm.

In precision optics, the operation analogous to edging is termed *centering*.   A spindle slightly smaller than the lens and with a

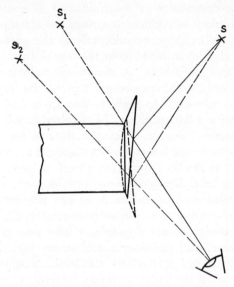

FIG. 169.

depression in the end is mounted in a lathe, and the lens is cemented to it with shellac.   The shellac is then softened by heating the spindle with a small flame while it is in rotation, and the lens is manipulated by means of a soft wooden stick until the image of a distant lamp reflected in the lens surface remains stationary.   Figure 169 illustrates the principle of this operation. When the lens is in the position shown by the solid lines, the image of the source S appears at S_1.   When the spindle has made half a revolution, the image appears at S_2, and thus the image seems to rotate in a circle of diameter S_1S_2.   When the lens is centered, the image remains stationary at some mean position.   For the very finest work the image should be truly stationary, but usually there is sufficient play in the lens cell to make a slight shift of the image permissible. After the lens is centered, it is turned to the proper diameter, either with a hand tool or with a diamond-charged milling tool or grinding wheel. If there are many lenses in the lot, a template is fitted to the spindle so that the grinding is stopped automatically when the lenses are reduced to the specified diameter. A precision of ±0.1 mm in diameter can easily be attained.

126. Working Prisms and Flats.—Prisms and flat plates, frequently called simply flats, are treated much like lenses except for the obvious modifications required by the difference in shape. Flats are cemented to a plane block and worked against a plane lap. Prisms are either cemented to a block having grooves of the proper shape or embedded in plaster of Paris, as shown in Fig. 168. The chief difficulty is to maintain a true surface figure. In addition, prisms must be constantly checked to insure the accuracy of their angles, and flats must be checked to prevent them from becoming wedge shaped.

A flat worked to spectacle quality is likely to be disappointing. It will doubtless be polished well enough, but more often than not it will be found to taper toward the edges. This can be detected by examining the image of a window formed by reflection at nearly grazing incidence. A piece of polished plate, or even selected window glass, usually has a flatter surface. If spectacle quality is required by reason of expense, it is well to have a large blank prepared and then to trim off the outer portions. Even then the piece may be wedge shaped, varying in thickness by as much as 0.2 mm in a hundred.

Round flats are edged exactly like lenses but rectangular ones are edged somewhat differently. If the glass is thin, the edge left by the glazier's diamond may be untouched. Such an edge is not satisfactory if the plate is more than about 4 mm or 5 mm thick because it is likely to be too irregular. It is almost certain to be unsatisfactory also in any pot opal, which cracks very erratically. A cheap way to edge the plate is to lay each edge in turn on the flat face of a grinding wheel. The tolerance demanded in a cut edge or an edge ground in this manner should not be closer than ±0.2 mm for a plate 2 mm thick. By the more refined methods of the precision-lens shop, a flat can be edged to ±0.1 mm without difficulty, and ±0.05 mm may reasonably be demanded.

The angle between the two faces of a flat or prism made to precision quality can be held within $\pm 2''$ for the most exacting purposes, but this is very expensive. A common tolerance is $\pm 1'$. Ophthalmic prisms are specified in *prism diopters*, 1 prism diopter being the power of a prism that deviates a ray by 1 cm at a distance of 1 meter. The customary tolerance is $\frac{1}{16}$ diopter.

127. Cementing.—Two optical parts can be brought into optical contact most conveniently by cementing them together with some substance of approximately the same refractive index. The cement that is most commonly used is Canada balsam, which is a mixture of turpentine and resins. For cementing glass, the balsam is freed from its turpentine by heat and cast into sticks. The removal of turpentine should be especially thorough if the cemented parts are to be subjected to heat in use.

The cementing should be done in a room as free from dust as possible, and cardboard covers should be used as a further protection. After the parts to be cemented have been thoroughly cleaned with alcohol and dusted with a camel's-hair brush, they are placed on a sheet of clean paper on an electric plate and heated slowly. A stick of balsam is then rubbed over the surfaces to be cemented, which should be in a horizontal position so that the molten balsam will spread evenly. It is important that the parts be brought to the right temperature to avoid discoloring the balsam. Ordinarily the balsam is light yellow, but it darkens if it is allowed to become too hot. In addition, a high temperature may cause bubbles to form that are not easily pressed out. Indeed, the greatest difficulty in cementing is to squeeze out all the bubbles and to prevent others from forming. If the proper temperature is maintained, the small bubbles that always form will usually migrate to the edges and disappear.

When the two surfaces have been covered with liquid balsam, one part is lifted from the plate and placed upon the other. In the case of lenses, the convex surface is placed upon the concave. The two are then pressed and rubbed together to squeeze out as much of the excess balsam as possible. Finally, the combination is set aside to cool, after which it is cleaned with kerosene or alcohol and ether.

If the combination is a lens, it must be trued. This can be done by heating it slightly and pressing it against an angle block. A better method is to mount the concave element in a chuck and center it, the convex element being then moved about until the image of a distant source remains stationary.

For cementing gelatin filters between glass plates, the balsam is used in its natural condition because the gelatin film would be ruined if heated sufficiently to melt the hard balsam. Cemented filters are baked for a long time, a matter of weeks, in a very cool oven to evaporate the turpentine. The edges of cemented filters should be painted with enamel to prevent the entry of liquids that would injure the balsam. This is a wise precaution in all cases.

Canada balsam and similar cements are not suitable for joints that become hot in use. Fusing the parts together in the ordinary manner would destroy the figure of the surfaces. However, it is possible to join two surfaces that have been worked to a close fit by holding them in contact for some time at a temperature slightly under the annealing temperature. In fact, if two surfaces that exactly match each other are brought into contact at ordinary temperatures in such a manner as to exclude the air, they will adhere firmly. The chief difficulty in performing this operation is in removing the dust from the surfaces. Moffitt has described a technique in which distilled water is sprayed against the surfaces during the operation. The thin film of water that remains between the surfaces after they are slid into contact is adsorbed by the glass within a few hours.

128. Aspheric Surfaces. Dropping.—Any surface having other than a plane or spherical form is said to be *aspheric*, but, in practice, such surfaces are usually either paraboloidal or ellipsoidal.[1] Aspheric surfaces are used to reduce the spherical aberration and thus increase the permissible relative aperture. They are seldom used except in instruments designed to cover a small field, which, curiously enough, represent the opposite extremes of image-forming requirements. On the one hand, relatively crude aspheric surfaces are used for searchlight mirrors and motion-picture condensers, where the image-forming requirements are not very severe. On the other hand, they are also used for the mirrors in the great astronomical telescopes, which represent the highest type of image-forming system.

Searchlight mirrors and mirrors used in motion-picture projectors are made by what is known as a *dropping* process. The stock is plate glass of the proper thickness and diameter, which is

---

[1] Usually they are known by the incorrect terms "parabolic" and "elliptical."

laid on the top of a hollow mold curved on the inside to the figure of the desired reflector. The mold and glass are placed in a furnace and heated until the glass becomes soft, whereupon it is sucked into the mold by pumping out the air. The pumping is stopped just as the glass touches the mold because a firm contact would cause pits on the surface. The dropping, as it is now called, is cooled, annealed, and edged to the required diameter. It is always made considerably larger in diameter than the finished reflector because the outer portions are not true to figure. The surfaces are cleaned on a buffing wheel and then the outside surface is silvered, coppered, and backed. The versatility of the dropping process can be inferred from the fact that it is used alike for stereopticon reflectors 3 in. in diameter and 3 mm thick and for searchlight mirrors 5 ft. in diameter and 1 in. thick. The chief importance of the process is in the manufacture of aspheric mirrors, of course, but it is also used for spherical mirrors because of the economy of time and material that it effects.

The surfaces of dropped mirrors are somewhat uneven, as might be expected. Spherical mirrors can be improved by grinding and polishing in the orthodox manner. Paraboloidal mirrors can be ground with a template by a special process. This process is based on the property of a paraboloid that its intersection with a plane parallel to its axis is a parabola whose form is independent of the distance of the plane from the axis. The template is an extremely hard metal blade about $\frac{1}{8}$ in. thick, one edge of which is cut into a parabolic outline. The dropping is rotated on a vertical spindle while the template, fed with abrasive and held in a vertical plane, is moved sidewise in a direction perpendicular to its own plane. The same process can be used for figuring a lens, such as a motion-picture condenser, except that the surface is previously rough ground with ordinary spherical tools. Another method is to grind by hand, testing constantly with a parabolic gauge. The demand for aspheric surfaces is so limited and the art of producing them so specialized that only a few firms are equipped to do this kind of work.

The figuring of mirrors for reflecting telescopes is very different from any other branch of the optician's art,[1] not only because the

---

[1] A detailed description of the method will be found in a monograph, On the Modern Reflecting Telescope, and the Making and Testing of Optical Mirrors, by G. W. Ritchey, published in the "Smithsonian Contributions to Knowledge," Vol. 34 (1904) and reprinted in *Sci. Amer. Supp.*, **58** and **59** (Dec. 24 and 31, 1904; and Jan. 7, 14, and 21, 1905).

mirrors are so large but also because an almost perfect surface is required. If a mirror is to be more than two feet in diameter, the difficulty of casting a disk of glass that is well annealed, sufficiently homogeneous to retain its figure, and free from defects near at least one face is considerable. Most of the large disks, including the 100-in. disk at Mount Wilson,[1] have been cast by the celebrated firm of St. Gobain in France. After the disk has been cast, the first operation is to grind and polish the two sides to permit inspection. One side is selected to be the face of the mirror, and the grinding of this side proceeds in the orthodox manner with metal tools mounted on counterbalanced arms, the disk lying on a platform under the tools. Frequently the center is ground almost to the finished depth with a small tool first and the working of the outer zones deferred until later. The fine grinding is done with a full-sized tool unless the mirror is more than two or three feet in diameter, in which case tools smaller than the disk are used. The polishing is done with a wooden tool covered with soft rosin cut into squares as described previously. This tool is shaped by pressing it on the mirror itself. It is operated by hand, two men grasping knobs on its back and giving it a peculiar motion over the rotating mirror. When the polishing is completed, the mirror is tested by means of the Foucault knife-edge test to be described in Sec. 135 of the next chapter. The last operation—parabolizing—consists in removing material from the center of the disk so as to shorten the radius of curvature at that point. It can be accomplished either by cutting away rosin from the outer portions of the polishing tool or by using a small tool and working harder at the center of the disk than at the edges. An idea of the delicacy of the operation can be gained by noting that the amount of glass removed at the center of the 60-in. mirror at Mount Wilson, which has a focal length of 25 ft., was only 0.015 mm.

The early makers of reflecting telescopes did not realize the necessity for parabolizing. Even Newton figured mirrors blindly until he obtained one that was satisfactory. Not the least of the difficulties of the operation is to prevent the disk from

[1] An extensive description of this instrument, which is the largest in the world, is not available, but a brief description will be found in the *Sci. Amer.*, Aug. 11, 1917. A detailed description of the 72-in. reflector at the Dominion Astrophysical Observatory, Victoria, B. C., has been given by the director, J. S. Plaskett, in *Dom. Astrophys Obs. Pub.*, **1**, 7, (1922).

heating because it changes its shape when it becomes cool. Changes in temperature affect its figure when it is in use also, and, to prevent this effect, fused quartz is proposed for future reflectors.

Although the preparation of large mirrors is exceedingly difficult, a reflecting telescope can be constructed quite easily by an amateur provided he limits himself to a 6-in. or a 10-in. mirror.[1] The procedure for such mirrors is somewhat different. Two disks of heavy plate glass are used, one for the mirror and one for the tool. They are worked together with abrasive until the upper disk, which is to be the mirror, has become concave to the requisite extent. The lower disk is then covered with rosin cut into squares as usual and the mirror is polished and parabolized on it as described above. In this case, the paraboloidal figure is readily attained by lengthening the stroke of the mirror on the tool to grind the center more than the edges.

129. Marking Glass.—There are three ways of marking glass—stamping, engraving, and etching. Stamping consists in applying an ink by means of an ordinary rubber stamp and then baking the stamped article. The base of the ink is albumin, which is coagulated by the heat and so binds the pigment to the glass. This method is rapid and fairly permanent, but it cannot be used for such things as scales, where accuracy is essential. Engraving consists in scratching the article with a diamond point. As compared with etching, it will make a finer line but the width of the line cannot be controlled readily. Etching consists in coating the article with a thin layer of wax, inscribing the design in the wax, and then subjecting the article to the action of hydrofluoric acid. The etched characters are usually filled with black or colored pigment. A surface that is to be etched should be polished on beeswax rather than on pitch because the acid acts more uniformly on a wax-polished surface. The tools for inscribing the etched and engraved characters are controlled mechanically. Scales are made in a dividing engine; letters and figures are made in a pantograph by tracing a large stencil of the character desired.

For writing on glass by hand, a diamond set in a metal handle to form a pencil can be used. Such a diamond pencil should be

[1] R. W. Porter has published very explicit directions in *Sci. Amer.*, **134**, February and March, 1926, for those who wish to embark upon this most fascinating pastime. See also "Amateur Telescope Making," edited by Ingalls and published by the Scientific American Publishing Company.

held vertically in use. It will be found to work best if one particular side is held away from the operator; this side should be found by trial and marked on the handle. The pencils made of a new alloy are also very satisfactory. For making temporary marks, a wax crayon can be used.

130. Chemical Silvering.—Many methods for silvering glass have been invented, but the following, which is a modification of one due to Brashear, gives excellent results. It can be described only briefly here, but a more extensive description[1] is available. The most important step in the process is cleaning the glass. If the surface is greasy, it should be washed first with some solvent such as alcohol or ether. It is then washed with pure nitric acid, being swabbed very thoroughly with as much pressure as its optical perfection will permit, after which it is rinsed with distilled water. Sometimes it is cleaned again with a strong solution of caustic followed by an application of French chalk. Commercial operators frequently use a saturated solution of stannous chloride. After the surface is cleaned, it must not be allowed to become dry but must be kept covered with distilled water until it is silvered.

The silvering should be done, if possible, on a freshly polished surface. If the surface is old, it can be treated with a 2 per cent solution of hydrofluoric acid for 2 or 3 min. before being cleaned. This is the most effective method of cleaning surfaces that are inaccessible to a swab, but it tends to spoil the polish and should not be used for surfaces of high quality.

A good silvering job requires much care. The materials must be chemically pure and the water must not contain harmful impurities. If the water turns a light blue or pink when silver nitrate is dissolved in it, it is probably too impure and either distilled or rain water must be used. A trial on a small mirror will definitely settle the question. The merest trace of chlorine, either free or in combination, will cause failure, and care must therefore be taken that the fingers do not contaminate the solutions. For Brashear's process, the four following solutions are required:

> *A.* Granulated sugar............................. 90 grams
> Nitric acid (sp. gr. 1.22)....................... 4 cc
> Alcohol (ethyl or rubbing)..................... 175 cc
> Distilled water, to make.... . ... 1000 cc

[1] *Bur. Standards Circ.* 389.

This reducing solution should be made up in advance and kept in stock because it improves with age. If it must be used at once, it can be improved by boiling, the addition of the alcohol being delayed until it is cool.

B. Distilled water............................ 300 cc
　　Silver nitrate............................. 20 grams

C. Distilled water............................ 100 cc
　　Potassium hydroxide....................... 10 grams

D. Distilled water............................ 30 cc
　　Silver nitrate, approximately............. 2 grams

To prepare the silvering solution, add strong ammonia gradually to solution B until the precipitate first formed just disappears; avoid an excess of ammonia. Then pour in solution C, whereupon the mixture will turn dark brown or black. Again add ammonia, stirring constantly until the solution just clears a second time. It should now be a light brown or straw color but transparent. Next add solution D slowly, stirring constantly, until there is quite a little suspended matter that the solution refuses to take up. Finally filter the solution through absorbent cotton.

When ready to silver, add about 130 cc of solution A and pour the resulting mixture at once upon the mirror without pouring off the water that was left to cover it after it was cleaned. At all times during the operations the solutions should be kept below 18°C. (64°F.), preferably about 15°C. (60°F.). While the silver is being deposited, keep the solution in motion so that the sediment will not settle on the silver coat. Very light swabbing with loose absorbent cotton will be found advantageous for large mirrors.

The silvering process requires from 3 to 8 min., and during this period the surface should not be exposed to the air for more than a second or two at a time. When the process is completed, the solution should be poured off and the surface rinsed thoroughly, being swabbed lightly with absorbent cotton if there is much bloom on it.

The volume of solution required in the silvering operation depends both upon the size of the mirror and the thickness of the coat desired. For most work, 1 gram of silver nitrate for each 40 cm^2 (or 6 sq. in.) of surface is ample; for thicker coats, such as are put on astronomical mirrors, 1 gram to each 27 cm^2 (or 4 sq. in.) may be used. In every case, the amount of solution *A* to be used should be in the ratio of 6 cc per gram of silver nitrate.

Second-surface mirrors are backed with some sort of protective coating. Cheap mirrors are backed with a gray paint, but most of those made in optical factories are backed with a tough black enamel. Mirrors that are to be subjected to extreme heat, such as the reflectors in stereopticons and motion-picture projectors, are backed with a heat-resisting material that is baked on. The composition of this backing is a trade secret. Several coats are applied, the result being a thick, rough, white coating. Another kind of backing, used where mechanical strength is required, consists of a thick layer of paint in which is embedded a sheet of wire mesh. Mirrors are frequently plated electrolytically with copper before the backing is applied.

First-surface mirrors are more difficult to protect because the light must traverse the protective coating. Lastina and Zapon lacquers are used for the purpose, as also is collodion. The difficulty in using such a coating is that, if it is too thick, it will dry in streaks and waves, and thus bring to naught all the care expended on figuring the surface; whereas, if it is too thin, it will exhibit interference patterns. If the mirror is so located in the optical system that these patterns are of no consequence, a commercial lacquer thinned six to one and carefully applied in the ordinary manner is satisfactory. If the mirror is located where these interference patterns would be visible, the lacquer can be thinned two to one and the mirror rotated while it is drying. Mirrors that are used only occasionally, like those in radiometric instruments, can be kept in a desiccator containing vessels of phosphorus pentoxide and potassium hydroxide. Coblentz states that a mirror preserved in this manner will retain its finish for years.

Mirrors can be half silvered by any of the slower processes for full silvering, but a process devised by Twyman[1] especially for the purpose is undoubtedly preferable. In this process four solutions are prepared according to the formulae on the next page. The object to be silvered is placed in a dish, cleaned with strong nitric acid swabbed over the surface with a bit of cotton or wool on the end of a rod, and then is placed in solution *D* for 5 min., after which it is rinsed in running water. The silvering solution is prepared by adding to 20 cc of *A* enough ammonia

[1] *Trans. Optical Soc. (London)*, **24**, 203 (1922–1923).

to redissolve the precipitate that forms at first, after which a slight amount of silver nitrate solution is added until the ammoniacal solution becomes a faint straw color.   Then the latter is made up to 100 cc with water and the object is suspended in it either face upward or face downward.   The reducing solution, which is prepared by mixing 5 cc each of *B* and *C*, is then added to the silvering

A. Silver nitrate............................   10 grams
    Water, to make.........................   100 cc

B. Formalin, 40 per cent solution.

C. Granulated sugar........................   400 grams
    Alcohol.................................   200 cc
    Nitric acid..............................   10 cc
    Water, to make.........................   2000 cc
Allow to stand two weeks.

D. Chromic acid............................   250 grams
    Sulphuric acid..........................   1500 cc

solution while the resulting mixture is stirred constantly.   When the mixture becomes reddish, it is poured off and some of the clear silvering solution, unmixed with reducing solution, is poured on. This is allowed to remain until the density of the deposit becomes correct, which requires only a few minutes.   The liquid is then poured off and the object is rinsed and dried.

Many notes on the process of silvering have appeared in the literature, and directions for depositing other materials are also available.[1]   For example, copper mirrors can be made chemically, and dark mirrors can be made by the deposition of lead sulphide.

131. The Burning-in Process of Platinizing.—Glass can be platinized by coating it with a mixture of organic materials containing platinum salts and then heating it.   Various methods have been described, but they are little used because the deposits produced by most of them are somewhat granular and consequently not suitable for most optical purposes.   To overcome this drawback, Rheinberg[2] has developed a technique of which the important feature appears to be that the components of the mixture evaporate at nearly the same rate so that the resulting deposit is uniform.   A typical formula is given as follows:

----

[1] An extensive bibliography will be found in the pamphlet "The Making of Reflecting Surfaces," published by the Optical Society of London.   A briefer but more recent bibliography will be found in the *Bur. Standards Letter Circ.* 32, mentioned previously.

[2] U. S. Patent 1,385,229.

Parts by
Volume

Collodion in methyl alcohol, 6 per cent solution........... 3
Chlorplatinic acid (H_2PtCl_6) in denatured alcohol, 6 per cent
    solution.. 3
Denatured alcohol................................... 3
Bismuth chloride, 1 per cent solution in alcohol......... 1

The last-named solution is made from a 5 per cent solution of bismuth chloride in denatured alcohol to which 5 per cent of hydrochloric acid is added. It is diluted to the proper extent with alcohol just before use because very weak solutions of bismuth chloride will not keep for any length of time.

The characteristics of the deposit are described by Rheinberg substantially as follows: At first, the collodion film chars and completely volatilizes, leaving the reduced platinum in an exceedingly fine state of division. With continued heating, the deposit becomes adherent although soft, but eventually it becomes wholly incorporated within the surface layer of the glass and is then exceedingly permanent. In fact, nothing that is not hard enough to damage the glass itself will damage the mirror. Neither will any chemical that does not attack the glass itself affect it, except aqua regia after prolonged immersion. The surface layer of the glass in which the platinum is incorporated is extremely thin, perhaps 200 mμ thick, so it may gradually be worn away, if, like a dental mirror, it is subjected to rough treatment.

132. The Electrical Deposition of Metals.—A glass surface can be coated with metal by bombarding it with atoms of the metal moving with a high velocity. These can be obtained from a metallic cathode in a gaseous discharge at low pressure and high potential, or by direct evaporation from a heated electrode in a vacuum. The first process, which is known as *sputtering*, is illustrated in Fig. 170. The cathode, which should be somewhat larger than the object to be plated, is placed about an inch from the surface of the latter. In the figure, a lot of prisms mounted in a clamp are shown in position for plating. A potential difference of about 1000 volts is employed and the chamber is evacuated until the edge of the Crookes dark space almost coincides with the surface to be plated.[1]

[1] The position of the edge of the dark space is of great importance. If it is not close enough to the surface, the deposit is soft; if it is beyond the surface, the deposit may blister.

The pressure is of the order of 0.005 mm of mercury. Platinum, gold, silver, and nickel can be plated satisfactorily by this process.

Neither the reflectance nor the transmission of the plated surface varies linearly with the time of plating, but the rate of deposition is slow enough to enable the process to be accurately controlled. Thus it is a fairly easy matter to prepare mirrors that reflect and transmit in any desired ratio. Such mirrors are very useful for many purposes, particularly in certain processes of color photography. Prisms for binocular micro-

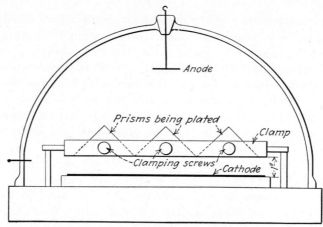

FIG. 170.—Apparatus for platinizing optical parts by sputtering. The figure shows a lot of prisms mounted in a clamp with the faces to be plated held above the platinum cathode. The prisms are placed in parallel rows, each row being held in a position with a clamping screw.

scopes are frequently plated by this method. An undesirable feature is that a platinized surface is very wasteful of light. A surface that reflects and transmits in equal proportions absorbs approximately 50 per cent of the incident light.

The plating of metals by the evaporation process, which has been described by Stuhlmann,[1] is accomplished conveniently by an apparatus like that sketched in Fig. 171. A wire of the metal to be deposited carries an electric current which heats it to incandescence. The surface to be plated is horizontal and the wire is moved across it at a constant rate, the pressure within the chamber being held at approximately 0.002 mm of mercury during the operation. The wire can be moved by means of a

[1] *Jour. Optical Soc. Amer.*, **1**, 78 (1917). The technique of evaporation and sputtering is described in detail in Chapter IV of Strong's "Procedures in Experimental Physics."

crank passing through a ground-glass joint in the base of the chamber or by means of a clockwork within the chamber. For depositing silver, a wire of about B. and S. No. 24 gauge made of an alloy of 85 per cent silver and 15 per cent platinum has been found by the present authors to be satisfactory. The function

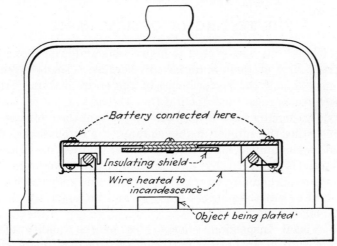

Fig. 171.—Apparatus for silvering optical parts by distillation. The piece to be plated is laid under the silver wire, which is heated and drawn along the tracks.

of the platinum is principally to impart stiffness to the wire at a temperature at which the silver evaporates freely. Because the ends of the wire are cooler than the center, the wire must be somewhat longer than the surface to be coated. Metals with a low boiling point, like zinc or tin, can be deposited by this process from their alloys, brass and bronze.

CHAPTER XVII

THE TESTING OF OPTICAL PARTS

Optical parts are subjected to many tests and inspections during the course of their manufacture because a single defective unit may impair the performance of the entire system. Many of these tests are so fundamental that the user of optical instruments occasionally finds it desirable to perform them for himself. In presenting the subject in this chapter, the emphasis has been placed on the underlying principles rather than on the details of the methods followed by any particular manufacturer. The methods may therefore be taken as typical, and they can usually be varied to suit the purpose required and the apparatus that is available.

133. Visual Inspection.—Some idea of the quality of the workmanship in an optical part can be gained by mere visual inspection. If the part is examined with a magnifier, the freedom of its surface from pits, scratches, grayness, insufficient polish, chipped edges, and cracks can be easily verified. Some surface defects, such as poor polish, scumminess, and waviness, can be detected even without a magnifier by simply illuminating the surface at nearly grazing incidence. Sometimes striae, stones, and folds in the glass are so prominent that they can be seen with the naked eye. Truing and centering can be tested with some little precision by noting whether the images of a distant light formed by reflection at the various surfaces lie in a straight line. Cemented lenses can be inspected visually for bubbles and blisters in the cement, for the color of the Canada balsam, and for particles of dirt or fuzz within the balsam.

The manufacturing defects and striae in a lens can be exhibited on a screen with the apparatus sketched in Fig. 172.[1] In this figure, S is a source of light, D a diffusing glass, A a screen containing a pinhole, C a collimating lens, L the lens being tested, P a photographic objective, and K a screen on which an enlarged

---

[1] This method of detecting striae is described in detail in *Bur. Standards Sci. Paper* 373.

image of L is formed. Faint striae can be made visible by closing the diaphragm of the objective and shifting the lens or the collimator to obtain oblique illumination. Of course, the screen and photographic objective can be replaced by a camera to make a permanent record of the results of the inspection.

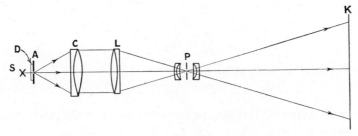

FIG. 172.

134. Index and Dispersion.—The index and dispersion of a sample of glass can be measured by means of a spectrometer as described in Sec. 201, Chap. XXVII. This method is tedious, however, and has the further disadvantage that the sample must be fairly large and in the form of a prism. For ordinary measurements, special instruments called refractometers, based on the critical-angle principle, are generally used instead. The type best suited for measuring the index of glass is due to Pulfrich. The principle on which it is based can be understood by reference to Fig. 173, where

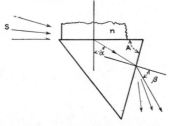

FIG. 173.

the sample, which has an index n, is shown in optical contact with a prism of index N and refracting angle A. A beam of monochromatic light from a source S passes into the sample and through the prism to emerge from the second refracting face of the latter. The ray incident horizontally on the interface between the sample and the prism emerges from the first face of the prism at an angle α to the normal, and from the second face at an angle β. Evidently, incident rays making an angle less than 90° with the normal to the first prism face will emerge from the second face below this first ray, but no rays can emerge above this one because such rays cannot enter the prism. Thus a telescope directed at the second face of the prism will show a bright band of light terminated at its upper side by a sharp boundary.

Working formulae for the instrument can be derived from the relations

$$\frac{\sin (\alpha - A)}{\sin \beta} = \frac{1}{N}$$

and

$$\frac{n}{N} = \sin \alpha,$$

which can be combined to give

$$n = \sin A \sqrt{N^2 - \sin^2 \beta} + \cos A \sin \beta. \tag{215}$$

For most types of Pulfrich refractometers, $A = 90°$ and, consequently,

$$n = \sqrt{N^2 - \sin^2 \beta}. \tag{216}$$

The instrument is shown diagrammatically in Fig. 174. The sample should be 15 or 20 mm square and at least 1 mm in thick-

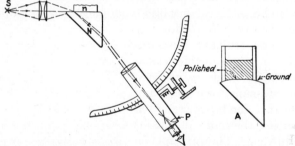

Fig. 174.—Diagrammatic sketch of the Pulfrich refractometer. A, the type of cell used for holding liquids.

ness. Monochromatic light from the source S is condensed on the front edge of the sample at its junction with the refractometer prism, and the telescope is placed in such a position that the band of light appears in the ocular. To insure optical contact of the sample, a minute drop of a liquid having a higher index is placed on it before it is set on the prism. A right-angle prism P allows the observer to look into the side of the telescope to see the interference fringes formed at the interface of the sample and prism. When the face of the sample is parallel to the surface of the prism, the interference pattern disappears. It is difficult to place the sample exactly parallel, and usually the sample is merely adjusted until the number of bands is reduced to fewer than three and these are made parallel to the direction of the light. Under these circumstances, the sample makes a negligibly small angle with the plane of the prism. With the sample in position, the arm of the tangent screw is clamped and the telescope is turned to bring the cross hairs into coincidence with the upper edge of the bright band. Inasmuch as the index is commonly specified for the *D*-line and the dispersion as a function of the difference between the *C*- and *F*-lines, it is convenient to use a sodium flame and a hydrogen tube successively as the source. The index for the *D*-line is determined by reading the divided circle, which can be done to a precision of 0.5' by means of a vernier; the dispersion is determined by reading the drum on the tangent screw for the *C*-, *D*-, and *F*-lines, which can be done to a precision of 0.1'. By this procedure, the computed dispersion is accurate to one or two units in the fifth decimal place, although the index for the *D*-line may be accurate to only five or ten units. Tables are generally supplied with the instrument to facilitate the computations.

This instrument is very rapid and easy to use but several precautions must be taken. The two faces of the sample through which the light passes must be flat and well polished, the bounding edge must be truly sharp, and the angle at this edge must be close to 90°. The faces must be pitch polished because a felt polisher rounds them so much that only a rough determination can be made. The sample must be free from striae because a very slight amount will make the *C*- and *F*-lines so hazy as to be unreadable. The hydrogen tube must be in good condition, or the *F*-line will be hazy and weak. The visibility in the blue end of the spectrum is so low that an excellent tube is required if the *G'*-line is to be measured.

The instrument itself is subject to numerous sources of inaccuracy,[1] of which five in particular should be emphasized:

1. The divided circle must be checked for eccentricity and a calibration curve made, if necessary.

2. The tangent screw must be adjusted so that the micrometer indicates the same angular differences between the *C*- and *F*-lines at all parts of the scale.

3. The refracting angle of the prism must be within 10″ of 90°. When the upper face becomes seriously scratched it must be refinished, and this is the maximum tolerance that should be allowed in the operation.

[1] See a paper by Guild, *Proc. Phys. Soc.* (*London*), **30**, 157 (1918). Reprinted in *Nat. Phys. Lab.*, *Collected Researches*, **14**, 273 (1920).

4. The zero error of the divided circle must be found. This is done by illuminating the cross hairs with an external source placed outside the prism P and moving the telescope until the images of the cross hairs reflected from the refractometer prism appear in the ocular coincident with the cross hairs themselves. This is the autocollimation method described in greater detail in Sec. 138.

5. With all these precautions, the values as measured on the different prisms may be different and they all may be different from those determined by means of a spectrometer. This is because the particular pieces of glass from which the prisms were cut may have slightly different indices from the samples measured to furnish data for the tables. With the aid of test pieces of known indices, a correction table for each prism can be made. Usually it is sufficient to use a different zero correction from the one determined directly. Sometimes the magnitude of the correction can be reduced by slightly altering the angle of the prism.

A liquid can be measured by cementing a cylinder on the prism as shown at A in Fig. 174, and putting the liquid in the cup

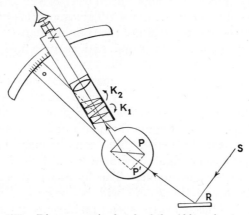

FIG. 175.—Diagrammatic sketch of the Abbe refractometer.

thus formed. The cylinder and prism must be well fitted so that the layer of the cement—Canada balsam, gum arabic, or whatever is appropriate to the liquid to be measured—will be thin.

Figure 175 is a diagrammatic sketch of another refractometer operating on the critical-angle principle. It was invented by Abbe, and its chief merit is that it is more rapid than the Pulfrich instrument. It is suitable for both solids and liquids having indices from 1.3 to 1.7, and is precise to about two units in the fourth decimal place. The essential features are a telescope, a refractometer prism P, and two Amici compensating prisms

K_1 and K_2 so arranged that they can be rotated simultaneously in opposite directions by means of a knob. These prisms disperse light without deviating it so that, by varying their relative positions, any amount of dispersion can be produced from zero to a maximum. Their function is to neutralize the dispersion of the sample and thus permit white light to be used. The observer looks into the telescope and rotates the arm carrying the prism until a boundary between a light and a dark area appears. He then adjusts the compensating prisms until the system is achromatized and the boundary appears sharp.[1] When the boundary is coincident with the cross hairs, the index is read directly on the scale to the third decimal place and by interpolation to the fourth place.

The Abbe refractometer was designed primarily to measure the refractive index of liquids, and as shown in Fig. 175 it is in the proper position for this purpose. The sample is placed between the refractometer prism P and an auxiliary prism P' made of the same glass, the separation of the two prisms being approximately 0.1 mm. Light enters the instrument from the reflector R, which may be a sheet of paper, a piece of ground opal glass, or, if more light is necessary, a mirror. Some light enters at grazing incidence, and the principle of the instrument can therefore be understood by following an argument similar to that for the Pulfrich refractometer. If the sample happens to be a solid, the instrument is swung about until the face of prism P is uppermost, the prism P' being moved out of the way. The sample is then placed on P as described for the Pulfrich refractometer. A felt polish of good quality is satisfactory for the face of the sample that is in contact with the prism. The adjacent face, on which the light is incident, need not be polished, but the edge between the two faces should be sharp.

Two other types of refractometers may be mentioned in this connection, although they are rarely used for inspecting optical parts. One is the crystal refractometer, which is similar to the Pulfrich except that, instead of having a prism, it has a hemisphere made of glass whose index is about 1.9. It is equipped with an analyzer so that the indices for the two rays of doubly refracting crystals can be measured. Another important type is the dipping refractometer, which is used for measuring the index

---

[1] This boundary will have a slight violet coloration extending into the dark area, but this is not especially annoying.

of liquids having a small range of index. It consists of a tube, at one end of which is a glass cylinder with a sloping face that acts as the refractometer prism. The observer looks into the opposite end of the instrument and, immersing the prism in the liquid, reads the index directly by noting where the boundary between the light and dark areas intersects a scale in the ocular. Several prisms of different index are supplied so that any index from about 1.3 to 1.7 can be measured.

The contact liquid commonly used in critical-angle refractometers for samples having an index less than 1.658 is α-monobromnaphthalene. For samples having an index greater than this but less than about 1.7, methylene iodide is satisfactory. With the Pulfrich refractometer, samples having a somewhat higher index can be measured by using methylene iodide in which sulphur has been dissolved by heat (see page 406).

One of the disadvantages of the Pulfrich and the Abbe refractometers for measuring solids is that the sample must be ground and polished in a particular manner. This means that the object to be tested must usually be mutilated and a certain amount of shop work must be done to prepare the sample. If it is not allowable to mutilate the object or if the facilities for working optical surfaces are not at hand, an immersion method can be used to determine the index.

The immersion method consists in finding a liquid having the same index as that of the sample and then measuring the index of the liquid. This method is extensively used by mineralogists, who can thus determine the indices of crystals to a few units in the fourth decimal place. The customary procedure is to place the specimen in a cell containing a liquid on the stage of a microscope and then to judge from the appearance of the crystal, as the microscope is racked up and down, whether the index of the liquid is too high or too low. Usually after about ten trials, a liquid is found that matches the index of the crystal to three decimal places, and somewhat greater accuracy can be obtained if necessary. For large specimens, such as lenses and pieces of glass, a microscope is not needed and examination with the naked eye is sufficient. A more refined procedure for such specimens has been described by Cheshire.[1]

135. Surface Curvature.—Instruments for measuring the radius of curvature of a surface are called spherometers. Figure

[1] *Phil. Mag.*, **32**, 409 (1916).

176 is a sketch of a type designed by Abbe that is commonly used in the laboratory. It consists essentially of a ring on which the surface to be measured is placed, and a plunger concentric with the ring that is pulled upward by the counterweight until it just touches the surface. The ring is carefully ground to a cross section as shown at A, so that a concave surface makes contact with the outer rim and a convex surface with the inner rim. The procedure in measuring a radius of curvature is first to place a glass flat on the ring and determine the position of the plunger by means of the scale and the reading microscope. The flat is then replaced by the surface to be tested and the scale

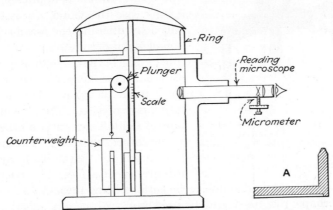

Fig. 176.—Diagrammatic sketch of the Abbe spherometer. A, an enlarged cross-sectional view of a ring, showing the shape of the edge.

is read again. The radius of curvature of the surface can be computed from the difference of the two scale readings and the diameter of the ring. If r is the radius of the appropriate rim of the ring and h the difference in the readings of the plunger, the radius of curvature of the surface is

$$R = \frac{r^2}{2h} + \frac{h}{2}. \tag{217}$$

The diameter of the rims of a spherometer can be measured on a comparator to ± 0.01 mm and the position of the plunger can be determined to ± 0.001 mm.[1] It is easy to compute on this basis that the error in measuring the radius of curvature of a

---

[1] This precision is meaningless, however, unless the errors of the scale are known. For methods of determining these errors, see Martin's "Optical Measuring Instruments," Chap. III.

surface having a radius of 200 mm and a diameter of 100 mm is approximately 0.1 mm. This type of spherometer is generally equipped with interchangeable rings and, for obvious reasons, the largest ring that will accommodate the object being measured

should be used. An even better plan is to use several rings and average the results.

Two other types of spherometers based on the same principle are in common use. One is the three-legged type illustrated in Fig. 177. The same formula is applicable, but in this case the value of r is determined by dividing the mean separation of the legs by the square root of three. This type as commonly made does not give very precise results, but a model developed by Guild[1] is extremely precise. The novel feature of Guild's design is a glass ball on the end of the screw. The instant of contact is determined by the appearance of a Newton's ring pattern where the ball touches the surface being measured.

Fig. 177.—A common type of spherometer. The needle above the divided circle flies upward when the rod makes contact with the surface being measured.

Perhaps the most widely used instrument for measuring curvature is the Geneva gauge, called colloquially by opticians the "clock." As will be seen in Fig. 178, it indicates the curvature of a surface in diopters in accordance with the convention described in Sec. 124 of the preceding chapter. Its use is confined almost entirely to spectacle lenses, of course.

The spherometer is not adapted for routine work in an optical shop, and the customary procedure is to use a set of test glasses instead, as described

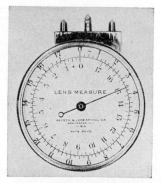

Fig. 178.—A typical Geneva gauge. (*By courtesy of Bausch and Lomb Optical Company.*)

in the preceding chapter. These test glasses are always made in pairs, one concave and the other convex, by grinding and polishing

[1] *Trans. Optical Soc.* (*London*), **19**, 103 (1918).

them on each other until both surfaces are spherical and of the same radius of curvature as judged by an interference test. The radius of curvature is then measured accurately on a spherometer in the laboratory. Test glasses are also made with plane surfaces, but the method of preparing them is somewhat different because three test glasses must be prepared instead of two to make sure that the surfaces are truly plane. The procedure in this case is to grind three blanks together, two at a time, in all possible combinations. They are then polished on a pitch lap, as described in the preceding chapter, and are tested by the interference method against one another. By setting up three simultaneous equations, each representing the number of interference rings formed by one of the combinations, the departure from flatness of each blank can

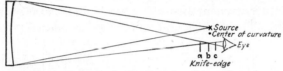

Fig. 179.—The Foucault method of measuring the radius of curvature of a reflecting surface.

be computed. The polishing process is continued until each test glass fits both the others perfectly in all positions, in which case they must all be plane.

An excellent method of determining the radius of a weak concave surface is to locate the center of curvature. This can be done readily by mounting an illuminated pinhole and a screen side by side at the supposed center of curvature of the surface. The exact center is found by moving the pinhole and screen together until the image of the pinhole is in sharp focus on the screen. The distance from the screen and pinhole to the surface is, of course, the radius of curvature. A somewhat better procedure is to substitute a pair of cross hairs for the screen and to use an ocular or magnifier for determining when the image formed by reflection at the surface is coincident with the cross hairs. Foucault brought this method to a high state of refinement by intercepting the reflected beam with a knife edge, as shown in Fig. 179. It is clear that if the knife edge is introduced at a, inside the center of curvature, the mirror appears to darken on the side from which the knife edge is introduced; if it is introduced at c, outside the center of curvature, the mirror darkens from the other side; if it is introduced at b, exactly at the center of curvature, the mirror darkens uniformly over its entire surface.

Since a paraboloidal surface has different radii of curvature in different zones, Foucault's method can be used to test the figure of a mirror such as would be used in a reflecting telescope. A diaphragm is placed over the whole mirror except for a narrow zone around the edge, and the center of curvature of this portion is determined. Then a diaphragm with a central hole is substituted and the new center of curvature found. If the surface is paraboloidal, the difference between the two centers should be equal to one-eighth of the square of the diameter of the mirror divided by the mean radius of curvature. For a 6-in. mirror of 4-ft. focal length, this difference between the centers is about $\frac{1}{10}$ in., an amount that is easily measured.

A better arrangement for testing paraboloidal surfaces is shown in Fig. 180. The pinhole and knife edge are placed at the focal

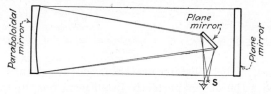

Fig. 180.—The Foucault method applied to a paraboloidal surface.

point of the paraboloid, and consequently the entire surface appears to darken uniformly if it is true to figure.[1] The procedure is analogous to testing a spherical surface at its center of curvature, which of course is also its focus.

The Foucault test can also be used for such things as test glasses and the polished blanks for Rowland gratings. Lenses can be tested in a similar manner by placing the pinhole at the object distance for which the lens is corrected (for a photographic or telescope objective, as far away as possible) and placing the knife edge at the focus. If spherical aberration is present, the lens will not darken uniformly for any position of the knife edge; if chromatic aberration is present, the disk will appear in different colors depending on the position of the knife edge.

136. Focal Length.—The characteristic of prime importance in a lens is its focal length. Special methods of measuring this quantity that are appropriate to particular instruments are

[1] For further details, see the paper by Ritchey cited in Sec. 128 of the preceding chapter.

described in later chapters. The methods described in this section are of more general application, and are sufficiently precise for all ordinary purposes if conducted with reasonable care. A number are applicable to positive lenses only, but, if a negative lens is to be tested, it can usually be combined with a stronger positive lens of known focal length. The unknown focal length can be computed from the measured focal length of the combination.

The equal-magnification method is perhaps the most precise of the simpler ones. The lens is set in a holder running on a track between an illuminated target and an ocular. The ocular and the lens are moved until the image of the target formed on a scale in the focal plane of the ocular is of the same size as the target itself. The focal length of the lens is then computed by

FIG. 181.—Optical system of the focal collimator.

subtracting the separation of the principal points from the distance between the target and scale, and dividing the difference by four. The separation of the principal points can usually be calculated with sufficient precision inasmuch as any error is divided by four. Although the lens can be moved a considerable distance without appreciably affecting the size or distinctness of the image, the same is not true of the ocular, and so the measurement is precise nevertheless.

A variation of this method is to place an illuminated pinhole and a knife edge at conjugate points by Foucault's method and compute the focal length. The greatest precision is obtained at approximately unit magnification. Some idea of the aberrations of the lens can be gained at the same time from the uniformity with which the lens darkens as the knife edge is moved.

Perhaps the most generally useful apparatus for measuring focal length is the focal collimator, which is deserving of a wider use than it enjoys at present. As shown in Fig. 181, it consists essentially of an illuminated target T at the focal point of the collimator C, and an observing microscope M with a scale S on the stage. The lens L to be tested is moved along the axis until the target is focused on the scale, a red filter usually being inserted in the path of the light to reduce the effect of chromatic aberration. It is clear that the total magnification of the target on the scale is

$$m = m_1 m_2 = \frac{y_2'}{y_1} = \frac{s_1' s_2'}{s_1 s_2},$$

where y_1 is the separation of two intervals of the target and y_2' the corresponding distance in the image measured on the scale. But s_1' and s_2 are equal and infinite, s_1 is the focal length f_1 of the collimator, and s_2' is the focal length f_2 of the lens being tested. Therefore,

$$f_2 = \frac{f_1}{y_1} y_2' = k y_2'.$$

Thus, if the constant k of the instrument is determined, the focal length of any lens can be measured by simply determining

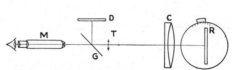

Fig. 182.—Sketch showing the method of calibrating the focal collimator.

the size of the image of the target on the ocular scale. To make the apparatus generally useful, several targets should be available with different intervals.

The method of determining k has been described by Cheshire[1] as follows: The target T in Fig. 182 is set approximately at the focal point of the collimator C. Light from the diffusing glass D illuminated by the source S is directed to the target by means of a piece of thin glass G. This light is reflected back through the collimator lens by the mirror R set on a divided circle. The target is placed exactly in the focal plane of the collimator by moving it until its image is in the plane with itself as seen through the microscope M. Then the table is rotated first in one direction until the left-hand end of the target is coincident with the right-hand end of its image, and then in the other direction until the right-hand end of the target is coincident with the left-hand end of the image, the divided circle being read each time. The difference in the readings is the angle subtended by the target at the

[1] *Trans. Optical Soc.* (*London*), **22**, 29 (1920–1921).

principal point of the collimator, and, since this angle is small, its reciprocal is the constant k. If the apparatus for this method is not available, an alternative but less precise method is to compute k from the size of the target and the focal length of the collimator.

Another instrument especially designed for the measurement of focal length is the Abbe focometer, for which the makers claim a precision of 1 part in 1000. In appearance this instrument resembles a microscope with an unusually long stage that can be slid in its own plane. The lens being tested should be smaller than about 100 mm in diameter and 50 mm in thickness. Its focal length, if positive, must be greater than about 100 mm, but, if negative, it may be of any value. With this

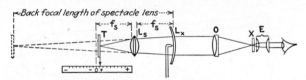

Fig. 183.—Optical system of a typical vertex focometer.

instrument, the principal points and the departure from the sine condition can be determined also.

The measurement of the focal length of ophthalmic lenses is of such importance that special instruments have been devised for the purpose. These are marketed under such names as "Lensometer," "Dioptrometer," and "Vertometer," but all are designed to measure the reciprocal of the back focal length of the lens. This quantity is called the *vertex power*, which, as will be shown in Sec. 152, Chap. XX, is the quantity of significance in lenses to be used as spectacles. Various systems used in these instruments have been described by H. F. Kurtz.[1] One that is common to several existing instruments is sketched in Fig. 183. The lens L_x under test is placed with the vertex that is to be nearest the eye against a fixed metal pointer at the focal point of the standard lens L_s. The image of a target T formed by both lenses is observed through a telescope consisting of an objective O and an ocular E. A fixation mark is placed on the plate X at the first focal point of the ocular to insure that the rays entering the telescope are parallel when the setting is made. The procedure in determining the vertex

[1] *Jour. Optical Soc. Amer. and Rev. Sci. Instruments*, **7**, 103 (1923).

power of L_x is simply to move the target along the axis of the system until its image is seen sharply focused in the telescope. The power is then read directly on the scale that indicates the position of the target. The standard lens must obviously be stronger than the strongest positive lens to be tested.

The task of measuring the power of ophthalmic lenses is complicated by the frequent use of cylindrical surfaces, which are prescribed to correct astigmatism, as explained in Chap. XX. Such lenses have two different powers in the two principal meridians. However, by using two sets of parallel lines at right angles to each other as a target, it is possible to determine the power in each of the principal meridians and also the azimuth of the meridians.

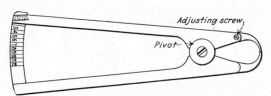

Fig. 184.—A type of caliper used for measuring optical parts.

137. Thickness and Separation.—Just as the micrometer caliper is the symbol of the mechanic, so it is of the optician. Perhaps the type of caliper that is easiest to use (and also the least likely to be injured in clumsy hands!) is what might be called the pincer type. This is sketched in Fig. 184. The points are pressed together with a spring, being separated for the insertion of the lens by squeezing the long arms. A more versatile tool is the Boley caliper, shown in Fig. 185. This can be used for either outside or inside measurements and, by means of the two parts marked a and b, for the measurement of depth. It is graduated in millimeters and the vernier reads to tenths.

The most precise type of thickness gauge is one that is based on the same principle as the spherometer illustrated in Fig. 176. The specimen to be measured is placed on a flat plate and a plunger drops vertically on it. A scale secured to the plunger enables the thickness to be determined to 0.001 mm from the difference of the readings made before and after the specimen is placed in position.

138. The Measurement of Angle.—The most general method of measuring the angle between two plane surfaces, such as two faces of a prism, is by means of a spectrometer, the optical system of which is illustrated in Fig. 186. The slit Z at one end of the collimator tube is illuminated in any convenient manner, as, for example, by focusing a source of light upon it. The light from

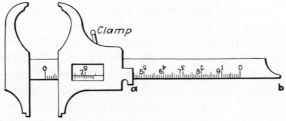

Fig. 185.—The Boley caliper.

the slit is made parallel (collimated) by the collimator lens C and falls on one face of the prism. The table supporting the prism is rotated until light reflected at this face enters the telescope objective O and is brought to focus in the plane of the cross hairs

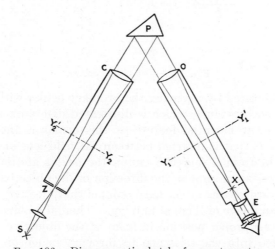

Fig. 186.—Diagrammatic sketch of a spectrometer.

X. The observer, by looking into the ocular E, then makes such further adjustment as is necessary to cause the image of the slit to be bisected by the cross hairs, after which the position of the prism table is read by means of a divided circle. The prism table is rotated until light is reflected into the telescope from the second face of the prism, and it is then adjusted again until the image of the slit is bisected by the cross hairs.   A second reading is made on the divided circle,[1] and the angle through which the prism table has been rotated is computed.   It is easily shown that the angle between the faces of the prism is the supplement of this angle.

There are certain adjustments that must be made before a measurement of this sort can be undertaken.   In the first place, the optical system must be so focused that the light from the slit is collimated where it strikes the prism and is then brought to focus in the plane of the cross hairs.   The ocular must also be focused properly, but since it is used merely as a magnifier, the only requirement is that the image of the cross hairs shall appear sharp to the observer.   The adjustment of a spectrometer is

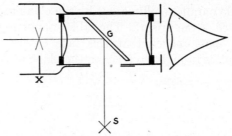

Fig. 187.—The Gauss ocular.

greatly facilitated by replacing the ordinary ocular with one of a type devised by Gauss, which is illustrated diagrammatically in Fig. 187.   The essential feature of this ocular is the piece of plane glass G that is inserted between the field lens and the eye lens.   Light from a source S enters the ocular and is reflected down the telescope tube in the direction of the objective.   If the cross hairs are located at the focal point of the objective, the latter will form an image of them at infinity.   Then, if a plane mirror is placed in the proper position in front of the objective, the light is redirected into the telescope to form an image of the cross

---

[1] All spectrometers that are designed for serious work are equipped with at least two verniers or reading microscopes located on opposite sides of the divided circle.   By reading both verniers each time and averaging the two values of the angle thus found, any errors due to eccentricity of the divided circle are eliminated.   For work of the most precise character, the accidental errors in the divided circle must, of course, be taken into consideration. An excellent description of the determination of these errors will be found in Chap. IV of Martin's "Optical Measuring Instruments."

hairs in the plane of the cross hairs themselves. Hence, to place the cross hairs at the focal point of the objective, one has merely to vary the distance between the objective and the cross hairs until the image of the cross hairs coincides with the cross hairs themselves. Most spectrometers are equipped with a rack and pinion to facilitate this adjustment. If a Gauss ocular is not at hand, the telescope can be trained on a distant object and adjusted until the image is formed in the plane of the cross hairs.

With the telescope thus focused for "parallel light," it is a simple matter to adjust the collimator for "parallel light" also. If the mechanical construction of the spectrometer permits the telescope tube to be swung around until its axis coincides with that of the collimator, one has merely to adjust the position of the slit with respect to the collimator lens until the image of the slit is formed in the plane of the cross hairs. An alternative procedure in the case of a spectroscope, in which the rotation of the telescope tube is usually limited, is to reflect light from the collimator into the telescope by means of a plane mirror.

The above adjustments relate to the focusing of the optical system, and the next step is to make the axes of both the collimator and the telescope accurately perpendicular to the mechanical axis about which the prism table rotates. This adjustment is made most conveniently by means of an autocollimating method similar to the one used for focusing the telescope. In addition to the Gauss ocular, a piece of black glass having plane-parallel faces is needed. The purpose of using black glass is simply to avoid the confusion that may be caused by the image reflected at the second surface in case the faces of the glass are not exactly parallel or the collimator and telescope are not perfectly adjusted.[1] This piece of glass is set on edge on the prism table in such a manner that light from the telescope is redirected back from the first surface in exactly the same manner as when the telescope was being focused. The leveling screws on either the prism table or the support for the glass are then adjusted until the image of the cross hairs coincides with the cross hairs themselves. The prism table is then rotated through 180° and, if the cross hairs and their image still coincide, the axis of the telescope

---

[1] A piece of colored glass or a cemented gelatin filter can be used instead of the black glass. In this case, the reflection from only one of the faces is considered, the difference in color making it easy to identify the image reflected from the second face.

must obviously be perpendicular to the axis of rotation. If they do not, the telescope must be rotated about the axis Y_1Y_1' in Fig. 186. The procedure is to bring the cross hairs approximately halfway to their correct position by rotating the telescope about this axis and the remainder of the distance with the leveling screws on the prism table. This process is repeated as many times as may be necessary, the adjustment becoming closer each time. With the telescope properly adjusted, it is a simple matter to swing it into line with the collimator and to adjust

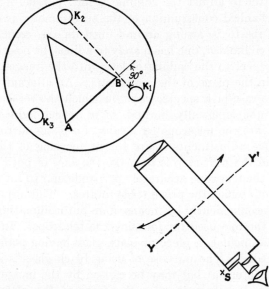

FIG. 188.—Diagrammatic sketch of an autocollimating spectrometer, showing the proper method of placing the prism.

the latter about the axis Y_2Y_2' until the cross hairs appear to bisect the length of the slit.

The instrument itself is now in adjustment, but the prism must be so placed on the prism table that the line of intersection of the two faces forming the angle that is to be measured is parallel to the mechanical axis about which the prism table rotates. In other words, both faces of the prism must be capable of being set perpendicular to the axis of the telescope. The autocollimation method is again applicable, but some care must be taken in placing the prism on the prism table to enable the second face to be adjusted without destroying the adjustment of the first. However, if the prism is placed in the manner illustrated in Fig. 188 so that one face is perpendicular to the line joining two of the leveling screws, adjusting the third screw merely rotates this face in its own plane. In the figure, the face AB is perpendicular to the line joining the leveling screws K_1 and K_2. This face should obviously be adjusted first, and then either of the other faces can be adjusted by means of the leveling screw K_3. It will be seen from this description that by far the greater proportion of the time required in measuring a prism angle with a spectrometer is spent in adjusting the apparatus and only a relatively small proportion in determining the actual data from which the prism angle is computed. This is quite generally true of precision optical instruments, and, therefore, such instruments are usually kept in adjustment in optical establishments by providing them with a suitable case, often with a lock and key.

It is evident that the collimator tube of a spectrometer is really unnecessary for the measurement of prism angles if the telescope is provided with a Gauss ocular or the equivalent. In fact, most modern goniometers are of the autocollimating type. The instrument that is represented in Fig. 188 contains a small right-angle prism in the ocular. This prism reflects light to a slit in the lower half of the field, and the reflected image of the slit is observed in the upper half of the field superposed upon a scale. The more elaborate goniometers are provided with a divided circle for measuring angles in a vertical plane as well as in a horizontal plane, a necessary modification if they are to be used for natural crystals and some special types of prisms. The adjustment of such an instrument involves merely the extension to three dimensions of the principles that have been outlined above.

It frequently happens in optical establishments that certain types of prisms are made in such quantities that special methods are employed for routine inspection. In general, these methods[1] are devised to indicate the departure from the specified angle directly rather than to measure the actual value of the angle itself.

139. Lens Aberrations.—The user of an optical system is rarely interested in methods of determining the particular

---

[1] F. E. Wright has discussed optical methods of testing prisms in *Jour. Optical Soc. Amer.*, **5**, 193 (1921). An instrument for testing prisms by autocollimation methods is described by Moffitt in *Jour. Optical Soc. Amer. and Rev. Sci. Instruments*, **7**, 831 (1923).

aberrations with which the system may be afflicted; he is content with methods for determining directly the suitability of the system for a specific purpose. The lens designer, on the other hand, is vitally dependent on methods for identifying and measuring the individual aberrations. It will be recalled from Chap. VI that the customary procedure in lens design of tracing a few selected rays through the system gives a somewhat incomplete picture of its performance. A sample is therefore constructed according to a provisional formula; and from quantitative tests of the aberrations exhibited by this sample, the

Fig. 189.—An elaborate type of lens bench. (*By courtesy of Bureau of Standards.*)

designer learns how the formula may be improved. Lens-bench methods, the Hartmann method, and the interferometric method yield this information in different ways. The lens bench furnishes information about every aberration separately (or in so far as the interrelationships between the aberrations permit) but it requires expensive apparatus and is very slow. The Hartmann method is rapid and requires comparatively simple apparatus but is suitable only for measuring spherical aberration and coma. The interferometric method is also rapid but requires costly apparatus, and the results obtained by it are not so readily interpreted.

Since the lens bench furnishes information about the individual aberrations directly, it will be described first. A photograph of an elaborate bench is shown in Fig. 189, the essential features being sketched in Fig. 190. A target T, illuminated by a source S, is placed at the focus of the collimator lens C, which, in effect,

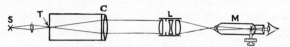

Fig. 190.—Optical system of the lens bench. The lens L is being tested.

places the target at infinity. The image of the target formed by the lens L to be tested is examined by means of the reading microscope M, which can be moved longitudinally along the track (or bench) on which the various units are mounted.

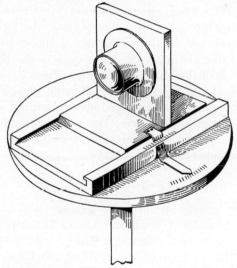

Fig. 191.—Sketch showing the principle of the nodal slide.

The lens is mounted in a special form of holder, known as a nodal slide, the principle of which is illustrated in Fig. 191. The entire nodal slide can be rotated about a vertical axis that is rigidly attached to the lens bench. In addition, the lens can be slid along the short track to vary its position with respect to the axis of rotation. It will be recalled from Chap. IV that every lens contains an axis, called the transverse axis, characterized by the property that rotation about it does not cause a displacement of the image. Hence, by watching the image of the source through the microscope and adjusting the lens until the image remains stationary as the lens is rotated slightly, the position of the transverse axis is found. When the object is at infinity, as it is in this case, the transverse axis coincides with the second nodal point. This type of mounting enables the second nodal point to be found and, by reversing the lens, the first nodal point can be found in a similar manner. Since the lens is in air, the principal points coincide with the nodal points.

Despite the straightforward nature of lens-bench determinations, much care must be taken in adjusting the apparatus and making the readings if the results are to be reliable.[1] The apparatus is first aligned and then the nodal slide is adjusted. The subsequent operations depend upon the aberrations for which the lens is to be tested. These operations are so self-evident that little description is necessary. Curvature of field and astigmatism are measured by rotating the lens about the second nodal point in 5° steps and sliding the microscope along the bench to bring the image in focus each time. If the field is flat, the distance of the image of the target from the second nodal point should be $f/\cos \alpha'$, where f is the axial focal length and α' the angle of the emergent ray passing through the second nodal point. This angle is, of course, the angle through which the lens has been rotated. If the shift necessary to restore the focus be d, the departure from a flat field, measured in the direction of the lens axis, is

$$\delta = f - (f + d) \cos \alpha'.$$

If the target consists of a vertical and a horizontal cross hair, the two are not in focus simultaneously for large values of α'. The locus of the images of the vertical cross hair defines the primary focal surface and the locus of the images of the horizontal cross hair, the secondary focal surface. The difference between the two at any angle is the astigmatic difference at that angle. The typical curves of the results of such a test on a photographic objective were presented in Fig. 48 of Chap. VI.

Distortion is measured by setting the lens for the best focus at each angle and measuring the lateral displacement of the image by means of the filar micrometer in the ocular of the

---

[1] Explicit instructions are given in *Bur. Standards Sci. Paper* 494.

microscope.   A distortion curve was shown in Fig. 51.   Lateral chromatism is measured by determining the position of the images at each angle when "monochromatic" filters are placed in front of the light source.   To avoid focus adjustments between colors, the test lens should be placed for best focus with light of approximately wave length 580 mμ.   The collimator can usually be left unchanged throughout the run except for the deep violet.   Axial chromatism is measured by placing the lens with its axis parallel to the bench and determining the amount of longitudinal displacement of the microscope that is required to bring the images successively into focus when various monochromatic filters are set in the path of the light.

Spherical aberration can be determined by placing a series of diaphragms containing holes equidistant from the axis over the face of the lens and locating the image of the target for each diaphragm in turn.   This is easy because the image appears double everywhere except at the focal point for the zone being tested.   The departure from the sine condition can be determined by a procedure that is exactly similar, except that the nodal slide is adjusted each time.   Inasmuch as the sine condition is measured by the equality of the ratio $h/\sin \theta'$ for parallel incident light, and this ratio is also equal to the focal length for each value of θ', the variation in the focal lengths as determined directly from the readings on the bench is also a measure of the departure from the sine condition.   Typical spherical-aberration and sine-condition curves of a photographic objective were given in Fig. 39.   For these tests it is advisable to omit the collimator because its spherical aberration, even if small, may be great enough to vitiate the results and, if the target is placed at a sufficient distance, the aberrations are not markedly affected. The chief difficulty is that the air currents in the room may make the image distorted and difficult to set upon.

Microscope objectives and motion-picture camera objectives cannot be tested on a lens bench of the usual construction, the former because of their short object distance and the latter because of their short image distance.   In either case, it might be possible to make samples on an enlarged scale for testing, although this is almost never done.   Some of the tests can be carried out by means of an ordinary microscope fitted with a scale to measure the longitudinal displacement of the tube. The procedure is to lay the lens on the stage and to place a mirror or reflecting prism of good quality underneath to reflect light from a distant target up through the lens.

For testing spherical aberration and coma, the Hartmann method[1] in a modified form is superior to the lens-bench method. The principle is illustrated in Fig. 192. The lens L to be tested is covered with a diaphragm S perforated with a row of holes along a diameter. An illuminated pinhole at a considerable distance is photographed, the plate being placed successively at A and B. Obviously the light passing through any given hole in the diaphragm will produce two spots on the plate; one at a distance a above the central spot, and the other at a distance b below it. By measuring a, b, and d, the point F', where the

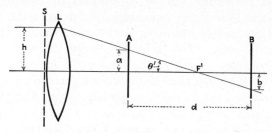

Fig. 192.—Sketch showing the principle of the modified Hartmann method of testing a lens for spherical aberration and coma.

pencil intersects the axis, can be computed. The variation of this distance for the various apertures represents the spherical aberration of the lens. Furthermore, the angle θ' that the pencil makes with the axis and the ratio $h/\sin \theta'$ can be computed for each aperture, and in this way the departure from the sine condition can be determined.

Lens-testing interferometers have been developed only recently and hence are little used. Twyman[2] has made one for photographic objectives and another for microscope objectives. These both consist essentially of a Michelson interferometer.[3] The lens is placed in one path, and the mirror at the end of that path is made spherical with its center at the focal point of the lens. The observer sees a contour map of the emergent wave front in terms of the wave length of whatever light is used. This

[1] Descriptions of this method can be found in *Bur. Standards Sci. Papers* 311 and 494.

[2] *Trans. Optical Soc. (London)*, **22**, 174 (1920–1921); **24**, 189 (1922–1923).

[3] See Sec. 207, Chap. XXVIII.

method is excellent for comparing the performance of well-corrected lenses, but the interpretation of the results in terms of the conventional aberrations is a matter of some little difficulty. It is claimed, however, that an observer can train himself in a few days to judge with fair accuracy the aberrations that are responsible for a given interference pattern.

CHAPTER XVIII

MISCELLANEOUS OPTICAL MATERIALS

The optical engineer and the scientific investigator use many other substances besides optical glass, although not by any means to the same extent. These substances may be divided into three general classes: Some are used as functional parts of optical systems to reflect, refract, or disperse light because of special properties, such as a high transmission or a high reflectance in some particular spectral region; some are used merely as light filters to absorb the radiation within certain spectral regions; and some find a place because of their ability to produce polarization. For a few of these substances the data available are bewilderingly abundant, whereas for others the data are very scarce. All that can be done in this chapter is to give data for the more important materials and to indicate where further information can be found.

140. Miscellaneous Varieties of Glass.—For many purposes, plate glass is a satisfactory substitute for optical glass. Unlike window glass, which is merely blown and has a very irregular surface, plate glass is polished in large sheets and consequently is fairly flat except at the very edge of the sheet. In fact, plate glass of selected quality is generally used for protecting the gelatin filters used by photographers and microscopists. Plate glass is available in thicknesses of $\frac{1}{8}$ in. to over 1 in. Ordinary varieties are green when viewed through the edges, but the visual absorption of a 2-mm piece when illuminated by white light is of the order of only 2 per cent in a direction normal to the surface. White varieties having a very low absorption are available, but they must be distinguished from other varieties that have been made to appear white by the use of decolorizers. These substances merely introduce additional absorption in such a region of the spectrum that the color of the glass is neutral. They do not eliminate the absorption that is responsible for the green color.

For diffusing light, ground glass and opal glass are commonly used. A very coarse grade of ground glass is made by grinding plate glass with crushed steel. A much better variety, which is entirely satisfactory for most purposes, is made by grinding with a 200-mesh abrasive. For a finer grain, such as is preferable in a focusing screen, the glass can be finished with a 600-mesh abrasive. If more diffusion is required than ground glass will produce, opal glass (sometimes called milk glass) can be used instead. The diffusing property of this type of glass is due to minute colloidal particles that are produced either by devitrification or by the addition of substances that will not melt in the furnace. Flashed opal, which consists of a thin layer of opal fused to a sheet of clear glass, is used more frequently than pot opal because of the very great absorption of the latter. All opals cause the transmitted light to become noticeably yellow by virtue of the selective effect of the scattering.

Uranium glass, which is a fluorescent yellow glass characterized by salts of uranium, is used for focusing ultraviolet spectrographs. Ordinary ground glass wet with acetone and smeared with anthracene can also be used for the same purpose.

141. Filters for the Visible Region.—The essential property of a light filter is its selective absorption, and it goes without saying that this property can be evaluated only by a spectrophotometric or a spectroradiometric analysis. One of the most common mistakes made by investigators with limited optical training is to assume that a colored material transmits only a narrow spectral band in the immediate vicinity of its dominant wave length. That this is seldom the case will be clear from an inspection of Fig. 193, which shows the transmission curves of a few typical colored glasses made by the Corning Glass Works. The only glass in this entire set that transmits a narrow portion of the visible region is that represented by curve 1, which is a deep red glass used for railway signals. Even this glass transmits in the infrared, so the effective cut-off on the long wave-length side is due to the eye and not to the glass.

Glass is colored by introducing salts of certain metals into the melt. Red glass is colored with copper, gold, or selenium. Copper produces such an intense red that it is usually used only for flashed glass. Gold produces a less intense color but it transmits a considerable amount of violet. This kind of glass is preferably called "ruby" to distinguish it from the reds that do not transmit violet. The color produced by selenium can be varied from red to orange but is difficult to control. A peculiarity of many red glasses of importance to the optical manufacturer is that their color is ruined by pressing. A signal red, for example, which in its original state has a high transmission in the red and a sharp cut-off in the orange, has a lower transmission in the red and a considerable transmission in the orange after being pressed. In fact, the characteristics of many colored glasses change even with relatively slight variations in temperature.

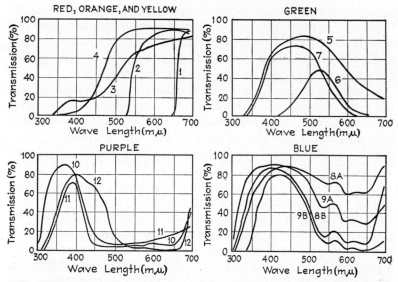

Fig. 193.—Transmission curves of a few Corning glasses (uncorrected for surface reflection). The names of the glasses and the thicknesses of the samples are as follows: (1) Red, G24, 0.88 mm. (2) Orange, G34, 1.50 mm. (3) Yellow, 100 %, 1.12 mm. (4) Yellow, G36–190 %, 0.60 mm. (5) Green, 100 %, 0.92 mm. (6) Sextant green, 1.66 mm. (7) G584, 4.10 mm. (8*A*) G55D–70 %, 0.97 mm. (8*B*) G55D–70 %, 6.22 mm. (9*A*) G50–77 %, 0.98 mm. (9*B*) G50–77 %, 3.39 mm. (10) G586A, 1.03 mm. (11) G172BW5, 5.27 mm. (12) Purple, 100 %, 5.03 mm. (*Bur. Standards Tech. Paper* 148.)

Yellow glass is colored by either iron in the ferric state, cadmium, or carbon. Such glass appears yellow merely because it absorbs the blue and violet, as can be seen from curves 3 and 4 of Fig. 193.

Green glass is colored by either chromium in the chromic state, iron in the ferrous state, or copper in the cuprous state. The color produced by chromium is a yellow-green, while that produced by iron or copper is a blue-green.

Blue glass is almost invariably colored with cobalt, with sometimes a little copper added. It is very reproducible. The high transmission in the red is frequently objectionable, especially in filters, but it can be removed by introducing chromium.

Violet glass is usually colored with manganese. Although the color produced by this element is markedly affected by the conditions in the furnace, some violet glasses are remarkably reproducible. They are little used, however, because of the low visibility in this region of the spectrum.

Purple glasses are similar to the blue ones except that the transmission in the green and yellow is very much lower and in general the transmission in the red is higher. (This does not happen to be true for the glasses illustrated, which are a blue-purple rather than a red-purple.) The transmission in the red can be easily detected by viewing a source of white light through the glass. The eye is unable to focus the red and the blue simultaneously, and hence the source appears to have a blue border. This circumstance makes it possible for a locomotive engineer to identify a purple signal at a great distance.

Colored glass is made in different forms according to the purpose for which it is intended. The types represented in Fig. 193 are cast in plates about 6 mm thick and either 6 in. square or 6 in. in diameter. These plates must be cut to size and ground and polished before they can be used. For ophthalmic lenses, the glass is made in the form of pressed blanks as usual. Colored glass is also available in large sheets like ordinary window glass. It is usually supplied in three weights, having thicknesses of 2.4 mm, 3.5 mm, and 5.0 mm. These values are only approximate and the actual thickness of a given sheet may be different by several tenths of a millimeter. Indeed, the thickness of a single sheet varies greatly from point to point.

Until within comparatively recent years, the experimenter who required a greater variety than the glass maker provided or who wished to isolate definite spectral regions was forced to prepare his own filter. A very popular method was to fix out an unused photographic plate and bathe it in a solution of dye. This type of filter is fairly inexpensive, even in comparatively large sizes, and very convenient when once prepared, but it has fallen into disuse with the advent of the Wratten gelatin filters.

These filters consist of thin films of gelatin in which appropriate dyes are incorporated. They are made by allowing the dyed gelatin to dry between two polished glass plates. The gelatin film is then stripped from the plates and cemented between pieces of plate or optical glass of the desired size. The transmission curves of these filters are given in the catalogue published by the makers, the Eastman Kodak Company. Almost a hundred different kinds are available, but perhaps those of most importance to the optical experimenter are the series of "monochromatic" filters. These are characterized by narrow transmission bands located at the following positions in the spectrum:

Name	Number	Maximum transmission, millimicrons
α	70	700
β	71-A	640
γ	72	610
δ	73	570
ϵ	74	530
η	75	490
θ	76	440

Practically all the Wratten filters transmit the infrared.

A still newer series of filters has been put on the market by the firm of Schott. These are made of glass but have the sharp cut-off characteristic of dyes. Compared with the gelatin filters, they are more expensive to prepare but they have the advantage that they can be used where the heat would ruin a gelatin filter. They are quite remarkable in their properties and are not to be confused with ordinary colored glass.

Although it is difficult to prepare filters that will transmit one portion of the spectrum to the exclusion of the others, it is yet more difficult to prepare filters that will absorb equally throughout the spectrum. The ordinary dark glass, which is colored with either manganese, iron and copper, or copper and nickel, is far from neutral, having transmission bands in the red and the deep violet. This type of glass, under the name of "smoke," is occasionally used in spectacles, and the curve in Fig. 194 distinctly shows the transmission bands. The black glass used for table tops is of a somewhat different type but also has a marked transmission band in the violet. The Wratten neutral filters, which are composed of a mixture of dyes in the proper proportions, are fairly neutral, as are also the Schott neutral filters. When none of these filters is available, a fogged photographic plate can be used. It is reasonably neutral if developed in a non-staining developer. For some purposes, a wire screen is an excellent neutral filter, the transmission being determined by the fineness of the mesh and the size of the wire.

142. Filters for the Ultraviolet and Infrared.—The spectral transmission of ordinary spectacle crown glass is shown by the

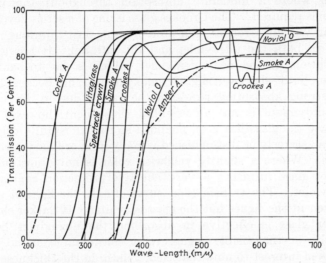

Fig. 194.—Transmission curves of several glasses in the visible and ultraviolet as determined by the Bureau of Standards (uncorrected for surface reflection). All curves are for a thickness of approximately 2 mm. (Curves for Corex and Vitaglass from *Bur. Standards Jour. Research*, **3**, 629 [1929] [*Research Paper* 113]; others from *Bur. Standards Tech. Paper* 119.)

heavy curve in Fig. 194. This curve is for a sample having a thickness of 2 mm, and the reflection loss at the two surfaces is included. It is typical of all kinds of ordinary glass except the dense flints, which absorb more of the ultraviolet.

The glasses whose cut-off occurs at shorter wave lengths than spectacle crown are used primarily on account of their property of transmitting the ultraviolet.[1] They are used principally for such purposes as hospital windows, where a

[1] The manufacture of these glasses is discussed by P. Davidovitch, *Jour. Optical Soc. Amer.*, **20**, 627 (1930).

high ultraviolet transmission is desired for therapeutic purposes. Although these glasses are fairly stable to ordinary sunlight, their ultraviolet transmission is greatly reduced by exposure to strong sources of radiation in the region below 300 mμ.

The glasses whose cut-off occurs at a longer wave length than spectacle crown are used primarily for spectacles to protect the eyes from the injurious effects of ultraviolet radiation. The smoke is a nearly neutral glass except for transmission bands in the red and deep violet, but its ultraviolet cut-off is not far from that of spectacle crown. It is made in several shades and is most useful where a moderate absorption throughout the visible region is required. The Crookes glass is one of a series developed by Sir William Crookes as a protection against injurious radiations in both the ultraviolet and the infrared. It has a high absorption in the near ultraviolet, which is due to oxides of cerium, but it also has a slightly smoky appearance because of the two strong absorption bands in the yellow due to didymium. The didymium is not an essential constituent, however, and recently the glass has been modified so that it is quite colorless and can scarcely be distinguished visually from ordinary spectacle crown. Where a slightly yellowish color is not objectionable, Noviol glass furnishes a very effective protection against the ultraviolet. The transmission curve of only the lightest shade is given in the figure but the glass is available in darker shades. Amber glass is effective in absorbing the ultraviolet but it absorbs in the visible region to a considerable extent also.

It is of interest to note that clear gelatin in the thickness used for Wratten filters has a cut-off in the ultraviolet similar to that of Vitaglass. Also, the Wratten No. 2 filter, which is dyed with aesculin, has a transmission very similar to that of Noviol O, whose curve is shown in Fig. 194.

The transmission curves of the optical materials that are most widely used in the infrared are shown in Fig. 195. Following the usual custom, the curves are for a thickness of 1 cm, a curve for spectacle crown of 2-mm thickness, as it is commonly used in spectacles, being added for comparison. Because the infrared region was formerly regarded as the seat of heat radiation, substances that are transparent in this region are sometimes said to be *diathermanous*. Most of them are also transparent to the ultraviolet, fluorite being useful to 120 mμ, quartz to 185 mμ, and calcite to 215 mμ. These substances are used so frequently for optical purposes that they will be described in greater detail in the following section.

Materials that are opaque to the infrared but transparent in the visible region are said to be *heat absorbing*.   They are used

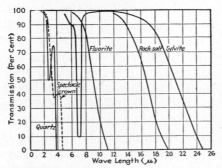

FIG. 195.—Infrared transmission of certain optical materials (corrected for surface reflection). The curve for spectacle crown is for a thickness of 2 mm. (*Bur. Standards Tech. Paper* 93.) The curves for the other materials are for a thickness of 10 mm. (*Bur. Standards Sci. Paper* 401.)

occasionally as filters in motion-picture projectors to prevent the film from burning when it is not in motion.   They are also used in photomicrography to prevent the slide from becoming over-heated.   One very effective type has been developed by Pfund. It consists of a sheet of glass coated with a thin layer of gold which, although it transmits approximately 80 per cent of the light from an incandescent lamp, absorbs all but about 20 per cent of the heat.   This type of filter should strictly not be called heat absorbing because the infrared radiations are reflected rather than absorbed.   There are other types of truly heat-absorbing filters, which are usually glasses in which ingredients have been incorporated to produce a high absorption in the infrared.   These glasses are

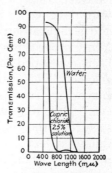

FIG. 196.

usually green in color. Since in this case the filter actually absorbs the heat, it may become so hot as to crack.   To prevent this, some of the newer types are made from a glass having a low coefficient of expansion. For scientific purposes, such as photomicrography, a water cell is often used to absorb the heat, and the transmission curve for a 2-cm thickness is shown in Fig. 196.   When water alone furnishes insufficient protection, there are many salts that may be added to increase the infrared absorption. Coblentz,[1] who has made a study of this subject, has stated that a 2.5 per cent solution of crystallized cupric chloride $(CuCl_2 + 2H_2O)$ is the most effective. The transmission curve of a 2-cm thickness is shown in Fig. 196, and it will be seen that such a solution absorbs nearly all the radiation beyond 800 mμ and still transmits rather freely in the visible region. Its color is blue, and consequently it tends to compensate for the yellowness of the usual artificial sources. It is of interest to note that water is very transparent to the ultraviolet, its limit of transmission lying below that of quartz.

The protection of the eyes from powerful sources of infrared radiation is quite as important as protection from the ultraviolet. Under certain circumstances, it may even be more important because, although exposure to the ultraviolet may produce intense pain, the effect is only temporary unless the radiations are of very short wave length. This is because the cornea absorbs the ultraviolet and the injury is therefore localized there. The eye media are fairly transparent to infrared radiations, however, and consequently a prolonged exposure to a copious source, such as a furnace, produces lesions which are irreparable. Indeed, it was to prevent the disease so aptly termed "glass-blower's cataract" that Crookes developed his well-known glasses. These were designed to have a high transmission in the visible region and a high absorption in both the infrared and the ultraviolet. Many other types of eye-protective glasses of this sort have since been developed, one new variety being intended for aviator's goggles. This variety is light green in color, its transmission curve being very similar in shape to the visibility curve of the eye. Despite the low transmission in the ends of the visible spectrum, the transmission in the green is so high that a 2-mm thickness has a total visual transmission of approximately 50 per cent. There are some operations, such as welding, for which protective goggles must have a high absorption in the visible region in addition to a well-nigh complete absorption in both the infrared and the ultraviolet. For such purposes, special welding glasses are available in several shades, which are commonly designated in accordance with the specifications laid down by the Federal Government.[2]

[1] *Bur. Standards Sci. Paper* 168.

[2] These are published as "Federal Master Specifications" and are changed from time to time. See also a paper by Coblentz and Stair, *Jour. Optical Soc. Amer.*, **20**, 624 (1930).

It is comparatively difficult to find filters that will isolate narrow regions of either the ultraviolet or the infrared, although a few glasses are available commercially for therapeutic purposes to isolate the vital-ray region (290 mμ to 310 mμ). Several combinations of filters especially designed for biological investigations have been described by Jones.[1] The most extensive compilation of data concerning the absorption characteristics of materials appears to have been made by Gibson.[2]

143. Materials with Special Optical Properties.—Many substitutes for optical glass are used in systems designed to transmit either the ultraviolet or the infrared.

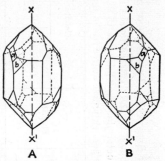

They are usually natural crystals, although liquids are occasionally used, and fused quartz, which is amorphous, is coming into prominence. Tables XXII and XXIII give the refractive indices of the more common of these materials. Most of them have been mentioned in the preceding section, but their peculiar properties are so important that they are worthy of a more extended discussion.

FIG. 197.—Quartz crystals. The form shown at *A* is left-handed and that shown at *B* is right-handed. The optic axis is indicated by *XX'*.

Quartz (SiO_2) is, next to glass, the most widely used optical material. It crystallizes in the hexagonal system, typical forms being those shown in Fig. 197. It has a specific gravity of 2.6 and a hardness of 7 on Mohs's scale. Because of its hardness it is very durable, but it is somewhat more difficult to work than glass, which has a hardness of approximately 5. Quartz is more widely distributed than any other mineral, but there are only a few isolated localities where it occurs in a form that is sufficiently flawless and transparent for optical use. This type of quartz was called rock crystal by the ancients, the term "quartz" being a Germanic word that seems to have appeared first about 1529 in Agricola's writings.

Quartz, in common with many other crystals, is doubly refracting. This subject will be discussed more extensively in

[1] *Jour. Optical Soc. Amer. and Rev. Sci. Instruments*, **16**, 259 (1928).

[2] "International Critical Tables," Vol. V, p. 271. See also *Jour. Optical Soc. Amer. and Rev. Sci. Instruments*, **13**, 267 (1926).

TABLE XXII.—REFRACTIVE INDICES OF CERTAIN SUBSTANCES TRANSPARENT IN THE ULTRAVIOLET

The values for water and carbon disulphide are those adopted by the "International Critical Tables" for 20°C. and reprinted by permission. Those for the other substances were determined by Gifford at 15°C.[1] All values are relative to air. The temperature coefficient is the change of index for the D-line per centigrade degree rise in temperature.

Wave length, millimicrons	Quartz		Fused quartz	Fluorite	Calcite		Water	Carbon disulphide
	Ordinary ray	Extraordinary ray			Ordinary ray	Extraordinary ray		
185.5 Al	1.67590	1.69007	1.5743	1.50989	....	....	....	....
199.0 Al	1.65092	1.66399	1.55199	1.49613	....	....	1.42572	....
226.5 Cd	1.61820	1.62997	1.52305	1.47754	1.81304	1.54914	1.39257	....
257.3 Cd	1.59625	1.60716	1.50371	1.46477	1.76050	1.53012	1.37349	....
274.9 Cd	1.58753	1.59813	1.49613	1.45966	1.74150	1.52266	1.36637	2.005
361.1 Cd	1.56347	1.57324	1.47511	1.44534	1.69316	1.50224	1.34738	1.738
404.6 Hg	1.55715	1.56671	1.46968	1.44153	1.68134	1.49691	1.34035	1.675
434.1 H (G')	1.55398	1.56341	1.46685	1.43963	1.67552	1.49424	1.33750	1.654
480.0 Cd	1.55013	1.55945	1.46357	....	1.66861	1.49110	1.33714	1.653
486.1 H (F)	1.54970	1.55899	1.46317	1.43707	1.66783	1.49074	1.33447	....
546.1 Hg	1.54617	1.55534	1.46015	1.43499	1.66165	1.48789	1.33300	1.628
589.3 Na (D)	1.54426	1.55337	1.45848	1.43385	1.65836	1.48639	1.33115	1.619
656.3 H (C)	1.54193	1.55095	1.45642	1.43252	1.65440	1.48457	1.33079	....
670.8 Li	1.54146	1.55047	1.45607	1.43226	1.65367	1.48427	1.33079	....
768.2 K (A')	1.53906	1.54800	1.45389	1.43095	1.64974	1.48255	1.32888	....
794.8 Rb	1.53851	1.54742	1.45340	1.43064	1.64886	1.48216	....	....
Temperature coefficient	−0.000005	−0.000006	−0.000003	−0.000010	0.000005	0.000014	−0.000079	−0.00080

[1] Proc. Roy. Soc., 70, 329 (1902); 73, 201 (1904); 84, 193 (1910).

TABLE XXIII.—REFRACTIVE INDICES OF CERTAIN SUBSTANCES TRANSPARENT IN THE INFRARED

The values are those given by Coblentz[1] and are relative to air. The values for quartz are for the ordinary ray.

Wave length, microns	Quartz, 18°C.	Wave length, microns	Fluorite, 20°C.	Wave length, microns	Rock salt, 20°C.	Wave length, microns	Sylvite, 15°C.	Wave length, microns	Carbon disulphide, 15°C.
0.5893	1.54424	0.5893	1.43384	0.5893	1.54427	0.5893	1.49044	0.434	1.6784
0.6950	1.54078	0.6867	1.43200	0.6874	1.53930	0.656	1.48721	0.485	1.6550
0.8007	1.53834	0.7665	1.43093	0.7858	1.53607	0.7858	1.48328	0.590	1.6307
0.9047	1.53649	0.8840	1.42980	0.8839	1.53395	0.845	1.48230	0.656	1.6217
0.9914	1.53514	1.0140	1.42884	0.9724	1.53253	0.884	1.48142	0.777	1.6104
1.0830	1.53390	1.0830	1.42843	1.0810	1.53123	0.9822	1.48008	0.823	1.6077
1.1786	1.53263	1.1786	1.42789	1.1786	1.53031	1.1786	1.47831	0.873	1.6049
1.2288	1.53192	1.3756	1.42689	1.5552	1.52815	1.584	1.47650	0.931	1.6025
1.3070	1.53090	1.5715	1.42596	2.0736	1.52649	2.3573	1.47475	0.999	1.6000
1.3685	1.53011	1.7680	1.42502	2.9466	1.52466	2.9466	1.47388	1.073	1.5978
1.3958	1.52977	1.8688	1.42454	4.1230	1.52156	4.125	1.47215	1.164	1.5960
1.4219	1.52942	1.9644	1.42407	5.0092	1.51883	4.7146	1.47112	1.270	1.5940
1.4733	1.52879	2.250	1.42258	5.8932	1.51593	5.8932	1.46880	1.396	1.5923
1.4972	1.52843	2.5537	1.42080	7.0718	1.51093	7.00	1.46625	1.552	1.5905
1.5414	1.52782	2.750	1.41956	8.04	1.5064	8.00	1.4630	1.745	1.5888
1.6087	1.52687	2.9466	1.41823	9.00	1.50100	8.8398	1.46086	1.998	1.5872
1.6815	1.52585	3.2413	1.41610	10.0184	1.49462	10.0184	1.45672		
1.7679	1.52462	3.5339	1.41376	12.50	1.47568	12.50	1.44570		
1.8487	1.52335	4.0000	1.40963	14.144	1.46044	14.144	1.43722		
1.9457	1.52184	4.4000	1.40568	15.3223	1.44743	15.00	1.4320		
2.0626	1.51991	5.0000	1.39908	15.912	1.44090	15.912	1.42617		
2.3573	1.51449	5.8932	1.38712	17.93	1.4149	18.10	1.4108		
2.6519	1.50824	7.0718	1.36805	20.57	1.3735	20.60	1.3882		
3.0939	1.49703	9.4291	1.31605	22.3	1.3403	22.5	1.3692		

[1] Bur. Standards Sci. Paper 401.

Chap. XXIX, and it must suffice here to state that a beam of unpolarized light incident on a doubly refracting crystal is divided into two beams: one moving with the same velocity in every direction, the wave front being spherical; and the other moving with a velocity that depends upon the direction of its path, the wave front being ellipsoidal. These two beams are plane polarized in perpendicular azimuths and are known as the ordinary beam and the extraordinary beam respectively. There is one direction in a quartz crystal, represented by the line XX' in Fig. 197, in which both beams travel with the same velocity. This is known as the *optic axis* and, since quartz contains but one such axis, it is known as a uniaxial crystal. The refractive index for the extraordinary ray represents its velocity in a plane perpendicular to the optic axis, where its velocity differs most from that of the ordinary ray. It is clear that if a lens is to be cut from crystal quartz, the lens axis should be made parallel to the optic axis of the crystal. In this case, all rays that are parallel to the axis behave as though the quartz were isotropic. The other rays are doubly refracted, but, since the birefringence of quartz is small, the effect is usually negligible unless the angles are very large.

Another property of quartz that must be taken into account by the instrument designer is its power of rotating the plane of polarization of a plane-polarized beam traversing it parallel to the optic axis. Quartz is one of the few solids to possess this property, although it is possessed by a large number of organic substances when in solution, notably certain sugars. The phenomenon was explained by Fresnel by assuming that a plane-polarized beam can be resolved into two circularly polarized beams rotating in opposite directions, and that these beams travel with slightly different velocities. It so happens that the two crystal forms shown at A and B in Fig. 197 behave oppositely, the left-handed component traveling more rapidly in the form shown at A and the right-handed component in the form shown at B. These forms are termed left-handed and right-handed respectively because the resultant effect on a beam of plane-polarized light is to rotate it in a left-handed and a right-handed sense respectively. Because of the difference between the velocities of the circularly polarized components within the crystal (which is equivalent to a difference in refractive index), a refracting system made of quartz will in general produce double images even when a beam traverses the system parallel to the optical axis.   The remedy is to construct the system out of symmetrical elements, an element of one variety of quartz being paired with a similar element made of the other.   Thus, it is the general practice in constructing spectrographs, for example, to build up a 60° prism from two symmetrical 30° prisms of each variety of quartz and to make the collimator from one variety and the camera lens from the other.   Frequently twin crystals of quartz are found.   These are composed of the two forms in alternate layers, but the opposite actions of the two forms do not neutralize, and such crystals are useless for optical systems.

Because crystal quartz occurs only in relatively small pieces, attempts have been made to prepare fused quartz of optical quality.   A vast amount of work on this problem has been done under the direction of Prof. Elihu Thomson at the Lynn Works of the General Electric Company.   The chief difficulty is the elimination of striae and bubbles.   The striae seem to result from slight differences in index between the crystals that comprise the raw material; and, as the quartz never really melts in the ordinary sense, these striae are usually present to such an extent that it has not been possible to use fused quartz in optical systems where images of high quality were required.   The bubbles likewise have difficulty in escaping from the melt, and as a consequence the final operation is to apply sufficient pressure to compress them into a small volume.   It is possible to obtain small pieces free from striae and bubbles, but they are of little value because pieces of crystal quartz of comparable size are not expensive.   Moreover, fused quartz is difficult to anneal thoroughly, and the stresses remaining in it are usually much greater than have been found to be permissible in glass.

Fused quartz possesses so many desirable properties that it would undoubtedly be extensively used if its faults could be successfully overcome.   Its isotropism alone would make it superior to crystal quartz because it would reduce not only the cost of the grinding and polishing operations but also the loss of material entailed therein.   Fused quartz would be superior to glass for such articles as condensers for projection apparatus because it has a low coefficient of expansion and is therefore less likely to crack when heated.   Its low coefficient of expansion also suggests its use for mirrors for reflecting telescopes since it would not have to be kept cool during the parabolizing operation. Fortunately, the light does not traverse the material in this case, and a method of manufacture based on this fact has been very successful. This method consists in grinding quartz crystals into the form of a powder, which is introduced into an oxyhydrogen flame and sprayed on a base of ordinary fused quartz until a surface coat of the desired thickness has been laid. At the present time, a 60-in. mirror is under construction and a 200-in. mirror is contemplated.

Calcite ($CaCO_3$) is widely distributed in the earth's crust, but with minor exceptions the only variety that is sufficiently transparent and flawless for optical uses is found in Iceland, whence arises the common term "Iceland spar." The specific gravity of calcite is 2.7 and its hardness is 3, being readily scratched with a knife. Calcite parts are easily damaged, not only by mechanical abrasion but also by acid vapors in the atmosphere. Like quartz, calcite crystallizes in the hexagonal system, but it is rhombohedral in form as shown in Fig. 198. It does not rotate the plane of polarization as quartz does but it is more strongly birefringent, as can be seen from Table XXII. This is a serious disadvantage because, if it is used as a prism in a spectrograph, the lines will appear single within only a small spectral region near the position of minimum deviation, where the rays within the prism are almost parallel with the optic axis. Moreover, the optic axis, indicated by XX' in the figure, is so placed within the crystal that, when a prism is cut, the loss of material is great. Calcite, therefore, is more commonly used in polarizing prisms than in dispersing prisms. The construction of these prisms will be explained in Sec. 211, Chap. XXIX.

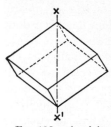

FIG. 198.—A calcite crystal. The optic axis is indicated by XX'.

When the mines in Iceland were first exploited, large and beautifully clear crystals were found, but their value for optical purposes was not realized at the time and most of them were broken up. The survivors are jealously retained by their owners and only comparatively small pieces are available commercially.

Fluorite (CaF_2) has a specific gravity of 3.2 and a hardness of 4, indicating that it can be scratched with a knife. The flawless, transparent variety that is of use in optical systems is found principally in the Alps and is known as fluorspar. It crystallizes in the isometric system and is cubical in form. Inasmuch as the three axes are indistinguishable from one another, the substance is not birefringent and behaves optically as if it were isotropic. Like calcite, it is available only in small pieces, a circumstance that prevents it from being used to achromatize quartz lenses, for which it is otherwise admirably suited. It is used in spectroscopic apparatus only where other materials are unsuitable and finds its widest application in constructing semi-apochromatic microscope objectives.

Rock salt, like fluorite, is cubical in its crystalline form and therefore not birefringent. Its specific gravity is 2.3 and its hardness is 2.5. It is widely used for infrared apparatus and according to Coblentz, "is uniformly transparent from 200 mμ to 12 μ." To prevent its surface from deteriorating, it should be coated with a lacquer that is transparent to the spectral region for which the apparatus is designed but impervious to water and other deleterious vapors. If not protected by lacquer, it must be carefully covered when not in use.

Sylvite or sylvine (KCl) is also cubical in form and not birefringent. Its low dispersion combined with the high cost of transparent pieces of sufficient size makes it of little use. Moreover, it has strong absorption bands at 3.18 μ and 7.08 μ. The materials previously described are more satisfactory except for the narrow region from 15 μ to 24 μ.

Water is rarely used although its high ultraviolet transmission combined with its cheapness as compared with quartz makes it of some value. One disadvantage of water is that its dispersion is low. Another is that, in common with other liquids, its temperature coefficient of index is high. It must, therefore, be maintained at a uniform temperature to prevent convection currents that injure the quality of the image.

Carbon disulphide (CS$_2$) is occasionally used for prisms because of its high dispersion. Its temperature coefficient is greater than that of water, and therefore the precautions mentioned above apply with even greater force. Although its limits of transmission are approximately 220 mμ and 5800 mμ, it cannot be used throughout this entire region because of the presence of absorption bands. There are several in the infrared beyond 4 μ, and there is one in the ultraviolet at 321 mμ. At these bands the phenomenon of *anomalous dispersion* appears, which requires a little explanation.

The conventional dispersion curve is like those of Fig. 52 in Chap. VI, and the type of dispersion thus represented is so common that it is said to be *normal*. If, however, the index of a transparent substance is measured over a long spectral region, the resulting plot of index against wave length will be found to be a series of discontinuous curves as shown in Fig. 199. The regions indicated by the heavy lines are the regions of "normal" dispersion. Discontinuities occur at the absorption bands, on one side of which the dispersion is "normal" and on the other, "anomalous." The absorption bands of carbon

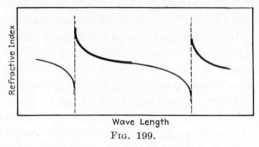

Fig. 199.

disulphide between 220 mμ and 5800 mμ are too weak to produce this effect in the complete form shown in Fig. 199, but they do cause slight irregularities in the dispersion curve.

The values of refractive index usually given in tables are referred to dry air at the same temperature and 760 mm pressure. If the values are to be reduced to vacuum, the index of the air must be known. Many researches upon this subject have been made, but it will suffice to give the following values obtained by Meggers and Peters:[1]

t	0°C.	15°C.	30°C.
n_D	1.0002916	1.0002764	1.0002624

In each case, the barometric pressure was 760 mm of mercury.

The dispersion of air is usually represented by the Cauchy formula instead of the Hartmann formula [Eq. (214) in Chap. XV]. The Cauchy formula is

$$n - 1 = a + \frac{b}{\lambda^2} + \frac{c}{\lambda^4}.\tag{218}$$

[1] *Bur. Standards Sci. Paper* 327. This also contains a summary of the previous data.

The curves obtained by Meggers and Peters are well represented when the following values are assigned to the constants and λ is expressed in millimicrons:

$t°C.$	a	b	c
0	2.876×10^{-4}	1.34	3.8×10^4
15	2.726	1.23	3.6
30	2.590	1.23	2.6

144. Reflecting Materials.—The materials used for mirrors are usually either metals or alloys. Determinations of the spectral reflectivity of six metals—silver, gold, platinum, copper, nickel, and steel—and four alloys were made by Hagan and Rubens in 1902. New determinations have been made of these substances since then, and many others have been examined. The data are published in various places and, as they are useful in selecting the proper material for a given purpose, the results of the more important determinations have been collected in Table XXIV. It will be noticed that the reflectivity of most metals is low in the ultraviolet but increases in the visible and near infrared to approximately 90 or 100 per cent, remaining almost constant throughout the remainder of the spectrum. This phenomenon is best exhibited by the substances that are the most metallic in their other characteristics, such as iron, platinum, tungsten, and, above all, silver. Substances that are less metallic or non-metallic in character, like antimony and carbon, exhibit the phenomenon to a much less degree. The same is true of alloys. The behavior of silicon is the opposite, the reflectivity in the ultraviolet being greater than in the infrared. The natural sulphides of certain metals, such as pyrites (FeS_2), molybdenite (MoS_2), galena (PbS), and stibnite (Sb_2S_3), behave the same way. In the table, stibnite has been chosen for illustration because its cleavage surfaces are smooth and bright and it can be obtained in fairly large pieces.

Some little care must be taken in interpreting the table. The specimens are so diversified in character and the methods used by the various investigators are so different that the values are not strictly comparable. Moreover, two specimens of the same material behave somewhat differently because of uncontrollable variations in the method of preparation. Nevertheless, the table indicates quite accurately the relation of the reflecting

TABLE XXIV.—SPECTRAL REFLECTIVITY OF SOME METALS AND ALLOYS*

Wave length, millimicrons	1 Lacquered silver	2 Silver	3 Aluminum	4 Antimony	5 Bismuth	6 Cadmium	7 Carbon	8 Chromium	9 Cobalt	10 Copper	11 Gold	12 Iridium	13 Iron	14 Lead	15 Magnesium	16 Molybdenum	17 Nickel	18 Palladium	19 Platinum	20 Rhodium	21 Selenium	22 Silicon	23 Tantalum	24 Tellurium	25 Tungsten	26 Vanadium	27 Zinc	28 Speculum metal	29 Stellite	30 Monel metal	31 Magnalium	32 Duralumin	33 Stibnite
200		27[1]	35[1]	33[1]	18[1]	23[1]	16[1]	36[1]	38[1]	32[1]	20[1]		26[1]	25[1]	21[1]	32[1]	45[1]	18[1]	39[1]		15[1]	74[1]	13[1]	21[1]	16[1]		22[1]	25[1]	39[1]		67	25[6]	51[6]
250		33	53	34	25	37	18	32	45	34	25		39	28	33	25	40	20	42		21	77	16	23	17		39	37	43		71	30	61
300		20	65		30	49	18	38	50	33	30		44	34	45	40	46	22	49		29	73	19		28		48	45	50		81	35	60
350		66	71	47	37	60	18	41	53	35			49	42			49	25	51		30	60	25	41			51	59	56				
400		84[2]	71		46[8]	61	21[2]			31[7]	33[7]		55[2]			44[2]	59[1]		48[2]		31[8]	34[2]	38[2]	49[2]	47[2]		54[4]	60[1]	64[4]		84	41	52
450		88			50		22		55	37	47			45		45	61		54		29			48	48		55	63	66	57[4]	84	46	50
500	69[3]	90	73[5]		52		23	55[2]		44	74				72[4]	46	63	29	58	76[2]	27	32	45	50	49	57[2]	56	64	68	58	83	48	49
550	74	91	80	53[2]	53						84		58			48	65				26			50	51		58	64	70	59	83	50	44
600	77	92			55		24	57	67[5]	72	89			62[2]			66		64		25									60	83	58	40
650	80	93			57			59		80	92		60			50					24	30		51	54		60	66	72	62	83		41
700		94		55	58		24	61	71	83		84					69		69	79	23		56			59	61	67		64			44
800	83	95	88	58			25			89	95	87	62		74	52	70		70	81		29	65	52	56	60	62	72	73	67	84		
1,000	88	97.2					27		77	93	97		65		75	58	74	75[5]	73	84		28	79	53	62	61	49	75	74	72	84		37
1,200	90	97.6	91	60			28	70		95	95	91	69			64	77	78	75	87		28	84	54	68	63	75	75	75	75	84		37
1,400	92	97.8					30			95	97		72			69	80		77	88			87	55	74	65	86	76	75	77			
1,600	93	97.9		65		95	32	76	81			93	74			74			78	90			88	57	78	66	90		76	79			
2,000	95	97.9		68			35						78		77	82			81	91		28	91		85	69	94		77	84			
2,500		98.0					40						82		79	86				92		28	92		89	72	95		79	87			
3,000		98.3					43						85		81	88		87	89	92		28	92		91	74	96		80	89			
3,500		98.4					46						88			89							93		92	77	96		81	90			
4,000							48						90		84	91		88	92	93		28	93		93	79	96		83	91	90		

TABLE XXIV.—SPECTRAL REFLECTIVITY OF SOME METALS AND ALLOYS*—(Continued)

Wave length, millimicrons	1 Lacquered silver	2 Silver	3 Aluminum	4 Antimony	5 Bismuth	6 Cadmium	7 Carbon	8 Chromium	9 Cobalt	10 Copper	11 Gold	12 Iridium	13 Iron	14 Lead	15 Magnesium	16 Molybdenum	17 Nickel	18 Palladium	19 Platinum	20 Rhodium	21 Selenium	22 Silicon	23 Tantalum	24 Tellurium	25 Tungsten	26 Vanadium	27 Zinc	28 Speculum metal	29 Stellite	30 Monel metal	31 Magnalium	32 Duralumin	33 Stibnite
5,000		98.5	93			96	51	81	85			94	92		86	92		90	94	93			93	60	94	82							37
6,000		98.6	94	70			52	85					93		88	93						28		63	95	85							
7,000		98.6	95			97	54	89	93			95	94		91	93		93	96	94			94	68	96	88							
8,000		98.8	97				56	92	96			95	94		93	94		95	95	94			94	72	96	90							
9,000		98.9		72		98	58	93	96			95			93	94		95	95	94				78		92							
10,000		99.0	97			98	59		97			96				95		97	96	95		28			96								38

In this table, the sources of information are indicated by superscripts as follows:

[1] HULBURT, *Astrophys. Jour.*, **42**, 205 (1915).
[2] COBLENTZ, *Bur. Standards Bull.*, **7**, 197 (1911) (*Sci. Paper* 152).
[3] COBLENTZ and KAHLER, *Bur. Standards Sci. Paper* 342 (1919).
[4] COBLENTZ, *Bur. Standards Sci. Paper* 379 (1920).
[5] COBLENTZ, *Bur. Standards Bull.*, **2**, 457 (1906) (*Sci. Paper* 45).
[6] COBLENTZ and HUGHES, *Bur. Standards Sci. Paper* 493 (1924).
[7] HAGEN and RUBENS, *Zeits. Instrumentenk.*, **22**, 42 (1902); *Ann. Physik*, **8**, 1 (1902).
[8] MEIER, *Ann. Physik*, **31**, 1017 (1910).
[9] DRUDE, *Ann. Physik*, **39**, 481 (1890).

For explanation see pp. 406–408.

* The values are expressed in percentage.

power in one part of the spectrum to that in another besides giving a good idea of the order of magnitude. It must be emphasized, however, that a high reflectivity alone does not determine the value of a material for practical use. Many of these materials are either very soft or difficult to prepare, and many others, although hard and capable of taking a high polish, tarnish and become dull in a short time. Speculum metal is an excellent example of this; the extent to which it deteriorates being well shown by the values given in the explanation of the table. One of the best materials for both the ultraviolet and the visible region is stellite, which has a high reflectivity, is hard, takes a high polish, and does not tarnish. It is extremely difficult to work, however.

The reflectivity of a metal is also of importance from a theoretical standpoint. It can be shown that, on the basis of the electromagnetic theory, the reflectivity of an electrical conductor at any wave length for normal incidence is given by the expression

$$R = \frac{n^2(1 + k^2) + 1 - 2n}{n^2(1 + k^2) + 1 + 2n},\tag{219}$$

which is analogous to Eq. (16) for a dielectric material. In this equation, n is the index and k is the *extinction coefficient* for the wave length in question. The meaning of the term "extinction coefficient" in this connection deserves some explanation.

Let the light traverse a layer of material of a thickness λ equal to the wave length of the light within the material. The extinction coefficient k is then defined by the fraction $1/\epsilon^{-2\pi k}$, where this fraction represents the reduction in the amplitude of the electromagnetic disturbance in passing through this layer. It can be readily seen that the value of k can be determined experimentally by measuring the transmission of very thin films. Usually at least two films of different thicknesses are measured to eliminate the effects of reflection at the surfaces. The value of n can be determined experimentally for even so strongly absorbing a substance as a metal by making it into the form of an extremely thin prism. The experimental error is large, as might be expected, and it is very likely that the material at the surface, where reflection takes place, is in an entirely different molecular condition than it is in the interior, where most of the absorption takes place. The direct measurement of n and k can be avoided by taking advantage of the fact that a beam of light incident at an angle is elliptically polarized. The subject of elliptical polarization cannot be discussed here, and it must suffice to state that the necessary measurements can be made very accurately. As an example of the correspondence between the values of reflectivity as computed from the constants n and k and the values determined by direct measurement, some results obtained by Tate[1] are presented:

	λ, milli-microns	n	k	$R_{cal.}$	$R_{obs.}$
Silver	460	0.270	12.02	0.911	0.905
	540	0.279	13.95	0.933	0.930
	700	0.308	16.87	0.957	0.953
Gold	460	1.662	1.098	0.362	0.370
	560	0.805	3.503	0.703	0.708
	680	0.617	6.255	0.859	0.853
Copper	460	1.570	1.440	0.463	0.460
	560	1.269	2.018	0.566	0.575
	700	1.035	3.688	0.778	0.786
Fuchsin	460	1.056	0.720	0.121	0.130
	560	2.400	0.498	0.261	0.260
	680	2.231	0.025	0.146	0.142

It is evident that the reflectivity varies in the same direction as k, which means that an opaque substance reflects most strongly in the portions of the spectrum where it absorbs most strongly. The same is true for transparent substances at strong absorption bands, a condition which is illustrated by the dye fuchsin, for which values are given above. Such a material is said to exhibit *metallic reflection*. In the portions of the spectrum where a medium is transparent, the value of k is approximately zero and Eq. (219) reduces to Eq. (16), which is Fresnel's well-known equation for the reflection at the surface of a transparent medium.

145. Other Materials.—The other materials used in optics, although of importance in special branches, are not of sufficiently general application to warrant more than passing mention. Such, for example, are Canada balsam, oil of cedar, and a few other liquids. Canada balsam is made from the sap of the North American balsam fir. Despite its name, it is strictly a turpentine and not a balsam, containing neither benzoic nor cinnamic acid. Approximately one-fourth of it consists of

[1] *Phys. Rev.*, **34**, 321 (1912).

essential oils, the remaining three-fourths consisting of resins, of which most are soluble only in alcohol but others only in ether. All are soluble in xylol, however, with which the balsam is commonly diluted for cementing microscope specimens. The refractive index of Canada balsam depends upon its composition. One sample of balsam in stick form, prepared for cementing lenses, was found by the authors to have the following indices: $n_C = 1.537$; $n_D = 1.540$; $n_F = 1.550$; $\nu = 42$. The measurements were made at room temperature but the sample was first heated for half an hour at 100°C. to simulate the effect of heating the balsam during the cementing operation.

Cedar oil comes from a variety of juniper and is used mainly as an immersion oil for microscope objectives. It is usually prepared so that its index is 1.515, which is near that of crown glass. Both Canada balsam and cedar oil absorb in the ultraviolet, and consequently glycerine is used for work in this region. At a wave length of 275 mμ, it has an index of 1.45.

Liquids for use with critical-angle refractometers must have an index higher than that of the sample whose index is being measured. The one most commonly used is α-monobromnaphthalene, which has an index of 1.66. For specimens of lower index, aniline, with an index of 1.56, is preferable. For specimens with a higher index, methylene iodide, with an index of 1.74, is satisfactory. Mercuric iodide dissolved in a saturated aqueous solution of potassium iodide has an index of 1.71 and can be used if methylene iodide is not available. For samples having an index much greater than 1.71, a saturated solution of sulphur and methylene iodide can be used. A considerable quantity of sulphur can be dissolved by heating the mixture gently, and the index of the liquid can thus be raised to approximately 1.77.

Explanation of Table XXIV

In all the cases, the angle of incidence is less than 20°, so the values are practically the same as for normal incidence. The values depend greatly upon the character of the surface, however, and the various specimens are described by the investigators as follows:

1. *Lacquered silver:* Freshly polished silver-on-glass mirrors coated with various water-white commercial lacquers properly diluted. The reflectivity diminishes after exposure to powerful sources of ultraviolet light.

2. *Silver:* (1) An opaque film of silver on glass, deposited chemically and polished with rouge and chamois. (2) Values adopted as standard by

the Bureau of Standards for all their mirrors on the basis of which their other values are determined. The justification for this procedure is given in their *Bulletin*, **10**, 43 (1913) (*Sci. Paper* 204).

3. *Aluminum:* (1) An opaque film deposited by cathodic sputtering in an atmosphere of mercury vapor. (5) A sheet of commercial metal given a high polish with Vienna lime and stearin oil.

4. *Antimony:* (1) A freshly split cleavage surface. (2) An opaque cathodic film. It is difficult to obtain a bright film by sputtering and cleavage surfaces are marred by numerous cracks, so the values given are not very reliable.

5. *Bismuth:* (1) An opaque cathodic film deposited in hydrogen. (8) A sample melted and then cooled by immersion in water; it was somewhat scratched in polishing.

6. *Cadmium:* (1) An opaque cathodic film deposited in hydrogen; this film is extremely soft. (5) A sample melted and cooled in a thin copper mold. It was filed, ground, and finally polished with Vienna lime and stearin oil.

7. *Carbon:* (1) An opaque cathodic film; time required four days. (2) Siberian graphite, cleavage surface polished on wet semi-matte glass. Manufactured graphite cannot be burnished free from pores and consequently its reflectivity at short wave lengths is low, being about 13 per cent at 1000 mμ.

8. *Chromium:* (1) and (2) Solid pieces of metal, polished. The solid metal is full of fine pores but cathodic films are entirely unsatisfactory.

9. *Cobalt:* (1) and (5) Polished sheet; rather irregular surface.

10. *Copper:* (1) Two opaque cathodic films. (7) A polished plate of purest commercial copper. For this sample, Hagen and Rubens find values in the ultraviolet lower than those given. Hulburt finds that electrolytically deposited films also have lower values, at least in the ultraviolet.

11. *Gold:* (1) Two thick cathodic films two days old. No further change with age was found but the films when fresh had a reflectivity of 40 per cent at 300 mμ instead of 34 per cent, the other values being the same. A fresh electrolytic film had the values given in the table. (7) Metal sheet, type of surface not stated.

12. *Iridium:* A thick polished plate, not perfectly free from pores.

13. *Iron:* (1) Hardened steel. (2) Iron, 99.8 per cent pure. Both samples took a very high polish.

14. *Lead:* (1) An opaque cathodic film, which was soft and bright like cadmium but tarnished quickly. (9) A rolled sheet.

15. *Magnesium:* (1) Sheet, buffed and then polished with dry rouge on chamois; fine scratches on surface. (2) Highly polished sheet, finished first on wet emery paper, then on tin oxide ("putty powder"), and finally on dry chamois sprinkled with putty powder.

16. *Molybdenum:* (1) and (2) Polished pieces of solid metal.

17. *Nickel:* (1) Film deposited electrolytically on a thin cathodic film. (7) Sheet, method of preparation not stated.

18. *Palladium:* (1) An opaque cathodic film. (5) Sheet, polished with Vienna lime and stearin oil. Would not take a good polish.

19. *Platinum:* (1) An opaque cathodic film.   (2) Type of surface not stated.

20. *Rhodium:* Type of surface not stated.   The accuracy of the results is stated to be low.

21. *Selenium:* (1) An old mirror prepared by melting the metal and pouring it on glass.   (8) Sample cast on glass and polished.   The surface had many fine pores.

22. *Silicon:* (1) A polished specimen marred by holes and scratches.   An opaque cathodic film reflects less strongly below 300 mμ and more strongly above.   (2) Sample remelted after coming from furnace and polished on fine emery paper covered with tin oxide and graphite.

23. *Tantalum:* A polished sample of very pure cast metal.   The surface of a sample that has been rolled or hammered becomes seriously contaminated during polishing.   Ordinary samples are so impure that the reflectivity is very much lowered in the near infrared.

24. *Tellurium:* (1) An opaque cathodic film.   It was polished with rouge on chamois before being measured.   (2) An opaque cathodic film deposited in hydrogen.   Very fine films can be made this way.   The reflectivity of a polished sample of the solid metal is much lower because of the pores between the crystals.

25. *Tungsten:* (1) A polished piece of solid metal.   It was well polished but had a few holes and fine scratches.   (2) A polished piece of solid metal with some pores.   These pores cause a reduction in the reflectivity, especially at short wave lengths.

26. *Vanadium:* Type of sample not stated; surface well polished.

27. *Zinc:* (1) A dense cathodic film deposited in hydrogen.   (4) A polished sheet.   Note the low value at 1000 mμ.

28. *Speculum metal:* An alloy of 68.2 per cent Cu and 31.8 per cent Sn, especially interesting because it is the material from which concave gratings are made.   (1) A sample freshly polished on pitch and rouge.   Seven days later the surface had tarnished so much that the reflectivities at 200 mμ and 300 mμ had dropped to 17 and 39 per cent respectively.   At these wave lengths, the reflectivities of an old mirror that had tarnished to a marked extent were 5 and 26 per cent, and rubbing off the oxide layer with chalk and alcohol raised the values to only 9 and 30 per cent.   (7) Method of preparation not stated.

29. *Stellite:* An alloy of chromium, cobalt, and molybdenum, the proportions being a trade secret.   (1) and (4) Both samples were pieces of sheet metal given a very high polish.

30. *Monel metal:* A natural alloy of 68 to 70 per cent Ni, 1.5 per cent Fe, and 28.5 to 30.5 per cent Cu.   The sample was sawed from a rod.   The surface was optically flat and highly polished.

31. *Magnalium:* An alloy of 69 per cent Al and 31 per cent Mg.   It is very difficult to prepare and tarnishes rapidly in air.

32. *Duralumin:* An alloy of 94 per cent Al, 4 per cent Cu, and small amounts of Mn, Fe, Mg, and Si.   The sample was not highly polished.

33. *Stibnite:* Natural antimony sulphide (Sb_2S_3).   A cleavage surface, optically flat and unusually brilliant.

CHAPTER XIX

THE DESIGN OF OPTICAL INSTRUMENTS

Until comparatively recently, optical instruments were always designed for visual use. This means that the eye was a part of every complete instrument and the designer was compelled to select the constants of the system accordingly. With the advent of photographic plates, radiometers, and light-sensitive cells, the design of optical systems became, in one sense, less restricted. The principles that had been followed in the design of visual instruments did not, in general, extend to the newer applications;

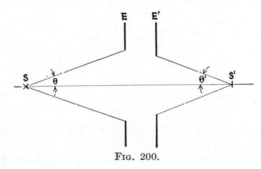

Fig. 200.

and, for this reason, it is necessary to treat the problem of design in its broader aspects.

146. The Distribution of Light in Optical Systems.—The calculation of the distribution of light flux within an optical system is comparatively simple when the source is so small that the system is incapable of resolving it. In Fig. 200, the point source S is imaged at S' by an optical system represented by an entrance pupil E and an exit pupil E'. The image at S' consists of a diffraction pattern described in Sec. 60, Chap. VII, where it was shown that 84 per cent of the flux entering the entrance pupil falls within the central diffraction disk. The radius of the disk was given by Eq. (164) as

$$z' = \frac{0.61\,\lambda}{n'\tan\theta'}.$$

Assuming, for the sake of simplicity, that the illumination is uniform within this disk, it will be seen that the illumination in the image of a point object is greater than the illumination in the entrance pupil in the inverse ratio of the area of the diffraction disk to the area of the entrance pupil, since the same flux traverses both.[1] The illumination in the entrance pupil is readily calculated by means of the inverse-square law from the intensity of the source and its distance from the entrance pupil.

When the source is of sufficient size to be resolved by the system, the computation of the illumination in the image is not quite so simple. In Fig. 201, let the circular source S be imaged

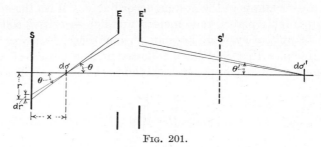

Fig. 201.

at S' by means of an optical system whose entrance and exit pupils with respect to these planes are at E and E' respectively. Let us then calculate the illumination on a small element of area normal to the axis, such as $d\sigma'$. To do so, we must first calculate the illumination on its conjugate $d\sigma$.

The illumination on $d\sigma$ can be found by dividing the source S into elements of such size that the inverse-square law can be applied to each, and computing the total illumination by integration. For convenience, let the source be divided into circular zones of radius r and width dr. The illumination dE at $d\sigma$ due to an elementary zone is given by

$$dE = \frac{dI}{x^2 \sec^2 \theta} \cos \theta,$$

where dI is the intensity of the elementary zone in the direction of $d\sigma$ and $x^2 \sec^2 \theta$ is the square of its distance from $d\sigma$. Since dI usually depends upon θ, the problem cannot be solved without making some specific assumption concerning the characteristics

[1] Neglecting the relatively small amount of flux distributed in the rings of the diffraction pattern and that lost by reflection and absorption within the instrument.

of the source. If it obeys Lambert's law of emission or reflection,

$$dI = 2\pi r \, drB \cdot \cos \theta,$$

where B is the uniform brightness of the surface when viewed from any direction, and $2\pi r \, dr$ is the area of the elementary zone. By substitution,

$$dE = \frac{2\pi r \, dr \, B \, \cos^2 \theta}{x^2 \sec^2 \theta}.$$

Now r can be evaluated in terms of θ by noting that

$$r = x \, \tan \theta$$

and therefore

$$dr = x \, \sec^2 \theta \, d\theta.$$

By making this substitution, the illumination at $d\sigma$ due to the area of the source within the angle θ is

$$E = \int_0^\theta 2\pi B \, \sin \theta \, \cos \theta \, d\theta,$$

which, on integration, becomes

$$E = \pi B \sin^2 \theta. \tag{220}$$

Since, by the property of entrance and exit pupils, all the flux that enters the one emerges from the other, it follows that the illumination on $d\sigma$ is to that on $d\sigma'$ in the inverse ratio of their areas. For an aplanatic system, the ratio of the areas can be found from the sine law [Eq. (129) in Chap. VI] to be

$$\frac{d\sigma}{d\sigma'} = \frac{n'^2 \sin^2 \theta'}{n^2 \sin^2 \theta}. \tag{221}$$

It is therefore evident that

$$E' = \left(\frac{n'}{n}\right)^2 \pi B \sin^2 \theta'. \tag{222}$$

If the refractive index of the image space is the same as that of the object space,

$$E' = \pi B \sin^2 \theta' \tag{223}$$

lumens/area when B is in candles/area. In other words, the illumination produced at any point on the axis of an aplanatic system by an extended source emitting or reflecting according to Lambert's law depends only on the brightness of the source and the size of the pencil of rays converging at that point.[1]

[1] The loss of light by reflection and absorption within the system is, of course, tacitly neglected.

This result is so fundamental to an understanding of the subject that it may be well to consider a specific example. In Fig. 202, the source S emitting or reflecting according to Lambert's law is imaged at S' by means of the aplanatic lens L. The lens is obviously the aperture stop, entrance pupil, and exit pupil with respect to the conjugate planes S and S'. Hence, the illumination on the axis in the plane of S' is obtained by simply multiplying the brightness of S by $\pi \sin^2 \theta'$, where θ' is the angle subtended at S' by the radius of the lens. Now consider the illumination at other points along the axis of the system. If one imagines the point to move toward the left from S', the illumination steadily increases between S' and M because of the increase in the value of θ'. At M, the source becomes

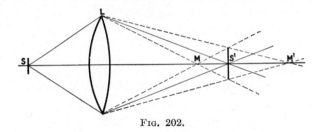

Fig. 202.

the aperture stop, and its image at S' becomes the exit pupil. Between M and L, the illumination decreases as the square of the sine of the half-angle subtended by S' at the point in question. When the point reaches L, the illumination computed by Eq. (220) for the object space is the same as that computed by means of Eq. (223) for the image space, as would be expected. If the point moves toward the right from S', the illumination decreases with L acting as the exit pupil until M' is reached. Beyond M', it continues to decrease with S' acting as the exit pupil.

It is of interest to note that Fig. 202 represents the optical system of the searchlight with the exception that a searchlight is usually focused so that S' is at infinity. Hence L is generally the exit pupil for all points at any considerable distance away. Since θ' is usually small, $\tan^2 \theta'$ may be written for $\sin^2 \theta'$, and the illumination is seen to decrease with the distance from L according to the inverse-square law. This consideration indicates the incorrectness of the common concept of a parallel bundle of rays extending with undiminished intensity to infinity. To be sure, the pencil originating at the point of the source which lies on the axis of the lens does become in the image space a bundle of rays that are parallel to the axis. It should be remembered, however, that, if the source is of finite brightness, the intensity of any point is zero. Hence, the energy in this bundle is infinitesimally small. The points of the source that do not lie on the axis produce bundles of rays in the image space which, although parallel to themselves, are not parallel to the axis. It will be seen, therefore, that the size of the source does not affect the illumination at points on the axis (except near the lens) but determines merely the spread of the beam.

The light-gathering power of lenses that are commonly used for very distant objects, such as telescope or camera objectives,

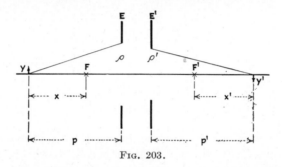

Fig. 203.

is most frequently expressed in terms of the f/-number. This quantity was defined in Chap. V as the ratio of the focal length of the system to the diameter of its entrance pupil. That this is a true measure of the light-gathering power for an object at infinity is clear from Fig. 203. By means of the sine law, Eq. (222) can be transformed into

$$E' = \frac{\pi B \sin^2 \theta}{m^2}, \tag{224}$$

which holds even if the refractive index of the image space differs from that of the object space. The lateral magnification between the object plane and the image plane is

$$m = \frac{y'}{y} = -\frac{f}{x},$$

where x is the distance of the object from the first focal point of the system. If x is very great, it may be assumed to be equal to p, the distance of the object from the entrance pupil.   Furthermore, θ is then small, so one may write

$$\sin \theta = \tan \theta = \frac{\rho}{p} = \frac{\rho}{x}.$$

With this substitution, Eq. (224) becomes

$$E' = \pi B \frac{\rho^2}{f^2} \tag{225}$$

$$= \frac{\pi B}{4} \cdot \frac{1}{(f\text{/-number})^2}. \tag{226}$$

Thus it will be seen that the illumination varies inversely as the square of the f/-number when the object is at a great distance.

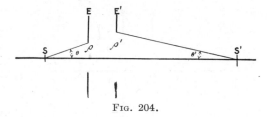

Fig. 204.

In systems that are commonly used with near-by objects, such as microscopes, the light-gathering power is generally expressed in terms of the numerical aperture.   This quantity was defined by Eq. (107) in Chap. V as

$$\text{N.A.} = n \sin \theta,$$

where n is the refractive index of the medium in the object space and θ is the angle subtended at the object by the radius of the entrance pupil, as shown in Fig. 204.   The complete form of Eq. (223) for the case when the object space and image space are of different refractive index is given by Eq. (222) as

$$E' = \left(\frac{n'}{n}\right)^2 \pi \cdot B \cdot \sin^2 \theta'.$$

The magnification between object and image is given by the sine law as

$$m = \frac{y'}{y} = \frac{n \sin \theta}{n' \sin \theta'} = \frac{\text{N.A.}}{n' \sin \theta'}. \tag{227}$$

By combining these two equations, the illumination in the image at S' is found to be

$$E' = \frac{\pi B \, (\text{N.A.})^2}{n^2 m^2}.$$ (228)

It will be seen that the illumination in the image is directly proportional to the square of the numerical aperture and inversely proportional to the square of the lateral magnification.

It frequently happens that the aperture stop of a system is not circular, in which case the integration is in general impossible to perform. The illumination can be computed, however, by means of an approximate formula involving the solid angle of the cone producing the illumination. For the case of a circular exit pupil, the solid angle ω' within the cone whose half-plane angle is θ' is given by

$$\omega' = 2\pi(1 - \cos \theta').$$ (229)

If θ' is small, $2(1 - \cos \theta')$ is very nearly equal to $\sin^2 \theta'$, so

$$E' = B\omega'.$$ (230)

For most optical systems, ω' is so small that this approximation is justified, and when an exit pupil is irregular in shape, it is the only simple method of computing the illumination. For example, in systems containing cylindrical lenses, the two planes can be treated separately, the solid angle being computed by multiplying together the plane angles in the two mutually perpendicular planes.

In designing optical instruments, it is well to keep in mind the relationship between θ', $\sin \theta'$, ω', the f-number, and the factor $(\pi \sin^2 \theta')$ that relates E' to B. This is facilitated by making a table such as Table XXV. Photographers who are accustomed to the f-system will find it convenient to note that an $f/8$ lens provides an illumination on the surface of the emulsion that is approximately $\frac{1}{100}$ th of the subject brightness, after making a reasonable allowance for the absorption of light within the lens. For example, an $f/8$ lens will produce an illumination of 1 lumen/meter^2 when the object has a brightness of 100 candles/meter^2, assuming the object to be at infinity.

The discussion so far has been confined entirely to the illumination at a point on the axis of the system. The same general principles apply to an extra-axial point, but a rigorous treatment of the problem would be rather complicated. It is usually sufficient for all practical purposes to use the approximation given by Eq. (230) and write

TABLE XXV

θ', degrees	sin θ'	ω'	$f/$-number	π sin^2 θ'
1	0.0175	0.0009	28.7	0.001
2	0.0349	0.0038	14.3	0.004
3	0.0523	0.0086	9.55	0.009
4	0.0698	0.0153	7.17	0.015
5	0.0872	0.0239	5.74	0.024
10	0.1737	0.0954	2.88	0.095
15	0.2588	0.2140	1.93	0.211
20	0.3420	0.3789	1.46	0.368
25	0.4226	0.5887	1.18	0.561
30	0.5000	0.8418	1.00	0.785
35	0.5736	1.1363	0.872	1.034
40	0.6428	1.4700	0.778	1.298
45	0.7071	1.8403	0.707	1.571
50	0.7660	2.2444	0.653	1.844
55	0.8192	2.6793	0.610	2.108
60	0.8660	3.1416	0.577	2.356
65	0.9063	3.6278	0.552	2.581
70	0.9397	4.1342	0.532	2.774
75	0.9659	4.6570	0.518	2.931
80	0.9848	5.1921	0.508	3.047
85	0.9962	5.7355	0.502	3.118
90	1.0000	6.2832	0.500	3.142

$$E' = B \, \Omega' \cos \alpha', \qquad (231)$$

where Ω' is the solid angle subtended by the exit pupil at the extra-axial point and α' is the angle made with the axis by the chief ray through this point. Now Ω' for an extra-axial point is less than ω' for an axial point in the same transverse plane for two reasons. In the first place, the projected area of the exit pupil is less at an extra-axial point by the factor cos α', and, in the second place, the distance of the point from the exit pupil is greater. Taking both factors into consideration,

$$\Omega' = \omega' \cos^3 \alpha'. \qquad (232)$$

By combining this with the previous equation, it is seen that the illumination at an extra-axial point decreases approximately as the fourth power of the cosine of the angle of obliquity of the chief ray. This result is based on the assumption that the field stops in the system do not interfere and cause a further vignetting of the image.

147. The Design of Visual Instruments.—The fundamental problem in the design of any optical instrument involves the proper correlation of the three fundamental quantities upon which its usefulness depends. These quantities are the light-gathering power, the resolving power, and the magnification. It was shown by Eq. (165) in Chap. VII that the resolving power of any optical instrument depends upon its numerical aperture, assuming it to be entirely free from aberrations. If full advantage of the inherent resolving power of an instrument is to be realized, the aperture stop of the entire system, including the eye, must lie within the instrument. However, if Eq. (223) is applied to the eye, it will be seen that the illumination on the retina depends upon the size of the cone of rays that converge on the fovea. Therefore, no optical instrument is capable of making an extended object appear any brighter than it appears to the unaided eye, and the brightness will be reduced unless the pupil of the eye is the aperture stop of the system. Full advantage of the inherent resolving power of an instrument can be obtained without sacrificing the light-gathering power by making the aperture stop of the instrument and the pupil of the eye equally effective in limiting the aperture of the entire system. Usually, the eye is so placed that its entrance pupil coincides in position with the exit pupil of the instrument, since placing the eye elsewhere merely introduces an additional stop that may unnecessarily restrict the field of view. When the two pupils coincide in position, they will be equally effective in limiting the aperture if they are of the same size. From the standpoint of optical theory, therefore, an optical instrument intended for visual use should be so designed that its exit pupil coincides in size and position with the entrance pupil of the eye.[1]

When the above condition is satisfied by a visual instrument, the magnification is given immediately by Eq. (129) as

[1] This conclusion applies also in the case of a point source, although for a different reason. In this case, all the flux that is collected by the entrance pupil of the instrument takes part in the formation of the diffraction pattern that is formed on the retina, assuming that the exit pupil of the instrument is not larger than the entrance pupil of the eye. The size of the diffraction pattern increases as the size of the exit pupil of the instrument is decreased. Therefore, with an instrument having a given entrance pupil, the illumination in the diffraction pattern on the retina is a maximum when the size of the exit pupil is the same as that of the entrance pupil of the eye. The amount of flux collected by an instrument depends, of course, upon the size of the entrance pupil. Thus it is said to be possible to see stars in the daytime with a telescope of sufficient size, because the telescope increases the apparent intensity of the stars but not the brightness of the sky.

$$m = \frac{y'}{y} = \frac{n \sin \theta}{n' \sin \theta'},$$

where m is the magnification between the object and its retinal image. The denominator $n' \sin \theta'$ depends upon the refractive index of the vitreous humor and the angle subtended at the fovea by the exit pupil of the eye. Although θ' varies somewhat with the adaptation level of the eye, it is ordinarily sufficient to distinguish in practice merely between instruments designed for daylight adaptation and those designed for use at night. It is evident that, for a given value of $n' \sin \theta'$, the magnification determined under the assumption that the exit pupil must coincide with the entrance pupil of the eye depends only on the numerical aperture of the instrument.

As a matter of convenience, it is desirable to distinguish the magnifying power of an instrument from the magnification as defined above. By definition, the *magnifying power* of an optical instrument is the ratio of the size of the retinal image when the instrument is used to the size of the retinal image formed by the eye alone.[1] Let m be the magnification between the object plane and its retinal image when the instrument is used, and let m_0 be the corresponding quantity for the unaided eye. When the instrument is used in the manner assumed above,

$$m = \frac{n \sin \theta}{n' \sin \theta'}.$$

For the unaided eye

$$m_0 = \frac{n_0 \sin \theta_0}{n' \sin \theta'},$$

where $n_0 \sin \theta_0$ is the numerical aperture of the eye. Combining these two expressions, the magnifying power of an instrument whose exit pupil coincides in size and position with the entrance pupil of the eye is found to be

$$M = \frac{m}{m_0} = \frac{n \sin \theta}{n_0 \sin \theta_0}. \tag{233}$$

Since, in this case, full use is made of the inherent resolving power of the instrument without reducing the brightness of the image, the value of M indicated by this equation is called the *normal magnifying power* of the instrument.

[1] The magnifying power of an instrument is sometimes called the *apparent magnification* to distinguish it from the *real magnification* of the retinal image.

To appreciate the full significance of this relationship, let us consider two concrete examples. In the case of an instrument that is used to view distant objects, such as a telescope, θ and θ_0 are both small and $n = n_0$. Therefore,

$$M = \frac{\sin \theta}{\sin \theta_0} = \frac{\tan \theta}{\tan \theta_0} = \frac{2\rho}{2\rho_0},$$

where 2ρ is the diameter of the entrance pupil of the telescope (usually the objective) and $2\rho_0$ is the diameter of the entrance pupil of the eye. Since the entrance pupil of the eye is approximately $\frac{1}{10}$ in. in diameter in the daytime, it may be remembered as a useful rule that the normal magnifying power of a telescope is ten times the diameter of its entrance pupil in inches.

A different situation arises in the case of a microscope because n and n_0 may be different if the objective is of the oil-immersion type. Moreover, the object distance with the unaided eye is rarely the same as the object distance with the instrument, so θ and θ_0 are no longer measured by the relative sizes of the two entrance pupils. In general, objects cannot be seen distinctly if they are less than 5 in. from the eye, even by young persons, and 10 in. (250 mm) is ordinarily assumed as the distance of comfortable vision. For an object at this distance, the numerical aperture of an eye having a 2-mm entrance pupil is 0.004. As a useful rule, therefore, the normal magnifying power of a microscope is roughly 250 times its numerical aperture.

The subject of magnifying power is commonly considered in its purely geometrical aspects. The procedure is to assume an object that subtends an angle measured by $\tan \alpha_0$ when viewed with the unaided eye. If an optical instrument placed before the eye forms an image (usually virtual) subtending an angle measured by $\tan \alpha$, the magnifying power is defined by

$$M = \frac{\tan \alpha}{\tan \alpha_0}. \tag{234}$$

With the aid of this equation, the magnifying power can be related to the constants of the elements composing the system. The defect of this treatment is that it takes no account of the resolving power or light-gathering power of the system. In a telescope, for example, this geometrical line of attack leads to the result that the magnifying power is the ratio of the focal length of the objective to the focal length of the ocular. Hence, by making the former very great and the latter very small, any magnifying power up to infinity is conceivably possible. However, the use of a magnifying power higher than normal causes the exit pupil of the instrument to be smaller than the entrance pupil of the eye. Consequently, the size of the diffraction pattern on the retina increases [Eq. (164)] at exactly the same rate as the magnifying power. A magnifying power higher than normal is therefore said to be *empty* because no more detail is visible. For example, the normal magnifying power for a telescope having an entrance pupil 1 in. in diameter is 10. If, by decreasing the focal length of the ocular, the magnifying power is increased to 20, the light-gathering power is reduced to one-fourth of the value it would have under normal magnification, and the resolving power is not increased. Conversely, if the magnifying power is diminished to 5, the diameter of the exit pupil of the instrument is twice that of the entrance pupil of the eye. Hence the pupil of the eye becomes the aperture stop of the entire system, and the entrance pupil is reduced to 0.5 in. in diameter. In this case the apparent brightness of the image is the same as with normal magnification but the resolving power is reduced one-half.

This discussion may be summed up with the statement that the principal feature to be observed in the design of visual instruments is the proper correlation of the magnifying power with the light-gathering power and the resolving power, which comes about automatically if the exit pupil of the instrument is made to coincide in size and position with the entrance pupil of the eye. In practice, it is quite customary to use a slightly higher magnifying power than the theory calls for because it is usually permissible to sacrifice light for the advantage of the easier seeing conditions that a slightly higher magnifying power affords. In a microscope, for example, the theory indicates that, since 1.6 is about the limit to the numerical aperture, the greatest useful magnifying power is approximately 400 times. Actually, magnifying powers as high as 1000 or more are frequently used to advantage when there is plenty of light available. This is in no way contradictory to the theory; it merely indicates a desire on the part of the microscopist to have a large image to study, even though it does not contain more detail. Of course, it has been tacitly assumed throughout this discussion that the resolving power of the instrument is limited by diffraction rather than by aberrations. The normal magnifying power may therefore be regarded as a limit for perfect image-forming systems, and the limit is lower for an actual system in the ratio of the actual to the theoretical resolving power.

There is so much history back of the design and use of visual instruments that the principles just discussed have become a tradition and the experienced designer accepts them as a matter of course. From his standpoint, the important problem is to reduce the aberrations to such an extent that the resolving power of the instrument is adequate for the purpose for which it is destined. The general procedure in lens design was discussed in Chap. VI, but the details depend so much on the particular form of the instrument that they must be deferred until later chapters. From the standpoint of the user of an optical instrument, the interrelationships between light-gathering power, resolving power, and magnifying power are of the utmost importance, since they determine the limitations of the instrument and therefore the manner in which it should be used. A lack of appreciation of these principles is common, with the result that optical instruments are frequently called upon to perform feats which, if interpreted in terms of their electrical or mechanical analogues, would at once appear ridiculous.

148. The Design of Non-visual Instruments.—Since the advent of satisfactory photographic plates, photoelectric cells, and similar physical detectors of radiation, many instruments that were formerly intended for visual use have been converted into non-visual instruments. There are, of course, a few non-visual instruments that have no visual counterpart, but, speaking generally, non-visual instruments have been merely adaptations of visual instruments. These adaptations have generally been made to permit observations in the regions of the spectrum where the eye is insensitive, to make the instrument recording, or to make it completely automatic by eliminating the operator— a feature that is highly desirable in the case of instruments that are to be used for routine purposes.

The most effective design of a non-visual instrument involves the proper correlation of the same factors that must be correlated in visual instruments—namely, light-gathering power, resolving power, and magnification. There are two important differences between the two types, however. In the first place, non-visual instruments contain no element analogous to the optical system of the eye, and hence the restrictions that have to do with the size and position of the exit pupil do not apply. In the second place, the human eye and the physical detectors respond to radiation very differently. Photographic plates, for example, respond, not to the illumination that they receive, as the retina does, but to the product of the illumination and the time of exposure. On the other hand, photoelectric cells respond to the total flux regardless of the area over which it is distributed. As a consequence, no general rules can be laid down for the design of non-visual instruments, but a word of caution may be interposed against the all too common tendency to adapt existing visual instruments to non-visual purposes without taking advantage of the removal of the restrictions that beset the visual instruments.

149. Mechanical Design.—Although it is not within the province of a work on optics to enter extensively into the subject of the mechanical design of instruments, a few general principles are sufficiently important to be mentioned. One very common mistake is to design the mechanical parts first and subsequently to fit the optical parts into the mechanical arrangement. The result of such a procedure is almost invariably a second-rate optical system, unless radical and expensive changes in the mechanical design are made. A far better way is to lay out the optical system first and then to build the rest of the instrument around it. Inasmuch as the behavior of every element in the system can be predicted mathematically, it is theoretically possible to design the system in its finished form on paper; but in practice it is usually found to be cheaper to prepare a tentative design and have the optical parts made according to the preliminary specifications. The performance of the system can then be tested by arranging the parts in their proper relative positions with clamps or other temporary devices. With such a set-up, the optimum arrangement can be determined and the physical form of the proposed instrument can be readily visualized.

The one feature of mechanical practice that is peculiar to optical design is the mounting of the lens elements. In general, the tube in which a lens is to be mounted is recessed to form a shoulder against which the lens is placed, and the only feature in which a choice remains is the manner of securing the lens. For temporary purposes, modeling clay or soft beeswax can be used. If the lens is to be removed frequently, the most convenient method of retaining it is to use a spring ring. This is simply a piece of spring wire bent into a circle so that when pressed against the lens it will remain in position by friction against the inside of the tube. A more elegant method of mounting a lens that is to be removable is to screw a threaded ring against it. If the lens is never to be removed from its mount, it can be burnished in place. This is done by placing the mount in a lathe and turning the thin edge of the tube over the edge of the lens with a rounded tool. Since the feather edge projecting above the lens must be short, the burnishing cannot be properly done unless the lens fits the mount rather closely. Nevertheless, burnishing is a very cheap and satisfactory method of mounting a lens. The customary way of mounting a complicated lens is to mount the separate elements in threaded cells that fit into a barrel. Aluminum and its alloys are frequently used for the sake of lightness, but cells made of these materials are likely to bind so tightly when screwed into the barrel that they cannot be removed without damage. This can be prevented by making the cells of brass, using aluminum only for the barrel.

The finest work of the optician can be ruined by a careless job of mounting. The glass maker takes great pains to release the stresses produced in the glass when it cools, but if the finished part is screwed tightly in its mount, stresses of equal or even greater magnitude may be produced. This is especially true when the mount makes contact at only a few points instead of over a wide area. If the glass part is composed of cemented elements, excessive pressure is particularly deleterious because in time the elements may become uncemented.

The interior of an optical instrument should be as nearly dead black as possible. Excellent lacquers for the purpose are obtainable commercially, but a satisfactory substitute can be made by mixing lampblack with as little very thin shellac as will stick to the metal. The disadvantage of this lacquer is that it can be easily wiped off. The threads and adjacent portions of retaining rings and lens mounts should never be lacquered because particles of the lacquer may get into the threads and cause the retaining ring to bind. The following method produces a lustrous black finish that is suitable not only for such parts but also for other parts where a slight sheen is not objectionable:

Prepare a saturated solution of cupric carbonate (green) in ammonia water (sp. gr. 0.90) and decant the clear solution. Thoroughly clean the part to be plated, preferably with emery paper, and immerse it as long as may be necessary. Then wash it in water to remove any undissolved particles of the carbonate and wipe it with an oily rag. This kind of plating is so easily rubbed off that it should be coated with a transparent lacquer if the part is to be subjected to much wear.

Formerly it was the custom to finish the exterior of optical instruments with orange lacquer, but nowadays black enamel is more generally used. This enamel may be either dull or glossy, a high polish on the metal surface being required for the latter. Frequently a crystal lacquer is used. It is particularly applicable to unfinished castings because its rough surface conceals the lack of finish on the metal. However, it collects dirt readily and is difficult to clean. To lighten the appearance of the instrument, certain portions can be nickel-plated, either bright or dull. Chromium is coming into extensive use but is somewhat more expensive than nickel. Occasionally, portions of instruments are black-plated by an electrochemical process in which a combination of nickel and nickel sulphide is deposited on the metal. The plated article is finished by being polished and then rubbed with oil. This kind of finish looks good and is fairly satisfactory even for moving parts, but it is less durable than nickel and therefore should not be used unless a black finish is necessary.

Lens mounts are frequently engraved with such information as the focal length, the name of the maker, and the serial number. The characters are engraved by means of a pantograph and then filled with a kind of wax. The finest filler is a gold or silver lacquer that is baked into the engraving.

150. Optical Drawings.—The veriest tyro knows that to enable a mechanic to build a piece of apparatus, he must furnish him with a drawing showing not only the essential dimensions but also the tolerances and the quality of finish desired; yet he will write to an optical manufacturer for "a two-inch lens of twelve inches focal length" without indicating the index of the glass, the relative curvatures of the two surfaces, or the permissible tolerances in thickness, diameter, or even focal length. He may not specify any surface quality at all, or he may ask for the "highest" quality without realizing what this term means to an optician. Any one who is not sufficiently acquainted with practical optics to know what quality is necessary and what tolerances are reasonable would do well to indicate the purpose for which the optical part is to be used. Customers are often reluctant to tell the manufacturer what they plan to do lest he steal their ideas. Aside from the fact that a reputable manufacturer would not stoop to such practices, the ideas are frequently so well known that, far from stealing them, the manufacturer can often make worth-while suggestions for their improvement.

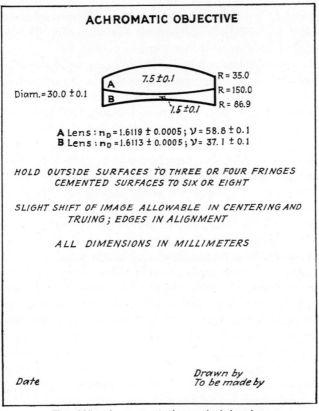

ACHROMATIC OBJECTIVE

Diam. = 30.0 ± 0.1

7.5 ± 0.1

R = 35.0

R = 150.0

1.5 ± 0.1

R = 86.9

A Lens : n_D = 1.6119 ± 0.0005 ; ν = 58.8 ± 0.1
B Lens : n_D = 1.6113 ± 0.0005 ; ν = 37.1 ± 0.1

*HOLD OUTSIDE SURFACES TO THREE OR FOUR FRINGES
CEMENTED SURFACES TO SIX OR EIGHT*

*SLIGHT SHIFT OF IMAGE ALLOWABLE IN CENTERING AND
TRUING ; EDGES IN ALIGNMENT*

ALL DIMENSIONS IN MILLIMETERS

Date

*Drawn by
To be made by*

FIG. 205.—A representative optical drawing.

The exact form of an optical drawing is not important provided the essential information is contained on it; yet a form that has been found to be especially satisfactory is shown in Fig. 205. This figure is a drawing of a doublet objective for a high-quality two-power Galilean telescope designed to cover a wide field. The diameters of the lenses are indicated at the left, the radii of curvature at the right,[1] and the thicknesses within the lenses themselves. The types of glass, quality of surface, and other pertinent information are given below. The dimensions are in millimeters, the customary unit used by opticians. To prevent misunderstanding, however, the unit in which the dimensions are given is stated on the drawing. Only one part of an instrument should be drawn on a sheet because the various parts may be put in work at different times or may even be made in different departments of the factory.

In general, it is a safe rule to follow the procedure that is customary for ordinary mechanical drawings, but the peculiar characteristics of optical parts must always be kept in mind. Thus the rim of a lens is never polished because no useful purpose would be served. In the case of a prism, on the other hand, the optician has no means of knowing which faces must be polished and which may be left fine-ground unless this information is furnished. The letter "P" on the traces of a prism face in the various projections is usually an adequate indication to an optician that the corresponding face is to be polished. Similarly, "G" can be used to signify that a face is to be left fine-ground. Sometimes the sharpness of the bounding edge between two faces of a prism is of importance. An optician "breaks" such an edge as a matter of course to prevent chipping. When an edge must be perfectly sharp, as in the case of a sample that is to be measured on the Pulfrich refractometer, it is necessary to indicate the fact. It goes without saying that if a definite bevel is required, the angle and size of the bevel must be specified. The specification of tolerances on all dimensions is especially important because the cost of an optical part depends in large measure upon the difficulty of working to the specified tolerances, as shown in Chap. XVI. Even if a dimension may be varied within wide limits, these limits should be stated because the manufacturer may thus be enabled to supply a stock part at a price considerably lower than he would have to charge for a special job.

---

[1] In this case, no tolerances are given for the radii of curvature because the lens is of precision quality and is to be compared with a test glass. In other words, the specified values for the radii indicate merely the test glass that is to be used, and fitting the surface to the test glass automatically specifies the tolerance for the radius. Unless tools and test glasses of the desired radii are known to be available, tolerances should always be given for radii.

CHAPTER XX

OPHTHALMIC INSTRUMENTS

The normal human eye was described in Chap. X, and now certain common abnormalities and the method of using spectacles to correct them will be considered. The branch of science that deals with the structure, behavior, and diseases of the eye is known as *ophthalmology* and the scientist who specializes in this subject is called an ophthalmologist. An oculist is a medical practitioner who has specialized in ophthalmology. He is therefore qualified to prescribe spectacles and also to treat the various diseases of the eye. An optometrist is trained to prescribe spectacles and to recognize the symptoms of eye diseases, although he is not qualified to treat them because of his lack of medical training. The optometrist in a small community is usually equipped to supply the spectacles as well, but in larger communities he more frequently furnishes merely a prescription which the patient takes to an optician to be filled.

151. Defects of Vision.—An *emmetropic* eye is, by definition, one that forms on the retina an image of an infinitely distant object when the accommodation is relaxed. The normal eye is very nearly emmetropic. When such an eye views a near-by object, the ciliary muscle tenses and allows the anterior surface of the crystalline lens to become more strongly curved. The normal individual at 10 years of age is able in this way to focus sharply on objects lying anywhere between the *far point* at infinity and the *near point* at about 7 cm in front of the eye. The range of accommodation becomes progressively less as the individual grows older, as is shown in Table XXVI, until in old age the power of accommodation is completely lost. This effect, which is called *presbyopia*, is due to a progressive hardening of the crystalline lens. It becomes a source of inconvenience as soon as the near point has advanced beyond the comfortable reading distance. If the far point of an eye is elsewhere than at infinity, the eye is said to be *ametropic*, as opposed to emmetropic.

The two simplest forms of ametropia are *myopia* and *hypermetropia*. These are illustrated in Fig. 206 at *B* and *C* respec-

TABLE XXVI.—RANGE OF ACCOMMODATION FOR AN EMMETROPIC EYE
All distances measured from the first principal point of the eye.

Age, years	Distance of near point, centimeters	Distance of far point, centimeters	Power of accommodation, diopters
10	7.1	∞	14
15	8.3	∞	12
20	10.0	∞	10
25	12.8	∞	8
30	14.3	∞	7
35	18.2	∞	5.5
40	22.2	∞	4.5
45	28.6	∞	3.5
50	40	∞	2.5
55	67	−400	1.75
60	200	−200	1.00
65	−400	−133	0.50
70	−100	− 80	0.25
75	− 57	− 57	0
80	− 40	− 40	0

tively, an emmetropic eye being shown at *A* for comparison. The cause of these defects lies principally in an incorrect relationship between the length of the eyeball and the radius of curvature of the cornea, where most of the refraction takes place. The curvature of the cornea is approximately the same for most individuals, but the length of the eyeball varies considerably. If the eyeball is too long, as in *B*, a bundle of rays from an infinitely distant point is brought to focus before reaching the retina. In other words, the far point of a myope is less distant than infinity. When the myope possesses the normal power of accommodation, as is usually the case, the near point is closer than that of an emmetropic eye. If the eyeball is too short, as in *C*, a bundle of rays from infinity is brought to focus behind the retina. Hence the distance of the far point of a hypermetrope is negative, corresponding to a virtual object located behind the eye. If the power of accommodation is normal, the near point is, of course, more distant than that of an emmetropic eye.

Hypermetropia is the more common defect, most "normal" eyes being slightly hypermetropic. But myopia, although less common, is more serious because our every-day activities tend to aggravate it. There is evidence to indicate that it is induced by excessive use of the eyes for near work, the extra-ocular muscles that converge the eyes acting in such a manner as to lengthen the eyeballs. Usually it appears at about the tenth year of age, when school work begins in earnest, and then it increases to an extent that depends upon the occupation of the individual and the structural characteristics of the eyeballs that he has inherited. The increase is most rapid before the twentieth year, when the eyes acquire their permanent shape. The danger is that as the retina increases in curvature, it may become injured mechanically, after which normal acuity cannot be attained even with suitable correcting lenses. In extreme cases, detachment of the retina may ensue.

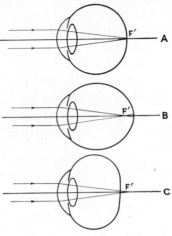

Fig. 206.—*A*, an emmetropic eye; *B*, a myopic eye; *C*, a hypermetropic eye.

In general, myopes become aware of their abnormality because of the difficulty of distinguishing distant objects. Hypermetropes, on the other hand, are prone to boast about the excellence of their vision, and, while they are still young, their power of accommodation may be ample to enable them to see

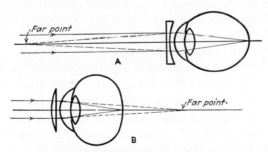

Fig. 207.—The action of spectacles in correcting ametropia. *A*, the effect of a negative lens in myopia; *B*, the effect of a positive lens in hypermetropia.

objects even as close as the normal reading distance. As they become older, or in any case if their hypermetropia is pronounced, focusing on near-by objects involves a considerable strain on the nervous system. The result is that they are likely to become aware of their abnormality because of headaches that follow a prolonged use of the eyes for close objects.

Myopia can be corrected by the use of a negative lens as shown at A in Fig. 207, and hypermetropia by the use of a positive lens as shown at B. Without a lens, a parallel bundle of rays would come to focus either in front of the retina or behind it, and the lens deviates the rays just enough to focus them on the retina. In other words, the power[1] of the lens should, in general, be just sufficient to image the far point of the individual at infinity.

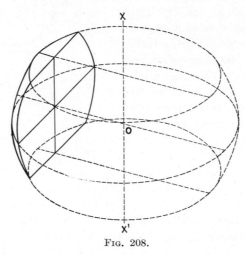

Fig. 208.

Another common defect of the eye is known as *astigmatism*, which is caused by the surface of the cornea[2] being roughly toroidal as shown in Fig. 208, instead of spherical. In other words, the power of the cornea is different in different meridians. This defect should not be confused with the aberration of spherical systems at oblique angles of incidence, although some of the

[1] In ophthalmic practice, it is customary to speak of the power of a lens rather than the focal length. The unit of power is the diopter and, as defined in Sec. 25, Chap. III, it is the reciprocal of the focal length in meters. The use of this quantity is a distinct convenience because, if the lens can be assumed to be thin, its power is simply the sum of the powers of the two refracting surfaces. Likewise, the power of two or more lenses in contact is the sum of their individual powers.

[2] A slight amount of astigmatism is occasionally produced by a deformation of the crystalline lens. Although this is a comparatively rare condition, it is of clinical importance because it often presages the onset of cataract.

effects are somewhat similar. For example, if an individual afflicted with astigmatism views a set of radial lines like those of Fig. 209, one line will be seen sharply and the others more or less blurred. In particular, the line at right angles to the one in sharp focus will be the most blurred. The annoyance suffered by the patient depends not only upon the amount of astigmatism but also upon the direction of the axis. A low degree of astigmatism is of little moment if the axis is horizontal or vertical, but it lowers the visual acuity considerably if the axis is oblique.

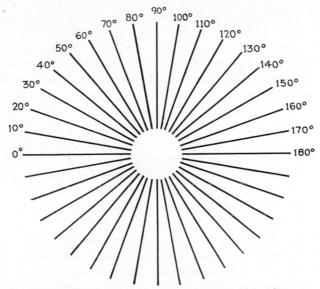

Fig. 209.—A typical chart for detecting astigmatism.

If the axes in the two eyes are not parallel, a relatively slight amount of astigmatism produces a severe strain on the ciliary muscles, which endeavor to overcome the error. Astigmatism can be corrected by the use of a lens whose surface is cylindrical, the power and azimuth of the cylinder being chosen to neutralize the defective curvature of the cornea.

A defect of the eye that is sometimes corrected with suitable spectacles, although it is not a refractive error, is called *heterophoria*. This is due to a disturbance of the relationship between the muscles that control the accommodation and those that control the rotation of the eye. When a normal individual directs his attention toward an object, the eyes not only accommodate themselves for the distance of the object but converge toward it as well, the brain having learned the proper accommodation-convergence relationship as a result of experience. If ametropia is present, a given amount of accommodation does not call into play the corresponding amount of convergence. The eyes do converge until both images of the object fall on corresponding portions of the two retinas, but the convergence is abnormal compared with the amount of accommodation. The presence of heterophoria is easily tested by viewing a distant light with a red filter over one eye and a green filter over the other. If the individual is normal, the two images will fuse automatically. On the other hand, if the individual suffers from heterophoria, the brain does not realize that the two images belong to the same source and does not make the requisite endeavor to fuse them. When an ametropia of long standing is suddenly corrected with spectacles, the heterophoria does not immediately disappear because the muscles have become accustomed to adopting a false accommodation-convergence relationship. It usually disappears in time, especially if suitable exercises are performed regularly.[1] Occasionally, the heterophoria persists and must be corrected by glasses that are prismatic. These can be made by grinding the refracting surfaces on a prism instead of a flat blank, but if they are of low power, they are more frequently made by decentering the lenses.

Heterophoria in its extreme form passes into *strabismus* or squint, a condition in which the extra-ocular muscles are unable to converge the visual axes of the two eyes on the same object. If the strabismus is of low degree, it can frequently be corrected by educating the muscles through special exercises after the patient has been fitted with suitable glasses. In severe cases, the only remedy is an operation in which certain of the extra-ocular muscles are cut and others are shortened.

152. Refraction of the Eyes.—In optometry, the determination of the refractive errors of an eye is termed "refraction." The method usually employed is subjective, consisting in trying various combinations of lenses while the patient observes a distant test chart. These lenses are inserted in a trial frame, one or more at a time until the patient's visual acuity becomes either normal or as high as possible. The prescription is then written down by noting the sum of the powers of the individual

[1] See Sec. 195, Chap. XXV.

lenses in the trial frame.   A typical prescription is given below:

	Sph.	Cyl.	Axis
O.D.	− .25	+2.50	95°
O.S.	0	+1.75	90°

The symbols "O.D." and "O.S." represent the Latin words *oculus dexter* and *oculus sinister*, which mean "right eye" and "left eye" respectively.   In this case, the prescription for the left eye calls for a cylindrical lens having a power of 1.75 diopters with its axis vertical.   The prescription for the right eye calls for a combination of a sphere having a negative power of 0.25 diopter and a cylinder having a power of 2.50 diopters with its axis inclined 5° from the vertical toward the temple.   This prescription is translated by the optician when he comes to grind the lens in a manner that will be described presently.

The method by which the optometrist determines the proper lenses for his patient depends to some extent upon the type of correction that must be made.   In general, he begins by determining the approximate correction with a retinoscope, which will be described in Sec. 155.   If the patient is so illiterate that a subjective examination would be impracticable, the glasses are prescribed solely on the basis of this preliminary examination. Ordinarily, however, a trial frame is fitted to the patient and the subjective examination is made, the patient observing a test chart bearing letters of various sizes.   If the patient is a myope, the optometrist begins with a negative lens that is slightly weaker than is indicated by the retinoscope.   He then tries lenses of increasing strength until the proper visual acuity is attained or until the acuity becomes as high as possible.   If the patient is a hypermetrope, the optometrist "fogs" him with a positive lens so strong that his accommodation cannot overcome it.   The ensuing procedure is then similar except that lenses of decreasing positive power are tried.   The patient is then directed to observe the astigmatic chart, which is of the general form illustrated in Fig. 209.   If he is afflicted with astigmatism, one line of the chart will be sharp and the others more or less blurred, the sharp one being in the meridian in which the eye has the highest power.[1]

[1] The reason is that, under the assumed conditions, the eye is myopic in this meridian and emmetropic in the perpendicular meridian.   Unless trial lenses are used, it is impossible to determine from the test chart which

Negative cylindrical lenses of increasing power are then inserted in the trial frame with their axes perpendicular to this meridian until all the lines appear equally distinct. Finally, the spherical lenses are usually varied slightly to make certain that the proper correction has been found. The optometrist does not necessarily prescribe the lenses that give the maximum acuity, but instead he attempts to take into account the condition of the patient's eyes. Thus, it is customary to prescribe a little less than the full correction for myopes because they are usually in the habit of holding objects excessively close to their eyes. Their ciliary muscles are therefore constantly under excessive strain, and they tend to remain somewhat tensed even when distant objects are being observed.

The test charts that are commonly used by the optometrist are cards bearing rows of letters, the letters in each row being progressively smaller in size. These letters, which are known by the name of their inventor Snellen, are shown at A in Fig. 210. It is customary to place the chart 20 ft. from the patient and to make the letters in the various rows of such a size that they would subtend an angle of five minutes of arc at distances of 10, 15, 20, 25, 30, 50, 80, 100, and 200 ft. respectively. The black strokes and the white spaces in these letters are made to subtend an angle of one minute of arc. For children and illiterates, charts are used containing a series of gothic E's, as shown at B in Fig. 210. In reading a chart of this type, the patient indicates the orientation of the letters with his fingers. The visual acuity of the patient is expressed as a fraction, the numerator being the distance of observation and the denominator the standard distance for the smallest letters that can be read. For example, if the smallest letters that a patient can read at 20 ft. are the ones that should be distinguishable at 60 ft., his vision is recorded as 20/60. The normal is, of course, 20/20, but some people with unusually keen vision have acuities as high as 20/15 or even 20/10.

---

meridian is the stronger since there is no means of knowing whether the meridian of highest or lowest power is in focus. Usually the strongest meridian is nearer vertical than horizontal, in which case the astigmatism is said to be "with the rule." If the strongest meridian is more nearly horizontal than vertical, the astigmatism is "against the rule." Usually the astigmatic axis departs appreciably from the horizontal or the vertical, in which case the astigmatism is said to be "oblique." Oblique astigmatism may, of course, be with the rule or against it.

Usually more than one lens at a time must be put in the trial frame to make up the required power, since the number of lenses in the set is necessarily limited. It is evident that the sum of the actual powers of the individual lenses is not equal to the true power of the combination because of the impossibility of placing the lenses in coincidence. In the cheaper trial sets, the error thus introduced is neglected. This is unfortunate because such sets usually contain so few lenses that several are ordinarily required to obtain merely the proper spherical power. The best sets contain enough lenses so that only two are required in all— one for the spherical power and one for the cylindrical. The lenses in these sets are designed in such a manner that the sum of the

FIG. 210.—Portions of charts for determining visual acuity. *A*, Snellen letters subtending an angle of 5′ at 20 ft. A person who can just read these letters at 20 ft. has an acuity of 20/20. *B*, E-chart for children and illiterates. The patient indicates the orientation of the E's with his fingers.

indicated powers is equal to the true power of a single lens placed at the standard distance from the eye. Even when such a set is used, however, the lens worn by the patient may be at a different distance from the eye, and may therefore have a different effective power. Trial lenses are usually flat, whereas spectacles of the better quality are meniscus for reasons that will be set forth in the next section. As a result, if both the trial frame and the spectacles are worn where the lenses just clear the eyelashes, the vertices of the spectacle lenses are farther from the cornea than those of the trial lenses. This difference is important in the case of pronounced hypermetropia because the second principal points are then in front of the lenses. The error is avoided by specifying the power in terms of the distance of the focal point from the vertex rather than from the principal point, the unit of power measured in this way being called the *vertex diopter*.

So far we have considered only the problem of finding spectacles that will form sharp images on the retina, and have given no consideration to the magnification that they might produce.

If spectacles produced an appreciable magnification, it would certainly be serious when the two eyes required different corrections (a condition known as *anisometropia*) because the images on the two retinas would then be of different sizes. However, it can be easily shown that if a thin lens is placed at either focal point of an optical system, the focal length of the system is unaltered. Now the first focal point of the eye is about 15 mm in front of the cornea, and hence, if spectacles are worn in this position, they produce no change in the size of the image. Actually, to avoid interference with the eyelashes, spectacles are worn slightly ahead of the focal point but not enough to cause any serious effect unless the anisometropia is very marked.

Occasionally, visual defects are encountered that cannot be corrected with spectacles. Sometimes the media of the eye are partially opaque or the retina is diseased. To distinguish such cases from those in which the only fault is a refractive error, a diaphragm pierced with a pinhole is placed over the eye. If the error is simply one of refraction, the vision will usually be improved. Otherwise, the condition is pathological and glasses may be useless.

153. Types of Spectacle Lenses.—The optician could fill the prescription for the right eye given on page 433 by starting with a flat blank and grinding a sphere with a power of -0.25 diopter on one side and a cylinder with a power of $+2.50$ diopters on the other. In the parlance of the optician, this would be called a flat lens. Such a lens is satisfactory enough when the wearer looks through the center of it, but the aberrations become serious near the edge. A vast improvement in the definition in the outer portions of the field of view came about with the introduction of the meniscus type of lens. In this type, the surface nearest the eye is concave, usually with a power of -6.00 diopters. If the prescription calls for a combination of sphere and cylinder, the front surface is made toroidal and the lens is said to be *toric*. A toroidal surface of spectacle quality can be ground with special tools having the shape of the desired surface. The grinding machine is especially constructed to move the tool in such a manner that it is not seriously deformed by the grinding.

Before grinding a toric lens, the optician must obviously transpose the prescription. For example, consider the method of grinding the lens for the right eye called for in the prescription referred to above. Let it be assumed that the surface nearest the eye is to be spherical and is to have a power of -6.00 diopters. In the meridian at 95°, the power of the front surface must be $+5.75$ diopters.[1] The power of the cylinder is greatest in the 5° meridian, and the power in this meridian must obviously be $+8.25$ diopters.

Astigmatism is the most important aberration of spectacle lenses, and to correct it, von Rohr computed a series of lenses in which the power of the surface nearest the eye is always such as to reduce this aberration to a minimum.[2] Such lenses give excellent definition over the entire field but are somewhat more expensive because every combination of spherical and cylindrical powers demands a different base curve. Recently, several firms have put on the market new types in which fewer base curves are required, a single curve serving for several lenses.

It was indicated in Table XXVI that the near point of an otherwise normal individual recedes beyond the comfortable reading distance sometime during middle life, usually at about 45 years of age. Of course, the presbyopia has existed since birth, but it becomes troublesome only at this time. The remedy is to wear glasses having sufficient positive power to bring the near point back to the conventional reading distance. More power might be used without impairing the acuity but it tends to upset the accommodation-convergence relationship.

If the individual has other refractive errors, he may wear two pairs of glasses after the presbyopia has become serious, one pair for distant use and the other for reading. More often, he will wear *bifocals*, as they are called. The first bifocals were made by mounting the distance lens in the upper half of the frame and the reading lens in the lower half. This is the kind that Benjamin Franklin wore. Later, the reading lens was made in the form of a thin wafer to be cemented to the lower portion of the distance lens. Many such lenses are in use today, but they have the disadvantage that the cement at the edge of the wafer collects dirt and the spectacles therefore become unsightly.

---

[1] This method of computation assumes the lens to be thin, which is not justified in the higher powers. It is impossible, of course, to describe the special methods by which the modern optician takes the thickness of the lens into account, but it may be stated that they are based on formulae developed from the first-order theory discussed in Chap. IV.

[2] For the procedure, see a paper by Southall, *Jour. Optical Soc. Amer.*, **5**, 398 (1921); **7**, 219 (1923).

An improved type of bifocal, known as the "Kryptok," is made by fusing a button of higher index into the blank.   The procedure is to grind a spot on the distance lens to the proper radius of curvature and then to fuse on a button of higher index.   When the lens is subsequently ground and polished in the ordinary manner, the reading portion is of higher power.[1]   The index of ordinary spectacle crown, which is used for the distance lens, is 1.523, and that of the button is usually 1.616.   For high values of the reading addition, glass having a still higher index is used for the button.

Another method of furnishing the reading addition is to grind a segment of the lens to a curve that is different from that on the rest of it.   This is known as the one-piece bifocal, and it has the advantage of being comparatively free from chromatic aberration.   It is expensive to make, however, and the edge of the reading portion is frequently as noticeable as that of a Kryptok.   In every case, the size of the button is adjusted by a skillful optician to the type of work that his patient is generally called upon to do.

154. The Ophthalmoscope.—In the remainder of this chapter, we shall describe instruments that are used either to detect diseases of the eye or to assist in determining the proper correction for errors of refraction.   Some of these instruments are especially interesting because they illustrate unusual applications of optical principles that are occasionally of value in other connections.[2]

The ophthalmoscope was the first instrument devised for examining the interior of the eye.   It was invented by Helmholtz in 1852, and in its original form consisted of a piece of glass used as a mirror, as shown in Fig. 211.   Light from a distant source was reflected into the patient's eye to form an image

---

[1] It goes without saying that the two types of glass must have the same coefficient of expansion and that the button must have the lower melting point.   In addition, if chromatic aberration is to be avoided for high values of the reading addition, the two glasses should have the same dispersive power.   This is not true of the ordinary Kryptok, for which the ν-value of the distance lens is about 59 and that of the button about 36 or less. However, in a newer bifocal known by the trade name "Nokrome," the ν-value of both lenses is approximately 55.

[2] The instruments used for testing binocular vision—the ability of the eyes to work together—belong to a different category from those used to examine a single eye.   They are essentially stereoscopes and will be described in Chap. XXV.

approximately on the retina (or *fundus*, as it is frequently known in medical terminology), and as the source had a finite size, a finite area of the fundus was illuminated. The observer then examined the fundus by looking directly through the glass. The instrument was soon improved by silvering the mirror, a small hole being left in the center for observing the eye. A few months later, Ruete improved the device still further by making the mirror concave so that the rays would come to a focus near the center of the eyeball and diverge from this point to illuminate a larger area of the fundus. This type of ophthalmoscope is in common use to-day. If both the patient's eye and the observer's eye are emmetropic and unaccommodated, the observer can see details in the fundus of the patient's eye, such as the blood vessels and the blind spot. If the patient's eye is

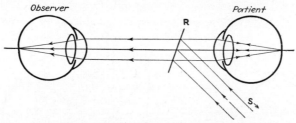

Fig. 211.—The optical system of Helmholtz's original ophthalmoscope.

ametropic, on the other hand, a suitable lens must be interposed. The strongest positive lens or the weakest negative lens required to make the details appear distinctly is the correction of the patient, provided the lens is placed at the same distance from the eye as the patient's spectacles will be worn. The difficulty in determining a patient's correction with the ophthalmoscope is in making certain that neither the patient nor the observer unconsciously accommodates. A practitioner learns to avoid accommodating by experience, and if a patient shows evidence of accommodating, a mydriatic, such as atropine, can be placed in his eye to paralyze the ciliary muscle.

The reflections from the various surfaces of the patient's eye, especially the cornea, are very annoying in the simple type of ophthalmoscope just described. These reflections are avoided in the more elaborate types, which are designed to fulfill the three following requirements:

1. The fundi of the patient and the observer must be conjugate.
2. The pupils of the patient and the observer must be conjugate.

3. The pupil of the patient's eye must be conjugate to the entrance pupil of the illuminating system.

Several instruments in which these conditions are fulfilled have been invented, but the type due to Gullstrand is the most common at present. One modification of his design is shown in Fig. 212. Light from a lamp S is focused by the condenser C on the slit A, which in turn is focused by a lens L_1 on the patient's pupil at A' near the edge, being reflected thereto from a transparent plate R. This plate is made slightly wedge shaped so that the light reflected from both surfaces will strike the pupil at the same

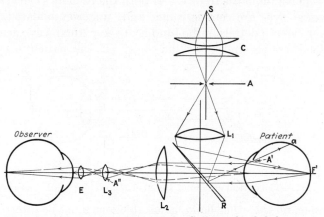

Fig. 212.—The optical system of the Gullstrand ophthalmoscope.

place. The rays diverging from A' illuminate the fundus, which is observed by means of an optical system composed of the lenses L_2, L_3, and E. E is an ocular, which is in reality compound but is drawn as a single lens for the sake of simplicity. The lens L_2 forms an image of the patient's pupil on L_3, so that a diaphragm placed here will block off the image A'' of the illuminated spot A'. The first condition given above is satisfied because the three lenses L_2, L_3, and E, with the optical system of the two eyes, form an image of the patient's fundus on that of the observer. The second condition is fulfilled because L_2 and E form an image of the patient's pupil on that of the observer, and the third condition is fulfilled because the patient's pupil is conjugate to the aperture stop A.

The appearance of the retina gives the oculist information concerning not only the condition of the eye itself but also the general physiological condition of the patient. As a result, the oculist not infrequently discovers evidences of morbid conditions existing elsewhere in the patient's body long before definite symptoms have appeared. It would be out of place here to discuss the various pathological conditions that can be detected by means of the ophthalmoscope. There is, however, a rather common disease of the eye that may be mentioned because it illustrates the use of the ophthalmoscope as a measuring instrument. This disease, which is known as *glaucoma*, is characterized by an increase in the pressure of the fluids within the eyeball. The first effect is to depress the blind spot since this is mechanically the weakest portion of the eyeball. The depression is easily detected with the aid of an ophthalmoscope by noting the difference in power required to focus sharply on the blind

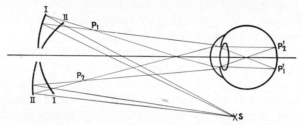

Fig. 213.—Sketch showing the principle of the retinoscope.

spot and on the surrounding portion of the fundus. The customary treatment for glaucoma is an operation known as *iridectomy*, in which a segment of the iris is removed. This has the effect of opening the ducts leading to the eyeball and thereby allowing the excess fluid to escape. If glaucoma is allowed to go untreated, the blind spot spreads and total blindness eventually results.

155. The Retinoscope.—The construction of the retinoscope is akin to that of the simple ophthalmoscope, but its action depends on the apparent motion of a spot of light across the retina.[1] In Fig. 213, a source of light S is placed at the side of the patient's eye while the observer holds a concave[2] ophthalmoscope mirror in position I. An image of S is formed at P_1, and, if the eye is properly accommodated, this image in turn is

[1] The theory is discussed at length by Southall, *Jour. Optical Soc. Amer. and Rev. Sci. Instruments*, **13**, 245 (1926).

[2] Some optometrists use a plane mirror but the principle of operation is the same, the only difference in the result being that the motions of the image are reversed.

focused on the patient's retina at P_1'.   If the observer now swings
the mirror to position II, an image is formed at P_2, and this in
turn is focused on the patient's retina at P_2'.   If the patient's
eye is not accommodated for the points P_1 and P_2, the images will
appear as circles of confusion.   Even so, a spot of light moving
in a direction opposite to that of the mirror will be formed on
the patient's retina.   The direction in which the spot *appears*
to move to the observer depends upon the refractive condition
of the patient's eye.   If the patient is hypermetropic, the images
of P_1' and P_2' are behind the eye and are erect.   Thus, to the
observer, the spot of light appears to move in a direction opposite
to that of the mirror.   If the patient is myopic, the images are
located in front of the eye and are inverted.   In this case, the
spot of light appears to move in the same direction as the mirror.
If the patient is emmetropic, the images are located at infinity
and hence do not appear to move at all.

In practice, the optometrist places himself about a meter
from the patient and tries various lenses in front of his eye until
there is no apparent motion of the spot across the patient's
retina as the mirror is rotated.   If the patient is astigmatic,
the edge of the spot may remain stationary in one direction but
not in a direction perpendicular to it unless a suitable cylindrical
lens is interposed.   When the proper lens combination has
been found, the optometrist subtracts one diopter from his
observations to allow for the fact that he is at a distance of 1
meter rather than at infinity.   Since the optometrist determines
the apparent motion of the spot of light by observing the edge
of the shadow, retinoscopy is often known as *skiascopy*.

156. The Ophthalmometer.—Since many of the refractive
errors of the eye, such as astigmatism, are the result of an improp-
erly shaped cornea, special instruments called ophthalmometers[1]
have been devised for measuring the radius of curvature of this
surface.   There are two general types of these instruments,
one invented by Javal and Schjötz and the other by Sutcliffe,
but the principle of operation is the same.   It consists in measuring the size of the image of a target formed by reflection at the
surface of the cornea.   The straightforward method of measuring
this image would be by means of a micrometer in the ocular

---

[1] They are sometimes called keratometers, although this term may occasionally lead to confusion with an instrument that was once used for measuring the distance of a spectacle lens from the cornea.

of the observing telescope, but the constant involuntary movements of the patient's eye make this method impracticable. The method adopted is to divide the reflected beam so that two images of the target are seen in the ocular, and to provide means for adjusting the deviation of the beams until the images are brought into coincidence. The various types of ophthalmometers differ widely in the manner by which the beams are divided,[1] but in all of them the deviation of the beam required to bring the images into coincidence is made to indicate the curvature of the cornea directly. It is customary to express the curvature

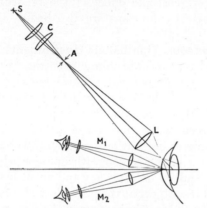

Fig. 214.—The optical system of the slit lamp.

in diopters of refraction. The normal radius is 7.83 mm and, since the cornea has an index of 1.376, the power of the normal cornea is 48.0 diopters.

Since an astigmatic cornea has different powers in different meridians, ophthalmometers are made rotatable about their optical axes to enable the power in any meridian to be measured. It is an easy matter to determine the meridians of greatest and lowest power, which are ordinarily 90° apart; and the difference in power represents the corneal astigmatism. The subjective examination discloses the total astigmatism, and the difference between the two is the lenticular astigmatism.

157. The Slit Lamp.—The media of the eye often contain opaque particles, which may be either congenital or the result of an injury. Such particles can be detected by means of an intense beam of light directed so that it will not blind the observer.

[1] HELMHOLTZ, "Physiological Optics," Vol. I, pp. 303 *ff*; English ed.

The combination slit lamp and binocular microscope sketched in Fig. 214 has been designed for this purpose. Light from a lamp S is focused by means of the condenser C on the slit A, and this slit is focused in turn by means of a lens L upon the portion of the eye being examined. The examination is made with a binocular microscope, which consists simply of two microscopes M_1 and M_2 directed upon the point to be examined.[1] Since the incident light does not enter the microscope, the field is dark and the particles stand out sharply against the background. Their positions can be estimated with considerable precision because of the stereoscopic effect of the binocular microscope. Certain pathological conditions are also readily detected in this way.

158. Miscellaneous Ophthalmic Instruments.—Many other instruments are used in ophthalmic practice, but most of them are comparatively unimportant. One large class that deserves mention, however, is designed for determining the boundaries of the field of view. A good representative of this class is the Bjerrum screen, which consists of a 2-meter square of black velvet placed 1 meter in front of the patient, who gazes at a white spot at the center of the screen with one eye while the other is covered. The oculist, holding a wand furnished with a small white or colored test object at the far end, stands beside the screen and moves the test object inward until the patient just perceives it "out of the corner of his eye." By moving the test object successively from all directions, the entire visual field can be mapped. The extent of the blind spot can be determined by placing the wand inside the area on the screen corresponding to the image of the blind spot and moving it outward. In this way, the progress of glaucoma can be followed. Other instruments of more elaborate design have been constructed for mapping the visual field. As a class they are known as perimeters or campimeters.

[1] A photograph of such a microscope is shown on p. 524.

CHAPTER XXI

PHOTOGRAPHIC OBJECTIVES

Photographic objectives range in quality from the simple lenses used in eighty-nine-cent cameras to the highly corrected ones used for aerial surveying, whose cost may run into four figures. The characteristic feature of all photographic objectives is their high relative aperture and the large field that they are required to cover. As was indicated in Chap. VI, it is impossible to fully correct an optical system of high aperture over a large field, and the designer is therefore compelled to resort to compromises. The great variety of objectives on the market is due to attempts on the part of designers to attain a compromise that is best suited to a particular purpose.

159. The Correction of Photographic Objectives.—A photographer's "rule of thumb" states that, for ordinary photographs, the focal length of the objective should be approximately equal to the diagonal of the plate. The corresponding field angle is 53°, which is in marked contrast to the field that a telescope objective is required to cover.[1] If an optical system is to cover such a large field, either the relative aperture must be low or the corrections must be imperfect. Since it is seldom permissible to sacrifice relative aperture, the definition must necessarily be distinctly inferior to that produced by an aberrationless lens whose definition is limited solely by diffraction. That such is the case is easily verified by measuring the image of a distant point formed by even a "well-corrected" photographic objective, which is rarely found to be less than 0.1 mm in diameter. On the other hand, a perfect lens with a relative aperture of $f/4.5$ should be capable of forming a diffraction pattern whose central disk is only about 0.005 mm in diameter. Fortunately, "needle-sharp" definition is seldom required of a photographic objective for several reasons. In the first place, excessive sharpness in the plane that is in focus draws attention to the lack of sharp-

---

[1] An ordinary eight-power binocular covers a field of only about 6° (that is, 3° on either side of the axis), and telescopes of higher power cover a field that is proportionately smaller. See p. 485.

ness in the other planes.   In addition, photographic emulsions are so grainy that a blur circle 0.1 mm in diameter is not objectionable.   Moreover, a very large proportion of photographs, especially portraits, are actually improved by softening the definition so as to obliterate the mass of unimportant details that would otherwise detract from the pictorial effect.   The one important branch of photography where the best possible definition is required is aerial surveying.   In this case, the relative aperture must be high because the exposures must be short, and so the improvement in definition is obtained by restricting the field.

Photographic objectives are so commonly used for objects at relatively great distances that they are ordinarily corrected for an object at infinity.[1]   The aberrations that are corrected depend upon the purpose for which the objective is to be used and the price that the purchaser is willing to pay.   Even the simplest lenses, such as those used in "Brownie" cameras, are corrected for chromatic aberration and have a field that is artificially flattened by the method described in Sec. 54, Chap. VI. The more highly corrected objectives, such as the anastigmats, are corrected for spherical and chromatic aberration, coma, astigmatism, curvature of field, and distortion.   A still higher type of correction is attained in objectives that are designed for photo-engraving.   These objectives are made especially free from distortion and, if they are to be used for making color-separation negatives, they are made apochromatic as well. The elimination of distortion is also especially important in objectives used for aerial surveying.

160. Meniscus Lenses.—The simplest type of photographic objective is a single positive lens of crown glass.   For reasons that were explained in Sec. 54, a lens of this sort should be of the meniscus type with a front stop.   This type of lens was apparently first used by Wollaston.   His lens had a focal length of 560 mm and was used to cover a field angle of 60°.   If reduced to a focal length of 100 mm, its constants would be as follows:

Relative aperture	$f/11$
Focal length	100 mm
Diameter of lens	18.0
Diameter of stop	9.1

[1] This is not true of objectives that are especially designed for enlarging or copying, which are generally corrected for unit magnification.

Distance from center of stop to first vertex....... 12.5
Axial thickness............................... 1.0
First radius of curvature...................... − 51.2
Second radius of curvature.................... − 25.6
Index of refraction (*D*-line)................... 1.505

Most modern "fixed-focus" cameras, either box or folding, are supplied with achromatic lenses of the meniscus type. These lenses have a relative aperture of approximately $f/11$, and at this or smaller apertures give results which are more than sufficient to meet the performance demanded of simple cameras. In fact, it is often found that a meniscus achromat gives a better image in the center of the field than some of the more highly corrected objectives.

161. Rapid Rectilinears.—The relative aperture of a simple meniscus lens cannot be increased without producing a serious deterioration of the image. Since a relative aperture of $f/11$ permits of snapshots only under favorable lighting conditions, a demand for a lens of greater light-gathering power was created as soon as the speed of photographic materials increased to a point where snapshots became possible. This demand was met by the so-called *rapid rectilinear* lens which, generally speaking, is constructed of two achromats, usually meniscus, with the stop between them. The two achromats are usually similar, so that the complete lens is symmetrical. As has been indicated in Chap. VI, such a lens is free from coma and distortion at unit magnification and sensibly so at all magnifications for which it would be used. It is also sensibly free from both lateral and axial chromatism. Whether the lens is symmetrical or not, spherical aberration is ordinarily corrected, and the field is flattened artificially by separating the elements properly. The largest aperture for which a lens of this type can be corrected satisfactorily is about $f/8$, so at best it transmits only twice as much light as a meniscus lens.

162. Anastigmats.—Before the new glasses were introduced in 1886, it was impossible to construct a lens free from astigmatism and curvature of field because the conditions for eliminating these aberrations were inconsistent with those for eliminating the chromatic aberrations. The new glasses enabled both conditions to be satisfied simultaneously and thus made possible the type of lens that is now known as the anastigmat. Modern anastigmats generally consist of two achromats, one constructed of the old glasses and the other of the new. Each achromat, although spherically corrected, is not corrected for astigmatism; but the astigmatism of the two is of opposite sign,

and hence the field of the combination is flat and stigmatic. This type of construction is well exemplified by the Protar lens, which was introduced by the firm of Zeiss about 1895. This lens is shown by the solid lines in Fig. 215,

FIG. 215.—Zeiss Protar.

and the specifications of one model, according to the German patent, are as follows, the elements of the lens being numbered in the order in which the light traverses them:

SPECIFICATIONS OF THE PROTAR OBJECTIVE
Focal length = 100 mm.   Relative aperture = $f/12.5$

Element	Index		Axial thickness, millimeters	Radii, millimeters
	n_D	$n_{G'}$		
I	1.4979	1.5074	0.48	−12.0
II	1.6227	1.6308	1.70	+44.2
III	1.5813	1.5952	1.50	− 9.3
IV	1.6275	1.6487	0.66	− 6.6
				−13.4

The diaphragm is 2.34 mm in front of the first element.

This lens is comparatively slow, but by using two such lenses in combination, one in front of the diaphragm and the other behind it, the relative aperture can be increased to $f/6.8$. More often the components are of different focal lengths and thus the photographer has at his command three focal lengths—that of the combination and that of each of the components. This type of lens, in which components of different focal length may be used either singly or in combination, is known as a *convertible anastigmat*.

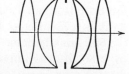

The principle of combining an old and a new achromat is often utilized in such a manner that it is not immediately evident.

FIG. 216.—Goerz Dagor.

The Goerz Dagor lens, for example, which is sketched in Fig. 216, consists of two symmetrical components, each component containing three cemented elements. The outer element of each component is constructed of one of the new glasses, and it combines, in effect, with the middle element to make an anomalous achromat. This element in turn combines with the inner element to form a normal achromat. The specifications for a wide-angle Dagor, which covers a 90° field, are given below. In accordance with custom, the data for only the front component are given, the rear component being similarly constructed and symmetrically placed with respect to the diaphragm. Since the rear component is sometimes used alone, the front component being temporarily removed, the characteristics of the rear component in regard to focal length, $f/$-number, etc., are given also.

SPECIFICATIONS OF THE DAGOR OBJECTIVE

	Complete objective	Rear component
Focal length	100.0	173.3
Relative aperture	$f/6.8$	$f/13.6$
Back focus	92.1	192.1
Distance from diaphragm to principal point	1.0	27.7

Element	Index		Axial thickness, millimeters	Radii, millimeters
	n_D	$n_{G'}$		
I	1.6122	1.6262	3.0	+20.8
II	1.5481	1.5613	0.9	−34.4
III	1.5120	1.5228	2.5	+ 8.5
				+21.1

The complete lens is symmetrical, the fourth (concave) surface facing the diaphragm, which is 2.7 mm away.

The Cooke triplet is a very different type of anastigmat, made originally in England by T. Cooke and Sons and now by Taylor, Taylor and Hobson. As shown in Fig. 217, this lens consists of two positive elements between which is a single negative element. The lens was designed by H. Dennis Taylor, who hit upon the novel expedient of eliminating astigmatism and curvature by making the power of the negative element equal to the sum of the powers of the positive elements. The negative element is made of glass whose dispersion

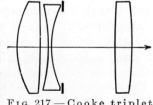

FIG. 217.—Cooke triplet objective.

is so chosen that the combination is chromatically corrected, and the radii of this element are such that spherical aberration and coma are corrected also.

The specifications for one type of Cooke triplet (Series IV) for use in hand cameras are as follows:

SPECIFICATIONS OF THE COOKE TRIPLET OBJECTIVE (SERIES IV)
Focal length = 100 mm.   Relative aperture = $f/5.6$

Element	Index		Axial thickness, millimeters	Radii, millimeters
	n_D	$n_{G'}$		
I	1.6110	1.6249	4.29	+ 19.4
(Air)	1.0000	1.0000	1.63	−128.3
II	1.5744	1.5935	0.93	− 57.8
(Air)	1.0000	1.0000	12.90	+ 18.9
III	1.6110	1.6249	3.03	+311.3
				− 66.4

The diaphragm is placed in the second air space against the second element.

This lens is made in several types, which are well suited to many

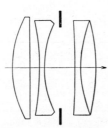

different purposes. One noteworthy type is the $f/4.5$ (Series II), which was designed for portraiture. The back element of this lens can be adjusted in position to introduce spherical aberration and thereby soften the picture. Another much used type is the process lens, which is excellent because of its freedom from distortion and its sharp marginal definition.[1]

FIG. 218.—Zeiss Tessar.

The success of the Cooke triplet led the firm of Zeiss to develop a lens which was similar except that the third element was a doublet, as is shown in Fig. 218. This lens, the Tessar, is perhaps the best known photographic objective to-day. Like the Cooke lens, it is made in many forms to meet varied requirements. The following specifications are for an early type:

[1] The final corrections of Cooke triplets are made by adjusting the air spaces, and consequently the user should never take such a lens apart. This does not mean that he should not remove the front and back elements in their cells to wipe off any deposit on the inner surfaces or on the negative lens, but this is as far as he may go safely. A damaged lens should be sent to the maker or his agent for repairing rather than to any other maker or optician.

SPECIFICATIONS OF THE TESSAR OBJECTIVE
Focal length = 100 mm.   Relative aperture = $f/5.5$

Element	Index		Axial thickness, millimeters	Radii, millimeters
	n_D	$n_{G'}$		
I	1.6113	1.6246	3.3	+ 21.5
(Air)	1.0000	1.0000	1.9	∞
II	1.6046	1.6225	1.1	− 74.2
(Air)	1.0000	1.0000	6.0	+ 20.8
III	1.5211	1.5340	1.1	−111.3
IV	1.6113	1.6251	3.0	+ 25.2
				− 36.7

The diaphragm is in the middle of the second air space.

The present trend in the design of anastigmats is in the direction of increased aperture, which is attained without sacrificing the definition by reducing the field that the lenses are required to cover.   Many of the recent objectives have been designed for motion-picture photography, where the focal length is commonly two or more times the diagonal of the film aperture. The standard objectives for motion-picture cameras have a relative aperture of $f/3.5$, and special objectives are available with apertures as great as $f/1.9$.   The present record for high aperture seems to be held by the Dalmac lens designed for 16-mm cameras, which has a relative aperture of $f/1.5$.

163. Wide-angle Objectives.—Photographs must often be made in cramped quarters.   It may be necessary, for example, to photograph a building from a point on the opposite side of the street or to photograph the interior of a room with the camera located in one corner.   Such photographs are commonly made with a lens whose focal length is short compared with the diagonal of the plate, for the purpose of embracing a large angle of view. The so-called *wide-angle* lenses, which are commonly sold for this purpose, are merely objectives that have been corrected to cover a larger field angle than the average objective.   These corrections are made at the expense of the relative aperture, which rarely exceeds $f/16$.

A distinguishing feature of wide-angle lenses is the shortness of the barrel or lens mount.   This is necessary to prevent the lens elements from acting as field stops.   It was shown in Chap. XIX that, even in the absence of a field stop, the illumination decreases as the fourth power of the cosine of the field angle. Ordinarily this decrease in illumination is not noticeable, but it may be serious in the case of wide-angle objectives.   Figure 219 shows the Goerz Hypergon lens,[1] which has features of consider-

able interest in this connection. This lens has a relative aperture of $f/22$ and it is anastigmatically flattened over a field of about 135°. Although it lacks spherical correction, it is free from distortion and is therefore eminently suitable for architectural photography, where a wide angle of view is often necessary.   The uneven illumination of the plate is overcome in a most ingenious manner by means of an auxiliary field stop in the shape of a star.   About one-sixth of the total exposure is made with the stop out of the way.   The stop is then swung into a position just

Fig. 219.—Goerz   Hypergon.
(*Courtesy of American-Goerz Optical Company.*)

in front of the lens and is kept rotating during the remainder of the exposure by means of a blast of air directed against the fan-shaped ends of the points.   The ordinary wide-angle lenses do not cover such an extreme field as the Hypergon and are of more conventional construction.   The type of Dagor described in the preceding section is an example.

Wide-angle lenses have often been accused of giving a false or violent perspective, when actually the fault lies not in the lens but in the manner of viewing the photograph.   This will be explained in Sec. 170.

164. Telephoto Objectives.—The magnification in the image of a distant object is directly proportional to the focal length of the objective.   Hence, if an inaccessible distant object is to be photographed, the straightforward method of securing an image of adequate size is to use an objective of long focal length.   This procedure ordinarily necessitates a proportionate increase in the distance between the objective and the plate, and few cameras are capable of sufficient extension to permit any great increase in magnification by this method.   In *telephoto*

[1] Now manufactured by Carl Zeiss, Inc.

objectives, which are designed especially for photographing distant objects, the principal points are located well in front of the objective, so that a long focal length is secured with a short back focus. The principle of this type of lens will be clear from Fig. 220. The positive element I nearest the object is followed at a distance less than its focal length by a negative element II. The lens sketched in this figure has elements of 33.3 mm and −20.0 mm focal length respectively, which are separated by a distance of 20.0 mm. If the elements are assumed to be thin, the first and second principal points are 100 mm and 40 mm respectively in front of the positive element. Thus, although

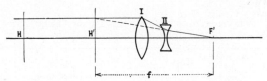

Fig. 220.—Sketch showing the principle of the telephoto objective.

the focal length of this combination is 100 mm, the back focus is only 40 mm.

The entire telephoto objective should preferably be designed as a unit, but telephoto attachments for ordinary objectives were formerly popular because of their comparative cheapness. These attachments consisted of a negative lens mounted in a barrel into which the photographer screwed an objective that he already possessed. They were generally designed so that the diaphragm of the positive lens was the aperture stop of the combination. This meant that the entrance pupil of the combination was of the same size as the entrance pupil of the positive lens alone, and consequently the relative aperture was reduced in proportion as the focal length was increased by the addition of the telephoto attachment.

The focal length of a telephoto objective depends upon the separation of its elements, as Eq. (76) in Chap. IV indicates. The focal length of the positive element is ordinarily less than that of the negative element; and, in any case, the separation must be less than the focal length of the positive element. In the older forms of telephoto objectives, the separation of the elements was made adjustable, the range being frequently sufficient to increase the focal length from three to twelve times that of the positive lens alone. It is clear that, if the lens is corrected for one value of the separation, the corrections will be impaired when the separation is altered. Hence a lens designed for such a wide range of magnifications may have to 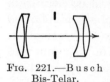 be stopped down to a small aperture to yield sharp images. Nowadays, telephoto objectives are usually made with a fixed magnification, thereby securing better definition at a large relative aperture but at a sacrifice of versatility.

FIG. 221.—B u s c h Bis-Telar.

An early type, known as the Bis-Telar, which is still used to some extent, is shown in Fig. 221. It was introduced by the firm of Busch in 1905 and its specifications are as follows:

SPECIFICATIONS OF THE BIS-TELAR OBJECTIVE

Focal length = 100 mm. Relative aperture = $f/8$

Element	Index		Axial thickness, millimeters	Radii, millimeters
	n_D	$n_{G'}$		
I	1.6140	1.6283	2.50	+ 9.16
II	1.6140	1.6360	0.30	−18.2
(Air)	1.0000	1.0000	10.50	+16.1
III	1.5900	1.6023	0.56	− 6.29
IV	1.5510	1.5669	1.40	+18.2
				−10.9

The diaphragm is in the middle of the air space.

As this lens has a back focus of 57 mm, it forms an image approximately twice the size of the image produced by an ordinary objective having the same back focus. Telephoto objectives with apertures of $f/4.5$ and even higher have been produced within the last decade. Such lenses are especially useful for recording the action in athletic events, which must ordinarily be photographed from the side lines or even from the grand stand.

Success in telephotography, especially at high magnifications, depends upon the recognition of three principles which apply only in part to ordinary photography. In the first place, the camera must be rigidly supported because a small amount of motion of the camera is serious on account of the high magnification. Telephotographs are also affected by the "boiling" of the atmosphere due to air currents of different temperature, an effect that is sometimes noticeable with a high-power binocular.

The third factor is the blue haze caused by the scattering of light in the earth's atmosphere. Panchromatic plates with a deep yellow or even a red filter should always be used when photographing distant objects. Infrared-sensitive plates with an infrared filter are even better.

165. Portrait Objectives.—One of the first applications of photography was to portraiture. The exposures required with the simple achromats that were available in the early days of the art ranged from 2 to 20 min., partly on account of the insensitivity of the photographic materials and partly on account of the small aperture of the lenses. To meet the demand for a faster lens, Petzval computed for Voigtländer in 1840 an $f/3.6$ lens particularly adapted for portraiture. Its construction is shown in Fig. 222. This lens had admirable definition at the center of the field but progressively poorer definition at the borders.

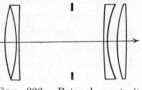

FIG. 222.—Petzval portrait objective.

Nevertheless, it fitted the requirements so well that lenses of this type are still in common use in many portrait studios. All the data of the original lens are not available, but the specifications of an early type of Petzval lens are given by von Rohr as follows:

SPECIFICATIONS OF AN EARLY TYPE OF PETZVAL OBJECTIVE
Focal length = 100 mm.   Relative aperture = $f/3.4$

Element	n_D	Axial thickness, millimeters	Radii, millimeters
I	1.517	4.7	+ 55.9
II	1.575	0.8	− 43.7
(Air)	1.000	33.6	+460.4
III	1.575	1.5	+110.6
(Air)	1.000	3.3	+ 38.9
IV	1.517	3.6	+ 48.0
			−157.8

The diaphragm is in the first air space 21.0 mm from the second element.

166. Testing Photographic Objectives.—The lens-bench test described in Chap. XVII is invaluable to the lens designer because of the fund of information that it gives concerning the performance of a lens. It is of little value to the user of a lens, however: first, because the apparatus ordinarily is unavailable; and, second, because the results are expressed in a form that only an expert can understand.   Fortunately, there are certain simple tests[1] that the user or prospective purchaser can make that will ordinarily furnish adequate information.   The results of such tests must be interpreted in terms of the purpose for which the lens is designed.   For example, spherical aberration and curvature of field may be permissible in a portrait lens, whereas in a copying lens they would be serious faults.   Similarly, a considerable amount of distortion, particularly barrel distortion, and a slight amount of astigmatism may be permissible in a landscape lens, whereas they would be fatal for many other purposes.

Spherical aberration can be tested by covering the central portion of the lens with a circular disk of cardboard and examining the image of a distant point at the center of the ground glass. If the ground glass must be moved to bring the image into focus again when this disk is replaced by a diaphragm with a small central aperture, the lens is afflicted with spherical aberration. The required displacement of the ground glass is a measure of the magnitude of the aberration.   Curvature of field can be detected by noting whether both the center and the margins of the field are in focus simultaneously on the ground glass.   Astigmatism can be detected by setting a large cross at some distance from the camera and examining the image, the camera being so directed that the image of the cross is at the corner of the ground glass. If the vertical bar and the horizontal bar of the cross are in focus at different positions of the ground glass, astigmatism is present. Coma can be detected by substituting an illuminated pinhole for the cross.   If coma is present, it will then manifest itself by the pear shape of the image.   If astigmatism is present also, the characteristic focal lines due to this aberration may mask the effect due to coma, but one of these aberrations is usually much more pronounced than the other.   To detect distortion, the camera should be focused upon a distant object that contains straight lines.   If an appreciable amount of distortion is present,

[1] In making many of these tests, the camera must be equipped with a ground glass if it does not have one already.   A further desideratum is that the ground glass should be as fine as possible.   J. T. Taylor recommends substituting for the ordinary ground glass a piece of glass which has been etched in the fumes of hydrofluoric acid.   The procedure in preparing such a glass, which should preferably be a piece of thin polished plate, is to suspend it horizontally above a lead tray containing either the acid or a mixture of calcium fluoride and sulphuric acid.

the image of such a line in the outer portion of the field will be curved.

Occasionally a lens will be found to suffer from a type of chromatism in which the focus for the rays to which photographic emulsions are most sensitive does not coincide with the focus for the rays that are brightest to the eye. This particular type of chromatism is sometimes given the name "chemical focus." Lenses that are achromatized for the *C*- and *F*-lines, and therefore have their minimum focal length near the middle of the visible spectrum, exhibit this aberration very markedly. Photographic objectives are therefore usually achromatized for the *D*- and *G'*-lines. Chemical focus can be detected by setting up in echelon formation a series of cards at various distances from the camera. A yellow or green filter should be placed over the lens while the camera is being focused, and a blue or violet filter should be substituted when the photograph is taken. It goes without saying that the photographic plate must be in exactly the same plane as the ground glass.

Special test objects for determining the over-all performance of objectives are used in routine examinations. A chart described by Jewell[1] for this purpose consists essentially of a set of radial lines resembling the chart shown in Fig. 209. The manner in which the images of these targets are distorted in the various parts of the field indicates not only the quality of the lens but also the type of aberration with which the lens is afflicted. To make such a chart is tedious and expensive, but an old calendar of generous size, such as is used in offices, will be found an excellent substitute. This should be torn apart and the various pages tacked to the flat side of a wall or building. One page should be put in the center, one at each of the corners, and the others in various intermediate positions. The camera should be secured firmly to some rigid support at a considerable distance away and should be focused very carefully. After the plate has been developed, it should be examined with a magnifier to determine to what extent the detail has been reproduced. Many calendars have the preceding and following months printed in smaller type, so this opinion is easily formed. The reason for using a large calendar is that the lens can then be used near the infinity position, for which it was probably corrected. On the other hand, if the lens is to be used for copying or enlarging, it

[1] *Jour. Optical Soc. Amer.*, **2-3**, 51 (1919).

should be tested at the magnification for which it is to be used in practice.

The focal length of a camera lens can be determined easily to within about 2 per cent in the following manner: Fit the lens to a camera and set the latter on a table covered with a piece of drawing paper. Focus the camera sharply on some distant object, such as a church steeple, and bring the image of this object to the very edge of the ground glass. Draw a pencil line on the paper along one side of the camera. Then turn the camera so that the image falls at the other edge of the ground glass and draw another line along the side of the camera as before. Remove the camera and make a diagram as shown in Fig. 223 on the drawing paper. In this figure, *AB* and *CD*

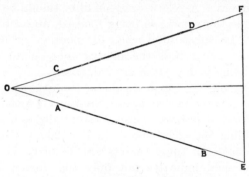

Fig. 223.

are the lines marked along the side of the camera and *EF* is equal in length to the width of the ground glass. Obviously, the length of the bisector of angle *EOF* is equal to the focal length of the lens.

The second principal point can be located roughly by focusing the camera for infinity and measuring the back focal length with a ruler. The difference between this quantity and the true focal length is, of course, the distance of the second principal point from the last vertex of the lens. Now, if the lens is reversed end for end, the first focal point can be found, and from this the position of the first principal point. If the principal points must be located more precisely, an improvised nodal slide can be fitted to the lens and the transverse axis located for an infinitely distant object.

167. Speed.—The light-gathering power of a photographic objective determines the rapidity with which the shutter can be operated for a given exposure of the plate.   This has led photographers to refer to the light-gathering power of the lens as its speed.   This quantity is expressed commonly by the f/-number, which was defined in Chap. V as the ratio of the focal length to the diameter of the entrance pupil.   As was indicated in Sec. 146, Chap. XIX, the f/-number is a measure of the light-gathering power of a lens only when the object is at a great distance.   Some of the older lenses were marked on the so-called *uniform system*.   A lens marked "U.S. 16" has also a speed of f/16, since the two systems were made to coincide at this point by definition.   In the uniform system, the number is proportional to the exposure time required for a given exposure, whereas the f/-number is proportional to the square root of the exposure

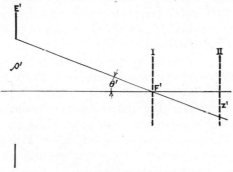

Fig. 224.

time.   The following table will make the relationship clear:

f-system	f/1	f/1.4	f/2	f/2.8	f/4	f/5.6	f/8	f/11.3	f/16	f/22.6
Uniform system...................				1	2	4	8	16	32	

The uniform system was practically abandoned as soon as the speed of objectives began to approach f/4.

The relative aperture of a lens can be determined by means of the following procedure: Focus the camera on a distant source, preferably at night.   The image of this source will be sensibly a point.   Then increase or decrease the distance between the lens and the ground glass by a known amount and measure the diameter of the resulting circle of confusion.   In Fig. 224, let the ground glass be moved from position I to position II.   It is clear that the ratio of the radius of the circle of confusion z' in the latter position to the distance between the two positions is tan θ'. The f/-number can be readily computed since

$$f/\text{-number} = \frac{1}{2 \sin \theta'},$$

as can be shown by combining Eqs. (223) and (226) of Chap. XIX.

168. The Transmission of Photographic Objectives. Flare.— It was shown in Sec. 15, Chap. I, that, when light is incident normally on a boundary between air and glass, approximately 4 per cent is reflected and hence only 96 per cent is transmitted. Therefore, as a first approximation, if an objective is composed of four separated elements (eight air-glass surfaces), the transmission is only $(0.96)^8$ or approximately 72 per cent. This value is in fairly good agreement with actual measurements of the image-forming light transmitted by photographic objectives, as would be expected from the fact that the absorption of light within the glass can usually be neglected. Occasionally glasses having a pronounced yellow color are used, and in such cases the absorption of the rays to which the plate is sensitive may be serious, but otherwise the difference in transmission between objectives having the same number of air-glass surfaces is hardly noticeable. There is, however, a very great difference between objectives in the manner of distributing the light that is reflected at the various surfaces. In a simple lens containing but two surfaces, for example, approximately 4 per cent of the light that is reflected at the second surface is redirected by the first surface to the plate. The curvature of the surfaces may be such that an image of the object plane is actually formed near the focal plane, and hence every bright area of the object will give rise to a *flare spot*. On the other hand, these images may be formed so far from the focal plane that the reflected light is spread diffusely over the entire area of the plate. The effect in the latter case is to degrade the contrast slightly, but this is usually of far less consequence than a series of flare spots, or *ghosts* as they are sometimes called.

A lens can be tested for flare by focusing it on a distant light at night. If flare exists, secondary images of the light will be visible at various points on the ground glass, and frequently images of the diaphragm will appear. Of course, the more elements there are in an objective, the greater the chance for flare, unless the elements are cemented. The flare is usually less pronounced when the lens is used at full aperture.[1]

In 1892, H. D. Taylor discovered that old photographic lenses whose surfaces have become slightly tarnished transmit more light than new lenses of the same construction. Surmising that the lens surfaces had been changed in some manner so as to reflect less light, he experimented and found that hydrogen sulphide and alkaline sulphides reduce the reflecting power appreciably. Experiments made during the war indicated that such materials as acid sodium phosphate, boric acid, copper sulphate, nickel sulphate, potassium dichromate, and many others produce the same effect, the extent depending not only on the chemical but also on the kind of glass and the condition under which the process is conducted. Not enough experimenting has been done to make the process commercially useful, and surely the novice should not attempt to improve his lens by this method.[2]

169. Depth of Field.—Even a perfectly corrected objective is incapable of forming on the plate a sharp image of more than a single plane of the object space. As was pointed out in Chap. V, however, there is ordinarily a certain region of the object space that is in satisfactorily sharp focus, and the distance between the near and far boundaries of this region is known as the depth of field. The mathematical expression for this quantity was given by Eq. (111) as

$$d = d_1 + d_2 = \frac{z'p}{m\rho - z'} + \frac{z'p}{m\rho + z'},$$

where d_1 is the depth on the far side of the object plane that is in sharp focus, d_2 is the depth on the near side, p is the distance of this plane from the entrance pupil of the objective, m is the magnification between this plane and the plate, ρ is the radius of the entrance pupil, and z' is the radius of the largest circle of confusion that can be tolerated. The depth of field is ordinarily of importance only when the object on which the camera is

---

[1] Occasionally stray light is reflected, not from the lens surfaces themselves, but from the interior of the lens mount. This is usually due to the use of too glossy an enamel for painting the mount, but it may also be due to the polishing of the enamel by the cloth used to wipe the lens. Painting the inside of the mount with a dead-black enamel as described in Sec. 149, Chap. XIX, will remedy the difficulty.

[2] Those who wish to experiment will find a good résumé on page 76 of the Ordnance Department publication cited in Chap. XV.

focused is fairly near the lens. In this case, $m\rho$ is large compared with z' and the preceding equation becomes

$$d = \frac{2z'}{m} \cdot \frac{p}{\rho} \,. \tag{235}$$

It was shown in Chap. XIX that the illumination on the plate depends upon the ratio ρ'/p', where ρ' is the radius of the exit pupil and p' is the distance of the exit pupil from the plate. But Eq. (106) of Chap. V states that

$$m = -\frac{\rho p'}{\rho' p},$$

and therefore

$$\frac{p}{\rho} = -\frac{p}{m\rho'} \,.$$

If this value of p/ρ is substituted in Eq. (235), the result is

$$d = -\frac{2z'}{m^2} \cdot \frac{p'}{\rho'} \,. \tag{236}$$

The negative sign results from the fact that the sign of z' was negative in Fig. 35, from which Eq. (111) was derived.

It is evident from Eq. (236) that all objectives have exactly the same depth of field when compared under the same conditions. In other words, for a given illumination on the plate, the ratio p'/ρ' is fixed (except for the slight difference in the loss of light within different lenses). Then for a circle of confusion of a given size, z' is fixed and the depth of field is seen to depend only on the magnification. In other words, if it is desired to photograph a man who is 6 ft. in height and obtain an image on the plate that is 2 in. high, the depth of field is the same regardless of what lens is used. Of course, the depth is increased if a smaller stop is used, but it is assumed that the stop is adjusted to provide the same illumination on the plate in all cases.[1]

The value of z' that should be chosen for substitution in the above equations depends to a great extent on the degree to which the objective is corrected. For the very finest lenses, a value of 0.05 mm (0.002 in.) is reasonable. It is manifestly absurd to assume a circle of confusion smaller than the smallest image of a point that the objective is capable of rendering, and hence a poor objective apparently has a greater depth of field than a well-

[1] For lenses of different focal lengths, the f/-number may be different since the camera is not focused for infinity.

corrected one.   This is undoubtedly the basis for the extravagant claims that are sometimes made for certain objectives by the manufacturers—claims that would certainly not be made if the majority of photographers were sufficiently conversant with optical principles to realize that a great depth of field is a sure indication of poor image quality.

When a negative is to be enlarged, the value of z' should ordinarily be smaller than is necessary otherwise—in fact, it should usually be smaller in direct proportion to the subsequent magnification.   Thus, in the example cited above, if the image of the man on the plate is only 1 in. high and the image on the print is to be 2 in. high, the circle of confusion formed by the lens should be half as large as before in order that it will be of the same size when the image is magnified in the enlarging camera.   However, the magnification between the object plane and the plate in the taking camera is only half as great in this case and, since the magnification appears squared in Eq. (236), the depth of field will evidently be doubled.   There is, therefore, a great advantage from the standpoint of depth of field in making the smallest possible negative and giving it all the subsequent enlargement that the graininess of the material will permit.

For practical purposes, it is convenient to have at hand a table giving the depth of field as a function of the magnification (or object distance) and the relative aperture.   Such a table can readily be prepared for a given lens by the aid of Eq. (111), but the values do not apply to other lenses, even of the same focal length and relative aperture, because the pupils and the principal planes may be differently located.   The table given on page 464 has been computed for a simple lens, in which both pupils and both principal planes coincide at the lens.   The first column gives the magnification between the object plane on which the camera is focused and the plate, and the second column gives the distance of this object plane expressed in terms of the focal length of the lens.

In computing this table, the diameter of the circle of confusion was assumed to be 0.1 mm (0.004 in.), which is ordinarily the smallest image of a point that can be obtained with a well-corrected objective.   In other words, this table applies for work of the most exacting character.   The depth of field is approximately proportional to the size of the circle of confusion—strictly proportional when the near and the far depths are the same.

Hence, if a larger circle of confusion can be tolerated, the depth of field can be obtained by multiplying the values in this table by the proper factor.

Table XXVII.—Depth of Field of a Thin Lens on the Basis of a Maximum Circle of Confusion 0.1 mm (0.004 in.) in Diameter
The upper number in each square is the depth on the far side of the object plane and the lower number is the depth on the near side.

Magnification	Distance of object plane	$f/4$	$f/5.6$	$f/8$	$f/11$	$f/16$
1	$2f$	0.03 in.	0.04 in.	0.06 in.	0.09 in.	0.13 in.
		0.03 in.	0.04 in.	0.06 in.	0.09 in.	0.13 in.
$\frac{1}{2}$	$3f$	0.10 in.	0.14 in.	0.19 in.	0.27 in.	0.59 in.
		0.10 in.	0.13 in.	0.18 in.	0.26 in.	0.55 in.
$\frac{1}{5}$	$6f$	0.49 in.	0.69 in.	0.98 in.	1.38 in.	2.07 in.
		0.47 in.	0.64 in.	0.93 in.	1.26 in.	1.82 in.
$\frac{1}{10}$	$11f$	1.82 in.	2.57 in.	3.76 in.	5.30 in.	8.09 in.
		1.71 in.	2.35 in.	3.31 in.	4.43 in.	6.25 in.
$\frac{1}{20}$	$21f$	7.2 in.	10.3 in.	15.4 in.	22.4 in.	36.2 in.
		6.3 in.	8.6 in.	11.9 in.	15.7 in.	21.4 in.
$\frac{1}{50}$	$51f$	4.0 ft.	6.1 ft.	10.0 ft.	16.6 ft.	38.6 ft.
		2.9 ft.	3.9 ft.	5.1 ft.	6.5 ft.	8.3 ft.
$\frac{1}{100}$	$101f$	19.6 ft.	34.0 ft.	75.0 ft.	305.0 ft.	∞
		10.2 ft.	13.0 ft.	16.4 ft.	19.6 ft.	23.6 ft.

This table applies strictly to a lens whose focal length is 5 in., but since the depth of field, when expressed in terms of the magnification, is very nearly independent of the focal length, the values hold well for a lens of any focal length unless the magnification or relative aperture is small.

Most inexpensive cameras are made of the fixed-focus type, and they are ordinarily constructed so that the total depth of field is a maximum. This is obtained by making the far depth infinite, which can be seen from Eq. (111) to result when $m\rho = z'$. Since from Eq. (51) $m = -f/x$, where x is measured from the first focal point, it follows that

$$x_h = -\frac{\rho f}{z'}. \tag{237}$$

If a camera is focused on an object plane at this distance from the first focal point, all objects will be in satisfactory focus from this plane to infinity. It is easily proved that, on the near side of this plane, they will be in focus down to a point midway between the object plane that is in focus and the entrance pupil of the objective. The distance x_h defined by Eq. (237) is called the *hyperfocal distance*.

170. Perspective Considerations in Photography.—It is manifestly impossible to reproduce a three-dimensional object space on a plane surface in such a manner that an observer possessing binocular vision will be entirely satisfied with the result. The best that can possibly be done is to make the reproduction satisfactory to an observer who possesses but a single eye. Even

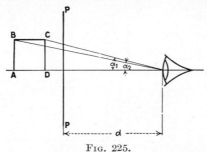

Fig. 225.

in this case, the photographic reproduction is not entirely true to nature because the image lies in a single plane; whereas, when the observer views the original object, some idea of the spatial relationships is gained by the amount of accommodation required to bring the various object planes into focus on the retina. Disregarding these inherent limitations, however, there are certain conditions that must be fulfilled if a photograph is to represent properly the perspective relationships of a three-dimensional object space.

Suppose that the observer in Fig. 225 views a three-dimensional object space, which is here represented for simplicity by the cube *ABCD*. The center of perspective is obviously the center of the entrance pupil of the observer's eye, as is easily seen by imagining the pupil to be contracted until only the chief ray from each point of the object space reaches the retina. A transparent glass plate *PP* could then be introduced at a distance *d* in front of the entrance pupil, and a drawing could be made upon it which, if skillfully executed, would constitute a satisfactory reproduction.   The problem is now to determine the conditions under which an optical system will produce an equally satisfactory photograph.

In Fig. 226, an optical system with entrance and exit pupils at E and E' forms an image of the cube $ABCD$ at $A'B'C'D'$. Since the entrance pupil of this system is the center of perspective for the object space, it should obviously be located at the same distance from the object as the pupil of the eye in the preceding figure.   Now imagine a photographic plate $P'P'$ located at a distance D from the exit pupil.   The chief ray from each point in the object space passes through the center of the exit pupil and intersects the plate in the manner indicated.   It will be obvious that if $\alpha_1' = \alpha_1$, $\alpha_2' = \alpha_2$, etc., the photographic plate

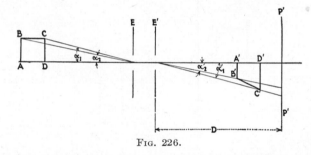

Fig. 226.

could be inserted at a distance D in front of the eye and would then constitute as satisfactory a reproduction of the geometry of the object space as the glass plate in Fig. 225.   In fact, if $D = d$, the two plates would be identical.   To satisfy the assumed condition, the angular magnification between the entrance pupil and the exit pupil must be unity.   Thus the pupils must lie in planes through the corresponding nodal points of the system. The simplest case for which this is true is a simple thin lens, in which the nodal points and the entrance and exit pupils can be assumed to coincide at the lens.   When the pupils do not lie in the plane through the nodal points, the perspective relationships are quite involved,[1] but the simple lens will suffice to illustrate a fundamental principle underlying any reproduction of space on a plane surface—namely, that the reproduction is

[1] This problem was discussed mathematically by Gleichen, "Die Grundgesetze der naturgetreuen photographischen Abbildung," published by W. Knapp (1910).

correct in its perspective relationships only when it is viewed from one particular distance. In the case of contact prints, this distance is equal to the distance of the negative from the exit pupil of the system at the time the picture was made, which is equal to the focal length of the lens if the camera is focused for infinity. For an enlargement, the viewing distance must, of course, be increased in direct proportion to the magnification produced by the enlarging camera.

The consequences of viewing a photograph from an incorrect distance are evident from Fig. 227, in which $P'P'$ is a photograph that faithfully reproduces the appearance of the cube $ABCD$ when the eye is in position E. Now, if the eye is moved to a position E', the brain has difficulty in interpreting the information

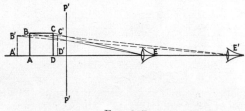

Fig. 227.

given by the photograph. If the size of the cube is known, its position on the axis can be inferred. The cube will appear distorted, however, because its depth dimension is apparently increased at the expense of the transverse dimensions. This relative increase in the depth dimension has the effect of making distant objects appear too small and near objects too large in comparison. Thus, in a landscape, distant mountains do not appear of sufficient height compared with the foreground; and, in a portrait, the nose of the subject appears excessively large. On the other hand, viewing the photograph from too close a distance has the opposite effect.

Photographers usually offer a somewhat different explanation for this phenomenon. Since photographs are customarily viewed at the conventional reading distance of 10 in., it is clear that this distance is ordinarily too great when a lens having a focal length less than 10 in. is used, and too small when a lens having a greater focal length is used. The photographer therefore associates the distorted perspective with the focal length of the lens. Focal lengths greater than 10 in. are rarely used, but focal lengths as short as 3 in. are frequently used in small folding cameras.[1] The type of perspective distortion illustrated in Fig. 227 is therefore the most common.   An example of the violent perspective that can be produced in this way is shown by the photograph reproduced in Fig. 228.   This photograph was made originally with a lens of 4.4 in. focal length, but after allowing for the reduction in making the cut, the proper viewing distance is 2.5 in. Only a myope is capable of accommodating for this distance, but an emmetrope can view the picture satisfactorily with the aid of a lens having a focal length equal to the proper viewing dis-

Fig. 228.

tance.   When viewed from this distance, the perspective relationships are correct.

It is important to distinguish between the choice of the proper viewing distance and the original choice of the center of perspective or point of view.   A house, for example, does not appear at its best when viewed from too close a distance and neither does it appear at its best from too great a distance.   The choice of the desired point of view should theoretically be made inde-

---

[1] The improvement obtained by enlarging a photograph made with a small camera is very largely due to the improvement in perspective.   It will be seen that a three-fold enlargement of a negative made with a camera having a lens of focal length 3.3 in. makes the perspective correct for viewing at the conventional reading distance of 10 in.   If the enlargement is to be hung on a wall, it is generally observed from a somewhat greater distance and hence a greater enlargement is desirable.

pendently of the focal length of the objective, which should be chosen with reference to the distance at which the photograph is to be viewed. However, practical limitations may prevent the photographer from carrying out this program. He may be unable to select the most desirable point of view, as, for example, when photographing a building in a city. If it must be photographed from the opposite side of the street, not only is the point of view too close for the best pictorial effect, but the focal length required to include the entire building on a plate of reasonable dimensions is too short.

One rule that is emphasized for beginners in photography is that the camera should never be pointed upward or downward. This rule is due to the fact that artists have always represented a subject by its projection upon a vertical plane; and so, although people are accustomed to the convergence of horizontal lines in a picture, they are unable to understand or interpret the convergence of vertical lines. The cameras used by professional photographers and advanced amateurs are usually provided with a swing back, so that the plate can be maintained in a vertical plane at all times. Some cameras are provided with a rising and falling front, which accomplishes the same result provided the lens has sufficient covering power. The owner of a camera that possesses neither of these adjustments can correct the distortion when making the positive by using a projection printer and inclining the negative and the positive material at the proper angles.

As indicated at the beginning of this section, no two-dimensional representation can ever be completely satisfactory, even for monocular vision, because the observer is not required to refocus his eyes for the different object planes. Inasmuch as only one plane can be in sharp focus in the photograph, the best that can be done is to focus the camera on the object of principal interest and then to regulate the diaphragm of the objective so that the depth of field in the photograph is the same as it would be to an observer accommodated for this plane. For a symmetrical objective, this condition is fulfilled when its entrance pupil is of the same size as the entrance pupil of the eye of the observer, but again practical considerations usually prevent this condition from being fulfilled. It may be stated, however, that when the requirements for obtaining true-to-nature photographs are met, the result is so lifelike, especially when viewed with only one eye, that it appears to be almost stereoscopic.

CHAPTER XXII

MAGNIFIERS AND OCULARS

Magnifiers and oculars are fundamentally very much alike, the chief distinction being that magnifiers are designed to magnify a real object and oculars to magnify the image formed by another optical system. The property of principal interest in either case is the magnifying power, and this can be discussed without making any distinction between the two instruments.

171. Magnifying Power.—The magnifying power of any optical instrument was defined in general terms in Chap. XIX as the ratio of the size of the image formed on the retina when the instrument

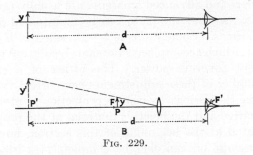

Fig. 229.

is used to the size of the retinal image for the unaided eye. It remains merely to interpret this definition in terms of the constants of a magnifier or ocular. In Fig. 229A, let a small object of height y be located at a distance d from the first principal point of the eye. The size of the retinal image obviously depends on the value of d; but, since the object cannot be placed closer than the near point of the eye, there is a definite limit to the size of the retinal image that can be formed by the unaided eye. In specifying the magnifying power of optical instruments, the value of d is arbitrarily assumed to be equal to the conventional reading distance of 10 in. or 250 mm.

Suppose now that a magnifier is placed before the eye as in Fig. 229B. To make the comparison fair, assume that the image P', which the magnifier forms of the object P, is located at the

470

same distance from the first principal point of the eye as before. In this case, the magnifying power of the instrument is simply

$$M = \frac{y'}{y},$$

where y' and y are the heights of the image and the object respectively. But y'/y is the linear magnification produced by the magnifier, and this quantity is given by Eq. (66) as

$$m = -\frac{x'}{f},$$

where x' is the distance of the image from the second focal point of the magnifier. This distance is negative, of course, by our sign convention. In general, the eye is located with its first principal point in the vicinity of the second focal point of the magnifier, and hence x' is approximately equal to 10 in. or 250 mm. The magnifying power of a magnifier is therefore

$$M = \frac{10}{f} \text{ (in.)} \tag{238}$$

$$= \frac{250}{f} \text{ (mm)}. \tag{239}$$

The positive sign indicates that the image is erect. It is clear that this equation holds also for an ocular, the only difference being that in this case the object is an image formed by another optical system. In a telescope or a microscope, for example, it is the image formed by the objective.

Both magnifiers and oculars are frequently focused so that the image is at infinity instead of at 10 in. from the eye, as assumed above. However, this requires only a slight displacement of the object with respect to the magnifier because the focal length of the latter is ordinarily so short that an image distance of 10 in. is practically infinite by comparison. Since the image subtends the same angle from the second nodal point of the magnifier as the object does from the first, the angle subtended at the eye when the image is at infinity is substantially the same as when the image is at 10 in. Furthermore, when the image is at infinity, the position of the eye with respect to the magnifier is unimportant. It follows, therefore, that the changes in the magnifying power of a magnifier or an ocular that are ordinarily brought about by varying the image distance are negligible, especially in view of the arbitrary assumption of 10 in. as the

distance that an object would be held for examination by the
unaided eye. An uncorrected myope would, of course, derive
less benefit from a magnifier than an emmetrope, but he also has
less need for one.

172. Types of Magnifiers.—An ordinary double-convex lens
is the simplest type of magnifier and is widely used for reading
glasses, watchmakers' loupes, and inexpensive pocket magnifiers.
As might be expected, the aberrations of a double-convex lens
cause the definition to deteriorate rapidly in the outer portion
of the field—the field that is covered sharply being rarely more
than 10° in angular extent. The system can be achromatized
by adding a concave lens of flint glass, and some of the monochromatic aberrations can also be reduced. Some high-grade
watchmakers' loupes are cemented doublets constructed in this
manner. Photo-engravers often use a magnifying glass consisting of two plano-convex elements of crown glass mounted with
their plane sides outward and the vertices of the curved surfaces
almost touching each other. This combination has a large field
free from distortion and is useful for magnifications up to three
or four times.

The magnifiers just described are useful primarily for relatively
low magnifying powers. For higher powers, more attention
must be paid to the correction of the aberrations. Lateral
chromatism is one of the aberrations that become serious in
the margins of the field. In some magnifiers, such as the one
shown at *A* in Fig. 230, this aberration is eliminated by properly
separating the two elements (see
Sec. 56, Chap. VI). The complete
elimination of lateral chromatism
requires that the object be placed
in contact with the lens surface if
the magnifier is to be symmetrical.
In other words, the *working distance*

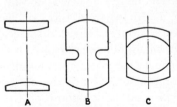

Fig. 230.—Types of magnifiers.
A, doublet; *B*, Coddington; *C*, triple
aplanat.

(*i.e.*, the distance from the object
to the nearest refracting surface)
would be zero. Hence, in practice,
the separation of the elements is made slightly less than the
condition for complete achromatism requires. At best, however,
the working distance is inconveniently short, especially in the
high powers; and the necessary proximity of the magnifier to the
object prevents the latter from being properly illuminated unless
it happens to be transparent.

An interesting type of magnifier is commonly credited to Coddington although it should really be ascribed to Sir David Brewster. Its prototype was a magnifier designed by Wollaston, which consisted of two plano-convex elements separated by a short distance. Their curved sides were outward and a diaphragm was interposed midway between their plane faces. Brewster improved this instrument by making it from a sphere of glass and cutting a groove about its equator to form a diaphragm. A modern form is shown at *B* in Fig. 230. It is a very fair magnifier but expensive to manufacture.

One of the best magnifiers now on the market is a cemented triplet consisting of a double-convex lens of crown glass between two negative meniscus lenses of flint, as shown at *C* in the figure. It is known under the trade name "Triple Aplanat." The field is large and the color correction excellent, so it may be used as an ocular as well as a magnifier. Since the elements are cemented, the loss of light is hardly more than with a single lens. It is especially meritorious as a magnifier because of its great working distance, which is nearly equal to that of a simple lens of the same power. A series of triple aplanats computed by C. S. Hastings is especially noteworthy.

The working characteristics of the three types of magnifiers just described are well shown by the following excerpts from the catalogue of the Bausch and Lomb Optical Company. All the types given in this list may be obtained either in tubular mounts for dissecting microscopes or in folding cases for carrying in the pocket.

TABLE XXVIII

Mag-nifying power	Focal length, milli-meters	Doublet		Coddington		Hastings Triplet	
		Working dis-tance, milli-meters	Field diam-eter, milli-meters	Working dis-tance, milli-meters	Field diam-eter, milli-meters	Working dis-tance, milli-meters	Field diam-eter, milli-meters
7	38	20.3	18	28.0	30	33.6	30
14	19	8.9	10	14.1	14	16.5	14
20	13	....	..	8.4	8	11.2	8

173. Types of Oculars.—As has been stated above, the only essential difference between an ocular and a magnifier is that the object for the latter is real, whereas the object for the former is the image formed by some other optical system. Oculars may therefore be designed to correct some of the residual defects in other elements of the system. In addition, oculars are frequently called upon to supply other functions not required of magnifiers. For example, it may be desired to introduce cross hairs or scales for purposes of measurement, or, if the image formed by the rest of the system is inverted, the ocular may be called upon to erect it. In the present section we shall describe the types of oculars that are used solely to magnify the image and then consider in later sections the types that perform other functions in addition.

It is clear that any of the magnifiers described in the preceding section can be used as oculars, and the triple aplanat is indeed excellent for this purpose. Such a lens gives a beautifully sharp and flat field of approximately 30° that is very free from chromatism and distortion. The loss of light and flare are at a minimum because there are only two air-glass surfaces, and hence this type of ocular is especially suitable for examining faint objects. The manufacturing cost is rather high, however, and the field is smaller than is desirable in optical instruments of high power.

The type of ocular that enjoys the widest use is credited to Huygens. It consists of two elements of the same kind of glass, usually spectacle crown, the ratio of the focal lengths varying from 3:1 to 1.5:1 according to the type of correction desired. These elements are separated by a distance equal to one-half of the sum of their focal lengths, and therefore the combination is free from lateral chromatism. The path of the rays through an ocular of this type is shown at A in Fig. 231. The objective (not shown) forms an image in the first focal plane of the ocular. This image is a virtual object for the ocular, which consists of the field lens FL and the eye lens EL. In most visual instruments, the objective is the aperture stop. The exit pupil (or eye point) is therefore the image of the objective formed by the ocular. It is generally close to the second focal point of the ocular and is indicated in the figure by EP.

If the image formed by the objective is at the first focal point of the ocular, the image seen by the observer is at infinity, which is usually the most satisfactory image distance for a person with the normal range of accommodation. It follows, therefore, that the field stop S should be located at the first focal point of the eye lens so that its image may likewise be formed at infinity. Also, if the ocular is to be provided with cross hairs or a scale, it should lie in the plane of the field stop S. The scale is then magnified by the eye lens alone; and, since the corrections that are provided by the field lens are lacking, the field that is sharply covered is small. Nevertheless, a micrometer ocular of this type is used to some extent in microscopy, but the scale is made very short and is placed at the center of the field.

The field of a Huygenian ocular is sharp out to about 25° and is very fair to 40°. Distortion and lateral chromatism

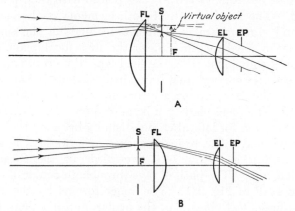

Fig. 231.—Path of rays through oculars. *A*, Huygenian type; *B*, Ramsden type.

are small, but the curvature of the field, which is convex toward the eye, is very pronounced. The longitudinal chromatism is about 50 per cent greater than that of a simple lens of the same focal length. To overcome these difficulties, the Huygenian ocular has been modified in several ways. A modification due to Mittenzwey, in which the field lens is meniscus, covers a field of approximately 50° with fair definition to the margin. Perhaps the most striking modification is a type patented by Tolles in the middle of the last century, although it was not original with him. It is similar in appearance to a Coddington magnifier, but the curvature ratio between the first and last surfaces is 1.5:1 instead of 1:1 and the groove that serves as diaphragm is at about one-third of the distance from the field end to the eye end. Although it is difficult to construct, it is superior to the two-lens type for high powers, not only because of its small loss of light and its freedom from flare, but also because of its extensive field and exquisite definition.   A further improvement has been described by Hastings in which the longitudinal chromatism is reduced by making the surface at the eye end concave and cementing a thin double-convex lens of flint glass to it.

An ocular devised by Ramsden is commonly used in instruments that are designed primarily for determining the size or direction of the object because it is better adapted for the use of scales or cross hairs.   This ocular consists of two plano-convex lenses made of ordinary crown glass placed with their plane sides outward.   The focal length of both elements is the same, and the lateral chromatism is corrected by making the separation equal to the focal length.   Since the first focal plane of such a system is coincident with the field lens, the cross hairs or the scale of the micrometer must lie against this lens.   Any specks of dust upon the lens surface are therefore plainly evident to the observer.   The focal plane can be moved forward at the expense of the correction for lateral chromatism by bringing the elements nearer together.   The prevailing custom nowadays is to make the separation approximately two-thirds of the focal length of the elements.   The path of rays through an ocular of this type is shown at B in Fig. 231.   The image formed by the objective is at the first focal point F of the ocular, and it is here that the field stop S and the cross hairs or scale of the micrometer must be placed.   It is evident that this type of ocular can be used as a magnifier, and it is therefore called a *positive* ocular in contradistinction to the Huygenian or *negative* type.

The field of the Ramsden ocular is of approximately the same size as that of the Huygenian.   The Ramsden ocular is about equally free from distortion, but its field is much flatter. Although the lateral chromatism is slightly greater than that of the Huygenian type, the longitudinal chromatism is only about half as great.   Many modifications of the Ramsden ocular have been devised, the purpose of most of them being to improve the chromatic correction.   One of the best known of these is the Kellner, in which the eye lens is an achromatic doublet.   In its modern form, this ocular gives an achromatic and orthoscopic field that in some models is as large as 50°.   Its most serious disadvantage is the pronounced ghost resulting from light reflected successively from the inner and outer surfaces of the field lens.

Inasmuch as it is desirable to interchange oculars freely, the tube sizes have been standardized. For telescopes, the standard diameter is 1.25 in. (31.8 mm); for microscopes, the standard diameter is 0.917 in. (23.3 mm).

174. Compensating Oculars.—It will be evident that the amount of lateral chromatism in an ocular can be readily varied by altering the separation of the elements, although this procedure affects the other corrections to some extent also. Oculars for large telescopes are provided with means for adjusting the separation of the elements and thereby securing the most satisfactory image by trial. Special oculars are available for use with apochromatic microscope objectives. These oculars are

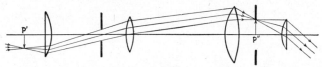

Fig. 232.—Path of rays through a four-lens erecting ocular.

overcorrected for lateral chromatism to compensate for the undercorrection of the objective. They are therefore known as *compensating* oculars. It is customary to make low-power compensating oculars of the Huygenian type and the high-power of the Ramsden. They can then be designed so that the first focal point lies the same distance below the shoulder that supports the ocular in the draw tube to eliminate the necessity of refocusing when one ocular is substituted for another.

A special type of Huygenian ocular has been found desirable for photomicrography, inasmuch as the image in this case is at a considerable distance behind the ocular instead of 10 in. in front of it. The eye lens of this *projection* ocular, as it is called, is made adjustable so that the image of the field stop and the image of the object under examination can be focused simultaneously upon the plate. Another type of ocular that is intended exclusively for photomicrography consists essentially of a negative lens. This gives a very large flat field when used with the objective for which it is designed.

175. Erecting Oculars.—All the magnifiers and oculars described up to this point form erect images of the objects they magnify. This may be an undesirable feature in an ocular, since the image formed by the rest of the system may have been inverted. Such instruments as opera glasses, field glasses, and terrestrial telescopes must necessarily be provided with erecting oculars to reinvert the image.

The simplest type of erecting ocular is a single negative lens. It will be discussed in Sec. 180 of the following chapter. A more complicated type that is widely used in terrestrial telescopes is shown in Fig. 232. The objective forms an inverted image at P' and the first three lenses of the ocular form an erect image at P''. Since this image is merely magnified by the eye lens, the image seen by the observer is erect also.

CHAPTER XXIII

TELESCOPES

In the strict terminology of optical theory, a telescopic system is one that forms an image at infinity of an infinitely distant object. In practice, however, the object may be located at a finite distance and the instrument may be adjusted to form an image at a finite distance also. In fact, there is no sharp distinction between telescopes on the one hand and microscopes on the other. Generally speaking, an instrument that is used to examine objects that would be held closer to the eye than 10 inches, if the accommodation of the observer would permit, is called a microscope, and an instrument that is used to examine objects at a greater distance is called a telescope.

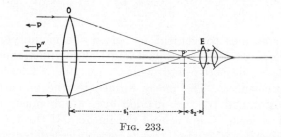

Fig. 233.

176. The Theory of Telescopic Systems.—Telescopes are constructed in a great variety of forms, but the same underlying principles are common to all. A very simple system will therefore suffice for illustration. In Fig. 233, suppose that an object of height y is located at P (not shown) at a distance s_1 in front of the objective O, which will be assumed to be thin. The objective forms an image at P' at a distance s_1' behind the objective, the height of the image being

$$y' = -\frac{s_1'}{s_1} y.$$

This image is observed by means of an ocular E, which forms a virtual image at P'' (not shown). Assuming the ocular to be thin, the height of the image at P'' is

479

$$y'' = -\frac{s_2'}{s_2}y' = \frac{s_1's_2'}{s_1 s_2}y, \tag{240}$$

where s_2 is the distance of P' from the ocular and s_2' is the distance of P''.*

If s_1 and s_2' are large compared with y and y'', the magnifying power of the telescope is

$$M = \frac{-y''/s_2'}{y/s_1},$$

since the numerator and denominator represent the angles subtended at the eye by the image and the object respectively. Substituting the value of y''/y obtained from Eq. (240),

$$M = -\frac{s_1'}{s_2}.$$

Since s_1 and s_2' are large, $s_1' = f_1$ and $s_2 = f_2$, where f_1 is the focal length of the objective and f_2 that of the ocular. Hence the magnifying power of a telescope when used under the assumed conditions is

$$M = -\frac{f_1}{f_2}. \tag{241}$$

It is sometimes convenient to regard the magnifying power of the telescope as the product of the individual magnifying powers of the objective and ocular. Imagine a telescope used without an ocular. The image formed by the objective must then be examined by the unaided eye, which must obviously be placed at least 10 in. behind the image. If the focal length of the objective is 10 in., the angle subtended by the image when viewed from this distance will be the same as the angle subtended by the object itself. Hence, the magnifying power of the objective is

$$M_1 = -\frac{f_1}{10} \text{ (in.)}, \tag{242}$$

the negative sign indicating that the image is inverted. The magnifying power of the ocular is given by Eq. (238) as

$$M_2 = \frac{10}{f_2} \text{ (in.)}.$$

---

* Since s_2' is negative whereas all the other distances are positive, y'' is negative and therefore the image is inverted. For many types of telescopes, notably astronomical and reading telescopes, this is no objection.

Hence, the magnifying power of the complete instrument is

$$M = M_1 M_2 = -\frac{f_1}{f_2},$$

which is the same as Eq. (241).

The magnifying power of a telescope can be measured very satisfactorily by means of the arrangement illustrated in Fig. 234. Two glass plates G_1 and G_2 are used to enable the eye to view the object around the outside of the telescope and at the same time to see the image formed by the telescope superposed upon it. The magnification can be read directly by sighting the telescope on a suitable scale. A picket fence or a brick wall may be used if nothing better is at hand. Another method that requires no auxiliary apparatus but gives results that are sufficiently precise for most purposes is to look through the telescope

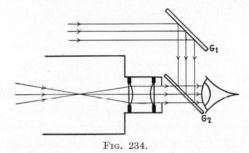

Fig. 234.

with one eye and observe the scale directly with the other. With a little practice the images formed by the two eyes can be made to appear in superposition.

The objective is the largest and most expensive part of a telescope and it should ordinarily be the aperture stop of the system. It is then the entrance pupil as well, since there are no lenses preceding it. The exit pupil is the image of the objective formed by the ocular. Since the objective is located at a considerable distance to the left of the first focal point of the ocular, the exit pupil is not far from the second focal point. If ρ represents the radius of the entrance pupil, the radius of the exit pupil is

$$\rho' = -\frac{f_2}{s_1'}\rho.$$

For a truly telescopic system, this becomes

$$\rho' = -\frac{f_2}{f_1}\rho. \tag{243}$$

In other words, the ratio of the size of the entrance pupil to the size of the exit pupil of a telescopic system is equal to its magnifying power. This circumstance provides an alternative method of measuring the magnifying power of a telescope. The procedure is to focus the telescope for infinity, locate the exit pupil, and compare its diameter with that of the objective. The exit pupil can be located readily by directing the telescope toward the sky and moving a piece of ground glass back and forth behind the ocular until the point is found where the emergent beam is smallest and most clearly defined. This sharply defined disk of light formed at the exit pupil is sometimes called the *eye circle* or *Ramsden circle*.

The useful magnifying power of a telescope is limited by its resolving power, as was made clear in Chap. XIX. It was there shown that if the entrance pupil of the eye lies in the plane of the exit pupil of the instrument, full advantage is taken of the inherent resolving power of the instrument when its exit pupil is no larger than the entrance pupil of the eye. On the other hand, the illumination of the retinal image is a maximum when the pupil of the eye is filled, and it decreases in proportion to the area of the exit pupil when the latter is smaller than the pupil of the eye. From the standpoint of optical theory, therefore, the magnifying power of the instrument should be chosen so that the exit pupil is of the same size as the entrance pupil of the eye. Practical experience has indicated, however, that it is usually desirable to depart somewhat from this condition. In other words, the better seeing conditions that result from using a magnifying power slightly higher than normal more than compensate for the loss of illumination in the retinal image. For the examination of terrestrial objects in daylight, the optimum size of the exit pupil is found to be in the neighborhood of 1.6 mm, which corresponds to a magnifying power approximately twice normal. For the examination of double stars, which are distinguished by means of their overlapping diffraction patterns, an even smaller exit pupil (or higher magnifying power) is generally employed. The usual practice for a telescope of moderate size is to use a magnifying power of 50 per inch of aperture, which results in an exit pupil only 0.5 mm in diameter. The fact that magnifying powers so much higher than normal are used in practice indicates that the resolving power of a good telescope is limited by diffraction rather than by aberrations.

The resolving power of a telescope depends upon the diameter of the objective and is independent of its focal length. Since the magnifying power depends upon the ratio of the focal length of the objective to that of the ocular, it is clear that varying both focal lengths in the same proportion merely varies the overall length of the telescope without affecting either the resolving power or the magnifying power. For obvious reasons telescopes are made as short as possible, and therefore the objective should have as high a relative aperture as is consistent with the type of correction required. The relative aperture of the objective is usually in the neighborhood of $f/15$ and rarely exceeds $f/12$. It should be noted that the focal length of the ocular that is required to produce normal magnification depends only on the relative aperture of the objective. Thus normal magnifying power is attained with an $f/15$ objective when the focal length of the ocular is 1.5 in. (40 mm) regardless of the focal length of the objective. For the reason set forth above, a magnifying power somewhat higher than the normal is usually desirable. In practice, therefore, the focal lengths of telescope oculars range from 1.5 in. down to 0.25 in., although 0.75 in. is the most common.

The field of view of the simple telescope illustrated on page 479 is limited theoretically by the diameter of the ocular. In practice, of course, the maximum field of view is limited by the aberrations of either the ocular or the objective, and it is desirable to insert a stop to limit the field to the region where the image is sharply defined. This stop in the case of the telescope on page 479 should be located at P' to make the image of the stop seen by the observer coincide with the image formed by the telescope.

If the eye is placed elsewhere than in coincidence with the exit pupil of the instrument, it may, of course, limit the field of view. In the simple type of telescope sketched on page 479, the exit pupil is at a considerable distance behind the ocular. This is an exceptional condition, and the eye point of most oculars is uncomfortably close to the eye lens. There are occasions, however, when it is desirable to locate the eye point well behind the eye lens. The outstanding example is the telescopic sight used on rifles, which must be designed with a view to protecting the eye from injury due to the recoil of the gun.

It has been assumed thus far that the telescope is to be used visually with an ocular to magnify the image formed by the objective. If the telescope is used to record the image on a photographic plate, the ocular is removed and the plate is inserted in the plane of the image formed by the objective.   Manifestly, there is no essential difference between a telescope used in this manner and a camera, except that the focal length of the objective is ordinarily longer than that of photographic objectives.   If a contact print made in a photographic telescope is viewed at the conventional reading distance of 10 in., the magnifying power is simply the ratio $f_1/10$ given by Eq. (242).

177. Refracting Telescopes.—The earliest telescopes were of the simple type discussed in the preceding section, and their performance, judged on the basis of our present-day standards, was very poor because of aberrations.   The spherical and chromatic aberrations were the most serious, but their effect was found to be greatly reduced by increasing the focal lengths of the lenses.   As a result, instruments over 200 ft. long came into use for astronomical observations.   With the invention of the achromatic objective early in the eighteenth century, the telescope became a more practical instrument because its over-all length could be greatly decreased.   Thus the refractor at the Yerkes Observatory, which is the largest of this type in the world, is only 65 ft. long, although its objective is $3\frac{1}{2}$ ft. in diameter.   Smaller telescopes of the same general form are used for a great variety of purposes, but they are still said to be of the astronomical type because this type was first used by astronomers.   The image is inverted, of course, but this handicap is more than offset by certain other advantages that will be apparent later.   One advantage that may be mentioned here, however, is the ease with which cross hairs or a scale can be inserted in the ocular.   This, together with the simplicity of construction, accounts for the wide use of the astronomical type in surveying instruments, such as levels and theodolites; in instruments for reading the deflection of a galvanometer mirror; and in many other scientific instruments, such as spectrometers and goniometers.

The principles underlying the design of all astronomical telescopes are generally the same notwithstanding the diversity in size and purpose of the various types.   The modern developments have been in the direction of improving the corrections of the instrument and adapting it to new purposes.   Since oculars have been discussed in the preceding chapter, we shall confine our attention to the design of objectives.

The aberrations of modern telescope objectives are ordinarily eliminated so completely that the resolving power approaches closely that of an ideal system. This is possible because telescopes for visual use are not required to have a high relative aperture and also because the field that must be covered is small. The field of view seen by the observer is rarely greater than 35° or 40°, being limited chiefly by aberrations in the ocular. The corresponding field in the object space is less in proportion to the magnifying power of the instrument. Thus the objective of a telescope with a magnifying power of 35 or 40 is required to cover a field of only 1°—that is, half a degree on either side of the axis. For this reason, the only aberrations that are of serious consequence in the objective are spherical aberration, coma, and longitudinal chromatism. The last aberration is the most difficult to correct, and the glasses should be chosen so that the secondary spectrum is eliminated as completely as possible.

Telescope objectives are so relatively simple in construction that semidirect methods can be followed in designing them. The classical treatment of the subject is by Harting[1] but many valuable papers, of which one by Moffitt[2] may be mentioned, have appeared since. Satisfactory corrections of the three aberrations mentioned above can usually be obtained with a doublet, which in small instruments consists of a double-convex crown element cemented to a plano-concave flint. The quality of an objective can be determined by the methods described in Sec. 139, Chap. XVII, but a better estimate of its performance under working conditions can be made by examining the image of a distant point source with an ocular of sufficient power to make the diffraction pattern visible. The appearance of this pattern when the ocular is racked back and forth through the focal point can be interpreted in terms of the individual aberrations by considering the principles discussed in Chap. VI. It may be added that the performance of many types of objectives is seriously affected by a relatively slight error in centering or squaring on, and that an objective should not be adjudged inferior until it is ascertained that these faults are not present.

When photographic methods were first introduced into astronomy, the photographic plate was simply inserted in the focal plane of the objective of an existing telescope. The chromatic

---

[1] *Zeits. Instrumentenk.*, **18**, 357 (1898).

[2] *Jour. Optical Soc. Amer. and Rev. Sci. Instruments*, **11**, 147 (1925).

errors of an objective designed for visual use are serious in the violet region, where the photographic plate is most sensitive. The other corrections are also inferior in this region of the spectrum, so it was found necessary to use color-sensitive plates and to remove the violet rays with a yellow filter. As soon as the importance of photographic methods was realized, special astrographic objectives were developed. In comparison with objectives designed for visual observations, these have a higher relative aperture, a larger field, and a different type of chromatic correction. It was found impractical to use the new glasses because the indices are so similar that deep curves are required. The elements would therefore have to be very thick and correspondingly expensive. Although the same difficulty arises when it is attempted to eliminate the secondary spectrum by using more than two elements, some notable triplets and even quadruplets have been produced. An especially interesting triplet is due to Steinheil. It is made in diameters up to 4 in. and works at a relative aperture of $f/4$ to $f/5$. This sort of objective must not be confused with an ordinary photographic objective of the same relative aperture because the former gives needle-sharp definition over a small field, whereas the latter gives mediocre definition over a large field. Wide-angle objectives are used for such purposes as the systematic survey of the heavens. An excellent objective of this type has been described by F. E. Ross.[1] It has a relative aperture of $f/14$ and gives critical definition over a field of approximately 30°.

The method of focusing a telescope deserves brief consideration. Figure 235 shows schematically the construction of the

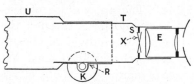

eye end of a telescope. The ocular E fits smoothly into a tube T to which the field stop S and the cross hairs X are permanently secured. The first operation is to direct the telescope toward an illuminated

FIG. 235.—The eye end of a spectrometer telescope showing adjustments.

surface and slide the ocular E back and forth until the cross hairs are in sharp focus. It is generally found to be most restful when the final image is placed as near the far point of the eye as possible. This can be accomplished by relaxing

[1] *Jour. Optical Soc. Amer.*, **5**, 123 (1921).

the accommodation[1] and withdrawing the ocular until the image is on the point of becoming blurred. With this adjustment made, the objective must be focused so that the image of the object is formed in the plane of the cross hairs. To accomplish this, the tube T is provided with a rack and pinion R. By turning the knob K, this tube can be moved back and forth in the main tube U at whose far end the objective is mounted.

For such instruments as theodolites, which are exposed to the elements, a draw tube of this sort is undesirable. Nowadays such instruments are frequently made with a fixed tube length and have a negative lens inserted between the objective and the ocular for focusing, as shown in Fig. 236. This lens is mounted in a tube fitted with a rack and pinion, and as the shaft that carries the pinion can be equipped with a stuffing box where it projects through the main tube, the instrument is water-tight.

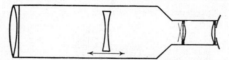

Fig. 236.—The optical system of a weather-proof theodolite telescope. The focusing is accomplished by moving the negative lens along the tube.

178. Reflecting Telescopes.—The first practical reflecting telescope appears to have been designed by James Gregory in 1663, but the first to be actually constructed appears to have been made about five years later by Newton, whose experiments had led him to believe that achromatic objectives were impossible. Although Gregory seems to have understood that the mirror should be paraboloidal to eliminate spherical aberration, the early makers did not know how to realize such a figure in practice. These mirrors were made of speculum metal, which is an alloy of copper and tin. Its disadvantages were that its reflectance was only about 65 per cent when new and that the mirror had to be refigured when it became tarnished. Present-day mirrors are made of glass on which silver is deposited chemically. They have a reflectance of upwards of 90 per cent when new, and when tarnished the old silver can be dissolved away and a new coat deposited.

With a reflecting telescope, some sort of apparatus must be introduced in front of the mirror to bring the image outside the

[1] Observers with little experience involuntarily accommodate for the ordinary reading distance when looking into an optical instrument.

tube where it can be examined. Sir William Herschel constructed many reflecting telescopes, the largest of which had an aperture of 48 in. and a focal length of 40 ft. To observe the image, he tilted the mirror slightly in its mount and looked at it over the edge of the tube through an ocular, as shown at A in Fig. 237. This arrangement has the advantage that the loss of light is at a minimum, but it is impractical for small telescopes because the observer's head would obstruct an appreciable proportion of the light. The commonest arrangement is that devised by Newton, which is shown at B in the figure. It consists merely of a first-surface mirror or a right-angle prism placed in

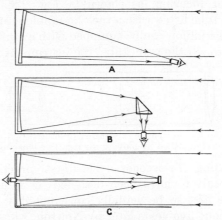

Fig. 237.—The optical systems of reflecting telescopes. A, Herschelian; B, Newtonian; C, Cassegrainian.

the tube to reflect the light through a hole in the side. The type of mounting devised by Cassegrain is shown at C in the figure. In this arrangement, the mirror is drilled with a central hole into which the light is reflected from a small hyperboloidal mirror, whose focus coincides with that of the large mirror. Thus the effective focal length is considerably increased. The type of mounting originally proposed by Gregory is somewhat similar except that the small mirror is ellipsoidal. Many of the large reflectors can be used in either the Newtonian or the Cassegrainian form.

The field of a reflecting telescope is exquisitely sharp in the center, but it is extremely limited in extent because the oblique aberrations, such as astigmatism and coma, are pronounced at only a short distance from the axis. The superior covering power of the refractor has therefore caused this type to be adopted for all but the very largest telescopes. The practical limitation to the size of refracting telescopes is set by the difficulty of obtaining disks of optical glass that are sufficiently homogeneous and free from striae and other defects. Moreover, unless the disk is annealed with extreme care, stresses will be set up that may prevent it from retaining its figure after it leaves the optician's hands. The difficulty of obtaining a satisfactory disk is also encountered in the case of the reflecting telescope, of course, but to a lesser degree because the light does not pass through the glass. On the other hand, the reflecting telescope presents some inherent difficulties. As it is swung from one part of the heavens to another, the mirror changes its position and the consequent flexure alters the figure of its surface. The same effect is produced on the objective of a refractor, but the changes in curvature of the various surfaces tend to compensate. Thermal changes are also more injurious to the performance of a reflector for a similar reason and therefore must be kept as small as possible. Many of these difficulties can be eliminated by using a material having a low temperature coefficient of expansion, and the improvements in the manufacture of fused quartz have led to experiments on the feasibility of making a 200-in. mirror of this material.

The advantage of the reflecting telescope lies in the fact that it is free from spherical aberration at its focus and is also inherently achromatic. It can therefore be made to have a very high relative aperture, usually in the neighborhood of $f/5$, the limit being set by the ability of the optician to work to the close tolerance that such a high relative aperture entails. Thus the exposures are short in comparison with those required by the ordinary refractor.

The mounting of a mammoth telescope is an engineering task of no small magnitude, but, as such instruments are few in number, it must suffice to state here that the tube is mounted on mutually perpendicular axes, one of which is parallel to the axis of the earth to enable objects to be followed as the earth rotates. A clockwork or motor keeps the instrument trained on the object under observation.

179. The Terrestrial Telescope.—The term "terrestrial telescope" is specifically applied to the type of telescope in which an erecting ocular of the type shown in Fig. 232 is used This type of instrument was very common before the invention of the prism binocular and is well known to everyone as the spy-glass of the old-time sea captain. The loss of light and the veiling glare caused by reflection at the large number of air-glass surfaces are serious faults. Moreover, the instrument must be inconveniently long, and it has therefore become practically obsolete.

180. Galilean Telescopes.—The first telescopes about which we have definite information were those built by Galileo in 1609. These were of the type shown in Fig. 238, the distinguishing feature being the negative ocular. The optical principles of this type of telescope are sufficiently different from those discussed in Sec. 176 to warrant some discussion.

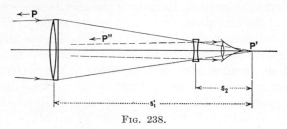

Fig. 238.

If an object of height y is located at P at a distance s_1 in front of the objective, the image formed by the objective is at P' at a distance s_1' to the right. The height of the image at P' is

$$y' = -\frac{s_1'}{s_1} y.$$

This image is a virtual object for the ocular. If the distance of P' from the ocular is s_2 and if its image at P'' is at a distance s_2', the height of the final image seen by the observer is

$$y'' = -\frac{s_2'}{s_2} y' = \frac{s_1' s_2'}{s_1 s_2} y,$$

which is identical with Eq. (240). If both P and P'' are at a great distance, the magnifying power is

$$M = -\frac{f_1}{f_2}$$

as before. However, f_2 is negative in this case, so the final image is erect.

If it be assumed, as before, that the objective is the aperture stop, it will be seen that the exit pupil, which is then the image of the objective formed by the ocular, is within the instrument at approximately the second focal point of the ocular.[1] It is therefore impossible to locate the eye at the exit pupil of the instrument, and the best that can be done is to place it as close to the ocular as possible. Even so, the pupil of the eye ordinarily becomes the aperture stop of the entire system. The entrance pupil is then the image of the pupil of the eye formed by the objective. It is located behind the observer and is magnified in the ratio f_1/f_2. As this ratio is equal to the magnifying power of the instrument, it will be seen that the magnifying power is always normal, as it should be.

If the eye is placed in coincidence with the ocular, the objective is obviously the field stop of the system. The half-angle of the field of view in the image space is therefore

$$\alpha' = \tan^{-1} \frac{d}{2(f_1 + f_2)},$$

where d is the diameter of the objective. Now

$$f_2 = -\frac{f_1}{M},$$

and with this substitution

$$\alpha' = \tan^{-1} \frac{d}{2f_1\left(1 - \frac{1}{M}\right)}. \tag{244}$$

The fraction $1/M$ is negligible in comparison with unity for large values of M, and in this case the equation becomes

$$\alpha' = \tan^{-1} \frac{d}{2f_1}. \tag{245}$$

The field of view in the image space of a Galilean telescope is therefore determined by the relative aperture of the objective. For an objective with a relative aperture of $f/12$, which is approximately the highest used in telescopes of the astronomical type, the total field angle $2\alpha'$ in the image space is only about 5°. To attain the field angle of 40° that is common for astronomical telescopes, the relative aperture of a Galilean telescope objective would have to be approximately $f/1.4$. Although the negative lens enables the designer to correct the instrument for a higher relative aperture than would be practical in an astronomical telescope, it is clear that the Galilean type cannot compete

[1] The focal points of a negative lens are crossed.

with the astronomical type in respect to the field of view. Since for small values of α', the field of view in the object space is

$$2\alpha = \frac{2\alpha'}{M},$$

it will be seen that the use of the Galilean type is limited to low powers.

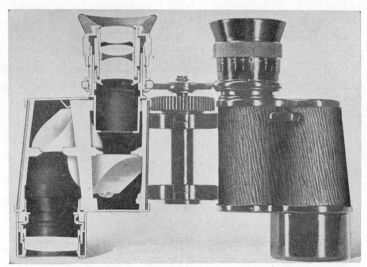

FIG. 239.—A typical prism binocular. One tube is cut away to show the arrangement of the optical parts. (*By courtesy of Bausch and Lomb Optical Company.*)

The chief advantage of the Galilean telescope is its short overall length, which makes it admirably suited for opera glasses.

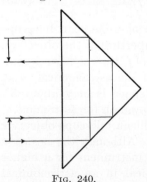

FIG. 240.

Moreover, since there are only four airglass surfaces, the images are very brilliant and free from flare. On the other hand, the small field of view is a serious disadvantage, and consequently the highest practical magnifying power is but a little more than two. One noteworthy type of Galilean telescope is marketed under the name "Sport Glass." Its magnifying power is only two, but, by careful design, its relative aperture has been made very high. It is therefore very short and compact, and its field of view in the object space is approximately 13°. The objective of this instrument was sketched in Fig. 205 of Chap. XIX.

181. Prism Binoculars.—The need for a compact erecting telescope magnifying six to ten times and covering a large field is met by the prism binocular. Such an instrument is shown in Fig. 239. As can be seen, it is essentially an astronomical telescope fitted with prisms which serve to diminish the length of the instrument and to invert and reverse the final image. Various types of prism systems are used, but the Porro system, shown in the figure, is the most common. It consists of two right-angle prisms, and, as can be seen from Fig. 240, one inverts the image but leaves it still reversed right and left. A second prism oriented in a perpendicular azimuth reverses the image. Prism binoculars are commonly made with magnifying powers of six, eight, and ten, the useful power being limited chiefly by the difficulty of holding the instrument steady. The diameter of the objective is commonly 25 mm or 30 mm for the six- and eight-power instruments. The size of the field of view varies somewhat, but it is approximately 6° to 8° in the object space. It is made large, at the expense of good marginal definition if need be, because otherwise moving objects would be difficult to follow.

CHAPTER XXIV

MICROSCOPES

The magnifiers described in Chap. XXII are sometimes called simple microscopes and, although they are eminently satisfactory for magnifying powers up to about twenty times, a compound microscope must be used when a higher magnification is desired. In its simplest form, the compound microscope is of the same type of construction as the astronomical telescope,

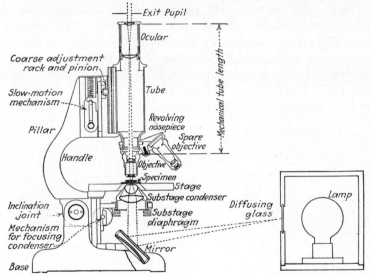

Fig. 241.—The essential features of a compound microscope, showing the path of the rays.

the chief point of difference being that the objective of a microscope is especially corrected for objects at a very close distance rather than for objects at infinity. The compound microscope is used so much more often than the simple microscope that the tendency is to use the term "microscope" to designate the former and "magnifier," the latter.

182. Magnifying Power.—The optical system of a typical compound microscope is illustrated in Fig. 241. It consists of an objective and an ocular, the specimen being laid on the stage under the objective. As in the astronomical telescope, the objective forms a real image at or near the first focal plane of the ocular, which in turn forms a virtual image for the eye to observe. A microscopic specimen is almost never self-luminous, and hence some means of illuminating it must be provided. For transparent specimens, the method shown in the figure is very widely used. A lamp illuminates a piece of ground glass, which acts as a secondary source. The light diffused from this glass is reflected at the plane mirror and is focused on the specimen by means of the substage condenser. The methods of illuminating opaque objects will be discussed in Sec. 184.

The magnifying power of a microscope is determined by the product of the individual magnifying powers of the objective and the ocular. Since the function of the objective is merely to form a magnified real image that is examined by the ocular, the magnifying power of the objective is evidently equal to the linear magnification between the object and its image. Thus

$$M_1 = m_1 = -\frac{x'}{f'},$$

where x' is the distance of the image from the second focal point and f' is the focal length[1] of the objective. The demands upon the objective are so severe that it can be corrected for only a single image distance. The present tendency among microscope manufacturers is to adopt 180 mm as the distance from the second focal point of the objective to the first focal point of the ocular. This is called the *optical tube length*. Since the image is formed by the objective very close to the first focal point of the ocular, x' may be taken equal to 180 mm and hence

$$M_1 = -\frac{180}{f_1} \text{ (mm)}. \tag{246}$$

The magnifying power of the objective expressed in this manner is frequently called the *initial magnification*, since the objective is the first element in the magnifying system. The magnifying power of oculars was discussed in Sec. 171, Chap. XXII, where it was shown by Eq. (239) that

---

[1] If the objective is of the oil-immersion type, the first and second focal lengths are different and the quantity f' in this equation is, of course, the second focal length.

$$M_2 = \frac{250}{f_2} \text{ (mm)} .$$

The magnifying power of the complete microscope is therefore

$$M = M_1 M_2 = -\frac{180}{f_1} \cdot \frac{250}{f_2} \text{ (mm)} . \tag{247}$$

An alternative method of computing the magnifying power of a compound microscope is to regard it as a single thick lens and apply Eq. (239) to the entire system. Thus

$$M = \frac{250}{f} \text{ (mm)} ,$$

where f is the focal length of the entire system. It is easily shown that, if the image formed by the objective lies in the first focal plane of the ocular, the focal length of the entire system is given by

$$\frac{1}{f} = -\frac{180}{f_1 f_2} \text{ (mm)} . \tag{248}$$

Hence, on substitution,

$$M = -\frac{180}{f_1} \cdot \frac{250}{f_2} \text{ (mm)} ,$$

which is the same as Eq. (247).

183. Resolving Power.—The objective of a microscope, like that of a telescope, should be the aperture stop of the entire system, and the exit pupil is therefore the image of the objective formed by the ocular. Since the objective is at a considerable distance from the first focal point of the ocular, the exit pupil is near the second focal point. This point is approximately 10 mm behind the eye lens, and consequently there is no difficulty in satisfying the primary requirement of visual instruments— namely, that the entrance pupil of the eye should lie in the same plane as the exit pupil of the instrument.

The early work of Airy on the resolving power of the telescope led to the suspicion that the finite length of a light wave must impose a similar limitation to the useful magnification of a microscope. That such was the case was found by the early experimenters with the microscope, who noticed that, when the magnification was increased beyond a certain limit, the image of a point became a spurious disk of light. The size of this disk was found to increase in proportion to the magnification as soon as this limit was reached, and hence no additional information about the object could be gained. It will be recalled from Chap. VII that the image of a point formed by a centered system of spherical refracting surfaces with a circular aperture stop consists of a central disk surrounded by rings of rapidly decreasing intensity. The central disk is the most important part of the diffraction pattern, and its radius was given by Eq. (164) of Chap. VII as

$$z' = \frac{0.61\,\lambda}{n'\tan\theta'}.$$

This can be written as

$$z' = \frac{0.61\,\lambda}{n'}\cdot\frac{\cos\theta'}{\sin\theta'}.$$

In microscopy, θ' is ordinarily so small that $\cos\theta'$ can be assumed to be equal to unity. Also, $n'\sin\theta'$ can be transferred to the object space by means of the sine law, Eq. (129); whence

$$z' = 0.61\,\lambda\,\frac{m}{n\sin\theta}. \tag{249}$$

According to the criterion discussed in Chap. VII, z' is the distance between two points in the image that can just be resolved. The corresponding separation of the points in the object is

$$z = \frac{z'}{m}.$$

The quantity z also gives a rough indication of the radius of the smallest circle in the object space that can just be distinguished from a point. Substituting z' in terms of z,

$$z = \frac{0.61\,\lambda}{n\sin\theta}$$
$$= \frac{0.61\,\lambda}{\text{N.A.}}. \tag{250}$$

This treatment of the resolving power of a microscope is based on the assumption that the object is self-luminous, whereas microscopic specimens are almost invariably illuminated from an external source. Abbe was the first to show that it is not permissible to assume in the case of a microscope that a single point of the object radiates light in all directions. By means of an elaborate analysis, he found that the fine structure of the object produces a diffraction pattern instead. That such must be the case will be evident when it is recollected that the fine periodic structure of a microscopic object will produce spectra

just like a diffraction grating.   Abbe showed that perfect images
can be obtained only if all the spectra are collected by the objective and take part in the formation of the retinal image.   If the
spectrum of zero order alone is allowed to enter the system, no
detail in the object appears.   At least one of the side spectra
must enter the system if any detail in the object that produces
it is to be distinguished.   As the numerical aperture of the microscope is increased, more spectra enter it and the resolving power
increases in proportion.

It would be out of place here to attempt to reproduce the work
of Abbe on the subject of microscopic vision.   The chief result
of practical importance is that the highest resolving power is
obtained when the source of light is focused on the object with a
condenser of such size that the beam fills approximately two-
thirds of the aperture of the objective.   This is called *critical
illumination*.   Abbe showed further that the finest detail which a
microscope can resolve is

$$z = \frac{\lambda}{(N.A.)_{obj.} + (N.A.)_{cond.}}. \tag{251}$$

If the numerical aperture of the condenser is equal to that of
the objective, as it is approximately for critical illumination,
this expression becomes

$$z = \frac{\lambda}{2(N.A.)}. \tag{252}$$

As a useful rule, therefore, the smallest separation of lines in
the object that can be resolved is equal to the wave length
of the light divided by twice the numerical aperture of the objective.   If the substage condenser is omitted, as it frequently
is for low-power work, the light striking the specimen is of
random phase.   Since $(N.A.)_{cond.} = 0$ in this case, the resolving
power of the microscope is only half as great.   The fact that
the resolving power is found by experiment to depend upon the
numerical aperture indicates that the optical system is so highly
corrected that diffraction and not aberrations limits the resolution.
It must be realized, however, that, although the diffraction of
light follows definite laws, the criterion upon which any formula
for resolving power is based must be arbitrary.   The important
feature to remember is that a limit does exist beyond which the
magnifying power cannot profitably be increased.   This limit
can be recognized very easily in any particular instance after a
little experience.

The question of the relationship between the magnifying power and the resolving power of visual instruments was discussed in Sec. 147, Chap. XIX, where it was shown that the normal magnifying power of a microscope is roughly 250 times its numerical aperture. At normal magnification, the exit pupil of the microscope is of the same size as the entrance pupil of the eye. Since the latter is then filled with light, the brightness of the object is the same as though the object were observed with the unaided eye, neglecting, of course, the absorption of light within the system. For reasons that are very similar to those discussed in the preceding chapter, experienced microscopists find that the best results are obtained with a magnifying power considerably higher than normal. This reduces the illumination of the retinal image in proportion to the square of the number of times that the actual magnifying power exceeds the normal, but the loss of light is not serious because plenty can always be obtained for visual work. However, if too high a magnifying power is used, the exit pupil of the system becomes so small that any minute particles floating in the humors of the eye cast shadows on the retina. These are sometimes mistaken by novices for particles floating in the specimen.

184. Types of Objectives.—A microscope intended for serious work is always provided with a battery of oculars and objectives. Since it is very desirable to substitute one ocular or objective for another without causing the image to go out of focus, some convention must be adopted for the positions of the focal points of both elements. For instruments whose optical tube length is 180 mm, which is the most common to-day, the second focal points of objectives (except those of very low power) are placed 32 mm below the shoulder that seats on the end of the microscope tube. The first focal points of the oculars are placed 12 mm below the shoulder that rests on the upper end of the tube. The distance from this end of the tube to the lower end, which is known as the *mechanical tube length*, is therefore 160 mm. The simplest microscopes have a fixed tube length, but the more elaborate ones have an adjustable draw tube engraved with a scale to indicate the mechanical tube length.

It has long been customary to designate objectives in terms of their focal length in millimeters. According to Eq. (246), this value gives the initial magnification when divided into 180. More recently, certain manufacturers have begun to designate their objectives in terms of the initial magnification itself, which is a great convenience because the magnifying power of the entire microscope is simply the product of this quantity and the magnifying power of the ocular.

Even the simplest microscope objectives are achromatized for two wave lengths and are corrected for spherical aberration and coma. They are known as achromats, and a modern low-power objective of this type is shown in cross section at A in Fig. 242. For most purposes these objectives are eminently satisfactory, but when the finest definition is required, apochromats[1] must be used.

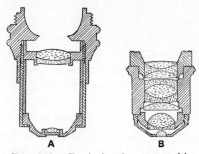

As was stated previously (see page 116), such objectives are achromatized for three wave lengths and are corrected for spherical aberration at two. A cross-sectional view of the lower portion of a 2-mm apochromat having a numerical aperture of 1.40 is shown at B in the figure. The most serious obstacle to the wide use of apochromats is their high cost, and therefore semi-apochromats, so called, in which fluorite is used for some of the lens elements, have been developed. Although their performance is but slightly inferior to that of the apochromats, their cost is considerably less.

Fig. 242.—Typical microscope objectives: A, a 16-mm achromat, full size; B, a 2-mm apochromat, $1\frac{1}{2}$ times full size.

Objectives for photomicrography must be selected by a different criterion than that applied to visual work. Since color filters are almost invariably used, it might seem that the chromatic errors of the objective would be less important. Even here, however, the superiority of the apochromat manifests itself because usually several filters must be tried, and the technique becomes involved unless the objective performs equally well with each. On the other hand, certain objectives, known as *monochromats*, have been designed to function with light of but a single wave length. They are used for work in the ultraviolet at 275 mμ because of the impracticability of achromatizing quartz lenses. Monochromats have even been designed for visual use, and because the monochromatic corrections can be so greatly improved, numerical apertures as high as 1.6 have been attained.

[1] The compensating oculars described on page 477 must be used with these objectives to correct the outstanding lateral chromatism.

The characteristics of microscope objectives are shown by Table XXIX below, which is taken from the catalogue of a leading manufacturer. To make the relationships clear, the types

TABLE XXIX.—CHARACTERISTICS OF THE MORE COMMON MICROSCOPE OBJECTIVES MADE BY THE BAUSCH AND LOMB OPTICAL COMPANY

Achromatic objectives

Focal length, millimeters	Numerical aperture	Type	Initial magnification	Working distance, millimeters
48	0.08	Dry	2	53
40	0.08	Dry	2.6	43
32	0.10	Dry	4	38
16	0.25	Dry	10	7
8	0.50	Dry	21	1.6
4L	0.65	Dry	43	0.6
4S	0.85	Dry	45	0.3
3	0.85	Dry	60	0.2
7	0.50	Water	26	2.0
4	1.00	Water	44	0.6
2.2	1.10	Water	81	0.15
1.9	1.25	Oil	97	0.15
1.9	0.80	Oil	97	0.35

Semi-apochromatic objectives

4	0.85	Dry	43	0.34
1.8	1.30	Oil	100	0.13
1.8	0.80	Oil	100	0.35

Apochromatic objectives

16	0.30	Dry	10	4.80
8.3	0.65	Dry	20	0.60
4	0.95	Dry*	45	0.18
3	0.95	Dry*	62	0.14
3	1.40	Oil	62	0.12
2	1.30	Oil	90	0.12

* With graduated collar to correct for cover-glass thickness. See page 506.

designed for special purposes are omitted. It will be noticed that the objectives of the very highest power are of the oil-immersion type, the purpose being to increase the numerical aperture by raising the value of the refractive index in the object space.[1] The immersion liquid is usually cedarwood oil, but

[1] Physically, the effect is to shorten the wave length of the light.

different manufacturers dilute it to obtain an index best suited to their particular objectives. For the best results, therefore, the oil supplied by the manufacturer should be used. The objective having a numerical aperture of 1.40 gives the highest resolving power, of course, but it is not a plaything for the novice because it is so likely to be injured. The front lens is hyper-hemispherical and therefore it cannot be securely mounted. The working distance is very short, and, if the objective should touch the cover glass, this lens might easily be knocked out of position. The water-immersion objectives are made because biologists frequently must study living specimens immersed in water and not because superior corrections can thereby be obtained.

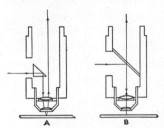

Fig. 243.—Standard types of vertical illuminators.

The proper method of cleaning objectives is to use lens paper or a soft lintless cloth. Only a very light pressure should be applied because the elements may otherwise be knocked loose. The back lens can be reached by a sliver of wood padded with lens paper or cloth. An objective should never be taken apart because the elements cannot be centered when they are replaced without special apparatus. If an objective is still cloudy after the first and last surfaces have been cleaned, it should be returned to the manufacturer for repairing.

In the past, the microscope has been especially identified with biology, but other sciences are now finding it to be a valuable tool. When modified somewhat by suitable devices for illuminating the specimen, it is widely used by metallographers. In this case, the light illuminating the specimen must be incident from above. The working distance of very low power objectives is so great that the specimen can be illuminated by directing a beam of light on it from a source beside the microscope. This is impossible with objectives of short focal length because the mount of the objective interferes. To overcome this difficulty, the illuminating beam is directed through the objective itself by means of a vertical illuminator. This apparatus consists optically of either a right-angle prism or a clear glass plate, as shown in Fig. 243. The objective is screwed into the illuminator and the combination is screwed into the body tube of the microscope. The illuminator occupies a considerable amount of space, and consequently the objectives used with it are made with especially short mounts. Even so, the standard mechanical tube length for these objectives is usually 190 mm. It is evident that both forms of vertical illuminator possess serious disadvantages. If the prism is used, the resolving power of the objective is diminished because the illuminating beam occupies one-half of the aperture. If the clear glass mirror is used, a certain amount of stray light is introduced. Nevertheless, excellent results can be obtained with either form.

Objectives are marked with their focal length or initial magnification, their numerical aperture, and, occasionally, the thickness of cover glass and the mechanical tube length for which they are corrected. It was formerly the custom to designate objectives by symbols, and if the maker's catalogue is not at hand, the focal length and numerical aperture must be determined experimentally. The focal length can be determined from the magnification produced by the objective. A stage micrometer, which consists of a slide on which a minute scale is engraved, is laid on the stage, and a micrometer ocular[1] is fitted to the instrument. The magnification between the stage micrometer and its image as seen in the ocular is measured for two different mechanical tube lengths. Then, by applying Eq. (52), it can be shown that the focal length of the objective is equal to the difference in the mechanical tube lengths divided by the difference in magnification. The numerical aperture can be found by suspending the objective at some distance above a dark-colored table top. The back lens of the objective is observed from a distance of 180 mm while a piece of paper is slid along the table top until its image just appears at the edge of the back lens of the objective. The numerical aperture can then be computed directly from the geometry of the arrangement. Evidently this method is suitable only for dry objectives. A special device invented by Abbe and called an apertometer must be used for oil-immersion objectives.

Although an objective made by a reputable manufacturer may be assumed to be of high quality, it is occasionally desirable to test its performance. The customary test objects are certain diatoms whose structure is well known. The method of using these to test objectives will be found in any textbook on microscopy. A few firms have on the market a device called an

---

[1] If the ocular is of the Huygenian type, the field lens must be removed.

Abbe test plate, which provides more definite information about the performance of an objective. This plate has six silvered spots under cover glasses of various thicknesses, the silver being ruled with a dividing engine in such a manner as to leave clear spaces of the same width as the intervening silver lines. No general rules can be laid down for the use of this test plate because the behavior of the different types of objectives is so different. It may be stated, however, that with a good apochromat or semi-apochromat, the edges of the lines should show hardly any trace of color when they are in focus. When they are inside the focus, a slight purple haze should encroach upon the dark lines, and when they are outside the focus, an apple-green haze should appear. When the lines are properly focused, the image should leave nothing to be desired. It must be remembered, however, that both apochromats and semi-apochromats have a noticeably curved field, and hence the outer portion and the center will not be in focus together.

185. Types of Condensers.—It is evident from Sec. 183 that, for critical illumination, the cone of light incident on the specimen should nearly fill the objective. For low magnifying powers, the numerical aperture of the objective is small and no condenser is needed. All microscopes are furnished with a double mirror as shown in Fig. 241, and the concave side can be used as a condenser in this case. For objectives having a focal length shorter than about 16 mm, some sort of condenser is required, the function of the mirror then being merely to deflect the light upward into the instrument. The so-called Abbe condenser is widely used. It is, however, neither chromatically nor spherically corrected, and at high powers pronounced color fringes appear at the edge of the field, which becomes ill defined. Both aplanatic and achromatic condensers are now available, and one or the other of these types should be used where critical definition is required at high power.

To avoid stray light, it is desirable to make the image of the source of light on the specimen no larger than the field covered by the objective. A certain amount of adjustment can be obtained by moving the lamp, but this procedure is usually inconvenient. Consequently, most condensers are constructed so that for low-power work, where a large field must be illuminated, the upper lens can be removed and the focal length thus increased.

A condenser that is used with an oil-immersion objective must have a drop of immersion oil placed on it before it is racked into position. If the slide on which the specimen is mounted is excessively thin, the oil will not fill the space between it and the front lens of the condenser. The remedy is to fill part of the space with a piece of cover glass oiled to the slide. It is possible to use an objective as a condenser, and adapters are available for fitting an objective in the condenser mount. Since the working distance of an objective is short, the specimen cannot be mounted on an ordinary slide in this case but must be mounted between two cover glasses. Special metal slides are available for mounting specimens in this manner.

186. The Adjustment of a Microscope.—The microscope is perhaps the finest example of the optician's art, but all the skill and care of designer and artisan will be brought to naught if the user does not adjust the instrument to operate under the conditions intended. If the instrument is fitted with a draw tube, the first adjustment is always to withdraw the tube to the graduation marked "160."[1] The elements of the microscope must be brought into alignment, but, fortunately for the novice, most microscopes are aligned once and for all at the factory. Sometimes the condenser can be centered, and if the objectives are fitted with sliding changers, they can be centered also. When such is the case, a suitable method of centering the condenser and objectives can be devised by a little thought.

After the instrument is aligned, the specimen should be placed in position and the source of light focused upon it by means of the condenser. The image of the source should be just large enough to cover the field. This condition can be brought about by using a condenser of the proper focal length and either moving the lamp or adjusting the diaphragm of the latter if it is provided with one. The next operation is to adjust the substage diaphragm. When it is wide open, the specimen will be seen to be bathed in a glare of light; but, as it is closed, this glare gradually disappears and the details in the specimen stand out sharply.

---

[1] If the instrument is provided with auxiliary apparatus, such as a sliding objective changer or a revolving nosepiece, the space occupied by it must be allowed for unless this has been done by the manufacturer. This precaution applies with especial force to old microscopes. Nowadays microscopes are almost invariably equipped with revolving nosepieces, and therefore the manufacturer makes the necessary allowance when graduating the draw tube.

As was stated above, the optimum results are produced when the aperture of the objective is approximately two-thirds filled. By removing the ocular and looking into the tube, it can be seen when this condition obtains. The ocular is then replaced and the instrument is ready for use. If the light is too bright, it may be reduced in intensity with neutral filters—never by closing down the substage diaphragm because this procedure lowers the resolving power.

Binocular microscopes are becoming popular. They possess two important adjustments in addition to those described. The separation of the oculars must be made to suit the interpupillary distance of the observer, and one ocular, which has a graduated collar, must be set to compensate for any anisometropia of the observer. In addition, the focusing must be done with due regard for the observer's accommodation-convergence relationship.

For the most exacting work it is necessary to correct for variations in the cover-glass thickness. Objectives are usually corrected for a thickness of 0.17 mm to 0.18 mm, and cover glasses especially selected for thickness can be obtained. If the cover glass varies much from the correct thickness, the resulting spherical aberration must be corrected by altering the length of the microscope tube. When the cover glass is too thick, the draw tube must be pushed inward; when it is too thin, the draw tube must be pulled outward. Experience is required to enable one to determine when the proper correction has been obtained, and the Abbe test plate mentioned above is useful for practice because the cover glasses of the separate specimens are of different thicknesses. This correction increases in importance as the focal length of the objective decreases. It is especially important for the 4-mm and the 3-mm objectives, and some microscopists do not use these objectives for this reason. In the case of oil-immersion objectives, the correction is almost negligible because the index of the oil is similar to that of the glass. Even in this case, however, it is desirable to adhere to the proper cover-glass thickness because the dispersion of the oil is somewhat different from that of the glass. Some high-power dry objectives are fitted with correction collars to compensate for variations in the cover-glass thickness by altering the separation of the lens elements.

One of the chief precautions to be observed in microscopy is not to allow the objective to come into violent contact with the slide. In focusing a dry objective having a focal length of 8 mm or less, the proper procedure is to lower the microscope until the objective is seen to be *almost* in contact with the cover glass, and then to rack it backward until the specimen comes into focus. For a 4-mm or a 3-mm objective, this should be done with the slow-motion knob. If the objective is of the oil-immersion type, the microscope should be lowered until the drop of oil just makes contact and then carefully lowered further with the slow-motion knob until the specimen comes into focus. Microscopes are constructed nowadays so that the slow-motion mechanism ceases to function when the objective touches the slide.

187. Photomicrography.—The technique of making photographs with the aid of a microscope is called *photomicrography.* From an optical standpoint, the only change required is to form a real image that can be recorded on a plate rather than a virtual image to be observed by the eye. Since objectives are commonly corrected for a single working distance, it is clear that the real image should be obtained by withdrawing the draw tube rather than by refocusing the objective. A very satisfactory procedure is to compute a table giving the tube length required at each magnification to keep the working distance of the objective constant at the value for which it was corrected.

One important problem in photomicrography is to obtain sufficient illumination to make the exposures reasonably short. With a source of a given brightness, the illumination on the plate depends, of course, upon the size of the cone of light that comes to focus there, as was shown in Chap. XIX. Now, from the sine law, the ratio of the numerical aperture in the object space to that in the image space is exactly equal to the linear magnification between the object and its image on the plate (for a dry objective). In photomicrography there is no quantity that corresponds to the normal magnifying power of a visual instrument, and hence there is a distinct advantage as regards time of exposure in making the magnification as small as is consistent with the graininess of the emulsion. In Fig. 241, the effective source of light is a piece of ground glass or the equivalent, and, although its brightness is high enough for the visual use of a microscope, the time of exposure would be very great if this system of illumination were used in photomicrography. As a consequence, most workers employ what is known as *Köhler illumination,* which is produced by a system like that sketched in Fig. 244. The source in this case is a ribbon-filament lamp like that shown in Fig. 79 of Chap. IX. An enlarged image of the filament is formed on the diaphragm of the substage condenser by means of the collector lens, and the substage condenser in turn focuses an image of this lens on the specimen. With this arrangement, the diaphragm at the collector lens acts as the field stop of the illuminating system and the diaphragm at the substage condenser acts as the aperture stop. The former can therefore be closed down until only the region of the object to be photographed is illuminated, and the latter can be regulated until the objective is properly filled and the image appears most satisfactory. If the collector lens and substage condenser are free from aberrations, it can be

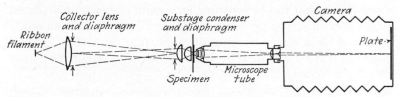

Fig. 244.—Apparatus for making photomicrographs using Köhler illumination.

shown that this method of illumination gives a resolving power equal to that obtained by the conventional arrangement.

An idea of the time of exposure required in photomicrography can be obtained by calculations involving the data on light sources given in Chap. IX and the sensitivity of photographic materials given in Chap. XI. Suppose, for example, that it is desired to make a photomicrograph of a specimen containing significant detail that is 0.0005 mm in size. Equation (252) indicates that for green light of a wave length of 500 mμ, the numerical aperture should be approximately 0.5. Most microscopists find it convenient to use a magnification approximately 500 times the numerical aperture. According to this rule, the magnification in this case should be 250 times, and the smallest detail in the object will be represented by a diffraction disk a little more than 0.1 mm in diameter. Although photographic materials are capable of recording somewhat finer detail, magnifying to this extent makes the graininess of the plate of little consequence. With a magnification of 250, the numerical aperture in the image space is

$$\frac{0.5}{250} = 0.002 \,.$$

Now, from Eq. (223) of Chap. XIX, the illumination on the plate is

$$E' = \pi B \, \sin^2 \theta',$$

where $\sin \theta'$ is the numerical aperture in the image space. At the temperature at which the filaments of lamps used in microscopy are generally operated, the brightness is in the neighborhood of 1000 candles/cm^2. The illumination on the plate in this case is therefore approximately 0.01 lumen/cm^2 or 100 lumens/meter^2 in the clear areas of the specimen. These areas should ordinarily receive an exposure approximately 100 times the inertia of the plate[1] in order that detail in the entire specimen may be recorded. With a photographic material having an H and D speed of 500, the inertia is 0.02 lumen-sec./meter^2 and the required exposure is therefore 2 lumen-sec./meter^2. The time of exposure must therefore be $\frac{1}{50}$ sec. This calculation makes no allowance for losses within the system, which are very great because of the large number of air-glass surfaces. In addition, the specimen is frequently stained and a color filter may be used, thus increasing the time of exposure still further.

It is coming to be realized that the combination of a microscope with a motion-picture camera is an exceedingly useful tool for both instruction and research. Processes that take place so slowly that they cannot be observed with the eye can be photographed at a slow speed. They can then be projected at the normal projection speed to accelerate the action and thus facilitate its study. The magnification required in *cine-photomicrography*, as this technique is called, is ordinarily low because of the great magnification of the image projected on the screen. Sometimes the ocular may be dispensed with entirely and the image formed by the objective allowed to fall directly on the film.

The most annoying feature about cine-photomicrography is the tendency of the image to quiver or to go out of focus because of the vibration of the camera. This can be greatly reduced by placing the microscope on a table and mounting the camera on a wall above it. With the usual type of optical

---

[1] This exposure gives a density of two when the plate is developed to a gamma of unity. If the plate is developed to a higher gamma, as it frequently is for the sake of increasing the contrast, the exposure may be somewhat less.

system, the slight relative displacements of camera and micro-scope due to the vibration will still be recorded on the film, but this can be avoided by a method described by one of the authors.[1] It consists in focusing the microscope visually, taking great care that the image is formed at infinity, and equipping the camera with an ordinary objective that is likewise focused for infinity. The apparatus is shown schematically in Fig. 245. By actual test, the camera can be moved by as much as $\frac{1}{4}$ in. either parallel to the optical axis or perpendicular to it without causing the image on the film to move perceptibly or to go out of focus.

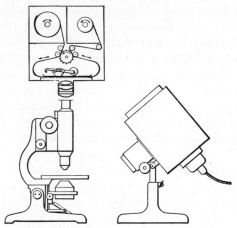

FIG. 245.—Apparatus for cine-photomicrography.

Even for ordinary photomicrography, this arrangement is very convenient because a single camera will serve any number of microscopes, and no additional adjustments are needed before the photographs are made.

188. Depth of Field.—It was shown by Eq. (235) of Chap. XXI that the total depth of field of any system forming a real image of an object that is not too distant is

$$d = 2\frac{z'}{m} \cdot \frac{p}{\rho},$$

where z' is the permissible radius of the circle of confusion, m is the linear magnification between the object and its image, p is the distance from the object plane that is in focus to the entrance pupil of the system, and ρ is the radius of the entrance pupil. The

[1] *Jour. Soc. Motion Picture Eng.*, **17**, 216 (1931).

ratio p/ρ will be recognized at once as the cotangent of θ, where $\sin\theta$ is the numerical aperture of the system for a dry objective. Since z' should be proportional to m, the depth of field is obviously fixed by the numerical aperture of the system. Stopping down the objective—a procedure that is permissible in ordinary photography—cannot be employed because the resolving power is reduced. Neither is it of any advantage to make a small negative and subsequently enlarge it, because m appears as the first power and not as the square.[1]

It is not often appreciated how extraordinarily small the depth of field of a photomicrographic camera really is. The smallest detail of the specimen that can be resolved is given by Eq. (252) as

$$z = \frac{\lambda}{2(\text{N.A.})}.$$

There is no reason for requiring the circle of confusion to be smaller than the image of an object of this size, and we may therefore set the value of z' in Eq. (235) equal to m times the value of z computed from the above equation. With this substitution, Eq. (235) becomes

$$d = 2z\frac{p}{\rho}. \tag{253}$$

But

$$\frac{p}{\rho} = \cot\theta = \frac{\cos\theta}{\sin\theta}$$

and

$$z = \frac{\lambda}{2n\,\sin\theta}.$$

Hence

$$d = \frac{\lambda\cos\theta}{n\sin^2\theta} = \frac{\lambda\,\sqrt{n^2 - (\text{N.A.})^2}}{(\text{N.A.})^2}. \tag{254}$$

For small values of the numerical aperture, the depth varies inversely as the square of the numerical aperture.

The depth of field of a microscope when used visually is much greater than it is when used photographically for two reasons. In the first place, the range of accommodation of the eye corresponds to a considerable depth of field, which can be added to the ordinary depth of the system itself. A more important

[1] The difference between this case and the one discussed in Sec. 169, Chap. XXI, is that photographic objectives were compared on the basis of equal exposures, whereas microscope objectives must be compared on the basis of equal resolving power and hence equal numerical aperture.

reason, however, is that the microscopist in studying a three-dimensional object is able to rack the microscope up and down so as to bring the various planes of the specimen into focus in succession.   As a result, there is built up in the brain a mental picture of the specimen that cannot be obtained from a photograph.   This factor is, of course, incapable of numerical evaluation, but we can evaluate the two other factors: first, the depth of field in a visual microscope for an observer lacking the power of accommodation; and, second, the additional depth resulting from the observer's power of accommodation.

Let us imagine first an observer focused on a real object at a distance of 250 mm in front of his eyes.   Since the resolving power of the unaided eye is about one minute of arc, it follows that the smallest circle that can be resolved in the object has a radius of 0.036 mm.   If we substitute this value for z in Eq. (110) of Chap. V and assume that the entrance pupil of the observer's eye is 2 mm in diameter, the total depth of field is 19 mm.   Therefore, if the observer looks through the microscope with a 2-mm exit pupil at a virtual image that is 250 mm from his eye, he is able to see distinctly all objects whose images lie within this range of 19 mm.   The corresponding range in the object space depends upon the longitudinal magnification of the system.   By combining Eqs. (94) and (96) in Chap. IV and assuming the medium at each end of the system to be air, it is easy to show that

$$dx = -\frac{dx'}{m^2}. \tag{255}$$

In other words, if the image is displaced by a distance dx', the corresponding displacement dx of the object is obtained by dividing by the square of the magnification.   Since the image is assumed to be formed at 250 mm, m is equal to the magnifying power given by Eq. (247).   Thus, if an observer has an unaccommodated depth of 19 mm with the unaided eye when viewing a real object at 250 mm, the corresponding depth in a microscope is simply this quantity divided by M^2.   For a microscope with a magnifying power of 100, the depth of field is 0.0019 mm.

Now consider the effect on the depth of field if the observer is able to accommodate for an object at infinity as well as one at 250 mm.   If a microscope is to form a virtual image at infinity, the object must, of course, lie in the first focal plane of the entire system. On the other hand, when it forms an image at 250 mm, which can be assumed to be measured from the second focal point of the system since that is very close to the eye point, the object must be located inside the first focal point of the system by a distance

$$x = \frac{f^2}{x'} .$$

But since f is given by Eq. (239) in Chap. XXII as

$$f = \frac{250}{M} \text{ (mm)},$$

and since $x' = 250$ mm, the displacement of the object plane required to form an image at 250 mm instead of at infinity is

$$x = \frac{250}{M^2} \text{ (mm)}. \qquad (256)$$

Thus for a microscope with a magnifying power of 100, the depth of field due to the observer's accommodation is 0.025 mm, which is considerably in excess of the factor calculated previously.

A comparison of this depth with that obtained in a photomicrograph is of interest. To secure the assumed 2-mm exit pupil in a visual microscope magnifying 100 times, the numerical aperture of the objective would be 0.4. Substituting this value in Eq. (254), the depth of field in the photomicrograph is 0.0024 mm, which is only about one-tenth of the depth of the visual microscope.

189. Dark-field Illumination. Ultramicroscopy.—According to Abbe's theory, the details in a microscopic specimen are visible by virtue of the diffraction patterns they produce. If a particle is too small to be resolved by the instrument, the result is a diffraction pattern on the retina whose size is independent of the size of the particle. However, the amount of light diffracted by the particle depends upon its size, so very small particles are invisible when viewed against the bright background. It is clear, therefore, that if the brightness of the background is diminished, particles can be distinguished that would otherwise be invisible. Of course, the shape of the particles cannot be determined but their existence can be recognized.

The method of reducing the brightness of the background is to use an illuminating system such that the direct beam will not enter the objective. This result can be achieved with an ordinary condenser by moving the substage diaphragm to one side, in which case the only light entering the objective is the light that is diffracted by the specimen. A method that makes a more efficient use of the condenser is to open the diaphragm fully and insert a central stop that is just large enough to block off the rays that would enter the objective. The type of illumination thus produced is known as *dark-field illumination* in contradistinction to the *oblique illumination* produced by moving the diaphragm sidewise. A type of condenser especially adapted for dark-field illumination is shown at *A* in Fig. 246. It consists of a plano-convex block of glass, the curved sides forming a paraboloid of revolution. The entering rays of light are reflected to its focus, which is brought into coincidence with the specimen. The

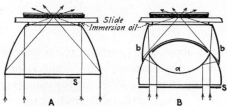

Fig. 246.—Condensers for dark-field illumination. *A*, a paraboloidal type; *B*, Siedentopf's cardioid.

diaphragm *S* blocks off the central rays, so the numerical aperture of the condenser varies from 1.1 at the diaphragm to 1.4 at the outer edge. It is evident that, if the numerical aperture of the objective is less than 1.1, the only light entering the objective is that diffracted by the specimen. A better type of dark-field condenser is the cardioid of Siedentopf, shown at *B* in the figure. As can be seen, the illuminating rays are reflected first at the spherical surface *a* and then at the cardioid *b*. This condenser, like the one just described, is free from both chromatic and spherical aberration, and, since it obeys the sine condition, it may properly be termed aplanatic. Under favorable conditions, particles as small as 0.000004 mm (4 mμ) in diameter can be seen under dark-field illumination.

190. Ultraviolet Microscopy.—It seems doubtful that it will ever be possible to make objectives having numerical apertures much greater than 1.4. On the other hand, the resolving power depends also upon the wave length of the light, which can be varied within wide limits. By using an apochromatic objective, it is possible to make photographs in violet light having a wave length in the neighborhood of 434 mμ (the wave length of the *G'*-line of hydrogen), and the resolving power is thereby increased 25 per cent over its value for green light at the maximum of visibility. The possibility of bettering this value by using ultraviolet light immediately suggests itself, and in 1904 Köhler designed an apparatus for making photomicrographs in light having a wave length of 275 mμ. The apparatus consists of a cadmium spark and a quartz monochromator to isolate the desired radiation. The optical elements of the microscope are similar to those of an ordinary microscope, but, of course, they are made of quartz and cannot be achromatized. Quartz must be used for the slide and the cover glass also, and the specimen must be mounted in glycerine because both glass and Canada balsam are opaque to ultraviolet light of this wave length.

The chief difficulties that present themselves in connection with this apparatus are those of aligning it and of focusing accurately. Once it is aligned it can be fixed in position, but it must be focused anew for each specimen. This can be accomplished by using an ocular furnished with a fluorescent ground glass, making a preliminary visual adjustment, and then taking several photographs, moving the slow-motion knob slightly between each. Trivelli and Foster[1] have recently devised photomicrographic equipment for light of 365 mμ that simplifies the technique enormously. The light is furnished by a mercury arc operating under conditions that make the radiations at 365 mμ very intense. The objectives are achromatized for 365 mμ and 546 mμ to permit the apparatus to be focused visually by light of the latter wave length. Since glass is fairly transparent at 365 mμ, no extensive changes are required in the accessory equipment. The specimens can be mounted with glass slides and cover glasses as usual, and Canada balsam can be used as the medium. Sandalwood oil is used as the immersion liquid because it is more transparent at 365 mμ than cedarwood oil. The resolving power of this apparatus with a numerical aperture of 1.40 is only 75 per cent of that of Köhler's apparatus, but it is a question whether the greater convenience does not more than compensate for this disadvantage.

Aside from furnishing greater resolving power, ultraviolet microscopy provides a means for studying specimens when all parts are equally transparent in the visible region but not in the

---

[1] *Jour. Optical Soc. Amer.*, **21**, 124 (1931).

ultraviolet, thus obviating the necessity of staining the specimen. Ultraviolet light must be used with caution in the study of living specimens, such as bacteria, however, because of its powerful bactericidal action.   Nevertheless, it is safe to say that a vast field for research will be opened by a convenient method of using short wave-length ultraviolet radiation in microscopy.

CHAPTER XXV

STEREOSCOPY

In monocular vision, information is obtained with respect to the distance of an object in a variety of ways. If the size of the object is known, its distance can be estimated from the angle it subtends. Even if its size is not known, the amount of accommodation required to bring it into focus gives some information regarding its location, provided it is not too distant. If the observer happens to be in motion, as on a railroad train, the distance of the object can be estimated from its apparent velocity, extremely distant objects appearing to be stationary and those in the foreground appearing to move rapidly. The same effect is produced to a lesser extent by simply moving the head.

A person possessing binocular vision ordinarily makes but slight use of these methods of estimating distances, as is easily demonstrated by attempting to thread a needle with one eye closed. Since the entrance pupils of the two eyes are not in coincidence, the images on the retinas are slightly dissimilar and this dissimilarity enables the brain to construct a mental picture of the scene in three dimensions. This circumstance is the basis of several important instruments that utilize the principles of binocular vision to enable the observer to form a three-dimensional picture of the object space. The entire psychophysical process leading to the interpretation of the object space by the brain of the observer involves physiology and psychology quite as much as physics, and therefore lies beyond the scope of the present volume. Nevertheless, the principles of *stereoscopy* itself—the method of representing a three-dimensional object space by means of an optical instrument adapted for use with both eyes—can be discussed from purely geometrical considerations. The binocular microscope and telescope and the stereoscopic camera are the principal stereoscopic instruments, and, for reasons that will appear later, they are becoming of increasing importance.

191. The Theory of Stereoscopy.—The principles upon which stereoscopic instruments operate are the same for all, but for simplicity the stereoscopic camera will be taken as an illustration. In Fig. 247, the pyramid ABC is photographed with a camera containing two lenses separated by a distance d, both lenses being focused on the plane AB at a distance x_0 from the entrance pupils. The image of A formed by the lens on the left is at A_L, and the image formed by the lens on the right is at A_R. Similarly, the images of B are at B_L and B_R respectively. The images of C are out of focus; but, if the depth of field is sufficiently great, the image formed by the lens on the left is at B_L and that formed by the lens on the right at A_R.*

Now suppose that the photographic plate is developed and that transparencies are made from it which are enlarged m times. Let the transparency made from the negative produced by the lens on the left be mounted as in Fig. 248 at a distance s' from the entrance pupil of the observer's left eye. Let the transparency made with the lens on the right be mounted at the same distance from the right eye. The point A_L' corresponds to the point A_L in the negative, B_L' to B_L, A_R' to A_R, and B_R' to B_R. By supposition, of course,

$$(A_L'B_L') = m(A_LB_L)$$

and

$$(A_R'B_R') = m(A_RB_R).$$

Now it follows from the geometry of Fig. 248 that

$$\frac{d'}{x_0'} = \frac{(A_L'B_L')}{s'} = \frac{(A_R'B_R')}{s'},$$

where d' is the interpupillary distance of the observer. But

$$\frac{A_LB_L}{s} = \frac{A_L'B_L'}{ms}$$

and

$$\frac{A_RB_R}{s} = \frac{A_R'B_R'}{ms},$$

from which

$$x_0' = x_0 \frac{s'd'}{msd}. \tag{257}$$

---

* This example is, of course, a very special case, but, as it leads to the same result as the more general treatment, it is chosen because of the simplification of the algebraic operations.

In other words, the observer looking at a pair of transparencies in the manner illustrated in Fig. 248 sees a pyramid whose base

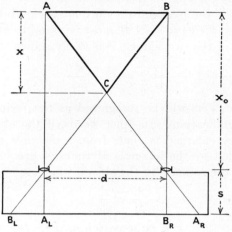

Fig. 247.

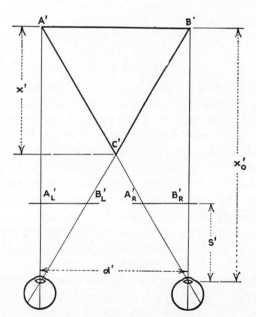

Fig. 248.

$A'B'$ appears to be at a distance x_0'. If the quantities in Eq. (257) are properly chosen, x_0' can be made equal to x_0—that is, the base of the pyramid will appear to be at the same distance from the eye as the actual object was from the camera.

To represent the spatial relationships properly it is necessary in addition that the pyramid should not appear to be distorted. In other words, the ratio $x'/A'B'$ must be equal to x/AB. From the geometry of the two figures, it is easily shown that

$$\frac{x'}{A'B'} = \frac{x}{AB} \cdot \frac{s'}{ms}. \tag{258}$$

The quantity s'/ms will be recognized as the reciprocal of the apparent magnification. In other words, if the observer views a transparency enlarged m times from a distance s', the visual angle subtended by the image is M times as great as the angle subtended at the camera by the object. Setting

$$\frac{1}{M} = \frac{s'}{ms}, \tag{259}$$

Eqs. (257) and (258) can be rewritten in the form

$$x_0' = x_0 \frac{d'}{Md} \tag{260}$$

and

$$\frac{x'}{A'B'} = \frac{x}{AB} \cdot \frac{1}{M}. \tag{261}$$

It is clear from Eq. (261) that, if the pyramid is to appear undistorted, M must be equal to unity. With this assumption, Eq. (260) indicates that, if the pyramid is also to appear at the proper distance, d must be equal to d'. It will be recalled from Sec. 170, Chap. XXI, that M must be equal to unity if the spatial relationships are to be properly represented in a single picture. Therefore the only additional requirement for orthostereoscopic results is that the separation of the camera objectives must equal the interpupillary distance of the observer.

Since the above conditions are rarely fulfilled by binocular instruments, it is of interest to consider the types of distortion that may result. If the magnifying power of the instrument is greater than unity, as is generally the case, Eq. (261) indicates that the depth of an object is magnified less than its transverse dimensions. The apparent distance of the object depends not only upon the magnification but also upon the separation of the entrance pupils of the instrument. For example, if the separation is too great, the reproduction has the appearance of a model on a reduced scale situated at a proportionately diminished distance from the observer.

It is clear that if M is equal to unity and the separation of the entrance pupils of the instrument is the same as that of the eyes, the ability to recognize relief in the object space with a perfect instrument is the same as with the unaided eyes. The minimum relief that is perceptible with the unaided eyes can be computed by the aid of Fig. 249. Let the point A lie at a distance a from the observer and the point B at a distance b, where a and b are both very large compared with the interpupillary distance d'. It can then be shown that

$$\alpha = d'\left(\frac{1}{a} - \frac{1}{b}\right). \qquad (262)$$

If A and B are to be visible in relief, it is reasonable to assume that α must be equal to or greater than the minimum angle that can be resolved, which has heretofore been considered to be approximately one minute of arc (0.00029 radian). From the above equation, the distance

$$AB = b - a = \frac{ab}{d'}\,\alpha. \qquad (263)$$

Thus, if a is 100 ft. and the observer has a normal interpupillary distance (62 mm), the distance AB is 14 ft. If B is at an infinite distance, Eq. (262) becomes simply

$$\alpha = \frac{d'}{a},$$

whence

$$a = \frac{d'}{\alpha}. \qquad (264)$$

In this case, a is the distance beyond which no relief is discernible. This is frequently called the *radius of stereoscopic vision*, and equals 200 meters (700 ft.) when $d' = 62$ mm and $\alpha = 1'$.

If an optical instrument has a magnifying power M and a pupillary separation d, it can be readily seen that Eq. (263) becomes

$$AB = b - a = \frac{ab}{Md}\alpha.$$ (265)

In corresponding fashion, Eq. (264) becomes

$$a = \frac{dM}{\alpha}.$$ (266)

The manner in which this increased ability to perceive relief is utilized in practical instruments will be discussed in the sections that are to follow.

An interesting type of distortion of the spatial relationships is produced when the binocular instrument is so arranged that the images are transposed. This is illustrated in Fig. 250, which is similar to Fig. 248 except that the transparency made with the lens on the right is placed before the left eye, and that made with the lens on the left is placed before the right eye. Since C' then appears to the left eye to coincide with A' instead of with B', and since to the right eye it seems to coincide with B' instead of A', the brain is led to assume that C is located behind the plane of AB. In other words, the relief is reversed—near-by objects appearing to be far away and distant objects appearing to be close at hand. This effect is said to be *pseudoscopic* in contradistinction to stereoscopic. A

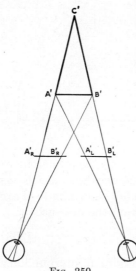

FIG. 250.

true pseudoscopic illusion is produced only when the brain is unable to obtain information about the spatial relationships in any other manner. In a landscape, for example, a previous knowledge of the relative sizes of the various objects and a realization of the positions of the shadows they must cast prevent the pseudoscopic effect from being produced. The best objects for exhibiting the pseudoscopic effect are those lacking any well-marked characteristics, such as spheres, cylinders, and other geometrical models. The effect is particularly striking in the case of a sphere, which takes on the appearance of the inner wall of a rubber ball. Stereoscopic photographs were made by aerial photographers during the war, and many of these exhibit striking pseudoscopic effects when transposed. Not only is the topography of the country reversed, but shell holes take on the appearance of mounds and the water in a reservoir stands higher than the top of the dam.

192. Binocular Telescopes.—Because the magnifying power of a telescope is always greater than unity, it follows from Eq. (261) that a true-to-nature representation of the object space is impossible. Fortunately, however, this inherent limitation is more than offset by the increased ability to separate the various planes in the object space when they lie at a great distance from the observer, as is shown by Eq. (265). This increased stereoscopic effect is brought about partly as a result of the magnification and in some cases partly by separating the objectives more than the oculars. In prism binoculars, for example, the separation of the objectives is approximately twice the interpupillary distance. Thus an eight-power binocular increases the radius of stereoscopic vision from 700 ft. to sixteen times this value or approximately two miles. Of course, the image appears to be sixteen times nearer, and the ratio of the depth dimension to the transverse dimensions is reduced eight-fold.

Although the primary purpose of separating the objectives in ordinary prism binoculars is to enable an erecting prism system to be introduced, certain types of telescopes are made with objectives separated by comparatively large distances to attain a pronounced stereoscopic effect. These stereoscopic binoculars are of especial value to an artillery commander because they enable him to estimate with great accuracy the spots where shells land.

One form of range-finder consists essentially of a binocular telescope with a scale in each ocular. This scale appears to the observer like a zigzag row of dots receding to infinity. These dots are superposed upon the scene itself, and every object in the scene appears to lie in the same plane as some one of them. It is not difficult to determine which dot coincides with an object, and the stereoscopic sense of a normal individual is so acute that the determination can be made very quickly. This is of importance in locating rapidly moving objects, such as airplanes, for which the coincidence type of range-finder is not suited because of its slowness of operation.[1]

---

[1] The coincidence type of range-finder is essentially a binocular telescope in which the image in one half of the field is formed by one objective and

One result of an increased separation of the entrance pupils in a binocular telescope is to increase the so-called *penetration effect.* It is clear that if observations must be made in a snow-storm or through underbrush, the object toward which the instrument is directed may be momentarily obscured from one eye but not the other. The greater the separation of the entrance pupils of the instrument, the greater the ability to see around an obstruction. Of course, the penetrating power of even a monocular instrument is ordinarily greater than that of the eye alone because of its larger entrance pupil.

193. Binocular Microscopes.—The principles just discussed apply with equal force to the binocular microscope. However,

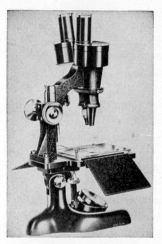

Fig. 251.—A typical two-tube binocular microscope for low powers. (*By courtesy of Bausch and Lomb Optical Company.*)

the objects examined by the microscope are frequently invisible to the unaided eye, so it is impossible to set up any standard of true-to-nature representation. Nevertheless, binocular microscopes are being used to an increasing extent. For magnifying powers below approximately seventy times, an instrument of the type shown in Fig. 251 is eminently satisfactory. Since the images must be inverted and reversed, an optical system similar to that of the prism binocular is used. At high powers, the working distance is so short that a single objective is used, the beam being divided so that the light entering each half of the objective passes into the corresponding ocular. This is done by means of a suitable prism system, which also assumes the duty of inverting and reversing the images. Such an instrument has in effect two entrance pupils of semicircular form, the centers of which subtend a considerable angle at the object.

that in the other half is formed by the other. The angular movement of a prism that is required to bring the images in the two halves of the field into coincidence is a measure of the distance of the object. An excellent discussion of range-finders will be found in the English translation of Gleichen's "The Theory of Modern Optical Instruments."

Many binocular microscopes that are not stereoscopic are on the market, and they are becoming popular among those who use microscopes for long periods at a time because of the increased comfort of viewing an image with both eyes rather than with one. Figure 252 shows the optical system that is frequently used in such micro-scopes. The beam from the objec-tive enters a prism as shown, where part of it is reflected at the half-silvered interface AB and part of it is transmitted. The two beams are then reflected into the oculars E_L and E_R. The coating of metal on the face AB is of the proper thickness to

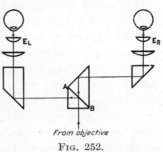

From objective

FIG. 252.

transmit approximately the same proportion of light that it reflects and thus the two images have the same brightness. When a stereoscopic effect is desired, a cap can be placed on each ocular to cover one half of each exit pupil.

Stereoscopic photomicrographs can be made with the instru-ment shown in Fig. 251 by attaching a camera to record both images. The method of viewing the photographs will be described in the following section. If this type of instrument is not at hand, or if the magnifying power is so great that it can-not be used, two photographs can be made in succession, the specimen being moved between the exposures. This movement

FIG. 253.

can be a rotation about an axis parallel to the stage of the microscope or it can be a translation of the specimen along the stage. A much more satisfactory procedure is to place a diaphragm of the shape shown in Fig. 253 against the back lens of the objective and to rotate it through 180° between the exposures. By all these methods, the entrance pupils for the two photographs are effec-tively separated and a stereoscopic result is therefore produced.

It is difficult to lay down any exact rules for the amount of stereoscopic effect that is desirable in either microscopy or photomicrography. At best the appearance of relief is obtained only within the limited depth of field of the system. Hence the proper correlation of magnification with the stereoscopic viewing angle varies considerably with the type of specimen and must be found by experiment.

194. Stereoscopic Photography.—The essential principles of stereoscopic photography were set forth in Sec. 191 in connection with the theory of stereoscopy. It was there shown that if a pair of stereoscopic photographs is placed before the eyes in the proper manner, as in Fig. 248, a three-dimensional representation of the object space is obtained. Unless some sort of viewing apparatus is used to assist the accommodation process, it is obviously necessary to place the transparencies or prints at least 10 in. from the eyes. Even so, the observer's accommodation-convergence sense would cause him to rotate his eyes until their axes intersect at the distance for which the eyes are accommodated rather than to diverge as shown in the figure. With practice, some observers are able to overcome their accommodation-convergence sense sufficiently to fuse the two images

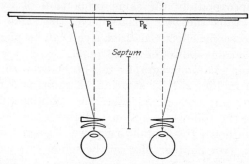

Fig. 254.—The path of the light rays in a prismatic stereoscope. The septum prevents the picture P_L on the left from being seen by the right eye and *vice versa.*

while keeping them sharply focused at the same time. Unless an observer is especially trained, however, an instrument known as a stereoscope is required for viewing stereoscopic photographs. About a generation ago, every parlor table boasted a stereoscope and a set of slides, but with the increased use of magazine illustrations and the introduction of the motion picture, the stereoscope went thoroughly out of fashion. This abandonment of the instrument was entirely undeserved because it is possible with two pictures to produce a lifelike representation that is beyond the ability of even the motion picture.

The most common type of stereoscope is shown in Fig. 254, and its operation is self-evident. Inasmuch as the objectives of stereoscopic cameras have focal lengths of approximately 5 in., the apparent magnification is unity only when they are viewed from this distance. Lenses of some sort are therefore necessary to assist the accommodation process of the observer. If these lenses have a focal length of 5 in., the axes of the eyes will be parallel. The individual photographs could then be no wider than the interpupillary distance, but, by introducing prisms as shown, the axes can be diverged so as to permit larger pictures to be viewed. In inexpensive stereoscopes, the prismatic effect is obtained by decentering the lenses. In precision instruments, rhombs are preferable because they avoid the distortion introduced by prisms.

An early type of stereoscope, invented by Wheatstone in 1838, is sketched in Fig. 255. The two pictures P_L and P_R are seen in the mirrors M_L and M_R. This type of apparatus is used to-day for viewing X-ray stereograms, which are so large

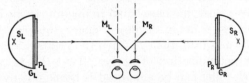

Fig. 255.—A type of stereoscope used for viewing X-ray stereograms.

that they cannot be conveniently mounted side by side. They are illuminated by the lamps S_L and S_R, pieces of opal glass G_L and G_R being placed as shown to make the illumination uniform.

Stereoscopic photographs can be made with an ordinary camera by photographing the scene twice, the camera being moved sidewise by the proper amount between the exposures. This procedure cannot be used if the object is in motion, so cameras especially designed for making stereoscopic photographs have two objectives of the same focal length, both shutters being arranged to operate simultaneously. Both pictures are made on the same film. By following through the various processes of development and printing, it will be seen that contact prints made from a plate or film exposed in such a camera must be cut apart and transposed to satisfy the primary requirement of stereoscopy—namely, that the left eye view the positive made with the left-hand lens and the right eye view the positive made with the right-hand lens. Ingenious cameras for making the original exposures in the proper relative positions on the film have been devised, but they are little used.

If there is no motion in the object space to record, stereoscopic photographs with a greatly enhanced relief can be made with a single camera by photographing from two widely separated points of view. This ability to enhance relief was used to great advantage by aerial photographers during the war. To keep out of range of anti-aircraft guns, it was necessary to fly at elevations of 10,000 ft. or more, and from such elevations the ground and objects upon it lie beyond the radius of stereoscopic vision for the unaided eyes. However, by making two photographs with the same camera several seconds apart, a stereoscopic pair can be obtained in which the relief is greatly exaggerated. One would expect the practical limit to the amount of exaggeration to be reached when the stereoscopic base is such that the nearest object appears to be at the conventional reading distance. Equation (260) shows that if two photographs are made with a stereoscopic base equal to one-fourth of the elevation above the nearest plane in the object space, this plane will appear to be only 250 mm from the eye when the prints are viewed under an apparent magnification of unity. That this is the practical limit to which relief can be enhanced is borne out by experience. It has been found that, when the base is equal to the altitude, an excessive strain is required on the part of the observer; but, when the base is reduced to one-tenth of the altitude, the observer feels that the relief could be enhanced still further without discomfort.

These stereoscopic photographs with enhanced relief were exceedingly useful during the war in locating gun emplacements, which, although skillfully camouflaged, necessarily extended several feet above the ground. In the stereoscope, the exaggeration of the depth dimension caused these emplacements to become conspicuous. In other words, the scene in the stereoscope appeared to the observer exactly as the original scene would have appeared to a giant with an interpupillary distance equal to the stereoscopic base.

One detail in the mounting of aerial stereograms is of sufficient interest to justify mentioning. The photographs are generally made with the camera pointed vertically downward, so the center of each picture can ordinarily be assumed to lie directly below the airplane at the time the exposure was made. Thus the two photographs represent slightly different portions of the terrain, and the stereoscopic effect is obtained only in the portion that is common to both. This is illustrated in Fig. 256, which shows two such photographs overlapped in register. The line of flight of the airplane is the line joining the centers *A* and *B* of the two prints, which, for obvious reasons, must be mounted on the stereoscopic slide so that the line of flight is horizontal. The dotted rectangle indicates the method by which a stereoscopic pair of photographs could be cut out.

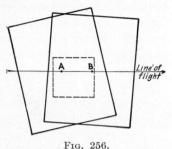

Fig. 256.

Stereoscopic photography is used to a limited extent in surveying. It is possible to prepare a map in this way from photographs made on the ground, and, if the camera is properly constructed and the base is accurately measured, excellent results can be obtained. Several ingenious instruments, known as stereo-comparators, have been devised for rapidly tracing the contours from a pair of stereoscopic pictures.

Many astronomical phenomena can be exhibited in a very striking manner with the aid of stereoscopic photography, the moon being one of the most interesting subjects. The period of rotation of the moon on its axis is exactly the same as its period of revolution about the earth, and hence, if its orbit were circular, it would always present the same side to the earth. Actually its orbit is somewhat elliptical and, as a consequence, it appears to oscillate slightly.[1] By making two photographs of the moon several days apart, the effect of a very great stereoscopic base is obtained.

A very interesting method of making a photograph that produces a stereoscopic effect without the use of a stereoscope was patented in 1903 by F. E. Ives. It is shown diagrammatically in Fig. 257, where O_1 and O_2 are the objectives of the camera, *P* is the plate, and *R* is a grating that causes alternate strips of the plate to be exposed through the two objectives. If the apparatus is properly designed, the plate when processed and viewed through a similar grating R' will produce a stereoscopic effect because each eye sees only the strips that constitute the image made through one of the objectives. Stereograms of this type were called by their inventor "parallax stereograms."

---

[1] This apparent motion is what astronomers term "libration."

Many attempts have been made to devise a satisfactory method for projecting stereoscopic pictures, especially stereoscopic motion pictures. It is desirable, of course, to project both images on the same screen; and, to satisfy the requirements for stereoscopic vision, some means must be provided to enable the left eye to see only the picture taken with the left-hand objective of the camera and the right eye only the picture taken with the right-hand objective. One method of doing this is to

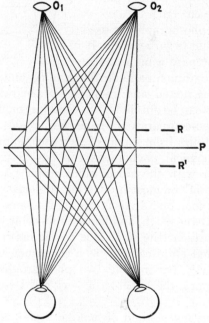

Fig. 257.

project the two pictures, either simultaneously or in rapid alternation, through red and green filters respectively. If the observers wear spectacles with a red filter over one eye and a green filter over the other, the requisite separation is obtained. If the filters are approximately complementary in color, the screen looks white. Stereograms of this type are known as anaglyphs. Another method of separating the pictures is to project the left-hand and right-hand pictures alternately and to provide each observer with spectacles in which a shutter covers first one eye and then the other in synchronism. The outstanding disadvantage of any of these methods is that the spectator must wear some viewing device. To avoid this difficulty, H. E. Ives[1] has devised a method based upon the principle of the parallax stereogram mentioned above. Although this method in its present form is hardly suitable for commercial projection, it embodies many ingenious tricks that are highly suggestive.

It may be remarked in passing that almost every invention for improving the motion-picture art is accompanied by the claim that it produces a stereoscopic effect. Not infrequently the term is used to describe the impression of depth that is produced when a single photograph is viewed under the proper conditions. If the meaning of the term is restricted, as it should be, to the reproduction of the spatial relationships by the aid of the observer's binocular sense, it is clear that such claims are absurd. An understanding of the requirements for producing truly stereoscopic results would save much time and trouble for both the inventors of "stereoscopic" projection schemes and the examiners in the patent office.

195. The Measurement of Binocular Sense.—A numerical evaluation of the binocular sense is an important part of the examination of aviators and may occasionally be required in certain clinical cases. Persons suffering from strabismus lack this sense entirely, of course, because the images do not fall on corresponding parts of their two retinas. Even persons suffering from heterophoria frequently lose it to some extent, partly because of the constant distortion of the accommodation-convergence relationship, but more because such persons tend unconsciously to suppress the image formed by one eye.

An ordinary stereoscope, such as is shown in Fig. 254, is suitable for a quantitative determination of the acuity of the binocular sense when suitable test slides are used. Such a slide might consist of a series of photographs of a double row of rods arranged as shown in Fig. 258, the separation of the two rows and hence the angle α being different for each photograph. When only a qualitative determination is required, simple figures like a hollow cylinder or an arrow piercing a ring are satisfactory. For children, a drawing of a bird in a cage is commonly used. A very effective object is a rock pile in which one of the rocks is slightly displaced sidewise between exposures. A person lacking binocular sense sees nothing unusual in the resulting picture, but to a

[1] *Jour. Optical Soc. Amer. and Rev. Sci. Instruments*, **18**, 118 (1929); *Jour. Optical Soc. Amer.*, **21**, 109 (1931).

person possessing binocular sense, the rock that was moved appears to stand out in mid-air.[1]

Stereoscopic slides can be used to train the eyes to work together in cases of strabismus and severe heterophoria. One

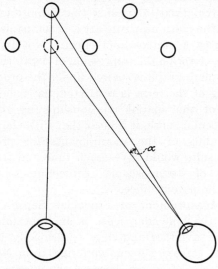

Fig. 258.

type of slide that is often used for this purpose consists of a series of words that appear to approach the observer from infinity. As

[1] The binocular sense of an individual is frequently utilized to detect a small change in a complicated scene or configuration. For example, a carpet may be compared with its master pattern by photographing both to the same scale and mounting the prints in a stereoscope with a red filter in front of one eye and a green filter in front of the other. Wherever the prints are identical, the two complementary colors are fused by the brain into a single image in black and white. On the other hand, the slightest difference between the two prints is immediately evident because the parts in question appear in color. This method was used to good advantage during the war for the detection of signs of activity by the enemy, a comparison of two aerial photographs taken on successive days indicating at a glance the trenches that had been dug during the interval. Astronomers used this method for the detection of new stars until the invention of the blink microscope. In this instrument, the new plate and an old plate are brought into register in the field of the ocular by means of a suitable optical system. The illumination is then switched from one to the other at a rate that is well below the critical frequency. This causes the new star to blink, since its image appears on only one of the plates, whereas the star images that appear on both plates remain constant in intensity.

the observer reads downward, he continues to fuse the image seen by the two eyes until the convergence required becomes excessively great, when the images are thereafter seen separately. The same result can be accomplished by using an ordinary slide and placing a Risley prism in front of one eye. This prism consists essentially of two ophthalmic prisms of equal power mounted so that they can be simultaneously rotated in their own plane at the same rate but in opposite directions. A ray of light passing through the pair of prisms is therefore deviated by a variable amount.

The least perceptible value of the angle α has been assumed in the discussion to be one minute of arc, because this is the approximate value of the resolving power of a normal eye. It is found, however, that a normal observer can perceive a much smaller angle than this stereoscopically, and a good representative value is 30''. Many people can detect an angle of 10'', and some especially keen individuals can detect an angle as small as 5''. Perhaps the most striking illustration of the extraordinary acuteness of the binocular sense is one given in 1859 by Dove and confirmed by Helmholtz. If two medallions cast from different metals but struck with the same die are viewed, one with the left eye and the other with the right, the resultant image appears curved simply because of the slight difference in the amount by which the two metals recover from the pressure exerted by the die.

CHAPTER XXVI

PROJECTION SYSTEMS

In general, a projection system is characterized by two distinguishing features: It usually forms a real image which is intercepted by a receiving surface, and it contains a source of light of high intrinsic brightness. The most typical instruments of this type are lantern-slide and motion-picture projectors, which form on a projection screen an image of the lantern slide or motion-picture film. Some projection systems, such as searchlights, spotlights, and signal lights, merely project an image of the source, which is usually formed at infinity. Others, which are used chiefly in the laboratory, record the deflection of a galvanometer or other measuring instrument by means of a spot of light that is projected on a screen or on a piece of photographic material.

196. Searchlights.—The optical system of the searchlight is represented schematically in Fig. 259. The source is the

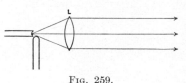

Fig. 259.

positive crater of an arc, which is located at the first focal point of the lens L, and hence the image of the arc is formed at infinity. This type of system was discussed in Sec. 146, Chap. XIX. It was there shown that, if the source obeys Lambert's law and the lens is aplanatic, the illumination at a point on the axis is given by the product of the brightness of the source and the solid angle subtended by the lens at the point in question.[1] This result leads at once to two rather important corollaries: first, the illumination at a point on the axis varies inversely as the square of its distance from the lens; second, the illumination depends only on the

---

[1] This is not true if the point is so close to the lens that the source is the aperture stop of the system. In this case, the exit pupil of the system is at infinity, and hence the illumination is independent of the position of the point.

intrinsic brightness of the source and not at all on its dimensions. In other words, increasing the size of the source merely produces a greater spread of the beam without increasing the illumination on an object within the beam.

Most light sources obey Lambert's law fairly well except for the obstruction of the light produced by the negative carbon or the supporting mechanism. Furthermore, lenses of low relative aperture are so nearly aplanatic, even when they are not especially designed with this end in view, that the conclusions reached above hold in practice to a close approximation. When the relative aperture is excessively high, however, the aberrations become so serious that an ordinary lens is inefficient. To remedy this difficulty, lenses of a type originally designed by Fresnel for lighthouses are commonly used. As can be seen from Fig. 260, a Fresnel lens may be regarded as a plurality of lenses, the curvature of the back surface of each zone being so chosen as to eliminate spherical aberration. Since Fresnel lenses are comparatively thin, their weight is less than that of an ordinary lens and they absorb a comparatively small amount of light.[1]

Fig. 260.

The Fresnel construction can be modified to distribute light in almost any desired manner. Thus, in a lighthouse lens, the light that would pass uselessly into the sky is directed horizontally where it can be seen from the surface of the water. Perhaps the best known modification of the Fresnel construction is in lenses for automobile headlights. These lenses are designed to distribute over the roadway the light that would otherwise reach the eyes of approaching motorists.

Large searchlights, such as are used for military purposes, usually contain a mirror instead of a lens. One important reason for this is the reduction in weight that can be effected, the difference in weight between a lens and a mirror 5 ft. in diameter being considerable. Moreover, the mirror is inherently free from chromatic aberrations; and, if it is paraboloidal in form, it is also free from spherical aberration when the source is imaged

---

[1] A similar type of construction is used in the lenses of signal lights to keep the thickness approximately the same for all zones, so that the color will appear to be uniform over the entire surface of the lens.

at infinity.[1] It goes without saying that the underlying principles are the same for both lenses and mirrors.

The mirrors used in projection systems are commonly silvered on the second surface, a procedure that is permissible because the glass of which such mirrors are constructed is so thin that it has no appreciable effect on the course of the light rays. Before practical methods of making aspheric mirrors were invented, spherical mirrors had perforce to be used. These suffer severely from spherical aberration when the image is formed elsewhere than at the center of curvature. This defect was remedied in large measure by the Mangin mirror, which is essentially a nega-

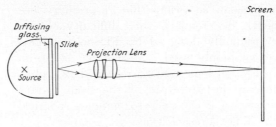

Fig. 261.

tive meniscus lens whose second surface is silvered. By choosing the radii properly, the spherical aberration can be corrected for any given position of the image.

197. Lantern-slide Projectors.—A lantern-slide projector consists essentially of an illuminating system behind the slide and a projection lens which forms an image of the slide on the screen. A very simple sort of projector is shown diagrammatically in Fig. 261. The source of light and a suitable reflector serve to illuminate an opal glass, which, because of its diffusing properties, becomes a secondary source of illumination. The projection lens is designed to form a sharp image of the slide on the screen. A photographic objective used in the reversed position would make an excellent projection lens, but, since the field to be covered is small, a simple triplet construction is generally used for reasons of expense.

The illumination on the screen depends only on the brightness of the opal glass and the solid angle subtended at the screen by the

---

[1] If the source is to be imaged at a point at a finite distance, the mirror should be ellipsoidal, the source being placed at one focus.

exit pupil of the projection lens.[1]   This solid angle is determined
by the projection distance (throw) and the diameter of the lens.[2]
The focal length of the lens is determined by the size of the
picture,[3] which should be chosen to satisfy the requirements of
true-to-nature representation.   From the principles that were
discussed in Sec. 170, Chap. XXI, it follows that the reproduction
on the screen should subtend the same angle at the eye of the
observer that the original scene subtended at the entrance pupil

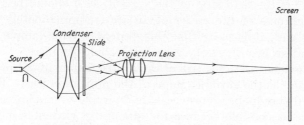

Fig. 262.—The optical system of a lantern-slide projector.

of the camera objective.   In practice, the lantern is generally
placed at the rear of the auditorium, and the focal length of the
projection lens is about twice that of the camera lens.   This
makes the perspective correct at a point midway between the
lantern and the screen.

The maximum brightness of a diffusing glass is so low that,
although the system shown in Fig. 261 is used in projection
printers for motion pictures and in enlarging cameras, it rarely
provides enough screen illumination for lantern-slide projection.[4]
For best results, the screen illumination should be approximately
10 foot-candles.   If the aperture of the projection lens is $2\frac{5}{16}$ in.
and the throw is 20 ft., the necessary brightness of the diffusing
glass can be computed by means of Eq. (223) to be 150 can-
dles/cm². A brightness as high as this could scarcely be obtained
with an illuminating system containing a diffusing element, and

[1] The screen illumination is always measured with the slide removed.

[2] Projection lenses are made in certain standard diameters.   The standard
diameter adopted by one leading manufacturer for lenses having focal
lengths of 10 in. or less is $1\frac{5}{8}$ in. (41 mm) and for those having focal lengths
of 10 in. or more, $2\frac{5}{16}$ in. (58 mm).

[3] In this country, the dimensions of lantern-slide plates are $3\frac{1}{4}$ in. × 4 in.
and the opening in the mask seldom exceeds $2\frac{3}{4}$ × 3 in.

[4] The same difficulty is encountered in the projection of opaque objects,
which can be done only with lenses having a very large aperture and even
then is practical only when the throw is short.

it is therefore common practice to make use of a system like that of Fig. 262. In this case, the source of light, which is here assumed to be the crater of a carbon arc, is imaged on the entrance pupil of the projection lens by means of a condenser. If the image of the crater more than fills the entrance pupil of the projection lens, it is obvious that the aperture stop of this lens is the aperture stop of the entire system. If the diameter of the condenser is larger than the diagonal of the slide, the mask in the slide is the field stop of the system, as it should be. Since the brightness of the crater of an arc is approximately 13,000 candles/cm², it is clear that this system provides ample screen illumination even for very great projection distances.

It is evident that the size of the source is immaterial provided its image fills the entrance pupil of the projection lens. From a practical standpoint, however, it is desirable to employ as small a source as possible because the amount of current required to operate an arc depends upon its size. This means that the magnification between the source and its image should be as great as possible. The limit is set by the aberrations of the condenser, which become serious as the focal length of the condenser is reduced. Moreover, to obtain a high magnification, the source must be placed so near the condenser that there is danger of pitting the latter by hot particles thrown off from the arc or even cracking it by the heat. Ordinarily, a magnification of approximately six times between the source and its image is found to represent the useful limit.

Nowadays, incandescent lamps are used more than arcs in lantern-slide projectors because they are much more convenient to operate and provide ample illumination unless the throw is excessively great. Special projection lamps are made with the type of filament shown in Fig. 263, all the coils of which lie in a single plane. By placing such a filament at the center of curvature of a spherical mirror located behind the lamp, an image of the filament can be formed between the coils of the filament itself. The result is a nearly uniform rectangle of light having a brightness approaching that of a tungsten surface at the temperature at which the lamp is operated. Since the filament is imaged at the aperture stop of the projection lens, it is clear that an image of the filament is not formed on the screen. Hence the illumination of the screen is uniform even though the brightness of the source is not.

198. Motion-picture Projectors.—The optical system shown in Fig. 262 is seldom used for projecting motion pictures because a frame of motion-picture film is smaller than the projection lens. Hence, with a condenser that is capable of a given magnification, a smaller source can be used if its image is formed on the film gate rather than on the projection lens. Imaging the source on the film gate imposes the additional requirement that the source shall be of uniform brightness. This condition is fulfilled by the high-intensity arc.[1] In case the light source is not sufficiently uniform in brightness to permit it to be focused upon

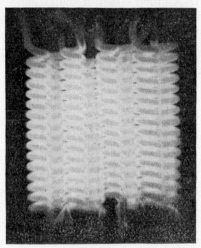

Fig. 263.—The filament of a projection lamp. A spherical mirror behind the lamp forms an image of the filament in the interstices between the coils themselves. (*By courtesy of General Electric Company.*)

the film itself, as frequently happens, the usual procedure is to form an image somewhere between the film gate and the projection lens—as close to the former as possible without causing the screen illumination to become appreciably non-uniform.

The requirements for a motion-picture projection lens are somewhat different from those for the lantern-slide projection lenses described above. The focal length is commonly in the neighborhood of five or six inches, and, since the frame is approx-

---

[1] With this type of source, an ellipsoidal reflector is frequently used instead of a condenser. The arc is placed at one focus and the film gate at the other, the constants of the reflector being such that the image is magnified six or seven times.

imately one inch across, the angular field to be covered is very small.   On the other hand, to produce sufficient screen illumination, the relative aperture must be high, a value of $f/2.5$ being not uncommon.   Until comparatively recently, a modified Petzval type of construction was used, but the higher magnification required by the smaller frame size of sound films has made it increasingly difficult to correct the aberrations of this type of lens satisfactorily.   With the possible necessity for projecting a wider film in mind, some designers have abandoned the Petzval construction in favor of types which, although more expensive to manufacture, give a much superior definition.   For the sake of interchangeability, projection lenses for theaters are made in two

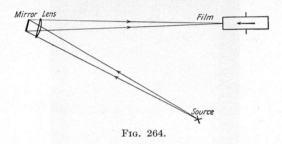

Fig. 264.

standard sizes, the external diameter for one series being $2\frac{1}{32}$ in. (52 mm) and that of the other series, $2\frac{25}{32}$ in. (71 mm).

The correction of the condenser is of considerable importance because, if spherical and chromatic aberrations are present, the homogeneity of the illuminating beam is destroyed—in other words, the film is not uniformly bright when viewed from the projection lens.   Now that practical methods for figuring aspheric surfaces in quantity have been developed, motion-picture condensers are commonly made of two elements, each having a weak spherical curve on the side toward the light and a strong parabolic curve on the other side.

199. The Optical System of Recording Instruments.—There are many measuring instruments of such delicate construction that a record of their deflections can be obtained only by optical means.   These instruments may be classed as projection systems because they usually contain a mirror that serves to project a spot of light on either a scale or a piece of photographic material. A typical arrangement, such as might be used for recording the deflection of a galvanometer, is shown in Fig. 264.   The light from a tiny lamp is reflected from a plane mirror attached to the galvanometer suspension and is brought to focus on the surface of the film by the lens. The film is assumed to be wound on a rotating drum to produce a record of the deflection as a function of time.

It is easily shown that the angular deflection of the beam reflected from the mirror is equal to twice the angle through which the mirror is rotated. The linear deflection of the spot on the film is, of course, proportional to the distance of the film from the mirror. The accuracy with which the trace can be read depends upon the ratio of the deflection to the size of the spot. Ordinarily, the lower limit to the size of the spot is set by the size of the diffraction pattern that is produced by the system. Since the diameter of the diffraction pattern increases at the same rate as the deflection when the distance of the film is increased, and, furthermore, since the illumination decreases approximately as the square of the distance of the film from the mirror, it is decidedly advantageous to place the film as near the mirror as possible. The ultimate limit is set by the graininess of the film.

A numerical example will make this point clear. Suppose that the mirror is 1 mm in diameter, which is not excessively small for an instrument with a delicate suspension. If the film is placed 1 meter away, the diameter of the diffraction disk is approximately 1.2 mm. By increasing the distance to 2 meters, the deflection would be doubled, but the size of the spot would be doubled also. Consequently, the uncertainty in reading the record would remain constant. It goes without saying that the figure given for the size of the diffraction disk represents a minimum value which is realized only if the optical system is perfect and the mirror is accurately flat.

In the system just described, the illumination and the size of the spot are limited by the condition that the mirror is the aperture stop, and one naturally wonders whether in some way this restriction cannot be removed. An analysis of this problem was published by one of the present authors[1] in connection with the optical system of the oscillograph and similar recording instruments. It was there shown, in effect, that if the system is designed with a view to making the exit pupil subtend a larger solid angle at the film, the result is inevitably to decrease the deflection just enough to compensate for the greater illumination

[1] *Jour. Optical Soc. Amer. and Rev. Sci. Instruments,* **14,** 505 (1927).

and smaller area of the spot of light.   In the limit, the mirror
itself might be imaged upon the film, but in this case the deflection would evidently be zero.   The simple system shown in
Fig. 264 is therefore as efficient as any system of spherical lenses
that can be devised.

If cylindrical lenses are used in the system, the condition that
the mirror shall be the aperture stop can be removed in part.
Although the mirror must always be the aperture stop in the plane
that is perpendicular to the axis of rotation, it need not be the
aperture stop in the plane of the axis.   In a system composed of
spherical lenses, the one condition imposes the other, but this is
not true of a system like that shown in Fig. 265.   In this figure,

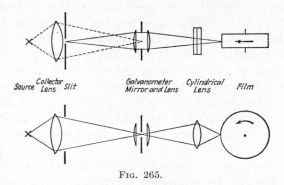

Fig. 265.

the upper diagram is a view in a plane perpendicular to the axis of
rotation of the mirror, and the lower diagram is a view in the plane
of the axis of rotation.   With the ordinary vertical suspension,
the upper diagram represents a plan view and the lower diagram,
a side elevation.   For simplicity, the mirror is represented merely
as an aperture—that is, as though it produced no deviation of
the beam.   The source of light is assumed to be imaged by a
spherical collector lens on the mirror in such a manner as to fill it
completely.   The lens at the mirror, which performs the same
function as the one shown in Fig. 264, is drawn twice because,
since the light traverses it twice, it behaves like two lenses.   A
cylindrical lens is inserted somewhat in front of the film so as to
image the mirror on the film in the lower diagram, but it has no
effect in the upper diagram.   Evidently this lens permits the slit
to be made very long without increasing the size of the spot.

The principles just outlined are applicable to other types of
recording instruments.   Instruments for recording sound on

motion-picture film have assumed especial importance of late.[1]
An oscillograph, which is essentially a high-frequency galvanometer, is used in one method, and a modified form of the
Einthoven string galvanometer in another. Both instruments
can be used to produce records of either the variable-width or the
variable-density type, although the oscillograph is better suited
to the former and the string galvanometer (or light valve) to the
latter.

[1] The peculiar problems that arise in this connection are discussed in a
paper by one of the present authors in *Trans. Soc. Motion Picture Eng.*, **12**,
760 (1928).

CHAPTER XXVII

SPECTROSCOPIC APPARATUS

All the image-forming instruments discussed in the preceding chapters are at least partially achromatized. We come now to a consideration of a class of instruments that are purposely made non-achromatic, usually by the insertion of a prism or other dispersing element, for the purpose of studying the spectral character of the radiation traversing the instrument. For obvious reasons, the object to be imaged by these instruments must be simple, so, unless the source is a point (such as a star) or a narrow line (such as the filament of a lamp), a slit is introduced in the apparatus where it can be focused either on the retina of the eye or on a photographic plate.

The most versatile instrument of the class we are about to study is the spectrometer. It was shown in Sec. 138, Chap. XVII, that this instrument can be used for measuring the angle of a prism by reflecting light first at one face and then at the other. If light is allowed to traverse the prism instead, the observer sees in the telescope a spectrum of the source; and, by setting the cross hairs on the image of a given spectral line, he can determine the deviation suffered by a beam of light of this particular wave length. The index of the prism can then be computed from the measured deviation and the refracting angle of the prism. Conversely, if one particular prism is always used, the divided circle can be calibrated to read wave lengths directly, and the instrument becomes a spectroscope. If the ocular is removed from a spectrometer or spectroscope and a second slit is placed in the plane of the cross hairs, radiation of any desired wave length can be isolated. An instrument arranged in this manner is called a monochromator. If the telescope is removed entirely and a camera is substituted for it, an image of the spectrum may be formed upon the photographic plate. Such an instrument is known as a spectrograph, and the photographic record of the spectrum is called a spectrogram. Most of the principles underlying these instruments have been discussed previously in other connections, and it only remains to develop the principles that are peculiar to the dispersing system.

200. The Theory of the Dispersing Prism.—A prism is used in spectroscopic apparatus so much more frequently than any other dispersing element that we shall consider it first. In Fig. 266,

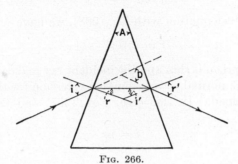

FIG. 266.

let a ray of light be incident at an angle i with the normal to one of the faces of the prism. We shall assume that this ray lies in a plane perpendicular to the line of intersection of the refracting surfaces. Let the angle between these surfaces be A. If the refractive index of the prism is n, the angle of refraction at the first surface is given by

$$\sin r = \frac{1}{n} \sin i. \qquad (267)$$

From the geometry of the figure, the angle of incidence at the second surface is

$$i' = A - r. \qquad (268)$$

The ray emerges again into the air after being refracted at this surface, the angle of emergence being given by

$$\sin r' = n \sin i'. \qquad (269)$$

Although these three equations can be combined in such a manner as to give r' directly as a function of i, n, and A, it is generally easier in a numerical case to compute each angle in turn by means of the separate equations.[1]

It is obvious that the deviation of the ray produced by the refraction at the first surface is

$$D_1 = i - r.$$

[1] Even in so simple a calculation as this, it is usually worth while to prepare in advance an argument like those shown in Chap. IV, especially if the calculation is to be repeated many times.

Similarly, the deviation at the second surface is

$$D_2 = r' - i'.$$

Hence the total deviation of the ray is

$$D = D_1 + D_2 = i - r + r' - i'. \tag{270}$$

Combining this equation with Eq. (268), we have

$$D = i + r' - A. \tag{271}$$

When the prism is thin and the incident ray makes only a small angle with the normal, a very simple expression for the deviation can be obtained. In this case, Eqs. (267) and (269) become respectively

$$i = nr$$

and

$$r' = ni'.$$

Substituting these values in Eq. (271) and noting from Eq. (268) that

$$i' + r = A,$$

the deviation is found to be simply

$$D = (n - 1)A. \tag{272}$$

This equation is of use in determining how nearly parallel the two faces of a plane-parallel plate must be to keep the deviation within given limits. For example, if the plate is to be placed before the eye, which may be assumed to have a resolving power of 1 minute of arc, the angle between the faces must not exceed about 2 minutes of arc if no perceptible deviation is allowable when the plate is introduced (assuming the eye is focused on an object at infinity). If the plate is to be placed before an optical instrument, the maximum permissible angle is less in proportion to the magnifying power of the instrument.

The variation in deviation with wave length is called the *dispersion* of the prism. If the prism is thin, an analytical expression for the dispersion can be obtained by differentiating Eq. (272) with respect to n, which gives

$$dD = dn \cdot A. \tag{273}$$

This equation can be expressed in a different manner by substituting for A its value in Eq. (272), which gives

$$dD = \frac{dn}{n-1} D.$$ (274)

If we substitute $n_F - n_c$ for dn, this becomes

$$dD = \frac{1}{\nu} D,$$ (275)

where $1/\nu$ is the dispersive power of the glass. Since the ν-value of the more common types of optical glass varies from about 28 to approximately 65, it will be seen that the dispersion from the C- to the F-line in the spectrum formed by a thin prism is from $\frac{1}{28}$ to $\frac{1}{65}$ of the deviation.

Except for the case of minimum deviation, which will be discussed presently, it is impossible to find a simple expression for the dispersion produced by a thick prism. For the general case, the dispersion can be determined when required by differentiating Eqs. (267), (268), (269), and (271) with respect to n, assuming the value of i to be constant.

Differentiating Eq. (271) gives

$$dD = dr'.$$

Equations (269) and (268) when differentiated give respectively

$$dr' = \frac{\sin i' + n \cos i' \dfrac{di'}{dn}}{\cos r'} dn$$

and

$$\frac{di'}{dn} = -\frac{dr}{dn}.$$

Combining these equations, we have

$$dD = \frac{\sin i' - n \cos i' \dfrac{dr}{dn}}{\cos r'} dn.$$ (276)

From Eq. (267), the value of $\dfrac{dr}{dn}$ is found to be

$$\frac{dr}{dn} = -\frac{\sin r}{n \cos r},$$ (277)

since the value of i is assumed to be constant. Equations (276) and (277) suffice for computing the angle dD subtended by a portion of the spectrum for which the difference of index of the prism is dn. In terms of wave length, the dispersion $dD/d\lambda$ of the prism can be computed by dividing Eq. (276) by $d\lambda$. The value of $dn/d\lambda$ appearing on the right-hand side of the resulting equation may be determined from the dispersion curve of the glass; but since it is equivalent to the quantity σ in Sec. 56, Chap. VI, it can be computed by means of Eq. (152) if the constants in Hartmann's formula are known. The values of σ for some representative types of glass are given in Table V, page 113.

It will be evident that by combining two or more prisms, a deviation can be produced without dispersion or a dispersion

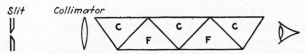

Fig. 267.—The optical system of the direct-vision spectroscope. The crown and flint elements of the prism are indicated by C and F respectively.

without deviation. Prisms of the latter type are used in direct-vision spectroscopes, which produce a dispersion of the light without deviating the central portion of the spectrum. The optical system of such an instrument is shown in Fig. 267.

There is one special case of considerable practical importance for which the mathematical relationships become simple. This is the case where the angle of incidence is so chosen that, for some specified wave length, the deviation produced by the prism is at a minimum. It can be shown that minimum deviation occurs when

$$i = r'. \tag{278}$$

This means that

$$r = i',$$

so that minimum deviation is obtained, as might be expected, when the ray traverses the prism in the symmetrical fashion illustrated in Fig. 266. The angle of incidence corresponding to minimum deviation is then

$$i = r' = \frac{A + D}{2}. \tag{279}$$

From Eq. (268)

$$r = i' = \frac{A}{2}, \tag{280}$$

and hence

$$n = \frac{\sin i}{\sin r} = \frac{\sin \frac{1}{2}(A + D)}{\sin \frac{1}{2}A}. \tag{281}$$

This form of the equation is convenient because the refractive index is so often determined experimentally by measuring the angles A and D with a spectrometer. The procedure required for measuring A was discussed in Sec. 138. To measure the angle of minimum deviation, one has merely to mount the prism as shown in Fig. 268, so that the image of a given line in the spectrum is visible in the telescope, and then to rotate the prism until the deviation becomes a minimum. The deviation is determined by reading the divided circle with the cross hairs set on the line in question, removing the prism, and resighting the

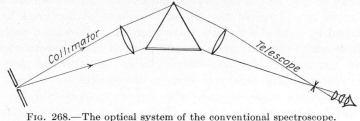

Fig. 268.—The optical system of the conventional spectroscope.

telescope on the undeviated beam. The difference between the two readings is the angle of minimum deviation.

When a prism is set at minimum deviation for a given wave length, the dispersion can be found by simply differentiating Eq. (281), which gives

$$dD = \frac{2}{n} \tan \frac{A + D}{2} \cdot dn \qquad (282)$$

$$= \frac{2}{n} \tan i \cdot dn. \qquad (283)$$

The usefulness of this equation will be clear from a numerical example. Suppose that a 60° prism is constructed from an ordinary silicate flint like O–103 in Table V, Chap. VI. Equation (281) shows that the angle of minimum deviation at 500 mμ is approximately 50°, and Eq. (279) shows that the corresponding angle of incidence is 55°. From the value of σ given in Table V for the assumed wave length, the value of dn corresponding to a difference of 1 mμ in wave length is 0.0001471. The index of refraction at this wave length is 1.6302, and hence the change in deviation dD corresponding to a difference of 1 mμ in wave length is approximately 0.00025 radian or about 0.9 minute of arc.

The case of minimum deviation is of considerable practical importance. As was shown above, it furnishes a convenient means for determining the refractive index of a substance. Indeed, this is a fundamental method since it depends only upon the measurement of angle and not upon the properties of any particular substance. Even when the prism is to be used for analyzing radiation, it should ordinarily be set for minimum deviation because the loss of light by reflection at the surfaces is then at a minimum. Moreover, the resulting symmetrical arrangement of the prism ordinarily gives the largest effective free aperture for a prism of a given size.

When the prism just discussed is used in a spectroscope, as shown in Fig. 268, it is obvious that even if the slit is infinitely narrow, the image of the slit in the plane of the cross hairs formed by light of a definite wave length is a diffraction pattern whose width depends upon the diameter of the telescope objective, assuming it for convenience to be the aperture stop of the system. The ability of such an instrument to resolve two spectral lines depends upon the dispersion produced by the prism and the resolving power of the telescope. For example, with the 60° prism considered above, the angular separation of two spectral lines that are 1 mμ apart in wave length is about 0.9 minute of arc. Since the resolving power of the unaided eye is 1′, the resolving power of the telescope must equal that of the eye to utilize the full resolving power of the prism. With a telescope of normal magnifying power, the diameter of the objective would be 3 mm and the prism need obviously be only large enough to fill the objective with light. If higher resolution is required, the entire system, including the collimator, prism, and telescope objective, must be proportionately increased in size. The resolving power of a prism evidently depends not only on its effective free aperture but also on its angle and the dispersive power of the glass from which it is made. A mathematical expression for the resolving power of a prism can be readily derived; and, on the basis of this expression, it is frequently stated that the resolving power of a prism made from a given type of glass depends only upon the length of the base. This statement is true provided the prism is the aperture stop of the system and the base is perpendicular to the bisector of the refracting angle.

In practice it is clearly impossible to use a slit that is infinitely narrow, and the calculation of the resolving power becomes exceedingly complex for a slit of finite width. The difficulty arises from the fact that the slit itself is rarely self-luminous—a difficulty similar to that encountered in connection with the resolving power of the microscope. As the apparatus is customarily arranged, the source is focused on the slit by means of a collector lens. If the source and the collector lens are sufficiently large to fill both the slit and the collimator lens, the system would at first glance appear to be used most effectively. If the source emits a continuous spectrum so that no question of resolution is involved, this system is indeed perfectly satisfactory. In fact, any other system can be used equally well provided both the slit and the collimator are filled with light. However, in work requiring the resolution of the fine structure of spectral lines and especially the measurement of the relative intensities of such lines, the most careful consideration must be given to the choice of the proper method of illumination and the proper width of slit to use under a given set of conditions. Recent papers by van Cittert[1] and by Stockbarger and Burns[2] may be consulted for references to the literature of the subject. The former paper is largely mathematical while the latter gives a very convincing experimental proof of the necessity for choosing the proper slit width for a given set of conditions.

We have so far considered the behavior of rays lying in principal sections of the prism—that is, in planes perpendicular to the line of intersection of the two refracting surfaces. It can be shown that the rays traversing the prism in other planes are deviated more than these rays. The result is that the rays from the top and bottom of the slit are deviated more than the rays from the center, and therefore the spectral lines are curved. This curve has been shown to be a parabola, the radius of curvature at the vertex for the case of minimum deviation being

$$\rho = \frac{n^2 f}{2(n^2 - 1)} \cot i, \tag{284}$$

where f is the focal length of the telescope or camera objective and i is the angle of incidence on the prism. The curvature changes but slowly with wave length, and hence in commercial apparatus the slit is often given the proper curvature to approximately neutralize the curvature of the spectral lines throughout the spectrum. This correction is of especial impor-

[1] *Zeits. Physik*, **65**, 547 (1930):
[2] *Phys. Rev.*, **37**, 920 (1931).

tance in a monochromator, in which case either the entrance slit
or the exit slit may be curved.

201. Prismatic Instruments.—A dispersing prism is used in
so many different types of instruments that only the salient
features of the more important types can be described here.
The spectrometer has already been discussed in Sec. 138, Chap.
XVII. It may be worth while, however, to mention Schuster's
method of focusing such an instrument, which is useful if a
Gauss ocular is not at hand. In this method, the telescope is
set for a deviation somewhat greater than the minimum, in
which case a given spectral line will be coincident with the cross
hairs for two positions of the prism. The procedure is to turn
the prism until the angle of incidence is *greater* than that for
minimum deviation and to adjust the *telescope* to bring the image
into focus. The prism is then turned to the other position, and

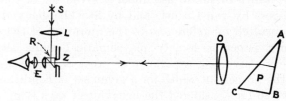

Fig. 269.—The optical system of the Abbe autocollimating spectrometer,

the *collimator* is adjusted to focus the image. This procedure
is repeated until the line is in focus for both positions of the
prism.

The method of determining the refracting angle of the prism
was described in Sec. 138, and it only remains to add that this
method is preferable to the method described in many textbooks
in which the beam from the collimator is split at the refracting
edge of the prism. The reason is that aberrations in the collimator and telescope reduce the accuracy of the latter method.

The Abbe autocollimating spectrometer is of considerable
importance because of its convenience of operation. As shown
in Fig. 269, light from the source S is reflected at the right-angle
prism R through the lower end of the slit Z, the lens L serving to
focus the source upon the slit. The beam from the slit is collimated by the objective O and enters the prism P. Part of this
beam is reflected at the second face AB and is brought to focus
by the objective in the plane of the slit. The image thus formed
is observed by means of an ocular E. The slit projects a trifle

above the prism R, and consequently it serves as an index for locating the image. Since the light is always reflected normally from the face AB of the prism P, it always traverses this prism at minimum deviation; and since it traverses the prism twice, it is evident that a 30° prism in this instrument is equivalent to a 60° prism when used in the ordinary manner.

The prism is mounted with its face AB on a ring that can be rotated in its own plane and can also be tilted in a perpendicular plane. To adjust the instrument, the prism table is first rotated until the face AB is nearest the objective. Then the prism is tilted until the image of the slit appears in the ocular between the jaws of the slit itself, the lower end of the image being coincident with the upper edge of the prism R. The prism table is then rotated until the face AC is nearest the objective, and the ring on which the prism is mounted is rotated until the image reflected from this face is in the same position as before. It is clear that the angle through which the prism table is turned between these two positions is the supplement of the refracting angle of the prism. The prism table is then turned until the image formed by refraction is located, and the amount of rotation necessary is, of course, the angle of incidence i. It can easily be shown that the index of the prism is

$$n = \frac{\sin i}{\sin A}, \qquad (285)$$

where A is its refracting angle. The great advantage of this type of spectrometer is the comparative facility with which determinations can be made. It also contains fewer moving parts and is less affected by mechanical strains, but it has the slight disadvantage that the light reflected at the face of the objective appears as stray light in the field.

A spectroscope is similar to a spectrometer except that the divided circle can be reduced to a mere rudiment or even dispensed with altogether. The spectrum is explored by moving either the prism or the telescope. If the telescope is movable, it can be provided with cross hairs, and then its angular position, when the cross hairs intersect the image of the slit, is a measure of the wave length of the line under examination. Another method is to use an auxiliary wave-length scale in such a manner that it appears to be superposed upon the spectrum.

The constant-deviation type of spectroscope, in which both the collimator and the telescope are fixed and the prism alone is movable, is of considerable importance. In this instrument, the rays entering the telescope must traverse the prism at a constant deviation for every wave length. This can be accomplished with the apparatus shown in Fig. 268 by reflecting the rays into the telescope from a plane mirror linked mechanically to the prism table so that it rotates simultaneously. Wadsworth[1] has designed several mechanisms by which this can be done, and he finally hit upon the very elegant arrangement shown in Fig.

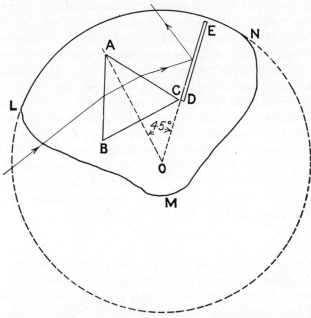

FIG. 270.—Sketch showing the principle of the Wadsworth prism system.

270. Here the prism *ABC* and the plane first-surface mirror *DE* are mounted on the prism table as shown. It can be demonstrated mathematically that the emergent ray that traverses the prism at minimum deviation makes an angle of 90° with the incident ray no matter what the wave length of the light or the dispersion of the prism may be. The angle between the incident ray and the emergent ray can be made to have any value whatever depending upon the position of the mirror, the only requirement being that the intersection between the plane of the mirror and a plane bisecting the angle *A* of the prism shall coincide with the axis of rotation *O*. In practice, of course, the

[1] *Phil. Mag.*, **38**, 337 (1894).

prism table is not a complete circle but has the form indicated by *LMN*. It may be noted that the autocollimating spectrometer described on page 552 is only a special form of the Wadsworth type.

A type of prism that itself performs the function of a mirror is shown at *a* in Fig. 271. This prism may be considered to be composed of the two 30° prisms *ABE* and *BCD* and the 90° prism *EAD*. The path of a ray traversing this prism at minimum deviation is shown. Since the angle *i* equals the angle *r'*

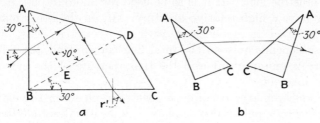

FIG. 271.

and the face *AB* is perpendicular to the face *BC*, it is evident that the emergent ray is perpendicular to the incident ray. Unlike the Wadsworth type, this prism causes a slight lateral displacement of the emergent ray as it is rotated, but this displacement can be minimized by properly locating the axis of rotation. One objection to this type of prism is the absorption of light due to the long glass path, which is serious in the violet region when flint glass is used. In addition, the free aperture of the prism is small compared with the dispersion that it produces. A system that avoids these difficulties is shown at *b* in the same figure. It consists of two 30° prisms so connected mechanically that they can be rotated simultaneously by equal amounts in opposite directions. This system is especially useful in instruments designed for the ultraviolet, partly because of the difficulty of obtaining large pieces of quartz and partly because a prism of right-handed quartz and one of left-handed quartz must be used in any case.

By substituting a slit for the ocular and cross hairs, a spectroscope becomes a monochromator. The constant-deviation type is especially convenient because the beam emerging from the instrument proceeds in the same direction regardless of its wave length. The requirements for a monochromator are rather different than for a spectroscope. In the first place, the usual function of a monochromator is merely to isolate a relatively narrow portion of the spectrum. For this reason, the slits can be wider than the slit of the spectroscope and the tolerances in the construction and calibration of the instrument are less severe. In the second place, a monochromator is generally used in conjunction with another optical system and must be designed with regard to the characteristics of the remainder of the system. If the monochromator forms part of a visual instrument, the requirements discussed in Sec. 147, Chap. XIX, for visual instruments must be met. If it is to be used for photography, it must usually have a high relative aperture. If, on the other hand, it is to be used in connection with photoelectric cells, whose response depends only on the total flux transmitted, the relative aperture is unimportant and the free aperture of the system is all that matters.

A monochromator becomes a spectrograph when the exit slit is replaced by a photographic plate. Since it is desirable to have all the lines in sharp focus, the plate must be tilted at the proper angle and must be given the proper curvature to suit the chromatic correction of the objective. In the ultraviolet, for which it is impractical to make achromatic objectives, the foci for the short wave lengths lie so much nearer the objective than the foci for the long ones that the plate must be tilted at a rather steep angle (approximately 60°) to bring the entire spectrum into focus. To facilitate focusing, the instrument should be provided with means for moving the camera lens parallel to the axis and for rotating the plate about an axis in its own plane intersecting the axis of the lens.

Spectrographs of many different types have been devised, especially for exploring the ultraviolet. One form due to Féry[1] is noteworthy because the prism itself serves not only as the dispersing element but as collimator and objective as well. As shown in Fig. 272, the refracting faces of the prism are spherical. The center of curvature of the first surface PQ is at A. Consider two rays of monochromatic light CP and CQ emerging from a slit at C so placed that $\angle CPA = \angle CQA = i$. After refraction at the first surface, the rays continue to M and N respectively as though they had come from B without being refracted. By making B the center of curvature of the second

---

[1] *Jour. Physique*, **9**, 762 (1910). Reprinted in *Astrophys. Jour.*, **34**, 79 (1911).

surface *MN* (which is silvered), the rays reflected from this face traverse their original path and come to focus at *C*. It can be shown that *B* and *C* lie on a circle through *A*, *P*, and *Q*; and, if the light is heterochromatic, it can be shown further that the foci for the various wave lengths all lie on this same circle. In practice, the slit is placed a little to one side of *C* and the plate a little to the other side.

A more common form of spectrograph was devised by Littrow. Its optical system is similar to that of the auto-

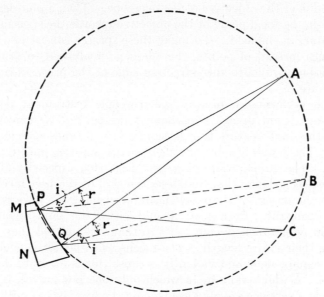

Fig. 272.—Sketch showing the principle of the Féry spectrograph.

collimating spectrometer shown in Fig. 269. Sometimes the objective is replaced by a concave mirror behind the prism.

Spectrographs are sometimes used for spectrophotometry. If the light entering one end of the slit passes through a cell containing a substance that absorbs selectively, and the light entering the other end of the slit passes through a neutral filter or rotating sector wheel, there are, in general, certain points along the juxtaposed spectra where the densities of the plate are equal. By making several spectrograms with the neutral filter or sector wheel absorbing a different proportion of light for each, it is evident that data can be obtained for plotting a spectro-photometric curve of the sample.

The spectrographs used in astrophysics are in a class by themselves because most of them are merely attachments for existing telescopes.[1] They are usually mounted at the eye end of a telescope in such a position that the image formed by the objective is focused on the slit. It is obvious that such an arrangement is not entirely satisfactory for making stellar spectra, not only because the telescope must be trained very accurately but also because only one star can be examined at once. For making rapid surveys of stellar spectra, therefore, a prism is usually placed over the objective of the telescope. Then a photographic plate in the focal plane of the objective records the spectra of all the stars in the field. To make these spectra consist of a series of lines instead of points, the telescope is allowed to drift in a direction parallel to the refracting edge of the prism during the exposure.

The performance of any spectroscopic instrument depends to some extent upon its mechanical design, but we can discuss only the single feature that is common to all types—namely, the slit. The jaws must be extremely sharp, smooth, and free from dust. The preparation of a first-class slit, especially if it is curved, is an operation that tests the skill of the best mechanic. Even the design of the mechanism for opening the jaws requires some thought. Both jaws should be in the same plane and should be parallel to each other so that when closed they touch along their entire length. The mechanism should be such that they cannot be closed violently because this is likely to dull the edges. A unilateral slit, in which only one jaw moves, is satisfactory if settings are always made on the fixed edge.[2] Bilateral slits, in which both jaws move simultaneously in opposite directions, are more difficult to construct. Both jaws must move at the same rate, remain parallel to themselves, and yet have no lost motion.

The difficulty in using a spectroscope or spectrometer of the usual type is that, if the slit is narrow, the cross hairs are difficult to see. Guild has proposed to use a very wide slit with a spider web in the middle between the jaws. In this case, the position

[1] See a series of papers in *Astrophys. Jour.* for 1895. The spectrographs for some of the famous telescopes have been described in this publication in 1900, 1902, 1904, 1912, and 1919.

[2] A slit of this type that is especially meritorious because of the delicacy with which the adjustments can be made has been constructed by de Gramont. It is described in *Rev. d'Optique*, **7**, 68 (1928).

of each spectral line is represented by a dark line in the middle of a bright band and the cross hairs can be very readily set to intersect the dark line. Another suggestion has been to use a comparatively wide slit and to place in the focal plane of the ocular a straight wire that nearly fills the image of the slit. The

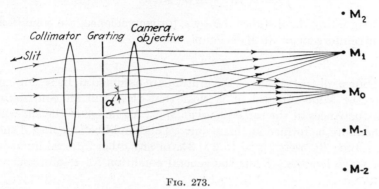

FIG. 273.

eye is able to estimate very accurately when the bright areas on the two sides of the wire are equal.

202. The Diffraction Grating.—The simple theory of the diffraction grating is illustrated in Fig. 273. Light entering a slit at the left of the figure is rendered parallel by the collimator

lens and falls on the grating, which we shall assume for the present is merely an opaque screen containing a large number of infinitely narrow rulings equally spaced. We shall make the further assumption that the light entering the slit is monochromatic. Then, from Huygens's principle, the rulings of the grating may be considered as secondary sources from which light radiates in all directions. Some of this light will of course continue in its

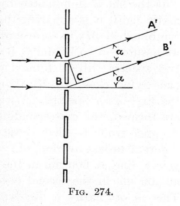

FIG. 274.

original direction and will be brought to focus at M_0 by the telescope or camera objective. Let us now consider the rays diffracted at an angle α with the original direction. These rays are brought to focus at M_1 by the objective; and, for the sake of clearness, an enlarged view of the grating showing two such rays AA' and BB' is given in Fig. 274. Manifestly, if the distance

BC in this figure is equal to one wave length, the disturbance from B will arrive at M_1 exactly one period behind the disturbance from A. Reinforcement will therefore take place. Now, from the geometry of the figure,

$$BC = AB \cdot \sin \alpha.$$

Designating the distance AB by e, for convenience, the condition for reinforcement at M_1 is simply that

$$e \sin \alpha = \lambda.$$

Since all the rulings of the grating are assumed to be separated by the same interval, it is clear that they will all contribute disturbances of the same phase at M_1. An image of the slit will therefore be formed at this point. This would be true also if the distance BC were equal to 2λ, 3λ, or any other integral number of wave lengths. Thus the general condition for reinforcement is

$$e \sin \alpha = m\lambda, \tag{286}$$

where m is any integer. Evidently a number of images, such as M_1, M_2, M_{-1}, M_{-2}, etc., will be formed on both sides of M_0, the limit to the number being set by the fact that $\sin \alpha$ cannot exceed unity.

If the slit is illuminated by white light instead of monochromatic light, it is apparent that light of all wave lengths will be combined at M_0 to form a white image of the source. If now we assume m to be unity, it is clear that, since α varies with λ, two spectra will be formed on opposite sides of M_0, the blue ends lying closer to M_0 than the red ends. These are called the first-order spectra. With $m = 2$, a second pair of spectra are formed, the corresponding portions of which lie at a greater distance from M_0 than those of the first order. The spectra of different orders overlap, of course. For example, the image of a yellow line at 600 mμ in the first order coincides with the line at 300 mμ in the second order, 200 mμ in the third order, etc. This is ordinarily a disadvantage, although it was turned to good use by Rowland in his classical determination of the wave lengths of the lines in the solar spectrum.

The dispersion produced by a grating can be determined by differentiating Eq. (286) with respect to λ, which gives

$$\frac{d\alpha}{d\lambda} = \frac{m}{e} \cdot \frac{1}{\cos \alpha}. \tag{287}$$

It will be seen that the dispersion is approximately proportional to the order of the spectrum and to the fineness of ruling of the grating.

The image of a spectral line formed in the plane of the cross hairs of the telescope or on the photographic plate is, of course, a diffraction pattern whose size depends upon the aperture of the system. Hence, it is clear that the resolving power of a grating depends upon both its size and the dispersion which it produces. A little consideration will show that the resolving power in the spectrum of a given order depends on the total number of lines of the grating that are effective in producing the spectrum. We may therefore write that the resolving power

$$\frac{\lambda}{d\lambda} = Nm, \tag{288}$$

where N is the total number of rulings and m is the order of the spectrum. If we consider the numerical example discussed in Sec. 200, where a prism was required to separate two lines 1 mμ apart at a wave length of 500 mμ, it will be seen that a grating containing only 500 lines will suffice in the first order, one of 250 lines in the second order, etc. Rulings as fine as 20,000 lines per inch are not uncommon, and hence, even in the first order, a grating less than 1.5 mm in size will resolve two lines that are 1 mμ apart.

Another consequence that can be deduced from Eq. (287) is that the spectrum produced by a grating is normal. In any practical application, the angle α is usually small, and consequently the value of $\cos \alpha$ is sensibly constant over a reasonably short angular interval. The value of $d\alpha/d\lambda$ is therefore approximately constant, and the linear separation of two lines in a spectrogram made with a diffraction grating is therefore very nearly proportional to the corresponding difference in wave length. It will be recalled that this is far from being true for the spectrum produced by a prism, which is much extended at the blue end in comparison with the red end.

We have assumed in this discussion that the grating consists of infinitely narrow rulings, but in practice such gratings would transmit an infinitesimal amount of light even if they could be prepared. The grating will function, however, if the rulings have a finite width and even if the intervening spaces are not completely opaque; in fact, the theory just developed holds equally well if the grating has any sort of periodic structure whatever. The only effect of varying the ratio between the transparent and the opaque portions of the grating is to vary the distribution of light among the various orders of spectra. For example, by making the opaque and transparent portions equally wide, the spectra of even orders disappear.

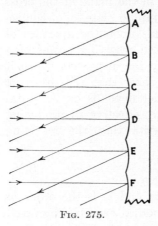

FIG. 275.

To see that the simple theory applies regardless of the type of ruling, let us consider the case of a reflection grating, which consists of a mirror scratched with parallel equidistant lines by means of a diamond point. A cross section of such a grating when enlarged might have the appearance shown in Fig. 275. The light incident upon the grating will be diffracted by each infinitesimal area of a grating element, but in any specified direction and for some point of each element indicated by A, B, C, etc., the disturbance produced in the resultant image will have the same phase as the resultant disturbance from the entire element. Since the simple theory applies to the rays diffracted at A, B, C, etc., it also applies to the rays diffracted by the entire grating. Here again the only effect of the form of the ruling is to vary the distribution of light among the various orders of spectra. Hence, by properly selecting the diamond point with which the grating is ruled, practically all the light can be concentrated in a single order.

The ruling of a grating is done with the aid of a dividing engine, which consists essentially of a carriage that can be moved along a track by means of a very accurate screw. The mechanical difficulties that are involved in the manufacture of a fine grating are of unbelievable magnitude. The most serious fault produced by a dividing engine that is anything less than perfect is a periodic error in the ruling. This may be due to a periodic error in the screw or in some part of the driving machinery. A ruling containing a periodic error produces not only the spectra characteristic of the nominal grating interval but also spectra corresponding to the interval of the periodic error. Such false spectra are termed *ghosts*. They can be detected by placing the grating in a spectroscope as usual, substituting a hole for the slit, and placing a prism against the grating with its refracting edge perpendicular to the ruling of the grating. The prism draws out each spectrum into a curve similar to the dispersion curve of the glass, and a little consideration will show that any images of the pinhole that do not lie upon this curve are due to ghosts produced by the grating.

A few gratings with 50,000 lines per inch have been ruled and at least one with 100,000 lines per inch. The ghosts in such fine gratings are so pronounced, however, that better results are obtained with coarser rulings. Most of the work on the fine structure of spectral lines is being done with gratings having 15,000 lines per inch. Such a grating 8 in. long, used in the fifth order, has a theoretical resolving power of 600,000. In other words, at 4000 Å., two lines 0.007 Å. apart should just be resolved.

The cost of even a moderately good grating is very high, but for many purposes replicas made by Thorp's process as modified by Wallace[1] are quite satisfactory. This process consists in pouring a layer of collodion upon an ordinary reflection grating, stripping it from the latter when it is dry, and mounting it between glass plates. The possibility of injuring a replica during the process of manufacture is considerable, and the price varies according to the quality.

Nowadays, reflection gratings are more widely used than transmission gratings.[2] If a grating is ruled on a concave mirror, it can be made to serve as its own collimator and camera objective. This was done by Rowland in 1882, and it was by means of such a grating that he made his classical determination of the wave lengths of the Fraunhofer lines in the solar spectrum. The essential features of Rowland's mounting[3] are shown in Fig. 276. The grating G forms an arc of a circle AGB (really a cap of a sphere of which AGB is the trace). The slit S and the photographic plate P lie on a circle SGP whose diameter is equal to the radius of curvature of the grating. It can be shown that the spectra also lie upon this circle. Sharp

---

[1] *Astrophys. Jour.*, **22**, 123 (1905).

[2] Replicas can be coated with platinum by cathodic sputtering for use by reflection.

[3] For the details of construction and adjustment, see a paper by Ames in *Phil. Mag.*, **27**, 369 (1889).

images of the slit can therefore be produced by curving the plate to coincide with the circle. The dispersion of the grating is so great that only a portion of even a single order can be photographed at one time. Some mechanical arrangement is therefore necessary to enable the entire gamut of spectra to be investigated. If the lines *SG* and *SP* represent two tracks mounted at right angles and the line *PG* represents a tie rod holding *P* and *G* at a fixed distance from each other, it is evident that the plate can be kept in focus by placing a swiveled truck under the grating *G* to ride on the track *SG* and another truck under *P* to ride on the track *SP*. This type of mounting has the advantage that a line in the second order coincides with the

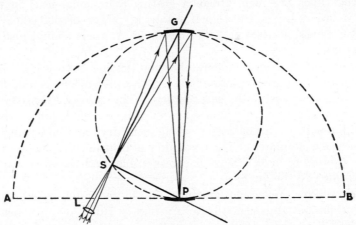

Fig. 276.—Sketch showing the principle of Rowland's mounting of the concave grating.

line in the first order having twice the wave length, and thus the spectral lines can be measured by the method of coincidences. On the other hand, the apparatus is large and is therefore difficult to maintain at a constant temperature. Moreover, the angle of obliquity for spectra of high order is so great that only the first few orders can be studied.

The method of coincidences has been shown by Kayser to be inaccurate, and therefore a form of mounting due to Eagle[1] is nowadays considered superior. In this mounting, the slit and plate are placed together as shown in Fig. 277. The various spectra are brought into focus by sliding the grating in the

[1] *Astrophys. Jour.*, **31**, 120 (1910).

direction *PG* and at the same time rotating it. The photographic plate must also be rotated about an axis in its own plane so that both ends of the spectrum will be in focus.[1]

It would take us too far afield to discuss the technique of spectroscopy in the infrared and ultraviolet regions. The instruments used in the infrared are essentially spectroradiometers; those used in the ultraviolet are spectrographs. The chief difficulty in exploring the extreme ultraviolet (300–100 mμ) is atmospheric absorption. The absorption of the gelatin of the photographic plate is also troublesome, but this can be overcome by the methods discussed in Sec. 93, Chap. XI. The pioneer in ultraviolet spectroscopy was Schumann, who devised

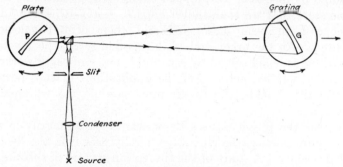

Fig. 277.—The optical system of the concave grating in Eagle's mounting. The plate is above the right-angle prism to prevent the latter from obstructing the beam returning from the grating.

a vacuum spectrograph to avoid atmospheric absorption. His apparatus was improved by Lyman,[2] who made the classical wave-length determinations in this region.

203. Applications of the Spectroscope.—The spectroscope[3] is undoubtedly the most powerful tool for investigating the nature of the universe that man possesses. In the early part of the past

[1] The similarity between the Féry, Littrow, and Eagle mountings is apparent at once. This circumstance has been turned to advantage by the firm of Hilger in the design of their "Universal" spectrograph. This versatile instrument can be used in a wide variety of ways by merely interchanging a few optical parts.

[2] *Astrophys. Jour.*, **23**, 181 (1906). This entire subject is well covered in his "The Spectroscopy of the Extreme Ultra-Violet."

[3] Although strictly the term "spectroscope" should be applied only to instruments in which the spectrum is viewed with the eye, it is frequently used loosely to mean spectroscopic instruments in general.

century, Auguste Comte remarked: "There are some things of which the human race must forever remain in ignorance; for example, the chemical constitution of the heavenly bodies." Yet he was in his grave little more than a decade (1868) before an element (helium) unknown on the earth was discovered in the sun.

We now know by means of the spectroscope not only the constitution of many of the stars but also their temperature, density, and stage of evolution. Our own star, the sun, has been virtually peeled into layers like an onion with the spectrohelio-graph,[1] invented by Hale about 1890. The motion of the stars and even of our own solar system through space has been measured by means of the Doppler effect; and, in the same way, double stars that we could never hope to resolve with the finest telescope have been discovered and their orbital velocities measured. At the other end of the cosmic scale, the mystery of the atom is being solved by a veritable army of eager workers. But, for a detailed account of the applications of the spectro-scope in these fields, the reader must consult the voluminous literature.

Whereas the physicist uses the spectroscope primarily in the field of pure science, the chemist generally uses it in the field of applied science. A study of the absorption spectra of substances yields much information about their chemical constitution. By causing a substance to produce its characteristic emission spectrum, the elements of which it is composed can be identified. This is often possible even when the proportion of an element is so small that the element is regarded as an impurity. This method of detecting impurities is of especial value when other methods are for some reason impractical. For example, the melting point of fusible plugs used in sprinkler heads and in the safety vents of steam boilers is raised to a dangerous extent by the presence of exceedingly minute traces of impurities such as

---

[1] This is similar to a monochromator with a photographic plate at the exit slit. The whole instrument, except the plate, is moved across the sun's image, and thus the photograph is taken in monochromatic light emitted by some particular element. Since the elements lie in layers, the com-parison with peeling an onion is evident. See *Astrophys. Jour.*, **23**, 54 (1906) for the final form of the instrument. The spectrohelioscope for visual observations was derived from the earlier instrument by adding an ocular to examine the exit slit and moving the instrument at a speed greater than the critical frequency. See *Astrophys. Jour.*, **70**, 265 (1929).

iron. To test these plugs individually by chemical methods would obviously be out of the question, but it is a simple matter to use the plugs as the electrodes of a spark gap. When this is done, some of the lines due to the impurities appear in addition to those of the predominant metals. As the proportion of the impurities is diminished, the lines due to them disappear in a characteristic order, leaving a few *persistent lines* or *raies ultimes* at the limit. Thus, the lines due to the impurities not only identify the impurities but also indicate the approximate proportion in which they are present. A striking feature about the *raies ultimes* is that they are not always the lines that are predominant when the element producing them is present in large proportions. A detailed description of spectrographic analysis by this method will be found in the *Bureau of Standards Scientific Paper* 444.

CHAPTER XXVIII

INTERFERENCE AND INTERFEROMETERS

The principle of superposition, which underlies all interference phenomena, was discussed briefly in Sec. 4, Chap. I. It was there shown that the combination of two light waves pursuing approximately the same path and having the same frequency

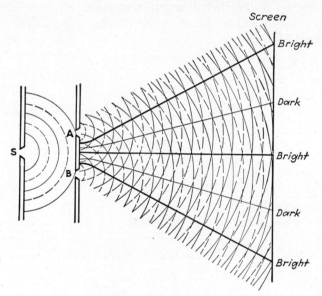

FIG. 278.—Young's experiment.

and plane of polarization produces a resultant sinusoidal disturbance whose frequency is the same as that of the components, and whose amplitude is

$$a = \sqrt{a_1{}^2 + a_2{}^2 + 2 a_1 a_2 \cos\varphi}, \tag{289}$$

where a_1 and a_2 are the amplitudes of the components and φ is the phase of one with respect to the other. If both components have the same amplitude, the resultant has double the amplitude of either when $\varphi = 0$, 2π, 4π, etc. On the other hand, when

$\varphi = \pi$, 3π, 5π, etc., the resultant amplitude is zero. This phenomenon is known as interference.

204. The Theory of Interference.—The phenomenon of interference was first correctly explained by Young about 1807. He used the apparatus sketched in Fig. 278. Light was caused to pass first through a pinhole S and then through two other pin-holes A and B. By Huygens's principle, A and B can be treated as the centers of two disturbances that impinge upon the screen. These disturbances reinforce each other at all points of the screen for which the distances to A and B either are equal or differ by an integral number of wave lengths. They annul each other for points on the screen for which the difference between

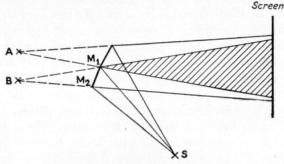

FIG. 279.—Fresnel's double mirror.

the two distances is an odd number of half wave lengths. As a result, a system of interference fringes is formed on the screen.

Young's explanation of the phenomenon was not immediately accepted because of the possibility that the light undergoes some modification in passing through the pinholes. This objection was removed by Fresnel, who obtained interference with the apparatus shown in Fig. 279. The mirrors M_1 and M_2 are inclined to each other at an angle of almost 180°, and hence images of the source S are produced at A and B. Where the beams from A and B overlap, as indicated by the crosshatching, a system of interference fringes appears. Since the interfering beams do not originate at pinholes with this apparatus, the objection to Young's experiment does not apply.

During the first half of the nineteenth century, several other ingenious methods of demonstrating interference phenomena were devised. Among these may be mentioned Fresnel's biprism, Lloyd's mirror, and Billet's split lens, a description of which will be found in any text on physical optics.   Experiments with these devices invariably indicated the essential correctness of Young's explanation of interference, and they played an important part in bringing about a general acceptance of the wave theory.   Actually, of course, such experiments indicate merely that the wave theory is capable of explaining interference.

In all the experimental arrangements for producing interference, it has been found necessary that the interfering beams be derived from the same source of light.   This is commonly explained by assuming that light is emitted in wave trains having a finite length.   Thus, although two wave trains derived from different sources will produce an interference pattern, two succeeding wave trains will, in general, have a different phase relationship and will therefore produce a pattern that is displaced with respect to the first.   Since a large number of wave trains are required to produce an effect on either the eye or a photographic plate, the screen appears to be uniformly illuminated. Schuster explains this failure to observe interference with two independent sources by assuming that no source emits radiation that is strictly monochromatic; in other words, that even a single spectral line represents a band of frequencies.   Since the phase relationships between the various frequency components are all different, the pattern produced by one frequency is masked by the patterns produced by the others.[1]

Let us assume for the moment the ideal case of a source that emits continuously light of only a single frequency.   Let this source be used in conjunction with suitable apparatus to form an interference pattern on the screen shown in Fig. 280, which may be either a ground glass or a photographic plate.   A more efficient arrangement for visual observation of the fringes is to dispense entirely with the ground glass and to look toward the oncoming light with the accommodation adjusted for the plane that the ground glass would have occupied.   The interference fringes are then formed directly upon the retina, since it is conjugate to the

[1] If the reader is familiar with Fourier analysis, he will immediately recognize that the two explanations are essentially equivalent because a wave train of finite length is resolvable into a spectrum composed of infinitely long wave trains of all possible frequencies.   The energy within a given band of frequencies is practically zero except in the immediate vicinity of the nominal frequency of the original wave train.   The longer the original wave train, the narrower is the band of frequencies for which the amplitude is sensibly different from zero.

plane of the ground glass. The observations are greatly facilitated by using either a magnifier or a telescope to examine the fringes, the former being used when the fringes are formed close to the eye and the latter when they are formed at a great distance.

At any point of the screen, such as P in Fig. 280, the phase difference between the two disturbances producing the interference has a definite value. This phase difference results from a difference in the length of the optical path of the two beams. It is easy to see that reinforcement takes place when the path difference $\delta = 0, \lambda, 2\lambda, 3\lambda$, etc., and annulment when $\delta = \frac{1}{2}\lambda, \frac{3}{2}\lambda, \frac{5}{2}\lambda$, etc. The ratio δ/λ evidently determines what may be called the *order* of the interference.

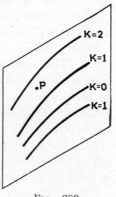

Fig. 280.

Thus the order of interference at P may be represented by

$$m = \frac{\delta}{\lambda} = K + \epsilon, \tag{290}$$

where K is an integer and ϵ a fraction.

Now let us suppose that the source emits light waves lying within the spectral band having a width $d\lambda$ and a mean wave length λ. By differentiating Eq. (290), it is found that

$$\frac{dm}{m} = -\frac{d\lambda}{\lambda}. \tag{291}$$

If the change in wave length represented by $d\lambda$ is to produce a negligible effect on the interference pattern, dm must be small in comparison with unity. Therefore, if the order of interference is high, the purity of the radiation, which is measured by the ratio $\lambda/d\lambda$, must also be high. The green line of mercury ($\lambda = 546.1$ mμ) is remarkably pure and produces observable fringes when the order of interference is nearly 800,000. This order of interference corresponds to a path difference of more than 40 cm. Unfortunately, this line is accompanied by satellites that complicate the interference pattern. The cadmium arc used by Michelson has a red line which is free from satellites and which produces observable fringes when the order of interference is 400,000. It will be recalled from Sec. 78, Chap. IX, that this radiation has been chosen as the primary standard of wave length. Buisson and Fabry found in 1912 that a discharge tube containing krypton in liquid air produces observable fringes when the order of interference is nearly 1,000,000. The inference is that the individual wave trains emitted by this source must contain at least one million waves.

When white light is used as a source, $d\lambda$ becomes nearly equal to λ. The interference pattern consists therefore of a white central fringe with a few colored fringes on either side. The pattern becomes so complex at higher orders that the fringes gradually blend into a uniform white field. For such purposes as the routine measurements in the machine shop or the testing of optical parts, only the first few orders are necessary and white light is therefore satisfactory. A greater number of fringes can be seen by placing a deep red filter in the path of the light.

205. Stationary Light Waves.—In the vast majority of interference phenomena, the interfering beams have substantially the same direction of propagation. This feature is not essential, however, for interference is observed between beams traveling in opposite directions. To see how interference takes place in this case, it is merely necessary to write the equations for the two waves and add them together. Let the displacement produced by one wave at any point along the direction of propagation be given at some particular instant of time by

$$y = a \sin x .$$

For a given value of x, the displacement varies with time in accordance with the expression

$$y = a \sin 2\pi f t .$$

Both expressions may be combined to give the general expression for a wave traveling in the positive direction of x:

$$y_1 = a \, \sin 2\pi\left(\frac{t}{T} - \frac{x}{\lambda}\right), \qquad (292)$$

wherein T is the period and λ the wave length. A similar wave traveling in the opposite direction would be represented by

$$y_2 = a \, \sin 2\pi\left(\frac{t}{T} + \frac{x}{\lambda}\right). \qquad (293)$$

If, in some manner, the two waves are combined, the resultant displacement at any point x and any time t is found to be

$$y = y_1 + y_2 = 2a \cos 2\pi \frac{x}{\lambda} \sin 2\pi \frac{t}{T}. \qquad (294)$$

This equation represents a sinusoidal disturbance in time whose amplitude is zero where $x/\lambda = \frac{1}{4}, \frac{3}{4}, \frac{5}{4}, \frac{7}{4}$, etc. Such points are known as *nodes*. The amplitude attains its maximum value $2a$ where $x/\lambda = 0, \frac{1}{2}, \frac{2}{2}, \frac{3}{2}$, etc., and such points are known as *antinodes*. The distance between successive nodes or antinodes is obviously $\frac{1}{2}\lambda$. Since the nodes and antinodes have fixed positions in space, this kind of interference is said to produce *stationary waves*.

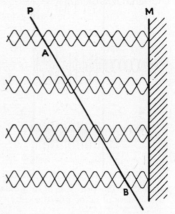

FIG. 281.—Sketch showing the principle of Wiener's experiment.

The phenomenon of stationary waves has long been known in the fields of mechanics and acoustics, and it was suggested as an explanation of the colors exhibited by some of Becquerel's photographs made in 1850. It was not until 1890, however, that Wiener demonstrated conclusively the existence of stationary light waves. His apparatus consisted, as shown in Fig. 281, of a plane mirror M upon which a parallel beam of monochromatic light was allowed to fall. Since the reflected beam had the same wave length and very nearly the same amplitude as the original beam, a stationary-wave pattern was produced. This pattern was recorded on a thin photographic emulsion P, which was inclined at a slight angle to the mirror. Upon development, the emulsion was found to exhibit an interference pattern consisting of parallel light and dark lines. This was to be expected because, wherever the emulsion coincided with a node, as at A and B, the silver halide should be unaffected. At other points, however, a developable image should be produced.

Soon after Wiener's experiment was published, Lippmann employed the phenomenon of stationary light waves as the basis of a process of color photography.[1] The plates used for this

[1] Although the subject of color photography is beyond the scope of this volume, this process deserves a brief description because of its theoretical interest. A comprehensive account of the methods that have been devised for making photographs in natural colors will be found in E. J. Wall's "The

process must be especially prepared because the grains of commercial plates are much too coarse. The plates are placed in the camera with the glass side facing the lens and the emulsion

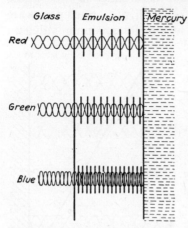

is backed with a reflecting layer of mercury, as shown in Fig. 282. Because of the stationary-wave pattern that is formed in the emulsion, the developed image consists of thin laminae whose separation is half of the wave length of the light that produced them. The plate is prepared for viewing by coating the back of the glass with a black varnish and cementing a thin prism to the emulsion side to avoid the annoying surface re-

FIG. 282.—The principle of Lippmann's process of color photography.

flection. When white light is then allowed to fall upon the laminae, the condition for reinforcement is satisfied for the wave length that produced them but not for other wave lengths. The existence of the laminae can be proved by examining a transverse section of the developed image under a microscope. When this is done, it is found that a node is produced at the boundary of the emulsion where the reflection takes place. This is explained by assuming that a wave is reversed in phase when it is reflected at the boundary of a denser medium. Although the complications of the Lippmann process have prevented it from being used to any great extent, it has the advantage over other processes of color photography that it is capable of reproducing spectral colors.

206. Interference at Thin Films. Newton's Rings.—The colors exhibited by a thin film, such as a soap bubble or a layer of oil on water, are familiar to everyone. Certain crystals, notably potassium chlorate, are composed of successive layers, and they also appear colored although they have no selective absorption in the ordinary sense. The first quantitative investigation of this phenomenon seems to have been made by Newton,

History of Three-color Photography," American Photographic Publishing Company.

who studied the colored rings produced when two spherical surfaces having almost the same radius of curvature are placed in contact. A hundred years later, Young showed that the phenomenon is due to interference between the beams reflected at the two surfaces.

The simplest case to investigate is that of a plane surface in contact with a spherical surface of large radius of curvature. Such a combination is shown in Fig. 283, where O is the center of curvature of the spherical surface and R is its radius. If monochromatic light is incident from above, some will be reflected

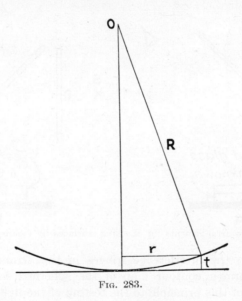

Fɪɢ. 283.

at the spherical surface and some at the plane surface. The point of contact is dark because, although there is here no path difference between the beams reflected at the two surfaces, the beam reflected at the plane surface is reversed in phase. This phase reversal is equivalent to a path difference of $\frac{1}{2}\lambda$ and therefore produces annulment. Annulment takes place also at points for which the thickness t of the air film equals $\frac{1}{2}\lambda$, $\frac{2}{2}\lambda$, $\frac{3}{2}\lambda$, etc. The result is an interference pattern consisting of a dark center surrounded by alternate light and dark rings, called *Newton's rings*. The value of t for any given ring cannot be measured conveniently, but it can be determined by measuring the radius r of the ring. Since, from the geometry of the figure,

$$r^2 = R^2 - (R - t)^2$$
$$= 2Rt - t^2,$$

and t^2 is negligible compared with $2Rt$, it follows that

$$t = \frac{r^2}{2R}. \tag{295}$$

The radii of the rings evidently increase as the square root of the natural numbers.

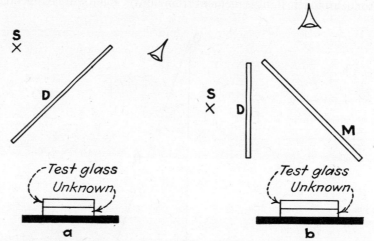

FIG. 284.—Two arrangements for checking surfaces by means of test glasses.

Evidently, the interference fringes in the arrangement just described form a contour map of the spherical surface. The application of this principle to the testing of the figure of optical surfaces was alluded to in Sec. 135, Chap. XVII, but we are now in a position to consider it in more detail. The apparatus that is ordinarily used in practice is represented schematically in Fig. 284a. The source S is an incandescent lamp, which illuminates the diffusing screen D. The optical part to be examined is laid on the table with the surface to be tested uppermost and a test glass is placed upon it. Let it be assumed for concreteness that the part is being tested for flatness, and that the test glass has a truly plane surface. If the surface of the part is also truly plane, it can be made to coincide with the test glass at all points and the field will therefore appear uniformly dark all over. This procedure is not followed in practice because of the danger of scratching the surfaces. Instead, the surfaces are placed in contact at only one point, leaving a wedge of air between. The result is a system of straight, parallel fringes, as shown at A in Fig. 285, where the point of contact is at c. Parallel fringes do not always indicate a true figure with the apparatus we have assumed because the pattern must be observed at an angle. For this reason, the arrangement sketched in Fig. 284b is better. The diffusing glass D is placed as shown, and the light from it is reflected downward by means of the clear glass plate M. The interference pattern can then be observed from a direction normal to the surfaces.

If the surface being tested is slightly convex, a Newton's ring pattern as shown at B in Fig. 285 results. Assuming that light

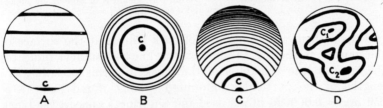

Fig. 285.—Typical interference patterns formed with test glasses.

with a mean wave length of 650 mμ is used and that the radius of the fifth dark ring is 50 mm, Eq. (295) shows that the radius of curvature of the surface is 770 meters. A concave surface would produce the same pattern except for the obvious differences resulting from the edge being in contact instead of the center. If the surface is convex, the test glass can be rocked upon it to move the point of contact. When it is at the edge, the pattern appears as shown at C in the figure.

If the surface of the part is irregular, the interference pattern may have an appearance like that shown at D. In this particular case, there are two points of contact, c_1 and c_2. If the corresponding portions of the surface under test are visualized as elevations on the surfaces, the similarity of the interference pattern to a topographic map is at once evident.

With the increasing importance of the quantity production of standardized machine parts, interference methods have found their way into the machine shop. A set of Johansson gauges used in conjunction with a plane test glass in either of the types of apparatus shown in Fig. 284 can be used for the extremely accurate measurement of thickness. In Fig. 286a is shown an arrangement for comparing a metal block—for example, a part of a machine or a gauge under construction—directly with a gauge of known thickness. Both block and gauge are "wrung" on a base plate[1] having a plane surface, and the test glass is

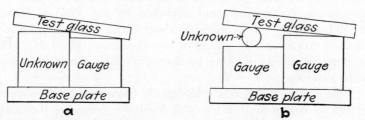

Fig. 286.—Typical arrangements for testing the thickness of objects by means of a gauge and a test glass.

laid upon them. The number of dark fringes at the surface of the gauge (neglecting the one at the line of contact) indicates the error in the thickness of the block in terms of half wave lengths of the particular light used. Thus, if red light ($\lambda = 650$ m$\mu = 0.000026$ in.) is used and ten fringes appear, the block is $10 \times 0.000013 = 0.00013$ in. thicker than the gauge. Another common problem in the machine shop is to measure the diameter of a spherical or cylindrical object—ball bearing, hairspring, or plug gauge, for example. A suitable arrangement is shown in Fig. 286b. If the difference in the thickness of the two gauges is equal to the nominal diameter of the object, it is obvious that the error in diameter can be computed directly from the number of fringes that are visible on the surface of the thicker gauge, the width of this gauge, and the distance of the object from the line of contact of the test glass and the gauge. Many other

[1] The process of "wringing" consists in sliding one part along the other in such a manner as to exclude air and dust. When the operation is properly performed, the two pieces stick together by the pressure of the air and can be removed only by sliding. The surfaces must be clean and must be covered with a light film of moisture, which is produced by breathing upon them. Two parts that are "wrung" together should be separated as soon as the test is completed or they may adhere permanently. It may be added that the Johansson gauges consist of metal blocks whose thicknesses are such that either singly or in combination any thickness within the capacity of the set can be obtained in steps of 0.0001 in. The precision of any combination less than 6 in. thick is said to be 0.00001 in., and the error of 0.000001 in. introduced by the film between the blocks is quite negligible.

arrangements similar to those just mentioned can be devised for special purposes.

207. The Measurement of Length. Interferometers.—Consider the ray I, in Fig. 287, which is incident on a plane-parallel plate having a thickness t and a refractive index n'. This ray gives rise to the ray R_1 on reflection at the first surface and the

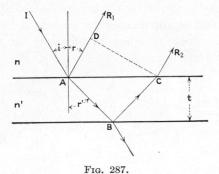

Fɪɢ. 287.

ray R_2 on reflection at the second surface. The path difference between the rays R_1 and R_2 is

$$\delta = n'(AB + BC) - nAD + \frac{\lambda}{2}$$

$$= 2n't \cos r' + \frac{\lambda}{2}, \tag{296}$$

where r' is the angle of refraction in the medium of index n'. The value of δ can be varied by varying either t or r. The fringes produced by varying t are called *fringes of equal thickness;* the fringes produced by varying r are called *fringes of equal inclination*. The production of fringes of equal thickness was discussed in the preceding section, and the production of fringes of equal inclination will be discussed in the present section. The distinguishing feature between the two cases is that, to observe fringes of equal thickness, the eye must be focused on the plate itself, whereas to observe fringes of equal inclination, the eye must be focused for infinity.

The method of producing fringes of equal inclination can be understood most readily in terms of an apparatus devised by Fizeau in 1849 for determining the separation of spectral lines. As shown in Fig. 288, the apparatus consists of a source S, a mirror R containing a hole for observing the fringes, and two glass disks M_1 and M_2. The upper surface of M_1 is inclined at a slight angle so that the reflected light does not enter the eye of the observer, and the lower surface of M_2 is blackened. The interference pattern that is produced is therefore the result of reflections at the lower surface of M_1 and the upper surface of M_2. If these surfaces are exactly parallel and are separated by an integral number of wave lengths, the point at the foot of the perpendicular dropped from the eye will be dark because of the reversal of phase suffered by the light reflected at the surface of M_2. This point is surrounded by alternate bright and dark rings, since the angle of obliquity increases the path difference between the interfering rays.

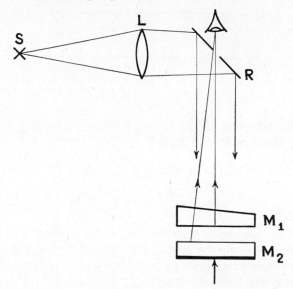

FIG. 288.—The optical system of the Fizeau interferometer.

Fizeau's apparatus was provided with a screw for moving the lower disk to increase or decrease the thickness of the layer of air between the disks. As the thickness of the layer is increased, the spot at the center becomes alternately bright and dark and the entire fringe system expands, new fringes appearing at the center of the field at approximately the same rate as the fringes disappear at the edge. As the thickness of the layer is decreased, the fringe system contracts, new fringes appearing at the edge of the field at approximately the same rate as the fringes vanish at the center. Obviously, a displacement of M_2 equal to half a wave length causes the center of the pattern to pass through one complete cycle. Hence, by counting the number of cycles through which the center of the pattern passes for a known displacement of M_2, the wave length of a monochromatic radiation can be determined.

Consider now the case where the source emits two monochromatic radiations having wave lengths λ_1 and λ_2. Suppose that the distance between the two disks is such that both radiations produce fringe systems with dark centers. The two fringe systems will then be superposed upon each other near the center of the field, which will have an appearance not unlike that produced

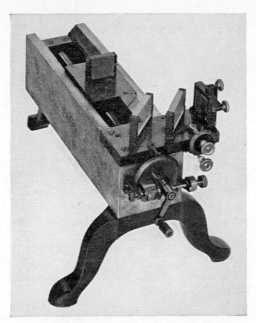

Fig. 289.—The Michelson interferometer.

by either radiation alone. If, however, one radiation produces a fringe system with a bright center and the other a system with a dark center, the two systems will be intermeshed in such a manner as to produce a uniformly bright field, provided the two radiations are of equal intensity. Suppose that, as the separation of the two disks is slowly varied, N_1 fringes of the radiation whose wave length is λ_1 are observed to appear or disappear at the center of the field between successive positions for which the field has the same appearance. The change in the path difference is obviously $N_1\lambda_1$, and this causes the appearance or disappearance of $N_1 \pm 1$ fringes of wave length λ_2, whence

$$N_1\lambda_1 = (N_1 \pm 1)\lambda_2$$

or

$$\lambda_2 = \frac{N_1}{N_1 \pm 1}\lambda_1. \tag{297}$$

Thus it is a simple matter to determine the wave length of an unknown radiation in terms of one that is known.

The instrument just described is known as an interferometer because it can be used to measure a length in terms of the length of a wave of light. The usefulness of the type just described is

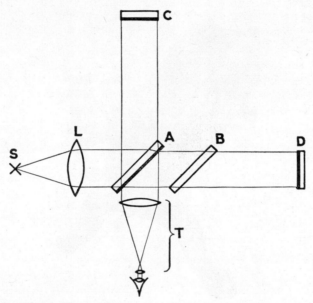

Fig. 290.—The optical system of the Michelson interferometer.

very restricted, however, and other types having a wider range of applications have been devised. One of the best known is the one designed by Michelson[1] for determining whether the earth is in motion with respect to the ether. Figure 289 is a photograph of a small model of this instrument. It consists, as shown by Fig. 290, of two first-surface mirrors C and D, a half-silvered mirror A, and a clear compensating plate B whose thickness is exactly equal to that of A. The lens L makes the light from the source S approximately parallel. The incident beam is divided at A, approximately one-half being reflected to the mirror C and the

[1] *Phil. Mag.*, **24**, 449 (1887).

remainder being transmitted to the mirror D.   The returning beams are recombined at A and enter the observer's eye to produce fringes of equal inclination.   These fringes are observed through the telescope T, which is necessary because of their small angular separation when the path difference is great. This apparatus is essentially equivalent to Fizeau's apparatus except for the important advantage that a substance can be introduced into one of the beams independently of the other.[1] The path difference can be varied by moving either C or D and, in contrast to Fizeau's apparatus, the path difference can be made equal to zero.   If the virtual image of D formed by reflection at A is parallel to C, the fringe system is a series of concentric circles as in Fizeau's apparatus.   Sometimes the instrument is used with the mirrors inclined at a slight angle, in which case the fringes are arcs whose direction of curvature depends upon whether the virtual image of D is in front of C or behind it. When the two coincide, the line of intersection is marked by a straight fringe that is achromatic in white light.   This fringe of zero path difference is easy to detect and serves as a useful point of reference.

The application of this interferometer to practical problems can be illustrated by the procedure developed by Michelson for measuring the standard meter in terms of the length of light waves.   This might have been accomplished by placing one of the mirrors, C for example, in coincidence with one of the scratches on the standard meter.   Then by moving C until it coincided with the other scratch and counting the number of fringes that appeared or disappeared at the center of the field during the operation, a direct measure of the number of light waves in a meter could have been obtained.   This procedure has two serious objections.   In the first place, there are 1,553,164 red cadmium waves in the standard meter, and to count the corresponding number of fringes would be a superhuman task.   In the second place, no radiation is sufficiently homogeneous to produce sharply defined fringes over a path difference as great as one meter.   Michelson therefore used nine etalons of the type shown in Fig. 291, each having approximately twice the length of the next shorter.   The shortest was 0.391 mm long and the longest

---

[1] This fact is the basis of Twyman's adaptation of the instrument for testing optical systems.   A brief description was given in Sec. 139, Chap. XVII.

100 mm (0.1 meter).   The length of the shortest was accurately determined in the manner described above, which was a comparatively simple operation since only 1200 fringes had to be

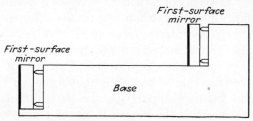

Fɪɢ. 291.—Diagrammatic sketch of an etalon used by Michelson in determining the length of the standard meter.

counted.   This etalon was then compared with the next longer, and the process was repeated until the number of fringes corresponding to the 100-mm etalon was found.[1]   The final operation was to compare this etalon with the standard meter.   To do this, an auxiliary meter was prepared and the etalon was provided with an arm on which a scratch was made.   The auxiliary meter

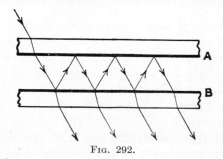

Fɪɢ. 292.

was placed on the interferometer beside the etalon, and the length of the auxiliary meter was stepped off ten times, the operation being started at one end of the auxiliary meter and finished at the other.   Finally the standard meter was compared with the auxiliary meter by means of a comparator.

The fringes obtained with either the Fizeau or the Michelson interferometer pass through their successive maxima and minima gradually, so the exact position of a fringe is difficult to estimate. The fringes are much sharper in interferometers that are based

[1] For the details of the procedure, see *Travaux et Mémoires du Bureau International des Poids et Mesures*, **9**, (1894) or Michelson's "Studies in Optics," University of Chicago Press, Chicago.

on the principle of multiple reflections between parallel plates. The formation of fringes in this case can be understood from Fig. 292, which shows two parallel plates with a light coating of silver on their adjacent surfaces A and B. If a ray of light is incident on these surfaces, the transmitted rays produced by the multiple reflections are parallel to each other and the path difference between any pair of adjacent rays is the same. These rays will therefore produce an interference pattern in a telescope focused for infinity. It can be shown that the intensity in the maxima of this pattern is

$$I_0 = \frac{T^2}{(1 - R)^2},\tag{298}$$

where R and T are, respectively, the reflectance and the transmission of the surfaces A and B. Calling δ the path difference between adjacent transmitted rays (in practice, approximately equal to twice the separation of the surfaces), the intensity at any other point can be shown to be

$$I = \frac{I_0}{1 + C \sin^2 \pi \dfrac{\delta}{\lambda}},\tag{299}$$

where

$$C = \frac{4R}{(1 - R)^2}.\tag{300}$$

At the minima, it is clear that the intensity is

$$I_{min.} = \frac{I_0}{1 + C}.\tag{301}$$

By examining Eq. (299), it can be seen that the sharpness of the fringes is determined by the value of C, which in turn depends upon the reflectance R of the surfaces. Taking R equal to 0.8, which is found to be the optimum value in practice, $C = 80$. The distribution of intensity in the fringe system under these conditions is shown in Fig. 293, which is a plot of I against δ/λ. The fringes are very narrow compared with the intervening dark spaces; and, since the intensity in these spaces is only $\frac{1}{180}$ of that in the maxima, the contrast is very marked. If the light consists of more than one monochromatic radiation, the patterns due to the separate radiations are clearly distinguishable, which is not the case for the Michelson or the Fizeau interferometer. This circumstance can be turned to advantage in analyzing spectral lines, as will be explained in the next section.

Fabry and Perot[1] have designed an interferometer based on the principle just discussed. It consists essentially of two parallel

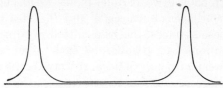

Fig. 293.—Plot of the intensity of the fringes produced by a Fabry-Perot interferometer.

mirrors whose adjacent faces are very accurately plane and whose reflectance is 80 per cent. The instrument is arranged as shown in Fig. 294, where the mirrors are represented by M_1 and M_2. The lens L forms a magnified image of the source S

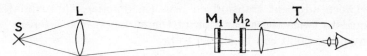

Fig. 294.—The optical system of the Fabry-Perot interferometer.

near the mirrors, and the fringes are examined with a telescope T. Mirror M_1 is movable in a direction normal to its surface. This instrument was used by Benoit, Fabry, and Perot in a repetition of Michelson's determination of the length of the standard meter. The manner in which the length of an etalon is measured with this instrument is indicated in Fig. 295. The etalon in this case

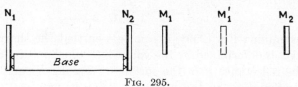

Fig. 295.

consists of two partially silvered mirrors N_1 and N_2, whose silvered surfaces face each other. White light from a source at the left of the figure is sent through the etalon and the interferometer mirrors M_1 and M_2 in turn. Consider a ray reflected first at N_2 and re-reflected at N_1. This ray interferes with another ray reflected first at M_2 and re-reflected at M_1. If $N_1N_2 = M_1M_2$, there is no path difference between the rays and the observer sees a uniform white field when all the mirrors are

[1] *Ann. Chimie Physique*, **22**, 564 (1901). Reprinted in *Astrophys. Jour.*, **13**, 265 (1901).

parallel. This condition can be readily detected because a slight motion of M_1 causes colored rings to appear. If the etalon is slightly rotated about a vertical axis, a straight, achromatic fringe bordered by curved, colored fringes indicates the vertical plane in which the path difference is zero, as with the Michelson interferometer. Now consider the effect of moving M_1 to M_1', where $M_1'M_2 = \frac{1}{2}N_1N_2$. A ray reflected once between N_1 and N_2 will interfere with a ray reflected twice between M_1' and M_2, and a uniform white field or a straight white fringe will again be seen. This is true also when $M_1'M_2 = \frac{1}{3}N_1N_2$, $\frac{1}{4}N_1N_2$, etc. The distance between the various positions of M_1 can be readily measured in terms of the wave length of any desired monochromatic radiation, and thus the distance between N_1 and N_2 can be computed. In determining the length of the meter, five similar etalons were used, each being twice as long as the next shorter. The length of the shortest, which was 62.5 mm, was found directly; and the length of the longest, which was approximately 1 meter, was found by comparing the etalons successively with one another. The 1-meter etalon was compared with the standard meter by means of a comparator.[1]

The interferometer is a valuable tool for the measurement of distances which are either excessively small or which must be determined with a degree of precision that makes other methods of measurement unsuitable. The two determinations of the wave length of the red cadmium line described above differed from each other by less than 5 parts in 10,000,000, and hence the wave length of this line is known to a greater degree of precision than is ever required in the ordinary measurements of distance. This establishes the wave length of this radiation as a unit of length whose constancy makes it unnecessary to maintain physical standards. To measure an unknown distance, one needs merely to count the number of fringes that appear or disappear in the field as the interferometer mirror is moved from one end of the distance in question to the other.[2] The cadmium arc is not always convenient but the radiations from other sources have

[1] See *Travaux et Mémoires du Bureau International des Poids et Mesures*, **15** (1913) for the details of the procedure.

[2] There are certain adjustments that must be made to an interferometer before it can be used. These are made most conveniently by following a systematic procedure, which is given in some detail in most treatises on physical optics and in advanced laboratory manuals such as Mann's "Manual of Advanced Optics" and Taylor's "College Manual of Optics."

since been determined by interference methods in terms of the red cadmium radiation with a precision that is entirely adequate for all practical purposes.

208. Interference Spectroscopes.—The interferometers described in the preceding section can be used to determine the wave lengths of the components of spectral lines. The procedure followed by Fizeau in his determination of the separation of the sodium lines was to count the number of fringes appearing in the field as the lower plate is moved between positions of uniform illumination. Michelson developed a method for analyzing still more complex radiations by means of his interferometer. The method consists in estimating the variation in the distinctness or "visibility" of the fringes as the interferometer mirror is moved. He defined visibility as

$$V = \frac{I_{\text{max.}} - I_{\text{min.}}}{I_{\text{max.}} + I_{\text{min.}}}, \qquad (302)$$

where $I_{\text{max.}}$ and $I_{\text{min.}}$ represent, respectively, the intensity of the bright fringe at a given point and the intensity of the adjacent dark fringes. The visibility varies in a characteristic manner for every type of complex radiation. Thus, for a radiation consisting of two components of equal intensity, the visibility varies periodically between zero and unity. Although the satellites of many lines were discovered by this method, there was no way of determining whether a given satellite was on the long or the short wave-length side of the principal line. Moreover, in the hands of one less skillful than Michelson, the method is quite impractical. On the other hand, the interferometers based on the principle of multiple reflections produce fringes of such sharpness that the fringe system is in effect an enlarged view of a limited portion of the spectrum. In this case, the problem of estimating the visibility does not arise.

It will be recalled from Sec. 202, Chap. XXVII, that the resolving power of a spectroscope is expressed by $\lambda/d\lambda$, where $d\lambda$ is the smallest distinguishable wave-length difference. For an interferometer, Eq. (291) shows that

$$\frac{\lambda}{d\lambda} = \frac{m}{dm}, \qquad (303)$$

where m is the order of interference. For example, if the fringes due to one component of the radiation are to lie midway between those due to the other, $dm = \frac{1}{2}$, and therefore

$$\frac{\lambda}{d\lambda} = 2m.$$

Thus the resolving power can be increased at will by increasing the order of interference. In the Fabry-Perot interferometer, this is done by moving the mirrors farther apart. The limit is reached when the order becomes so great that the inhomogeneity of the components causes the interference pattern to become indistinct. When absolute values of wave length are not required and the only problem is to analyze the structure of a spectral line, the Lummer-Gehrcke plate[1] is more convenient because it is less complicated and therefore less difficult to keep in adjustment. It consists essentially of a thick plane-parallel plate as shown in

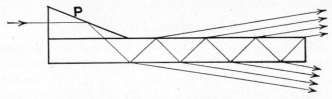

Fig. 296.—The Lummer-Gehrcke plate.

Fig. 296. The radiation to be examined is isolated with a monochromator, rendered parallel by a lens, and caused to enter the plate as shown through one face of the prism P. This prism is cemented to the plate to prevent the heavy loss of light by reflection that would otherwise occur. The rays suffer many internal reflections within the plate and emerge in a condition to interfere. The resulting fringes are viewed by means of a telescope placed either above or below the plate. The surfaces of the plate are not silvered, a high reflectance being attained by causing the reflections to take place near the critical angle. A very high resolving power can be attained, 500,000 being a typical value. The chief difficulty in manufacturing and mounting a Lummer-Gehrcke plate is to keep the faces parallel. A slight departure from strict parallelism will introduce ghosts similar to those produced by an imperfect diffraction grating. These ghosts can be detected in the manner described in Sec. 202, by crossing another plate with the one in question.

Michelson's echelon grating[2] is another device for analyzing

[1] *Ann. Physik*, **10**, 457 (1903).

[2] *Astrophys. Jour.*, **8**, 37 (1898)

radiation. As shown in Fig. 297, it consists of a pile of plane-parallel plates arranged in step formation. Each step is made to have the same height and width so that the retardation of the various portions of the beam varies in arithmetical progression. The plates usually have a thickness of approximately 10 or 20 mm

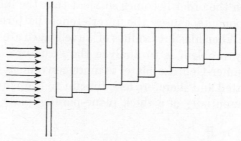

Fig. 297.—The Michelson echelon grating.

and each extends 1 or 2 mm beyond its neighbor. As many as 30 plates can be used before the absorption of light becomes excessive. The expression for the resolving power of an echelon is the same as that for an ordinary diffraction grating, which is given by Eq. (288) in Chap. XXVII as

$$\frac{\lambda}{d\lambda} = Nm,$$

where m is the order of the spectrum and N is the number of lines in the grating. In the case of the echelon, m is the path difference, expressed in wave lengths, between rays passing through adjacent plates. This path difference is evidently

$$m = (n - 1)\frac{t}{\lambda},$$

where t is the common thickness of the plates. Substituting $t = 20$ mm and $\lambda = 0.0005$ mm, the value of m is found to be equal to 20,000. The corresponding value of $\lambda/d\lambda$ is 600,000 when 30 plates are used. As this resolving power can now be attained with ruled gratings, the echelon grating no longer possesses the unique importance that it did at the time of its invention. One of its serious disadvantages is the small separation of the successive orders of spectra.

209. Miscellaneous Applications of Interference.—Interference methods are generally employed whenever a length, an angle, or a displacement must be measured with high precision. Many ingenious arrangements have been devised to meet special conditions, but they are all based on the principles discussed in the preceding section.[1] There are, however, two important applications of interference that are sufficiently different to warrant special mention.

One of these applications is the determination of indices of refraction. Since the quantity measured by an interferometer is the *optical* path difference, it is clear that the index of a sub-

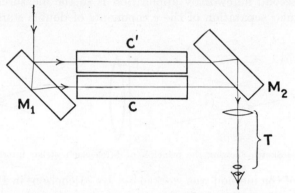

Fig. 298.—The optical system of the Jamin interferometer.

stance whose thickness is known can be found by inserting it in one of the beams of an interferometer and measuring the amount by which the optical path is altered. This method is especially valuable for gases, whose indices differ but slightly from unity. An early type of interferometer for this purpose was devised by Jamin,[2] and the principle of the instrument is illustrated in Fig. 298. It consists essentially of two thick mirrors M_1 and M_2. A beam of approximately parallel light is incident on M_1, where it is divided into two interfering beams. These are reflected at M_2 into a telescope T. Two evacuated cells C and C' having the same length are inserted, one in the path of each beam. The gas under examination is then allowed to enter one of the cells slowly and the resulting displacement of the fringe system is noted. From the known length of the tube and the increase in

---

[1] The field of interference measurements is well covered by Fabry's monograph, "Les Applications des Interférences Lumineuses," published by the *Rev. d'Optique*.

[2] *Ann. Chimie Physique*, **49**, 282 (1857).

the path difference, the index of refraction is easily computed. A more common type of instrument was designed by Löwe[1] after an apparatus designed by Lord Rayleigh[2] for measuring the indices of argon and helium. These interferometers are often used in the analysis of a mixture of gases to determine the proportion in which the components are present.[3] For example, the Löwe type is made in a portable form for determining the presence of a dangerous concentration of carbon monoxide in coal mines.

The second noteworthy application is to the measurement of the angular separation of the components of double stars. The

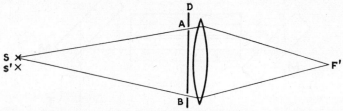

Fig. 299.—Sketch showing the principle of Michelson's stellar interferometer.

theory of the method was worked out by Michelson[4] in 1890. A complete discussion of the theory would be out of place here but the principle will be clear from Fig. 299. Let it be assumed that the two stars S and S' are so small that they can be treated as points. In other words, if these stars are observed in a telescope in the ordinary manner, two overlapping diffraction patterns similar to those of Fig. 60 in Chap. VII will be formed in the focal plane F'. If now a diaphragm D containing two apertures A and B is placed in front of the objective, one of the components, S for example, will produce a system of parallel fringes. The central fringe will be located at F' where the two paths AF' and BF' are equal. The component S' will produce a similar system of parallel fringes with the central fringe in a slightly different position. If the two components are of equal intensity, the two systems will intermesh to produce a uniformly bright patch of light when the angular separation of the two components is

[1] *Zeits. Instrumentenk.*, **30**, 321 (1910). See also Martin's "Optical Measuring Instruments," Chap. IX.

[2] *Proc. Roy. Soc.*, **59**, 198 (1896).

[3] See *Bur. Standards Tech. Paper* 131.

[4] *Phil. Mag.*, **30**, 1 (1890).

$$\alpha = \frac{\lambda}{2\,AB}.$$ (304)

Hence by varying the distance between the apertures until the fringe systems intermesh in this manner, the angular separation of the components can at once be determined. In practice, A and B are located at the opposite ends of a diameter of the objective and their effective separation is altered by rotating the diaphragm about the axis of the telescope.[1]

Since the diffraction patterns that are produced when a telescope is used in the ordinary manner without the diaphragm are merely manifestations of the phenomenon of interference between the various portions of the wave front entering the objective, it is not immediately obvious that the insertion of the diaphragm should increase the effective resolving power. The difference between the two cases is simply that in ordinary telescopic vision the recognition of the dual character of the overlapping diffraction patterns is more difficult than the determination of the separation of the apertures for which the interference patterns produce a uniformly bright field. If Eq. (304) is compared with the customary equation for the resolving power,

$$\alpha = 1.22\frac{\lambda}{D},$$

which was derived in Sec. 61, Chap. VII, it will be seen that, by inserting the diaphragm, the resolving power of the telescope is more than doubled. This method is applicable only to the case of objects like double stars and does not permit the resolution of finer detail in extended objects.

The usefulness of this method has been extended by Michelson[2] in an ingenious manner by mounting a system of mirrors outside the telescope as shown in Fig. 300. This arrangement was first tested with the 100-in. reflector at the Mount Wilson Observatory in a determination of the diameter of the star α Orionis (Betelgeuse), which was known to be comparatively near and was suspected of being very large. The interference fringes exhibited by a single star can be shown to vanish when the angle subtended by the star is

---

[1] A description of the application of this method to the determination of the angular separation of the components of α Aurigae (Capella) has been given by Anderson, *Astrophys. Jour.*, **51**, 263 (1920).

[2] *Astrophys. Jour.*, **53**, 249 (1921).

$$\alpha = 1.22 \frac{\lambda}{AB} \cdot \qquad (305)$$

The distance AB in this arrangement is the distance between the mirrors M_1 and M_4. Experiments showed that when the distance between the mirrors was 121 in. (3070 mm) the fringes disappeared. The angle α subtended by the star was computed

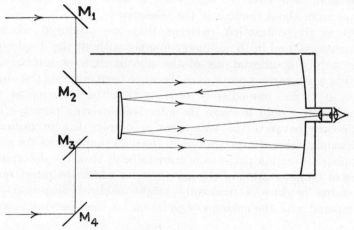

FIG. 300.—The optical system of the stellar interferometer as applied to the 100-in. Hooker reflector used in the Cassegrainian form.

to be 0.047 second of arc, assuming the effective wave length to be 575 $m\mu$. This star is so close that it appears to describe an orbit whose semi-diameter subtends an angle of 0.018 second of arc as a consequence of the motion of the earth around the sun; and, since the semi-diameter of the earth's orbit is 92,900,000 miles, it is easy to compute that the diameter of α Orionis is 240,000,000 miles.

CHAPTER XXIX

POLARIZED LIGHT AND ITS APPLICATIONS

All light sources of practical importance emit radiation that exhibits little evidence of polarization. For this reason, the optical instruments based on the phenomena of polarization are provided with some element, such as a Nicol prism, for polarizing the natural light supplied by the source. The use of such instruments is therefore limited to a few highly specialized applications, an adequate discussion of which would be beyond the scope of this volume. A general knowledge of the subject is essential nevertheless, but this involves the comprehension of a comparatively few basic principles.

210. Double Refraction.—Most of the phenomena that have been discussed hitherto could be interpreted by assuming that light is some sort of wave motion, and it was not necessary to raise the question as to whether the displacements are longitudinal or transverse. The early experimenters believed the displacements to be longitudinal, like those of sound waves, and they were therefore unable to explain what Huygens called the "strange refraction" of calcite, which was discovered by Erasmus Bartholinus in 1669. Bartholinus noticed that a ray passing through calcite is divided into two rays which are deviated by different amounts, and that one ray is deviated even when the incident ray is normal to the surface of the crystal. This effect is illustrated in Fig. 301. The *ordinary* ray O is undeviated, but the *extraordinary* ray E is deviated in the manner shown. This effect is called *double refraction* or *birefringence*. Huygens demonstrated that the principle he had devised for determining the behavior of ordinary rays can be applied to the extraordinary rays if the wavelets are assumed to be ellipsoidal instead of spherical. The procedure is illustrated by Fig. 302, where the circles represent the wavelets whose envelope is the ordinary wave front and the ellipses represent the wavelets whose envelope is the extraordinary wave front. In other words, the ordinary ray travels at the same velocity regardless of its direction within the crystal, whereas the velocity of the extraordinary ray depends upon its direction. There is one direction, however, for which the two velocities are equal, and this is represented in Huygens's construction by making one axis of the ellipses (in the case of calcite, the minor axis) equal to the diameter of the circles. This direction, which is indicated in Fig. 302 by XX', is called the optic axis of the crystal.[1] It should be noted that the optic axis is a direction and not a line.

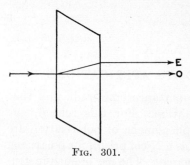

Fig. 301.

Since the velocity of the ordinary ray is the same as that of the extraordinary ray along the optic axis, the refractive indices are the same also. The value of the refractive index for the ordinary

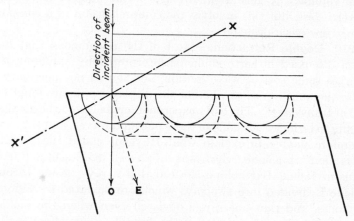

Fig. 302.—Huygens's construction for calcite. The optic axis is indicated by XX'.

ray is, of course, independent of the direction of propagation, and its value for calcite at the D-line is 1.6584. The refractive index for the extraordinary ray varies from this value to a minimum of

[1] In many crystals, the wave fronts together form a fourth-order surface. The intersection of this surface with a reference plane containing the axes of greatest and least elasticity consists of a circle and ellipse intersecting each other at four points; these points, taken by diametrically opposite pairs, determine two directions along which waves polarized in any azimuth travel with the same velocity. Crystals thus possessing two optic axes are called *biaxial* in contradistinction to the degenerate *uniaxial* crystals described in the text. Although of the greatest interest to the crystallographer, biaxial crystals are little used in optical instruments.

1.4864 in a direction perpendicular to the optic axis. Calcite is sometimes called a *negative* crystal because the index is less for the extraordinary ray than for the ordinary ray. Crystals like quartz, in which the index is greater for the extraordinary ray than for the ordinary ray, are known as *positive* crystals. In a negative crystal, the *minor* axis of the ellipsoidal wavelets in Huygens's construction must be assumed to be equal to the diameter of the spherical wavelets. It should be noted that in any uniaxial crystal the direction of propagation of the extraordinary ray is not perpendicular to the wave front except when the ray is either parallel or perpendicular to the optic axis.

Although Huygens was able to devise a construction that would indicate the paths of the rays in a doubly refracting medium, he was laboring under the belief that the vibrations are longitudinal and therefore he could not bring forth a convincing reason for the existence of the two rays. This task was not accomplished until a hundred years later, when Young made the bold hypothesis that light waves are transverse. Then it was an easy step to the assumption that the action of a doubly refracting crystal is to separate natural light into two components whose vibrations take place in mutually perpendicular planes. Experiments have since indicated that the direction of vibration at any point in the ordinary wave front is perpendicular to the plane containing the ray in question and the optic axis, and that the direction of vibration at any point in the extraordinary wave front lies within such a plane.

211. Methods of Producing Plane-polarized Light.—The simplest device for obtaining plane-polarized light from a beam of natural light is a crystal of tourmaline. This is a uniaxial crystal which has the peculiar property of absorbing the ordinary and extraordinary rays in different proportions. If the thickness of the crystal is more than about 2 mm, the ordinary ray is almost completely absorbed whereas the extraordinary ray is absorbed only slightly. Unfortunately, the absorption is somewhat selective as to wave length, and the transmitted beam is therefore colored. For this reason, tourmaline is seldom used except for demonstration purposes.

The most widely used device for producing polarization is the Nicol prism, which was devised early in the nineteenth century by William Nicol. In its original form, it consisted of a natural rhomb of calcite, split as shown at *a* in Fig. 303 and cemented together with Canada balsam.   The behavior of this prism can be seen from Fig. 304, which represents a plane passing through the corners *A*, *B*, *C*, and *D*.   The optic axis is indicated by *XX'*,

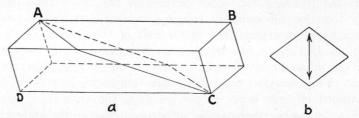

Fig. 303.—Diagrammatic sketch of a Nicol prism.   The direction of vibration of the emergent beam is indicated in the end elevation at *b*.

and the approximate values of the angles are shown.   When a ray of natural light is incident on the end face of the prism, it is divided into an ordinary and an extraordinary ray.   At the interface, the critical angles for the two rays are different because of the difference between the two indices.   The form of the

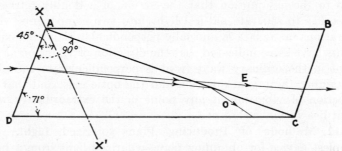

Fig. 304.—Cross section of a Nicol prism through the corners *A*, *B*, *C*, and *D* in Fig. 303.   The values of the angles are those of Nicol's original prism. The optic axis is indicated by *XX'*.

prism is such that the ordinary ray makes an angle of incidence that is greater than the critical angle, but the extraordinary ray makes an angle of incidence that is less.[1]   Hence, the ordinary ray is totally reflected toward the side of the prism, where it is absorbed by a coating of black lacquer.   The extraordinary ray continues on its course and emerges from the face *BC* in its

[1] Although Canada balsam is commonly used in the construction of polarizing prisms, any substance such as linseed oil, poppy oil, etc., may be used provided its index is lower than that of calcite for the ordinary ray. In the Foucault prism, which is used for ultraviolet light, the two parts are separated by a layer of air.

original direction. The plane of vibration of this ray lies in the plane of the paper. This plane is known as the *principal plane* of the prism. It contains the short diagonal of the end faces, as shown at *b* in Fig. 303.

The field of this type of prism is approximately 24°, being limited on one side by the angle for which the reflection for the ordinary ray ceases to be complete and on the other by the angle for which total reflection for the extraordinary ray takes place. The field is unsymmetrical about a line through the center of the prism.

Many modifications of the Nicol prism have been devised to increase the field, to make the field symmetrical, to decrease the amount of calcite required, or to eliminate the slight elliptical

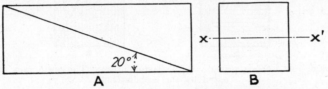

Fig. 305.—Side elevation and end elevation of typical Glan-Thompson prism. The optic axis is indicated by *XX'*.

polarization produced at the slanting end faces.[1] The most common type to-day is the Glan-Thompson prism shown in Fig. 305. The angle of the interface varies according to the use for which the prism is intended but is usually in the neighborhood of 20°. A prism of this type has a field angle of approximately 40°.

These polarizing prisms are designed to transmit one of the beams produced by the double refraction and to absorb the other. Sometimes it is desirable to transmit both beams, as in the case of the Rochon prism shown at *A* in Fig. 306. This prism consists of two wedges of calcite cut with their axes as indicated by the crosshatching. In the first half of the prism, both the ordinary and the extraordinary rays travel with the same velocity. In the second half, the ordinary ray continues at the same velocity, but the extraordinary ray travels more rapidly and is therefore deviated by an amount that depends upon the angle of the interface. The Wollaston prism shown at *B* in Fig. 306 deviates both beams in opposite directions. The ordinary ray in the first half

[1] An extensive survey of these various types has been given by Thompson in " Proceedings of the Optical Convention of 1905," p. 216.

of the prism becomes the extraordinary ray in the second half and *vice versa*. Therefore one ray is deviated by the same amount that a Rochon prism would deviate the extraordinary ray, and the other is deviated by very nearly the same amount.

It was found by Malus in 1808 that the light reflected at the proper angle from the surface of a non-conductor is plane polarized.[1] A few years later, Sir David Brewster showed that the

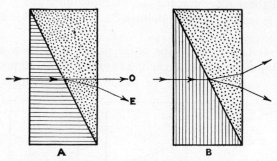

Fig. 306.—*A*, Rochon prism. *B*, Wollaston prism. The optic axes are indicated by the crosshatching.

condition to be satisfied for complete polarization is that $i + r = 90°$, a condition which obtains[2] for glass when the angle of incidence is approximately 57°. This method of producing polarized light is useful in practice when a beam of large aperture and small field is required, as in a projection lantern. It has the disadvantage, however, that the proportion of light reflected is small, as is shown by Fig. 11 in Chap. I. For this reason, a pile of plates is often used instead. Of course, the light transmitted by the pile is never completely polarized, but the amount of polarization becomes greater as the number of plates is increased. The angle of incidence for which the polarization of the transmitted light is a maximum is somewhat less than the Brewsterian angle, but it approaches this angle as a limit as the number of plates approaches infinity.

[1] As shown in Sec. 15, Chap. I, the plane of vibration in the reflected beam is normal to the plane of incidence, which is defined as the plane containing the incident ray and the normal to the surface. It will be recalled that the term "plane of polarization," which is sometimes used, refers to a plane that is normal to the plane of vibration.

[2] In practice, it is found that the light is not completely polarized even at this angle, the reason probably being a contamination of the surface of the glass.

With conductors of electricity, notably the metals, the conditions are quite different. The reflecting power for light polarized in all azimuths is high at all angles of incidence, and there is no angle at which the reflecting power for the beam vibrating in the plane of incidence becomes zero. Moreover, a beam of plane-polarized light, in general, becomes elliptically polarized on reflection. Even non-conductors, such as glass, produce a slight amount of elliptical polarization, probably because of strains existing at the surface of such materials. These phenomena are exhaustively treated in the standard textbooks on physical optics. They are, however, of little practical importance except that they must be guarded against in using polarizing instruments.

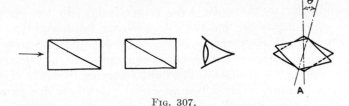

FIG. 307.

If two Nicol prisms[1] are placed in the same beam as shown in Fig. 307, the intensity of the beam emerging from the second prism depends upon the azimuth of this prism with respect to the first. Let a represent the amplitude of the beam transmitted by the first Nicol. Then if the principal plane of the second Nicol coincides with that of the first, the amplitude of the beam emerging from the second Nicol will also be a, neglecting losses by absorption and reflection. If the principal planes are at right angles to each other, the Nicols are said to be *crossed* and the amplitude of the beam emerging from the second Nicol is zero. At an intermediate position, as shown at A in the figure, the amplitude of the emergent beam is evidently equal to $a\cos\theta$, where θ is the angle between the two principal planes. Since the intensity is proportional to the square of the amplitude, it follows that

FIG. 308.

[1] Although the particular form of polarizing prism that was devised by Nicol has been largely superseded, the term "Nicol prism" is commonly used to denote any type of prism that produces a single beam of plane-polarized light from natural light.

$$I = I_0 \cos^2 \theta, \qquad\qquad (306)$$

where I_0 is the intensity of the beam that is incident on the second Nicol and I is the intensity of the emergent beam. This is sometimes called the *law of Malus*. It should be noted that, if the second Nicol is rotated through 360°, the intensity passes through two maxima and two minima.

212. The Production of Circularly and Elliptically Polarized Light.—Consider the uniaxial crystal shown in Fig. 308, whose optic axis is perpendicular to the plane of the paper. Let a beam of plane-polarized light of amplitude a be incident normally on the face of the crystal as shown, and let the plane of vibration make an angle θ with the optic axis. This beam can be represented by two components $a \cos \theta$ and $a \sin \theta$ vibrating parallel and perpendicular to the optic axis, respectively. In the crystal, these components become the extraordinary beam and the ordinary beam. Because the direction of propagation was assumed to be normal to the optic axis, both beams traverse the same path but at different velocities. The light emerging from the crystal therefore consists of two beams whose vibrations are parallel and perpendicular to the optic axis. The resultant motion of an ether particle acted upon by these vibrations can be readily found by applying the customary method for compounding two mutually perpendicular vibrations of the same frequency. In the present case, the amplitudes of the component vibrations depend upon the angle θ; and the phase difference depends upon the thickness of the crystal and the difference in velocity for the ordinary and the extraordinary beam. An expression for the resultant motion will be found in any text on physical optics, and it will be sufficient to state here that, in general, the orbit of an ether particle is an ellipse. In special cases, however, the orbit may become a circle or even a straight line. Hence, a crystal of this kind is capable of converting a beam of plane-polarized light into elliptically, circularly, or plane-polarized light.

To produce circularly polarized light, the phase difference must be $\pi/2$ and the azimuth angle θ must be $\pm 45°$. Since a phase difference of $\pi/2$ is equivalent to a path difference of $\frac{1}{4}\lambda$ between the component vibrations, a crystal of this thickness is known as a quarter-wave plate. If such a plate were made of quartz,[1]

---

[1] Mica and selenite are most commonly used. Mica is especially convenient for improvising quarter-wave plates because of the ease with which thin sheets can be split off.

which at the *D*-line has indices of 1.5443 and 1.5534 for the ordinary and the extraordinary ray respectively, its thickness would be 0.016 mm. When the azimuth of the incident vibration is other than ±45°, the emergent beam is elliptically polarized with the axes of the vibration parallel and perpendicular, respectively, to the optic axis. Conversely, a quarter-wave plate will convert elliptically polarized light into plane-polarized light if its optic axis is parallel to the proper axis of the elliptical vibration. It will convert circularly polarized light into plane-polarized light regardless of its azimuth.

A crystal whose thickness is such that it produces a path difference of λ (or any integral number of wave lengths) obviously does not cause the emergent vibration to differ in any manner from the incident vibration.[1] On the other hand, a crystal for which the path difference is $\frac{1}{2}\lambda$ produces plane-polarized light having an azimuth angle $-\theta$, whatever the azimuth angle θ of the incident vibration may be. Such a crystal is known as a half-wave plate.

213. The Analysis of Polarized Light.—The problem in analyzing polarized light is to determine whether the beam is elliptically, circularly, or plane polarized. If it is plane polarized, the azimuth of the vibration must also be determined. If it is elliptically polarized, the azimuths of the axes of the ellipse and the ratio of the lengths of the axes must be determined. Sometimes polarized light is contaminated by natural or unpolarized light, but this complication will be considered in a later section.

The first step in investigating the state of polarization of a beam of light is to determine whether it can be extinguished with a Nicol prism alone. If so, the beam is plane polarized and the plane of vibration is perpendicular to the principal plane of the Nicol prism—that is, to the shorter diagonal of its end face. Should there be no position of the Nicol for which extinction takes place, the beam is either circularly or elliptically polarized. If the original beam is circularly polarized, its intensity will remain constant as the Nicol is rotated. This is true for natural light also, but circularly polarized light can be differentiated by introducing a quarter-wave plate, which converts the circularly polarized beam into a plane-polarized beam. Extinction can then be produced when the principal plane of the Nicol is at 45°

[1] As will be shown in Sec. 216, a pronounced effect is produced when the light is heterochromatic.

with the optic axis of the quarter-wave plate.   If the beam is elliptically polarized, its intensity will vary between a maximum and a minimum as the Nicol is rotated but will never become zero unless a quarter-wave plate is introduced at the proper azimuth.   When the Nicol and the plate are set for extinction, the azimuth of the latter indicates directly the orientation of the axes of the ellipse.   The ratio of the lengths of the axes is equal to the tangent of the angle between the optic axis of the plate and the principal plane of the Nicol, as can be readily seen by making a vector diagram representing the action of the plate.

The quarter-wave plate is not used for analyzing polarized light when a high degree of precision is required because the exact

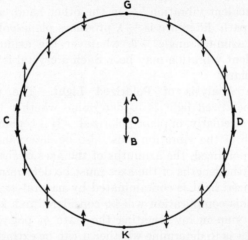

Fig. 309.—Distribution of scattered radiation about a particle *O* vibrating in the direction *AB*.

setting for extinction is difficult to determine.   It has the further disadvantage that a single plate is suitable for only a very limited range of the spectrum.   Many ingenious devices, such as the Babinet compensator, have been developed for facilitating the analysis of polarized light, but an adequate description would be beyond the scope of this volume.

214. Polarization by Scattering.—Although the practical methods of polarizing light have already been described, the fact that the light scattered by small particles is plane polarized is of some importance.   The scattering of light was discussed in Sec. 71, Chap. IX, but to understand how the polarization is produced, the mechanism must be examined more closely. In Fig. 309, let O be a minute particle of matter upon which a beam of light is incident. Let it be assumed that the direction of this beam is normal to the plane of the paper and that the vibrations take place along the line AB. Since light waves are of high frequency, the particle O is unable to vibrate in synchronism and there is therefore a relative movement between the particle and the ether. This causes the particle to emit secondary radiation. The effect of this radiation should be zero in the direction of G and K; for a displacement in this direction would have to be transmitted longitudinally. The effect should be a maximum in directions such as OC and OD, which are normal to AB. The

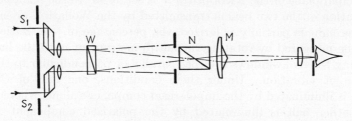

Fig. 310.—The optical system of a Martens photometer designed especially for transmission measurements.

light scattered in these directions should be completely plane polarized, the plane of vibration being parallel to AB. This should be true even when the primary beam is unpolarized, as can be seen by imagining the vector AB to rotate constantly about an axis normal to the paper.[1]

Tyndall's experiment demonstrated most strikingly the truth of the foregoing conclusions. A large part of his success was due to his care in producing very minute particles, since the polarization becomes less complete as the size of the particle increases. Sky light is due to the scattering of comparatively large particles,

[1] Although under some conditions the scattering of light by small particles may produce polarization, a piece of opal glass makes a very effective depolarizer. The reason is obvious when it is realized that, in the simple theory of scattering, it is assumed that the waves produced by each particle are transmitted unhindered to the observer. In a piece of opal glass, on the other hand, the particles are so densely packed that the secondary displacements produced by the original wave cause in turn tertiary disturbances when they impinge upon other particles. The effect at an external point is therefore the resultant of a large number of disturbances emanating from different portions of the glass and polarized in all possible azimuths.

and it is therefore only partially polarized as can be readily verified by looking at the sky through a Nicol prism.

215. The Polarization Photometer.—The extent to which sky light is polarized can be determined by means of an instrument designed by Martens. This instrument was discussed briefly in Sec. 107, Chap. XIII, and the optical system of a modern form is shown in Fig. 310. Two beams of light from the same portion of the sky are allowed to enter the windows S_1 and S_2 and are polarized in mutually perpendicular planes by the Wollaston prism W. These beams illuminate the two halves of a photometric field, which is provided by the biprism M. If the light is unpolarized, the two halves of the field will balance when the principal plane of the Nicol prism N is set at 45° to the planes of vibration of the two beams transmitted by the Wollaston prism. If the light is partially polarized, the percentage of polarization can be measured by rotating the entire instrument until the line joining the two windows is either parallel or perpendicular to the plane of vibration. Under these conditions, one half of the field is illuminated by the unpolarized component alone, whereas the other half is illuminated by the polarized component in addition. From the setting of the Nicol prism when the fields are balanced, the proportion of polarized light in the incident beam can be computed.

This instrument is frequently used as a photometer because of its compactness and simplicity of operation. It is especially convenient for measuring the transmission of a substance, and the method of using it for this purpose will be described. The instrument is first directed toward a source of uniform brightness, such as an illuminated sheet of opal glass or a surface of plaster of Paris. If the instrument is in perfect adjustment, the azimuth of the Nicol prism for a brightness match is 45°, but the match will usually occur at an angle φ which is slightly different from 45°. The substance whose transmission is to be measured is then placed in front of one of the windows of the photometer, and the Nicol is again adjusted to produce a brightness match. The transmission can be shown from the law of Malus to be

$$T_1 = \tan^2\varphi \cot^2\theta_1, \qquad (307)$$

where θ_1, the azimuth of the Nicol prism at the balance point, is assumed to be obtained with the sample in the beam that makes θ_1 greater than 45°. If the substance is then placed in the other beam and a second photometric setting is made, the transmission is

$$T_2 = \cot^2 \varphi \, \tan^2 \theta_2 . \tag{308}$$

These equations can be combined to eliminate φ, the result being

$$T = \cot \theta_1 \tan \theta_2 . \tag{309}$$

Thus it is unnecessary to determine the value of φ unless the substance under examination is suspected of producing polarization, which will be indicated by a difference between the values of T_1 and T_2. In such a case, it is preferable to use some other type of photometer.

The most common use of the polarization photometer is for the determination of the density of photographic images. In this case, the precision required is not high; and, because of the large number of routine measurements that must be made, it is desirable to simplify the procedure as much as possible. It is customary to determine the density from a single value of θ_1 and to subtract therefrom the density corresponding to the angle φ. The error in a single determination of the density made in this way is usually less than the variation in density from point to point of a photographic plate.

In the derivation of the above equations, it was assumed that the scale of the instrument is adjusted properly with respect to the optical parts. The procedure in checking an instrument is to place a small lamp in front of one of the windows and a magnifier in front of the ocular in such a position that the filament is in focus. The Nicol is then rotated until the extinction point is reached. Some means is always provided for rotating either the scale, the index, the Nicol, or the Wollaston with respect to the other elements mentioned; and the movable element should be adjusted until the scale reading is either exactly 0°, 90°, 180°, or 270° at the extinction point. If the instrument is directed at a diffusely reflecting or transmitting surface of uniform brightness, the photometric field should then balance when the scale reading is 45°, 135°, 225°, or 315°. If the instrument is dirty,[1] this will rarely be the case; but, as was shown above, no error is thereby introduced.

The Martens photometer was converted by König into a spectrophotometer by the addition of a dispersing prism as shown

---

[1] Polarizing prisms should be cleaned with even greater care than a fine surface of optical glass because of their extreme softness.

in Fig. 311. In this figure, A is a side elevation and B is a development in plan view. An image of the entrance slit Z is formed in light of different wave lengths at the exit slit Z'. Thus the entire spectrum can be explored by rotating the elements at the right of the prism P about an axis parallel to its refracting edge. This adjustment is clearly shown by Fig. 145 in Chap. XIII, which is a photograph of one form of the instrument. Although the various elements are arranged differently than they

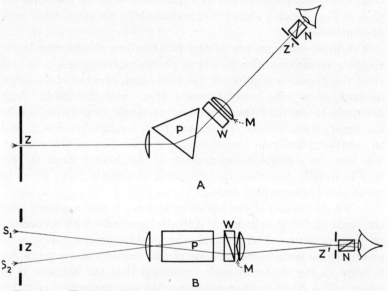

Fig. 311.—The optical system of the König-Martens spectrophotometer illustrated by Fig. 145 on page 286. A side elevation is shown above, and a development in plan view is shown below.

are in the photometer just described,[1] the action of the Wollaston and Nicol prisms is exactly the same.

216. Rotatory Polarization. The Polarimeter.—If a beam of light is passed in succession through two Nicol prisms whose azimuths are perpendicular to each other, the beam will of course be totally extinguished. Upon inserting a plate of quartz with its faces normal to the optic axis, the light is restored to a certain extent and one of the Nicols must be rotated to extinguish it again. Evidently, the quartz has rotated the plane of polariza-

[1] The arrangement shown in Fig. 310 is slightly better because a refracting surface between the Wollaston and the Nicol produces a slight amount of elliptical polarization, and thus the beam cannot be completely extinguished.

tion of the incident beam. This phenomenon is exhibited by many substances, both solids and liquids, and is of such great importance that substances exhibiting it are said to be *optically active*. The rotation is found to be proportional to the thickness of the substance and, in the case of a solution, to the concentration.[1] It also depends upon the wave length of the light (varying roughly as the inverse square), and this circumstance gives rise to *rotatory dispersion*.

The phenomenon of rotatory polarization was discussed in Sec. 143, Chap. XVIII, in connection with quartz, and it was explained on the hypothesis that an incident beam of plane-polarized light is equivalent to two circularly polarized components rotating in opposite senses, one traveling with a greater velocity than the other. The sense in which the emergent beam is rotated depends upon which of the components travels faster. Thus some substances are right-handed (dextrorotatory), some are left-handed (laevorotatory), and some, such as quartz, appear in both forms.

By measuring the amount of rotatory polarization, it is possible to determine very quickly the concentration of an optically active substance in the presence of one that is optically inactive. For example, ordinary sugar (sucrose) is dextrorotatory in an aqueous solution because of the asymmetry of its molecule. Since the tariff on sugar is based on the proportion of pure sucrose, the polarimeter is widely used by customs officers for determining the purity of sugar imports. Polarimeters especially designed for testing sugar are called saccharimeters.

The simple form of polarimeter just described consists merely of two Nicol prisms, which are known, respectively, as the polarizer and the analyzer. The precision obtainable with this form of instrument is low because the position of the analyzer for complete extinction is difficult to locate with certainty.[2] This difficulty was overcome in 1860 by Jellett, who designed a polarizing prism of such a type that the field seen by the observer is divided into two halves of adjustable brightness like an ordinary photometric field. The type of Jellett prism that is used to-day

---

[1] This is not strictly true if the solution is very concentrated or if the range of concentrations is excessive.

[2] The principles underlying the design of polarimeters are discussed extensively by Skinner, *Jour. Optical Soc. Amer. and Rev. Sci. Instruments,* **10,** 491 (1925).

is a modification due to Cornu. It consists of a Nicol prism
with a wedge-shaped section removed, as shown at *A* in Fig. 312.
The two parts of the prism are then cemented together as shown
at *B*, the result being that the planes of vibration for the two

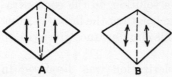

A   **B**

FIG. 312.—Construction of the
Cornu-Jellett prism.

parts make a small angle with each
other. This angle is called the
half-shadow angle. Evidently
there is no position of the analyzer
for which the two beams are extinguished simultaneously, but
there is a position for which they
are of equal intensity. The sensitivity is highest when the half-
shadow angle is small, but because of the reduction in illumination, an angle of 2.5° is the practical minimum, even for very
transparent samples.

Another half-shadow device that is sometimes used is due to
Laurent. It consists of a half-wave plate covering one half of
the polarizer, which is an ordinary Nicol prism. A sheet of glass
whose optical thickness is equal to that of the half-wave plate
covers the other half. The action of the device can be understood from Fig. 313, where the optic
axis of the half-wave plate is shown
by the crosshatching. The vector
OA represents the azimuth of the
beam emerging from the polarizer
and passing through the glass, and
the vector *OA'* represents the azimuth of the other half of the beam
after traversing the half-wave plate.
It will be remembered from Sec. 212
that θ' is always equal to θ. The
half-shadow angle is evidently 2θ.
The operation of the instrument is
the same as for the Cornu-Jellett prism, but it is necessary, of

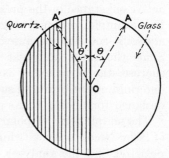

FIG. 313.—Construction of the
Laurent half-shade plate. The
crosshatching indicates the optic
axis of the quartz.

course, to use light of the wave length for which the half-wave
plate was designed. On the other hand, the half-wave plate has
the advantage that the sensitivity can be varied by rotating
the polarizer.

A device that is superior to either of those just described is
due to Lippich. The optical system of a typical polarimeter
incorporating the Lippich prism is shown in Fig. 314. Light from

the source S passes in turn through the collecting lens C, the polarizer P, and the Lippich prism L.   This prism consists merely of a small Nicol prism covering one half of the field.   The light then traverses the sample X and the analyzer N, and enters the

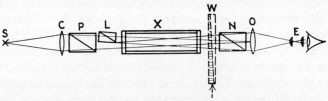

Fig. 314.—The optical system of the Lippich polarimeter.

telescope represented by an objective O and an ocular E.   The telescope is focused on the near face of the Lippich prism, the edge of which becomes the dividing line of the photometric field. The half-shadow angle in this case is determined by the orientation of the Lippich prism with respect to the polarizer.

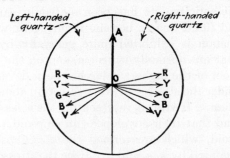

Fig. 315.—Construction of Soleil's biquartz.

The types of half-shadow devices hitherto considered suffer from the disadvantage that monochromatic light must be used on account of the rotatory dispersion of the sample.   To allow heterochromatic light to be used, Robiguet developed a polarimeter in which the biquartz plate of Soleil is the half-shadow device.   This plate consists of semicircular disks of right-handed and left-handed quartz placed side by side, as shown in Fig. 315. The disks are cut perpendicularly to the optic axes and are 3.75 mm thick, which is sufficient to rotate yellow light by 90°.   If the plane of vibration of the incident beam contains the vector OA and the principal plane of the analyzer, yellow light is extinguished for both halves of the field and the latter appears a uniform purple.   By a slight rotation of the analyzer, one half of the field becomes reddish and the other half, bluish. This device has many faults, however, and modern polarimeters designed for heterochromatic light are based on the principle of compensating the rotation of the sample by means of a quartz wedge. These instruments have an optical system like the one shown in Fig. 314 with the addition of the compensating wedge W. This wedge consists of a wedge of glass cemented to one of quartz with its optic axis as indicated by the crosshatching. The function of the glass wedge is to keep the optical path constant for all settings. Unless the rotatory dispersion of the sample is greatly different from that of quartz, the error due to the dispersion is trifling. This type of instrument has the further advantage that monochromatic light can be used if desired, in which case the dispersion does not affect the results. The wedge must, of course, be calibrated for the particular kind of light source and sample for which the instrument is to be used. Most saccharimeters are of this type.[1]

217. Photoelasticity.—It has been stated in earlier chapters that glass and fused quartz become birefringent when stressed. This phenomenon is exhibited quite generally by transparent substances that are normally isotropic, and on the basis of it an engineering tool of the highest value has been developed.

Let us consider the stresses in every direction about a point in a stressed medium. If vectors representing the stresses are drawn, it will be found that their envelope is an ellipsoid. Let the axes of this ellipsoid, which are termed the *directions of principal stress*, be designated by p, q, and r. Since the stresses in only two dimensions can be studied optically, the stress in the r direction must be kept equal to zero to avoid complicating the problem. The ellipsoid then reduces to an ellipse with axes p and q. The

---

[1] In saccharimetry, a solution containing 26.000 grams (weighed in air) of the sample per 100 cc of water is measured in a tube 200.0 mm long at 20°C. A linear scale on the wedge is divided into "sugar degrees," 100°S representing pure sucrose. Thus the scale indicates the purity directly. The instrument is calibrated by means of a quartz control plate, which, if 1.5934 mm thick, represents 100°S when yellow light is used. The source is an incandescent lamp with a 15-mm cell containing 6 per cent potassium bichromate solution. An ordinary polarimeter with monochromatic light can be used as a saccharimeter by noting that 100°S corresponds to a rotation of 40.763°(circular) for the mercury green line ($\lambda = 546.1$ mμ) or 34.620° for the sodium line. The subject of saccharimetry is treated at length in *Bur. Standards Circ.* **44.**

axis of p is taken as the direction of the compressive stress and the axis of q as the direction of the tensile stress.

Under the influence of the stresses, the substance undergoes a deformation that alters its internal structure so as to make it birefringent.[1]   In most substances, the ray vibrating in a plane parallel to the direction of the compressive stress travels more rapidly than the ray vibrating in the direction of the tensile stress.   A beam of natural light is therefore decomposed into two plane-polarized components having a path difference

$$\delta = C (p - q)t \,, \tag{310}$$

where t is the thickness of the substance and C is a quantity that is proportional to the difference $(n_e - n_o)$ between the indices for the two components.   The constant C is sometimes referred to as the *index of forced double refraction.*[2]

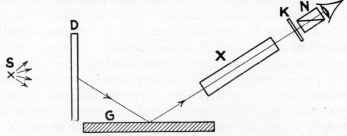

Fig. 316.—The optical system of a strain tester for optical glass.

The phenomenon of forced double refraction can be utilized very simply to detect internal stresses within blocks of optical glass by means of the apparatus sketched in Fig. 316.[3]   The

[1] It is important to note that the birefringence is caused by the stresses and not by the resulting strains.   If a substance is strained beyond its elastic limit, the birefringence disappears when the stress is removed although the substance has acquired a permanent set.

[2] This quantity can obviously be expressed as the retardation in millimeters of one component of the beam with respect to the other per millimeter thickness of the material when a uniform unidimensional stress of 1 gram/mm² is applied.   Expressed in these units, the indices found by Heymans and Allis for some materials used in photoelasticity are as follows: camphor celluloid, 12.1×10^{-8}; plate glass, 2.5×10^{-8}; fused quartz, 3.4×10^{-8}.   Transparent bakelite, which has been developed more recently, has an index of forced double refraction that is approximately five times that of celluloid and obeys Hooke's law over a far greater range of stresses.

[3] "The Manufacture of Glass and of Optical Systems," *Ordnance Dept. Doc.* 2037, p. 206.

diffusing glass D is illuminated by a light source S. The light entering the eye is reflected from a plate of black glass G at the polarizing angle, the proper adjustment being determined by setting the Nicol prism N for extinction and moving it up and down until the brightness of the field is a minimum. The sample of glass X is then placed in the beam as shown; and, if it is in a state of stress, it restores the light in the field. The amount of light restored and its color at any given point depend upon the directions and magnitudes of the principal stresses at that point. If the directions of principal stress are parallel and perpendicular to the plane of polarization, the field remains dark. If the directions of principal stress make some other angle with the plane of polarization, the light is partially restored and the color of the field depends upon the stress difference $(p - q)$. As the stress difference increases, the color changes from black to straw, orange, red, blue-green, straw, etc, the colors repeating themselves until they fade out in the fourth or fifth order. The precision of the method can be increased considerably by introducing a sensitive-tint plate K in front of the analyzer. This plate retards yellow-green light by a full wave length and therefore causes the field to appear purple where the specimen is free from stress. In regions where stress is present, however, the path difference between the ordinary and the extraordinary beam is increased or decreased, and some color other than green is extinguished. Thus the field becomes either blue or orange. The order of colors from the unstressed region outward is similar to that described above, but the colors are more pronounced.[1] The sensitivity of the method can be judged from the fact that a change in the path difference of 10 mμ produces a perceptible change in color. A path difference of this order of magnitude per centimeter of thickness is quite permissible in optical glass.

The scope of the photoelastic method has been greatly extended by several workers, especially Coker,[2] and the procedure devel-

---

[1] The sensitive-tint plate can be used with heterochromatic light in a polarimeter in lieu of a half-shade device. The analyzer is set to restore the sensitive purple, which, because of the pronounced hue change caused by a slight deviation from the correct position, can be located more precisely than the position for extinction when the plate is not used.

[2] See a series of papers in *Engineering* for 1911, 1916, 1920, and later. See also a series in *Gen. Elec. Rev.* for 1920 and 1921. A comprehensive summary of the technique of photoelasticity will be found in a paper by Delanghe in *Rev. d'Optique*, **7**, 237 and 285 (1928).

oped by them is now in common use for studying the stress distributions in contemplated engineering structures.   It consists essentially in making a model of the structure out of some transparent isotropic material, subjecting the model to a load similar to the load to which the structure itself will be subjected, and studying the stress distribution within the various members by means of polarized light.   The first operation is to determine the directions of principal stress, which can be done by placing the model between crossed Nicols.   Wherever the stress directions are parallel and perpendicular to the plane of polarization, the field is dark.   Thus the field is traversed by dark lines, called *isoclinics*, along which the directions of principal stress have a certain constant inclination.   A plot of these isoclinics is made.   Both Nicols are then rotated through a certain known angle and the new isoclinics are plotted.   Thus a map of the isoclinics as shown at A in Fig. 318 is prepared, each isoclinic representing the locus of points for which the directions of principal stress are constant.

The portions of the field for which the directions of principal stress make an angle other than $0°$ or $90°$ with the plane of polarization have a brightness that depends upon the angle.   The hue is constant, of course, if the light is monochromatic.   Where the angle equals $45°$, the maximum amount of light is restored. The value of $(p - q)$ can then be found by introducing a Babinet compensator or equivalent device in the beam and adjusting it until the retardation it produces is equal in magnitude but opposite in sign to that produced by the specimen.   By this procedure the field becomes dark again, of course.   The scale on the compensator indicates the quantity $C(p - q)$, and to compute $(p - q)$ itself, the value of C must be known.   This can be determined by cutting a strip of the same material and subjecting it to a uniform unidirectional tensile stress of known magnitude. Indeed, the strip itself can be used as a compensator if it is oriented so that the direction of the stress applied to it is perpendicular to the direction of maximum tensile stress within the specimen at the point under consideration.   If it has the same thickness as the specimen, the load that must be applied to effect compensation evidently indicates the value of $(p - q)$ directly.

When the light is heterochromatic, as is the case in practice, the portions of the field outside the isoclinics are colored because of the rotatory dispersion of the specimen.   Every band of constant color, which is termed an *isochromatic*, is the locus of points for which the value of $(p - q)$ is the same.   The second step in making a photoelastic analysis is to plot the isochromatics and to determine the value of $(p - q)$ for each.   Such a plot is shown at B in Fig. 318.   The value of $(p - q)$ can be determined with a compensator as described above.   When the compensator is adjusted for one point in an isochromatic, it need only be rotated to effect compensation at any other point.   A selected isochromatic can therefore be traced by simply rotating the compensator.

The difficulty with using plane-polarized light is that the isochromatic pattern is complicated by the presence of the isoclinics.   Moreover, the specimen must be rotated to distinguish the isoclinics from the neutral axis, where there is no stress.

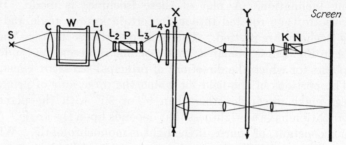

Fig. 317.—The optical system of a typical apparatus for the photoelastic analysis of stress.

Both drawbacks can be avoided by using circularly polarized light, in which the isochromatic pattern is the same for every orientation of the specimen and the isoclinics disappear.   The apparatus used by Coker and Kimball[1] is sketched in Fig. 317. Heterochromatic light from a source S is collimated by a lens C and passed through a water cell W to prevent overheating the Nicols.   It is polarized by a Nicol prism[2] P and is converted into circularly polarized light by a quarter-wave plate J.   It then passes through the specimen X, the compensator Y, a second quarter-wave plate K, and an analyzing prism N.   Images of X and Y are formed in superposition on the screen.   The second quarter-wave plate is placed with its axis perpendicular to that of the first.   It thus neutralizes the effect of the first for the points of the specimen where $(p - q)$ equals zero.   Hence, where the field is dark, the specimen is unstressed.   The other portions

---

[1] *Gen. Elec. Rev.*, **24**, 73 (1921); *Jour. Optical Soc. Amer.*, **5**, 279 (1921).

[2] The purpose of the lenses L_1, L_2, L_3, and L_4 is to permit a large field of the specimen to be examined with a polarizing prism of reasonable size.

of the specimen produce elliptical polarization, which is not neutralized by the second plate, and therefore an isochromatic pattern appears on the screen.

The information furnished by the foregoing procedure gives directly the value of $(p - q)$ for all points of the specimen. Although the values of p and q themselves can be computed from the isoclinic and isochromatic patterns, the operations are extremely tedious. An experimental method of determining these quantities was devised by Coker. It consists in measuring the change in thickness at each point of the stressed specimen and then computing $(p+q)$ from these data and the elastic moduli of the substance. This gives two equations in p and q, from which

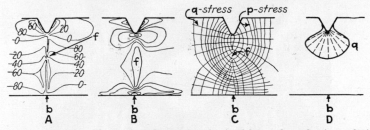

Fig. 318.—Sketches illustrating the results obtained by a photoelastic analysis.

their individual values can be calculated. An optical method for accomplishing the same result has been devised by Favre.[1]

The importance of the photoelastic method lies in its ability to analyze the stresses within a specimen that is too complicated to be treated in any other way. For example, the stress distribution within a uniform beam subjected to a bending moment can be readily computed, but the problem becomes exceedingly complex when a notch is cut in the beam. Figure 318 illustrates the treatment of this case by the photoelastic method.[2] The beam is supported at b in the various sketches and is loaded at the ends. The isoclinics are shown at A and the isochromatics are shown at B. The neutral point is at f in these sketches. The directions of the p- and q-stresses are shown at C by curves to which the stresses are everywhere tangent. These curves are sometimes called *isostatics*. Since the directions of p and q are mutually

[1] For a description of these methods, see the paper by Delanghe, *Rev. d'Optique*, **7**, 237 (1928). More recent papers are those by Favre, *idem.*, **11**, 1 (1932) and Solakian, *Jour. Optical Soc. Amer.*, **22**, 293 (1932).

[2] See a paper by Maris, *Jour. Optical Soc. Amer. and Rev. Sci. Instruments*, **15**, 203 (1927).

perpendicular at every point, the two sets of curves are orthogonal. They are also either normal or parallel to the free boundaries of the specimen, since the normal stress at a free boundary is zero. Thus the p-isostatics are normal to the upper surface, which is in tension, and the q-isostatics are parallel to it. At the lower surface, which is in compression, the opposite condition obtains. The zero isostatics intersect at the neutral point f. The stress distribution along any section of the specimen can be plotted when p and q have been computed. Thus the tangential stress along the boundary of the notch is shown at D, this stress

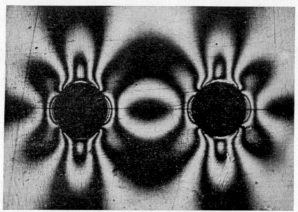

Fig. 319.—The isochromatic pattern about two rivet holes in a member subjected to a vertical tensile stress. This photograph was made with circularly polarized light of wave length 546.1 mμ. (*From a thesis by Joseph Harrington, Jr., by courtesy of the Mechanical Engineering Department of the Massachusetts Institute of Technology.*)

being of course a tension. The stress is indicated by the length of a vector normal to the boundary at any given point and extending to the curve.

Within the last decade, the stresses in many engineering structures, such as eye bolts, gear wheels, and ship's propellers, have been studied by the photoelastic method. Even when a theoretical treatment of such structures is possible, the experimental method is ordinarily more rapid. For example, Fig. 319 shows the isochromatic pattern about two rivet holes in a member subjected to a vertical tensile stress. Although it has been found possible to determine the stress distribution theoretically in this case, the mathematical treatment is so involved that the solution of the problem requires weeks of computation. The same result can be achieved by the photoelastic method in as many days.

INDEX

750